SUPERFLUID HYDRODYNAMICS

NORTH-HOLLAND SERIES IN

LOW TEMPERATURE PHYSICS

EDITORS

C. J. GORTER, R. DE BRUYN OUBOTER, D. DE KLERK

VOLUME 3

NORTH-HOLLAND PUBLISHING COMPANY – AMSTERDAM · LONDON
AMERICAN ELSEVIER PUBLISHING COMPANY, INC. – NEW YORK

SUPERFLUID HYDRODYNAMICS

Seth J. PUTTERMAN

Physics Department, University of California
Los Angeles, California 90024

and

Research Fellow of
the Alfred P. Sloan Foundation

1974

NORTH-HOLLAND PUBLISHING COMPANY – AMSTERDAM · LONDON
AMERICAN ELSEVIER PUBLISHING COMPANY, INC. – NEW YORK

Library of Congress Catalog Card Number: 74-75578
North-Holland ISBN for the series: 0 7204 1250 1
North-Holland ISBN for this volume: 0 7204 1258 7
American Elsevier ISBN: 0 444 10681 2

Publishers:
NORTH-HOLLAND PUBLISHING COMPANY – AMSTERDAM
NORTH-HOLLAND PUBLISHING COMPANY, LTD. – LONDON

Sole distributors for the U.S.A. and Canada:
AMERICAN ELSEVIER PUBLISHING COMPANY, INC.
52 VANDERBILT AVENUE, NEW YORK, N.Y. 10017

PRINTED IN THE NETHERLANDS

Preface

In April 1968 during my second year as a graduate student at the Rockefeller University I was one afternoon surprised to see upon entering my thesis adviser's office, a large pile of books and papers dealing with superfluidity. My adviser G. E. Uhlenbeck proceeded to ask me if I knew of any other works on this subject. I replied by asking what had brought about this shift of emphasis away from relativistic thermodynamics. His answer was that changing fields was a time tested means of renewing himself and to bring it about he had committed himself to give a course on superfluidity (along with T. M. Sanders, Jr.) in the 1968 summer school at the University of Colorado. In this way he assured me that his course would also fulfill the first requirement of Ehrenfest: that the teacher learn something.

Through the hospitality of M. Uberoi it was made possible for me to take a small part in that summer's program. My thesis and this book are the outgrowth of that summer's study. I have throughout tried to adhere to G. E. Uhlenbeck's philosophical admonitions on physics and this subject, e.g.:

> 'One must watch like a Hawk to see how Planck's constant comes into the hydrodynamics.'
>
> 'The major role of the microscopic theory is to derive the phenomenological theory.'

In many ways I am indebted to his many and continued criticisms and qualms.

The literature on superfluid helium is enormous and I have not attempted to refer to even a finite fraction of it. The goal has been to select those papers which have a direct bearing on the central theme as expressed in the Introduction. When this is done, one finds that the distance from the foundations or starting point (say classical hydrodynamics) to the frontiers of research is actually quite short. Furthermore, no fancy or specialized mathematical tricks are required at any stage so that it is hoped that this book will be readable by people in other fields and perhaps also by advanced undergraduates. Since classical hydrodynamics (the one fluid model) has become a secret subject in most physics departments a short discussion of the Euler and Navier–Stokes equations with some representative applications has been included for completeness.

I should like to acknowledge the contributions of many people to the writing of this book. The chapter on the condensed ideal Bose gas relied heavily on the contributions of M. Kac and G. E. Uhlenbeck. R. de Bruyn Ouboter was of major assistance in the development of the ideas presented on superconductivity. Much of the work on that subject was performed while at Philips Research Laboratory and I am indebted to H. B. G. Casimir, D. Polder and J. Volger for hospitality and many valuable discussions. Much of the emphasis on the importance of a hydrodynamic attack on superfluidity has resulted from R. J. Donnelly's influence on the field as for instance is reflected partly through his book 'Experimental Superfluidity'. I have also enjoyed valuable conversations with him. All of the discussions of He II films and speculations on the macroscopic uncertainty principle depended strongly on the contributions of I. Rudnick. I am also indebted to him for valuable criticisms and suggestions concerning aspects of this book too numerous to list.

Finally, I should like to thank T. Bomba, B. Chernow and C. Coppersmith for assistance with the preparation of the manuscript, and D. Moran and D. Stewart for assistance with the preparation of the figures.

Table of Contents

Introduction

Superfluids display quantum effects on the macroscopic level and obey hydrodynamics on the microscopic level [1].

At the famous Florence conference of 1948 on the foundations of quantum statistical mechanics Wolfgang Pauli [2] maintained:

> 'The otherwise so important difference between classical and quantum mechanics is not relevant in principle for thermodynamic considerations.'

This point of view was motivated by the observation that the macroscopic description of the behavior of liquids and gases as contained in the equations of hydrodynamics and the formulation of the laws of thermodynamics are independent of the particular mechanics used to describe the motion of the individual atoms on the microscopic scale. The revolution that brought physics from the Newtonian mechanics to the quantum mechanics left the thermo-hydrodynamics unchanged and for this reason Pauli and others regarded quantum mechanics as micromechanics.

In nature there exist systems, referred to as superfluids, whose macroscopic behavior changes radically as their temperature is lowered past a transition point. A striking property of superfluids is the ability to flow without any measurable resistance. So far the substances to fall into this category are liquid helium and various metallic substances called superconductors in which an electric current encounters no resistance. Superconductivity was discovered in 1911 by H. Kamerlingh Onnes [3], who also was first to liquefy helium. The superfluidity of helium four was discovered only about thirty years later.

It is now clear that superfluidity reflects the operation of quantum theory on the macroscopic level. This fact, and the implied conflict with the view expressed by Pauli's remark was first (1935) and continually emphasized by F. London and H. London [4]. They pointed out that

Notes p. XXI

due to the quantum theory the qualitative macroscopic description of these systems had to be quite different from those of the other, or classical fluids. The main reason for interest in superfluids lies in their unusual macroscopic quantum properties and it is for this reason that the largest part of this book is directed towards developing the hydrodynamics, and formulating the thermodynamics of superfluids. We will also discuss the experiments which played a crucial role in bringing the quantum revolution to the macroscopic domain.

F. London always thought of a superfluid as being a system in which a macroscopic fraction of the particles was locked into the ground state because of the low temperature. This picture leads naturally to the so-called two fluid model in which the superfluid system is considered as being composed of two interpenetrating fluids: the normal fluid which behaves classically and flows according to the macroscopic description appropriate above the transition temperature, and the superfluid which is the macroscopically occupied quantum ground state. The frictionless flow through narrow constrictions is now interpreted as a flow of the superfluid component as ground state transformations must be reversible. Since a single quantum state has no entropy the experimental observation by Kapitza [5] in 1940 of a superflow between two vessels, which was associated with a zero entropy flow must be taken as at least a qualitative verification of London's picture.

The characteristic length which determines the role played by quantum mechanics in any situation is the de Broglie wavelength. In classical fluids the de Broglie wavelength of the constitutive particles is generally much smaller than the mean free path and this accounts for the classical macroscopic description. The de Broglie wavelength of particles in the superfluid ground state is effectively infinite or in a confined geometry determined by the size of the container. Thus for a superfluid the scales are turned and the de Broglie wavelength of a macroscopic number of the particles is much greater than the mean free path. No matter how slowly or over what length an external constraint is varied it must be changing at least as fast as the macroscopic de Broglie wavelength of the superfluid. So quantum effects will always dominate. For instance, no matter how long the wavelength of an imposed temperature variation, it will propagate away not by diffusion (as in classical fluids) but as a travelling wave (second sound).

In terms of these remarks the central problem dealt with in this book can be reformulated as: what is the thermo-hydrodynamic description of

Notes p. XXI

a system for which a finite fraction of particles are in a state with macroscopic de Broglie wavelength much larger than the mean free path.

In the case of superfluid helium (He II) the most successful macroscopic or continuum theory was presented by L. D. Landau [6] in 1941, and is referred to as the two fluid hydrodynamics. The development of these equations is an excellent example of how a phenomenological theory proceeds. First, one must determine, based on experiment, how many variables are required to describe the state of the system. For He II this basic assumption is that eight variables are a complete set. That is three more than are needed for a classical fluid, they being the three components of velocity of the superfluid component. Next, one asks what are the most general equations consistent with this assumption and the macroscopic first principles such as: mass, energy, momentum conservation, Galilean covariance and the first and second laws of thermodynamics. In this way one is led to the Landau two fluid hydrodynamics provided that one also assumes that the circulation of the additional or superfluid velocity field is conserved. The arguments are presented in Chapter I along with some experiments which test the two fluid hydrodynamic theory.

This phenomenological approach has the advantage of being quite independent of any microscopic model used to describe the system. It has the disadvantage of not proceeding from first principles as evidenced by the need for instance to make an assumption on the number of independent macroscopic degrees of freedom.

In these macroscopic equations which are most certainly different from the thermohydrodynamics of say water, Planck's constant does *not* appear. Thus from the macroscopic point of view one could perhaps at this point still doubt whether He II is a quantum fluid. This situation changed in 1948 when at the same Florence conference at which Pauli delivered the above remark, Lars Onsager [7] proposed that the circulation of the superfluid would be quantized in integral multiples of Planck's constant divided by the mass of a He^4 atom. According to Onsager vorticity in He II must be quantized and the number of allowed macroscopic states of a superfluid is limited by the quantum theory.

This fundamental advance of Onsager is a natural outcome of the ideas of F. and H. London and brings quantum mechanics into the macroscopic domain in striking fashion. A number of experiments have now verified the Onsager quantization and in particular its consequences for rotating superfluid helium. Since quantization rules out distributed

Notes p. XXI

vorticity the superfluid cannot rotate smoothly like a classical fluid executing solid body rotation. Instead it rotates around an array of 'singularities' or quantized sources of vorticity. This unique quantum thermodynamic equilibrium state has been observed by Packard and Sanders [8] in 1969.

The Landau two fluid hydrodynamics supplemented by the Onsager quantization forms the basis of the macroscopic description of He II. These equations, when modified to include dissipative effects (Chapter II) provide the basic description of the flow of He II in just the same way as the Navier–Stokes hydrodynamics describe classical fluids. In Chapter III various applications of the superfluid hydrodynamics are presented and it is seen that starting from these basic equations one can discuss the propagation and absorption of sound as well as the motion of, and drag on, quantized vortices. In Chapter IV thermal fluctuations are incorporated into the macroscopic theory in systematic fashion and again the same equations which describe the four Brillouin peaks observed in light scattering, also describe the Brownian motion of quantized vortex lines.

If one accepts the idea of London that the superfluid is a macroscopic number of particles moving coherently in a single quantum state, then there is room to expect that the hydrodynamics of He II might work well in describing the motion of the superfluid in microscopic geometries. In this way the two fluid hydrodynamics of He II would have a greater range of applicability for He II than the Navier–Stokes theory for classical fluids. The observation [1] and description of propagating collective waves on the surface of one atomic layer thick He II films by measurements of associated temperature variations must be taken as evidence in favor of this point of view. These experiments which were performed in the laboratory of I. Rudnick in 1973 are discussed in Chapter V.

We see that not only do quantum effects manifest themselves on the macroscopic level but the normally macroscopic hydrodynamic theory works on the microscopic level. This incredible mixing of the scales is unique to superfluids and central to interest in them.

The Landau two fluid theory supplemented by the Onsager quantization has strong similarities with the Old Quantum Theory in which the Bohr–Sommerfeld quantization condition was used to select a discrete set of allowed states. As the Old Quantum Theory had shortcomings in that it did not take into account the wave particle duality one naturally

Notes p. XXI

expects that the Landau two fluid theory plus quantization will have comparable shortcomings. This is a current problem and the situations in which it may arise are discussed in Chapter VII.

The macroscopic theory of superconductivity is developed in parallel with that of He II in Chapter IX.

As in other branches of physics the theory of superfluidity proceeds on two levels, the phenomenological and microscopic. Phenomenologically the goal is to find, by combining guess work with the macroscopic first principles, a simple theory unifying as many experiments as possible. This still leaves open the question of understanding the relationship of superfluidity to the microscopic first principles. We consider this question briefly in Chapter VIII.

There are many problems that can be attacked from the microscopic approach; for instance, one can try to calculate the equation of state for the density as a function of pressure and temperature. However, from the point of view of the hydrodynamics, the main question involves understanding how in a single component system there can exist two 'fluids' with independent velocities one of which has a quantized circulation. We will see that these particular properties can be understood simply in terms of the model of a condensed non-interacting quantum gas obeying Bose statistics as originally proposed by F. London [9].

First in 1924 Einstein [10] remarked on a peculiar phase transition that took place in this ideal system. It appeared that as a result of the symmetric statistics a finite fraction of the particles dropped into the ground state for low enough temperature. In 1938 F. London proposed that this behavior was characteristic of the transition to He II and that the macroscopically occupied single particle state with de Broglie wavelength determined by the container, should be thought of as qualitatively similar to the superfluid fraction in He II. While the ideal Bose gas is a fruitful model for the most unusual properties of He II, it naturally gives a very poor description of the equations of state. The inclusion of interactions so as to rectify this situation and still explain the two fluid model remains a major outstanding problem.

Most precisely the title of this book should be 'Hydrodynamics of Superconductors and Superfluid Helium Four'. There may exist other superfluids with no guarantee that their hydrodynamics will be the same as He II or superconductors. A notable possibility is superfluidity in He^3 at a temperature one thousandth of that at which the He II transition occurs [11]. In order to allow for different superfluids one must first

Notes p. XXI

define the concept. We will work with London's definition that in a superfluid a single quantum degree of freedom becomes macroscopically occupied with the operational consequence that transformations of this degree of freedom correspond to no entropy transfer. The additional macroscopic variables needed for describing the superfluid will correspond to this quantum degree of freedom. In the superfluid phase(s) of He^3 one will certainly have to introduce the superfluid velocity as an extra macroscopic variable. If this is the only new macroscopic variable the hydrodynamics will be isomorphic to that of superfluid He^4. However, one might, for instance, also be forced to introduce an intrinsic superfluid 'spin' angular momentum as an additional macroscopic variable. In this event the He^3 hydrodynamics would be a generalization of the He^4 equations of motion. The recipe for generating the phenomenological theory would then still follow the same lines as for He^4 with the conservation of angular momentum now playing a much more important role as a macroscopic first principle.

Notes

[1] J. Scholtz, E. O. McLean and I. Rudnick, Phys. Rev. Letters **32** (1974) 147.

[2] W. Pauli, Discussion remarks on p. 166 of Supplement to Nuovo Cimento Vol. VI, Series IX (1949); they can also be found in: *Collected Papers* (Interscience, New York, 1964) Vol. II p. 1112. See also W. Pauli and M. Fierz, Z. Phys. **106** (1937) 572 (*Collected Papers,* Vol. II, p. 797) and J. von Neumann, Z. Phys. **57** (1929) 30 [*Collected Works* (Pergamon Press, New York, 1961) Vol. I, p. 558].

[3] H. Kamerlingh Onnes, Proc. Roy. Acad. Amsterdam **13** (1911) 1903.

[4] F. London and H. London, Physica **2** (1935) 341. F. London, *Une Conception Nouvelle de la Supraconductibilité,* Act. Sci. et Ind. No. 458, Paris (1937); *Superfluids* (Wiley, New York, 1950) Vol. I.

[5] P. L. Kapitza, J. Phys. USSR **5** (1941) 59; Phys. Rev. **60** (1941) 354.

[6] L. D. Landau, Zh. Eksp. Teor. Fiz. **11** (1941) 592; J. Phys. USSR **5** (1941) 71.

[7] L. Onsager, Nuovo Cimento Suppl. No. 2 to Vol. 6 (1949) p. 249.

[8] R. Packard and T. M. Sanders, Jr., Phys. Rev. Letters **22** (1969) 823.

[9] F. London, Nature **141** (1938) 643; Phys. Rev. **54** (1938) 947; *Superfluids* (see Ref. [4]) Vol. 2, p. 40.

[10] A. Einstein, Sitzber. Preuss. Akad. Wiss. (1924) 261; (1925) 3.

[11] H. Kojima, D. Paulson and J. Wheatley, Phys. Rev. Letters **32** (1974) 141.

CHAPTER I

Hydrodynamics of He II on the Level where Dissipative Effects are Ignored

1 Introduction: Classical Hydrodynamics on the Non-dissipative (Ideal) Level

Helium liquefies at 4.2 °K. Between this temperature and 2.17 °K this liquid (He I) behaves like an ordinary fluid. But as the temperature is lowered below $T_\lambda = 2.17$ °K it transforms into a second fluid phase (He II) which exhibits strikingly different dynamical properties. For instance, Allen and Misener [1] and Kapitza [2] found in 1938 that at these low temperatures the liquid helium could flow through narrow capillaries (about 10^{-4} cm in diameter) with no measurable resistance. This observation led Kapitza to refer to the liquid as a 'superfluid'. Based on this experiment one might simply expect that viscous effects are absent in He II and that the dynamical properties of He II would be especially accurately described by the classical ideal fluid, or Euler, equations of motion. It soon turned out that a number of experiments indicated that this is not the case. For instance, other methods of measuring the viscosity yielded non-vanishing results (this is the viscosity paradox which we return to in Chapter II) indicating that there are dissipative effects present in He II. Even in experimental arrangements where these dissipative effects can be ignored one finds, as will be discussed in § 2, that the Euler equations do not correctly describe the dynamical properties of He II. So not only don't the Euler equations give an especially accurate description of the flow of He II, they do not even give the appropriate description of its motion on the level where dissipative effects can be neglected.

The equations of motion of He II on the ideal level were first presented in complete form by Landau [3] in 1941. The goal of this chapter is to motivate and discuss these equations. Since the Euler equations form the pattern for the generalization to the Landau equations and since it is always crucial to understand the relationship of the new theory to the old theory we first review the Euler equations and some of their consequences.

The basic fact upon which the Euler equations are built is that knowledge of five independent variables in a small volume of fluid (or so to speak, at a 'point' in the fluid) constitutes complete information about this volume element (or 'point'). The five variables can be chosen as the mass density $\rho(\boldsymbol{r}, t)$, the specific entropy $s(\boldsymbol{r}, t)$ and the three components of the fluid velocity $\boldsymbol{v}(\boldsymbol{r}, t)$, where $\boldsymbol{r}$ is the location of the volume element under consideration and t is the time. That for an ordinary fluid in the approximation where dissipative effects can be ignored (the Euler level) any property of its flow must be a function of the five variables ρ, s, $\boldsymbol{v}$, cannot be proven from the mascroscopic or phenomenological point of view. It is the starting assumption and any investigation of this point must start from the microscopic laws of motion for a large number of molecules colliding according to Newton's laws.

The differential equations which determine the time development of these five variables follow from what can be called the 'macroscopic first principles'. From the principle of conservation of mass one obtains the equation of motion for ρ:

$$\frac{\partial \rho}{\partial t} + \nabla \cdot \rho \boldsymbol{v} = 0. \tag{1-1}$$

By integrating Eq. (1) over a given volume one finds after applying Gauss' law to the divergence:

$$\frac{\mathrm{d}}{\mathrm{d}t} \int \rho \, \mathrm{d}V + \int \rho \boldsymbol{v} \cdot \mathrm{d}\boldsymbol{S} = 0, \tag{1-2}$$

where $\mathrm{d}V$ is an element of volume and $\mathrm{d}\boldsymbol{S}$ is an element of the surface bounding the volume in question. Since ρ is the mass density, the $\int \rho \, \mathrm{d}V$ is the mass within the volume and hence Eq. (1-2) states that the change of mass in time within the volume is entirely accounted for by the mass flux through a surface bounding the volume; which is what is meant by conservation of mass. From Newton's law applied to a continuum follows an equation of motion for the velocity:

$$\rho \frac{\mathrm{D}\boldsymbol{v}}{\mathrm{D}t} = -\nabla p + \rho \boldsymbol{K}, \tag{1-3}$$

Notes p. 83

where

$$\frac{\mathrm{D}\boldsymbol{v}}{\mathrm{D}t} \equiv \left[\frac{\partial}{\partial t} + (\boldsymbol{v} \cdot \nabla)\right] \boldsymbol{v} \tag{1-4}$$

is called the substantial derivative of the velocity, and is the acceleration of a given fluid particle as one follows its motion. Eq. (1-3) states that the mass density of a fluid particle multiplied by its acceleration equals the forces acting upon it. These derive from the gradient of the fluid pressure p, and the external force per unit mass $\boldsymbol{K}$ (which in the case of gravity is just $\boldsymbol{g}$).

In deriving (1-3) we have assumed that the stresses within a fluid do not depend on the deformation (e.g., $\nabla\rho$) in the Euler approximation. This assumption called Pascal's law distinguishes a fluid from a solid. It is equivalent to asserting that on the Euler level the highest order spatial derivative of the basic variables is first order as opposed to third order in a solid.

On the Euler level we neglect dissipative effects and hence the equation of motion for the entropy is a conservation law:

$$\frac{\partial \rho s}{\partial t} + \nabla \cdot \rho s \boldsymbol{v} = 0. \tag{1-5}$$

Eqs. (1-1,3,5) are five equations for the five basic variables which determine the state of the fluid provided that they are supplemented with an equation of state giving the pressure as a function of the density and specific entropy: $p = p(\rho, s)$. Again from Pascal's law one concludes that p cannot depend on the deformation (i.e., $\nabla\rho$, ∇s), on the Euler level. When also supplemented by the boundary condition that the perpendicular component of the velocity must vanish at stationary solid boundaries these equations determine the behavior of the fluid at time $t > t_0$ given knowledge of its behavior at time 't_0' [4].

In addition to the macroscopic first principles of mass conservation, and Newton's law, one can rightly argue that a fluid's motion should also conform to the principles of momentum conservation (when $\boldsymbol{K} = 0$) and energy conservation. Since (1-1,3,5) form a complete set of equations for a classical fluid the principles of energy and momentum conservation must be consequences of these equations. We show this as follows. First from (1-1,3), with $\boldsymbol{K} = 0$ one finds the law of momentum conservation:

$$\frac{\partial J_i}{\partial t} + \frac{\partial P_{i\alpha}}{\partial r_\alpha} = 0, \tag{1-6}$$

Notes p. 83

where $\boldsymbol{J} = \rho \boldsymbol{v}$ is the momentum density, we sum over repeated indices and $(r_1, r_2, r_3) = (x, y, z)$;

$$P_{ij} = p\delta_{ij} + \rho v_i v_j \tag{1-7}$$

is the stress tensor. When $\boldsymbol{K} \neq 0$ momentum is not conserved and the right hand side of (1-6) becomes $\rho\boldsymbol{K}$. To interpret (1-6) integrate it over a given volume and apply Gauss' law to find:

$$\frac{\mathrm{d}}{\mathrm{d}t}\int J_i \,\mathrm{d}V + \int P_{i\alpha}\,\mathrm{d}S_\alpha = 0.$$

Thus the change of momentum within the volume is due to the momentum flux across a surface bounding the volume, and P_{ij} is the momentum in the ith direction to flow per second across a unit area perpendicular to the jth direction.

The momentum to flow per second across a surface element $\mathrm{d}\boldsymbol{S}$ forming the boundary between the fluid and a solid wall must be the negative of the force exerted by the fluid on the wall. We thus find that this force is $P_{ij}\,\mathrm{d}S_j$. But since the velocity perpendicular to a solid wall vanishes we find that the force exerted by an Euler fluid on an element of surface $\mathrm{d}\boldsymbol{S}$ of a solid wall is $p\,\mathrm{d}\boldsymbol{S}$. The law of conservation of angular momentum follows from (1-6) by calculating $\partial(\boldsymbol{r} \times \boldsymbol{J})/\partial t$.

In order to discuss energy conservation one needs an expression for the energy density U in terms of ρ, s, $\boldsymbol{v}$. The energy density is taken to be equal to the sum of the internal U_0 plus kinetic plus potential energy densities:

$$U = U_0 + \tfrac{1}{2}\rho v^2 + \rho\Omega, \tag{1-8}$$

where $\boldsymbol{K} = -\nabla\Omega$ ($\partial\Omega/\partial t = 0$). By the first and second laws of thermodynamics U_0 is given by

$$\mathrm{d}U_0 = \mu\,\mathrm{d}\rho + T\,\mathrm{d}\rho s, \tag{1-9}$$

where μ is the chemical potential and T the temperature. In terms of the internal energy per gram $\varepsilon = U_0/\rho$ the first and second laws take the more familiar form

$$\mathrm{d}\varepsilon = T\,\mathrm{d}s - p\,\mathrm{d}(1/\rho), \tag{1-10a}$$

where

$$p = -U_0 + \rho\mu + \rho s T,$$

Notes p. 83

or equivalently:

$$\mathrm{d}\mu = -s\,\mathrm{d}T + (1/\rho)\,\mathrm{d}p, \tag{1-10b}$$

and we note that $1/\rho$ is the volume of a unit mass of fluid.

From (1-1,3,5,8,9) the energy conservation law is found to be

$$\frac{\partial U}{\partial t} + \nabla \cdot [\rho \boldsymbol{v}(\mu + sT + \Omega + \tfrac{1}{2}v^2)] = 0. \tag{1-11}$$

A number of basic theorems apply to the special flows for which s can be regarded as constant (isentropic flow). In this case the fluid is described by the four variables ρ, $\boldsymbol{v}$ and the four equations (1-1,3); with Eq. (1-5) being identically satisfied. Since s is constant, Eq. (1-3) becomes

$$\frac{\mathrm{D}\boldsymbol{v}}{\mathrm{D}t} = -\nabla(n + \Omega), \tag{1-12}$$

where $n = \varepsilon + p/\rho$. From (1-12) one obtains the Kelvin circulation theorem

$$\frac{\mathrm{D}}{\mathrm{D}t}\oint \boldsymbol{v} \cdot \mathrm{d}\boldsymbol{\ell} = 0, \tag{1-13}$$

which expresses the fact that the circulation (line integral of $\boldsymbol{v}$ around a closed fluid contour) does not change as one follows the motion of the fluid particles making up the contour. In time a closed fluid contour will distort as the fluid particles which comprise it move according to the equations of motion; Eq. (1-13) states that as the contour distorts its circulation remains invariant. To derive (1-13) one must note that the substantial derivative of an element of contour $\mathrm{d}\boldsymbol{\ell}$ (i.e., the change in $\mathrm{d}\boldsymbol{\ell}$ as one follows the motion of the fluid particles) is $\mathrm{D}\mathrm{d}\boldsymbol{\ell}/\mathrm{D}t = \mathrm{d}\boldsymbol{v}$, which is the increment in velocity between fluid particles separated by a distance $\mathrm{d}\boldsymbol{\ell}$ on the contour. With this in mind we evaluate the substantial derivative of the circulation as follows:

$$\frac{\mathrm{D}}{\mathrm{D}t}\oint \boldsymbol{v} \cdot \mathrm{d}\boldsymbol{\ell} = \oint \frac{\mathrm{D}\boldsymbol{v}}{\mathrm{D}t} \cdot \mathrm{d}\boldsymbol{\ell} + \oint \boldsymbol{v} \cdot \frac{\mathrm{D}\mathrm{d}\boldsymbol{\ell}}{\mathrm{D}t}$$

$$= -\oint \nabla(n + \Omega) \cdot \mathrm{d}\boldsymbol{\ell} + \oint \boldsymbol{v} \cdot \mathrm{d}\boldsymbol{v} = -\oint \mathrm{d}(n + \Omega - \tfrac{1}{2}v^2),$$

where we have used (1-12). As the integral over a closed contour of the gradient of a single valued function vanishes, this expression vanishes leaving us with the Kelvin theorem (1-13). The Kelvin theorem in turn

Notes p. 83

implies (by use of Stokes' law) that if at $t = 0$ the vorticity $\nabla \times \boldsymbol{v}$ is zero everywhere it will stay zero. This is the theorem of Lagrange which can also be proven directly by writing (1-12) in the form

$$\frac{\partial \boldsymbol{v}}{\partial t} = -\nabla(n + \Omega + \tfrac{1}{2}v^2) + \boldsymbol{v} \times (\nabla \times \boldsymbol{v}) \tag{1-14}$$

from which one obtains by taking the curl

$$\frac{\partial}{\partial t}(\nabla \times \boldsymbol{v}) = \nabla \times [\boldsymbol{v} \times (\nabla \times \boldsymbol{v})], \tag{1-15}$$

so that if $\nabla \times \boldsymbol{v} = 0$ everywhere at $t = 0$ (1-15) tells us that the time derivative is zero and hence it will stay zero. It should be emphasized that the Euler theory in no way requires $\nabla \times \boldsymbol{v} = 0$; what we have shown above is that it is consistent with the Euler theory to consider the special case where $\nabla \times \boldsymbol{v} = 0$ everywhere for all times.

From (1-14) one obtains Bernoulli's law which states that, for stationary flow ($\partial \boldsymbol{v}/\partial t = 0$), $n + \Omega + \frac{1}{2}v^2$ is constant along a streamline (a path parallel to the fluid velocity). If $\nabla \times \boldsymbol{v}$ vanishes throughout the fluid one obtains the stronger Bernoulli law

$$\partial\phi/\partial t + n + \Omega + \tfrac{1}{2}v^2 = \text{constant throughout the fluid}, \tag{1-16}$$

where $\boldsymbol{v} = \nabla\phi$.

When the flow may be regarded as incompressible (ρ = constant) then one has also a Kelvin theorem and a Bernoulli law. In this case the Bernoulli law is, from (1-3),

$$p/\rho + \Omega + \tfrac{1}{2}v^2 = \text{constant along a streamline}, \tag{1-17}$$

for stationary flow. One also has from (1-1) that $\nabla \cdot \boldsymbol{v} = 0$.

A simple experimental application of Bernoulli's law consists of observing the flow of fluid between two levels in an external gravitational field ($\Omega = gz$) as shown in Fig. 1. If the cross-sectional area of outflow at the lower level is small compared to the area of the upper level then to a good approximation $\boldsymbol{v} = 0$ at the upper level and the flow is stationary. If the free surfaces are at the same pressure (such as will happen for a container of water exposed to the atmosphere) one finds, from application of (1-17) to a streamline which runs between the two levels, that the velocity of outflow is $(2g\Delta z)^{1/2}$ where Δz is the level difference (Torricelli's formula).

Notes p. 83

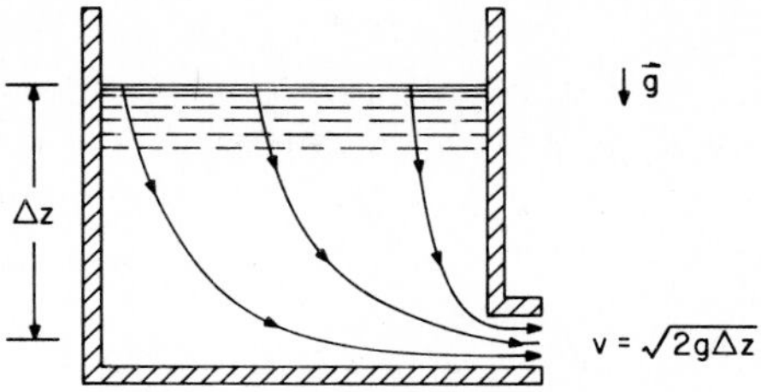

Fig. 1. Illustration of Torricelli's law for the flow of a fluid between two levels in an external gravitational field.

A flow field of special interest is one for which $\nabla \times \boldsymbol{v} = 0$ everywhere along and near a closed path yet the circulation of this contour is non-zero. Using Stokes' law to transform the circulation line integral we find $\int \boldsymbol{v} \cdot \mathrm{d}\boldsymbol{\ell} = \int \nabla \times \boldsymbol{v} \cdot \mathrm{d}\boldsymbol{S}$ where the surface integral goes over the surface spanned by the contour. If $\nabla \times \boldsymbol{v}$ vanishes everywhere then we see that there must be zero circulation. Since we stipulate that some circulation is present there are only two ways to keep from violating Stokes' law: (1) there can be a 'singular' region inside the contour in which $\nabla \times \boldsymbol{v} \neq 0$; (2) there can be a 'singular' region inside the contour in which there is no fluid, thus forbidding the use of Stokes' law in the first place.

We will first consider the special case in which this singular region is in the shape of a very thin cylinder (called a vortex line or vortex core). Since $\nabla \cdot \nabla \times \boldsymbol{v} \equiv 0$ for any $\boldsymbol{v}$ it follows from Gauss' theorem that a vortex line cannot terminate in the fluid. It must end on a boundary or close into itself (vortex rings). For simplicity let the singularity extend along the z axis of an infinite fluid. Then by symmetry requirements one looks for a velocity field which depends only on the distance r from the z axis and lies in a plane perpendicular to the z axis. The only velocity field to satisfy this requirement, $\nabla \times \boldsymbol{v} = 0$ everywhere except at the singularity, and vanish at infinity is

$$\boldsymbol{v} = (\gamma/r)\hat{\boldsymbol{e}}_\theta, \tag{1-18}$$

where γ is a constant which determines strength or circulation $(2\pi\gamma)$ of the line and $\hat{\boldsymbol{e}}_\theta$ is a unit vector circling the z axis.

If compressibility effects can be neglected then one can use the Bernoulli theorem (1-17) to derive the pressure distribution of a vortex line in an infinite fluid:

$$p = p_\infty - \rho\gamma^2/2r^2, \tag{1-19}$$

Notes p. 83

where p_∞ is the pressure far from the core. As one approaches the core r decreases and so does the pressure. The pressure cannot decrease without limit and thus it is common to say that the core has a finite radius which for instance might be chosen so that the negative pressure does not exceed the tensile strength, or the cavitation head for the particular problem under consideration.

When a vortex is not straight and when solid boundaries interfere with the flow field and when compressibility effects need to be considered Eq. (1-18) no longer describes the velocity field of a vortex line. But if the vortex line is the only source of vorticity in the fluid ($\nabla \times \boldsymbol{v} = 0$ everywhere except at the line) then regardless of the complicated velocity field all contours which encircle the line have identical circulations. This is made clear from Fig. 2. On the one hand the circulation of the

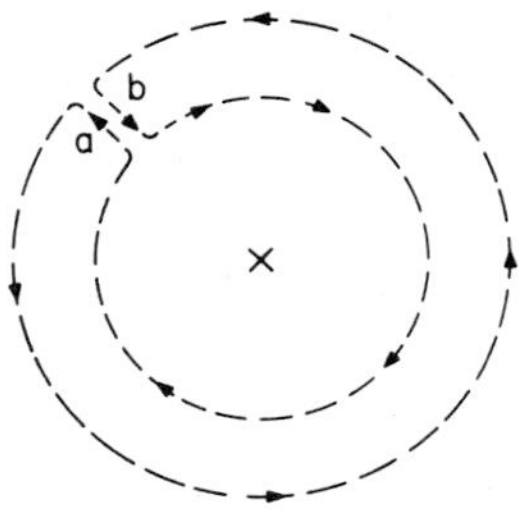

Fig. 2. Integration contour used to demonstrate that the circulation of a vortex (located at the '×') is independent of the contour.

contour of integration indicated by the arrows is equal to the difference of the circulations of the inner and outer contours taken separately, as the contributions from 'a' and 'b' cancel. On the other hand the circulation of the indicated contour is zero since by Stokes' law we can convert the circulation for this path into an integral of $\nabla \times \boldsymbol{v}$ over a surface which is not pierced by the vortex line and hence on which $\nabla \times \boldsymbol{v} = 0$ everywhere. Thus the circulations for the inner and outer contours are equal, and one can conclude that the circulation is a property of the vortex singularity.

For situations in which the Kelvin circulation theorem can be applied one obtains the very important result that a vortex line moves with the local fluid velocity at the core. In other words at a stationary vortex line the fluid velocity perpendicular to the core must vanish. This conse-

Notes p. 83

quence of Kelvin's theorem, which is called the Helmholtz theorem, can be proved by considering a small fluid contour which initially encircles a vortex line. If the vortex is not moving at the local fluid velocity then at a later instant the contour will no longer encircle the vortex line, and its circulation will have changed in violation of the Kelvin theorem.

In concluding this section we discuss the propagation of sound according to the Euler equations. To begin with we investigate the behavior of the Euler equations when the fluid experiences a small disturbance from a homogeneous ($\boldsymbol{K} = 0$) equilibrium state. In equilibrium the density and specific entropy are constant. Hence in the present situation we can take

$$\rho = \rho_0 + \delta\rho(\boldsymbol{r}, t),$$

$$s = s_0 + \delta s(\boldsymbol{r}, t), \tag{1-20}$$

where the deviations $\delta\rho$ of the density, and δs of the specific entropy are small compared to the constant equilibrium values ρ_0 and s_0. In equilibrium the velocity can be taken to be zero so that off equilibrium we put

$$\boldsymbol{v} = \delta\boldsymbol{v}(\boldsymbol{r}, t), \tag{1-21}$$

where $\delta\boldsymbol{v}$ is small in some sense yet to be specified. Now we substitute (1-20,21) into (1-1,3,5) and retain only those terms which are linear in the small quantities $\delta\rho$, δs, $\delta\boldsymbol{v}$; finding

$$\frac{\partial\delta\rho}{\partial t} + \rho_0\nabla\cdot\delta\boldsymbol{v} = 0, \tag{1-22}$$

$$\rho_0\frac{\partial\delta s}{\partial t} + s_0\frac{\partial\delta\rho}{\partial t} + \rho_0 s_0\nabla\cdot\delta\boldsymbol{v} = 0, \tag{1-23}$$

$$\rho_0\frac{\partial\delta\boldsymbol{v}}{\partial t} = -\left(\frac{\partial p}{\partial\rho}\right)_s\nabla\delta\rho - \left(\frac{\partial p}{\partial s}\right)_\rho\nabla\delta s. \tag{1-24}$$

Eqs. (1-22,23,24) are linear differential equations with constant coefficients [we treat $(\partial p/\partial\rho)_s$, etc., as constant since their variation leads to second order terms which can be neglected] and a solution in terms of exponentials is suggested. Thus we guess a solution of the form

$$\delta\rho = \rho'\exp(i\boldsymbol{k}_0\cdot\boldsymbol{r} - i\omega t), \tag{1-25}$$

$$\delta s = s'\exp(i\boldsymbol{k}_0\cdot\boldsymbol{r} - i\omega t), \tag{1-26}$$

$$\delta\boldsymbol{v} = \boldsymbol{v}'\exp(i\boldsymbol{k}_0\cdot\boldsymbol{r} - i\omega t), \tag{1-27}$$

Notes p. 83

where $\rho', s', \boldsymbol{v}'$ are the constant amplitudes of the travelling plane wave solutions which we guess. By substituting (1-25,26,27) into (1-22,23,24) one immediately verifies that in order for there to exist a non-trivial solution the waves must be longitudinal (i.e., $\boldsymbol{v}'$ must be parallel to $\boldsymbol{k}_0$). We assume this and are led to the relations

$$-i\omega\rho' + ik_0\rho_0 v' = 0, \tag{1-28}$$

$$-i\omega\rho_0 s' - i\omega s_0\rho' + i\rho_0 s_0 k_0 v' = 0, \tag{1-29}$$

$$-i\omega\rho_0 v' + i\left(\frac{\partial p}{\partial \rho}\right)_s k_0\rho' + i\left(\frac{\partial p}{\partial s}\right)_\rho k_0 s' = 0. \tag{1-30}$$

These are three homogeneous equations in three unknowns and in order for there to exist a non-trivial solution the determinant must vanish. As a consequence, we find the dispersion law

$$\frac{\omega^2}{k_0^2} = \left(\frac{\partial p}{\partial \rho}\right)_s \equiv u^2, \tag{1-31}$$

where u is referred to as the speed of sound.

We have just shown that small disturbances propagate through the fluid at this speed. Also a disturbance of the fluid at angular frequency ω will lead to a travelling wave of wavelength $2\pi/k_0$. Since Eqs. (1-22, 23,24) are linear any superposition of travelling waves will also satisfy the equations of motion provided that their space and time variations obey the dispersion law (1-31). The variation of quantities within the sound wave follows from (1-28,29,30). In particular we see that the sound wave is isentropic and involves variations only in the density (or pressure):

$$s' = 0, \tag{1-32}$$

$$\rho' = \rho_0 v'/u. \tag{1-33}$$

Returning to the question concerning what assumption must be made about $\delta\boldsymbol{v}$ in order to linearize the Euler equations, we now see from (1-33) that one must take $v'/u \ll 1$; otherwise ρ'/ρ_0 could become large. One can easily verify that in this approximation we are justified in dropping $(\delta\boldsymbol{v}\cdot\nabla)\delta\boldsymbol{v}$ compared to $\partial\delta\boldsymbol{v}/\partial t$ in going from (1-3) to (1-24).

Lastly we remark that the travelling wave solution which we have found is according to the Euler equations undamped. This is to be expected since on the Euler level entropy is conserved and there can be no absorption, or dissipation of mechanical energy into heat.

Notes p. 83

2 *The Kapitza Experiment and the Landau Two Fluid Equations*

In many experimental arrangements the flow properties of He II seem to obey the Euler equations. For instance, in the flow out of a vessel Allen and Misener [5] have verified that the Torricelli law (see § 1) remains valid. Furthermore the propagation of sound was found by Findlay et al. [6] to obey the relation (1-31), where we note that $(\partial p/\partial \rho)_s$ can be independently determined by static thermodynamic measurements of the equilibrium properties of the fluid.

However, in other experimental situations the Euler equations apparently give a highly inadequate description of the dynamical properties of He II. One of the most striking phenomena to demonstrate this was the fountain, or thermochemical, effect which was discovered by Allen and Jones in 1938 [7].

They observed that when two vessels, (A and B in Fig. 3) containing He II were connected by a superleak S, which is a very narrow constriction less than 10^{-4} cm in width, a heating of the inner vessel led not only to an expected temperature difference ΔT but also to a flow of liquid into the inner vessel and thus also to a level, or pressure difference, Δp, between the two vessels. According to the Euler equations a temperature difference can lead to a flow, or convection of liquid, but the entropy law (1-5) stipulates that the fluid velocity $\boldsymbol{v}$ must be in the same direction as the entropy flow, $\rho s \boldsymbol{v}$. In the fountain effect, the fluid flow opposes the heat flow!

The inverse of this experiment is the mechanocaloric effect which was first described by Daunt and Mendelssohn in 1939 [8]. They observed the behavior of the temperature of two vessels initially at the same temperature, when He II was allowed to flow say under the influence of gravity, from one vessel to the other through a superleak. Their results indicated that the temperature of a given vessel increased as the liquid flowed out. One might try to attribute this to dissipation, or friction encountered in flow through the superleak, except that one also knows that this flow can take place at zero pressure head, thus suggesting that it is a reversible flow. To further add to the paradox they found a cooling of the container into which the liquid flowed.

The landmark experiment of Kapitza in 1941 provided a clear and quantitative unification of the above observations [9]. His apparatus (Fig. 3) consisted of an inner vessel A which was adiabatically insulated

Notes p. 83

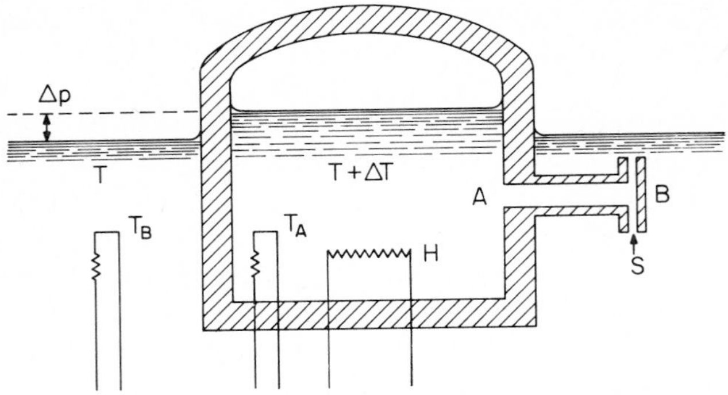

Fig. 3. Apparatus used for observation of the fountain effect.

from an outer vessel B. They were connected by a superleak S; T_A, T_B are thermometers used to measure the temperature of the He II in the respective containers, H is a heater through which the liquid in A can be heated. The advances made possible by Kapitza's experiment were due to his ability to accurately measure the temperatures, the heating rate $\dot{W}$, and the pressure (level) difference Δp, in the steady state and in the approach to it.

A typical experiment started with the temperatures and levels equal. Then as heat was supplied to A its temperature increased and fluid also flowed in through the superleak leading to a level difference. After some time and for a given $\dot{W}$ a steady state is reached where $\dot{W}$ is balanced by heat losses to the walls. It was found that not only in the steady state, but also in the approach to it, that the chemical potentials at the same level on either side of the superleak are equal or

$$\mu(p_A, T_A) = \mu(p_B, T_B), \tag{2-1}$$

where p_A, p_B are the pressures at A, B in Fig. 3. For small temperature and pressure differences the thermodynamic relation $d\mu = -s\,dT + dp/\rho$ leads to

$$\Delta p = \rho s \Delta T. \tag{2-2}$$

If the pressure difference is due to a level difference Δz in the external gravitational field then $\Delta p = \rho g \Delta z$ and we find that at 2 °K for instance, a $\Delta T = 10^{-3}$ °K leads to a level difference of 9.6 cm since $s = 9.6 \times 10^6$ erg/g °K, at this temperature.

Notes p. 83

These results (2-1), (2-2) hold only when $\dot{W}$ is small enough. There is apparently a critical value of $\dot{W}$. For heat inputs greater than this critical value, ΔT rises faster than predicted by (2-1). We will return to this critical phenomenon later and restrict ourselves here to the subcritical flow since it already reflects the basic properties of He II.

Besides demonstrating Eq. (2-1), Kapitza was able to draw another conclusion from his experiments. Since the cross-sectional area of the inner vessel A is known one can find from the change of Δp with time the volume flow rate $\dot{V}$ through the superleak. One then finds that in the beginning of the experiment when ΔT is very small that the heating rate $\dot{W}$ is much greater than can be accounted for by the heat necessary to increase by ΔT the temperature of the fluid already in A, plus the heat losses to the walls. The only other place to which the heat can go is into warming up the incoming fluid. He concluded that incoming fluid was deficient in heat content by the amount $\dot{W}/\rho\dot{V}$ per gram. Kapitza found that this quantity was equal to $T_A s_A$ where s_A is the entropy per gram of the fluid in A! Thus a gram of fluid which flows through the superleak does not carry with it the entropy which a gram of fluid has in vessel B, but instead carries no entropy and behaves as though it were at the absolute zero of temperature. This result shows that the flow of He II (at least through a superleak) is quite different from that of an Euler fluid where a flow of liquid always involves a flow of entropy [see (1-5)].

This last result of Kapitza explains the mechanocaloric effect as follows. The fluid to flow out of a vessel through a superleak carries no entropy so that the fluid to remain behind has the same total entropy distributed over less mass, which means that it has a higher temperature. In a similar way the container into which the zero entropy fluid flows is cooled.

Equation (2-1) is referred to as the H. London relation since he predicted in 1939 that a quantitative investigation of the fountain effect would yield data consistent with this relation [10]. In his derivation of (2-1) he considered the situation under which two vessels of He II connected by a narrow capillary (superleak) can be in equilibrium. For vessels A and B in Fig. 4 to be in equilibrium it must be possible to exchange mass between them reversibly through the superleak S. Let the exchange be accomplished by pushing in the piston of container B changing its volume by $\mathrm{d}V_B$. As a result of the increase of mass in A its volume may change by $\mathrm{d}V_A$. The net work done on the combined system in the mass transfer is thus

$$-p_A \,\mathrm{d}V_A - p_B \,\mathrm{d}V_B. \qquad (2\text{-}3)$$

Notes p. 83

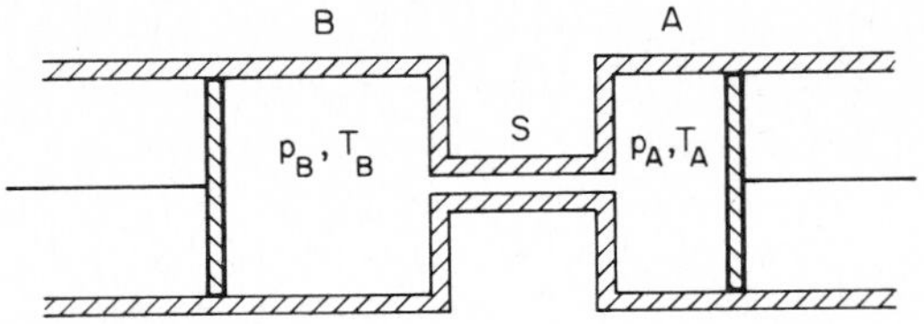

Fig. 4. Simplified arrangement useful for investigating the thermodynamics of the thermo-mechanical (i.e., fountain) effect.

In the course of this mass transfer the energies of A and B will respectively change by

$$\begin{aligned} dE_A &= \mu_A\, dM_A + T_A\, dS_A - p_A\, dV_A, \\ dE_B &= \mu_B\, dM_B + T_B\, dS_B - p_B\, dV_B, \end{aligned} \tag{2-4}$$

where M_A, S_A is the net mass, entropy in vessel A. As we put in no heat from outside the change in total energy must equal the work performed:

$$-p_A\, dV_A - p_B\, dV_B = dE_A + dE_B. \tag{2-5}$$

Also, if the process is to be reversible we must have

$$dS_A + dS_B = 0, \tag{2-6}$$

which states that the net change in entropy vanishes (again note that no heat is put in from outside in this process). From Eqs. (2-4,5,6) we find for the condition of reversibility

$$(\mu_A - \mu_B)\, dM_A + (T_A - T_B)\, dS_A = 0, \tag{2-7}$$

where we have also used the fact that there is no net change in the mass of the system: $dM_A = -dM_B$. In order to satisfy (2-7) for all possible processes (i.e., all possible dV_A and dV_B) the two terms on the left hand side must separately vanish since they are independent. London noticed that there are two ways of accomplishing this. First one could take $\mu_A = \mu_B$ and $T_A = T_B$. This is the usual condition for thermodynamic equilibrium. In ordinary fluids and in He II such equilibrium states can be found. London observed that a solution to (2-7) also existed if $\mu_A = \mu_B$ and $dS_A = 0$. That is: the chemical potentials are equal but there is no restriction on the temperature. For an ordinary liquid an exchange of mass always implies an exchange of entropy and hence this equilibrium state is not observed. But London guessed that such an equilibrium state could exist in He II and was in fact the fountain effect.

Of course if one waits long enough dissipative processes within the fluid will lead to an entropy flow which will even out the temperature difference in any arrangement such as in Fig. 4. What London had in mind is that for He II there exists a limit in which the superleak can be regarded as 'ideal' in that it permits a mass flow without an entropy flow (i.e., it acts like an entropy filter). This is the limit in which the above thermodynamic procedure is valid and in which the fountain effect can be regarded as an equilibrium state. In thermodynamics one often has in mind some limit in which the behavior of the system can be regarded as reversible. For instance in the osmotic pressure effect one talks of a discontinuity in chemical potential (and thus pressure) for the equilibrium state where a semipermeable membrane separates two solutions of different concentrations. There too, after a very long time, dissipative processes will lead to an equalization of pressure for any given experimental arrangement. And here also one can consider the state with an osmotic pressure difference as an equilibrium state only in the limit that the membrane is an 'ideal' semipermeable membrane.

One can question that the fountain effect is an equilibrium state from another point of view. According to London one has found that there is a pressure difference across the superleak. Yet we know that the fluid can flow without friction in the narrowest capillary, so why doesn't the fluid accelerate, and how can we have a steady state, no less an equilibrium state.

Questions like these indicate that a complete understanding of the fountain effect can only come from an investigation of the dynamical equations of He II. London's contribution here was to focus our attention on the fact that the fountain effect is basically a reversible process [11].

The dynamical equations for He II on the reversible level were first presented by Landau in 1941 [3]. In order to explain that in some cases (e.g., Torricelli flow) the entropy of He II flowed with the center of mass velocity $\boldsymbol{v}$ as though it were an Euler fluid, while in other cases there could be a mass flow with no entropy flow, Landau postulated that the velocity of flow of entropy was for He II a new variable, *independent* of $\boldsymbol{v}$. Thus in order to describe the state of He II one must know in addition to the center of mass velocity, the velocity $\boldsymbol{v}_{\mathrm{n}}$ of the entropy flow, at each point in the fluid.

Notes p. 83

As with the Euler fluid the equation of conservation of mass takes the form

$$\frac{\partial \rho}{\partial t} + \nabla \cdot \rho \boldsymbol{v} = 0. \tag{2-8}$$

In contrast with the Euler fluid the equation of conservation of entropy (which expresses the fact that we approximate the flow as being reversible) takes the form

$$\frac{\partial \rho s}{\partial t} + \nabla \cdot \rho s \boldsymbol{v}_{\mathrm{n}} = 0, \tag{2-9}$$

where $\boldsymbol{v}_{\mathrm{n}}$ is independent of $\boldsymbol{v}$. Let the density of mass to move with velocity $\boldsymbol{v}_{\mathrm{n}}$ be designated by ρ_{n} then since $\rho_{\mathrm{n}} \neq \rho$ (if $\rho_{\mathrm{n}} = \rho$ then we clearly must have $\boldsymbol{v}_{\mathrm{n}} = \boldsymbol{v}$ which would contradict the requirement that $\boldsymbol{v}_{\mathrm{n}}$ be independent) we define $\rho_{\mathrm{s}} = \rho - \rho_{\mathrm{n}}$. The quantity ρ_{s} is the density of mass which does not have any entropy and hence it is called the superfluid density. It moves at the superfluid velocity $\boldsymbol{v}_{\mathrm{s}}$. By contrast ρ_{n}, $\boldsymbol{v}_{\mathrm{n}}$ are referred to as the normal fluid density and velocity. The superfluid velocity is related to the other quantities by an equation expressing that the total mass flow is the sum of the flows of super and normal components:

$$\boldsymbol{J} \equiv \rho \boldsymbol{v} = \rho_{\mathrm{n}} \boldsymbol{v}_{\mathrm{n}} + \rho_{\mathrm{s}} \boldsymbol{v}_{\mathrm{s}}. \tag{2-10}$$

The idea that at each point in the fluid there are two independent velocity fields (say $\boldsymbol{v}_{\mathrm{n}}$, $\boldsymbol{v}_{\mathrm{s}}$) is referred to as the two fluid model. The two 'fluids', normal and super, exist throughout the entire volume interpenetrating each other and moving with independent velocities.

The lack of flow of entropy across the superleak in Kapitza's experiment can be understood in terms of this two fluid dynamics by saying that in a narrow constriction $\boldsymbol{v}_{\mathrm{n}} = 0$ and hence only the superfluid which transports no entropy can flow. Of course we have not proven that $\boldsymbol{v}_{\mathrm{n}} = 0$ in such a geometry. A proof of this point must wait until we consider the dynamics of He II when dissipative processes are included. At that time (Chap. II) we will see that the normal fluid has a viscosity just like an ordinary Navier–Stokes fluid. Its viscous interaction with the narrow walls then strongly impairs its flow through the superleak. The narrower the superleak the harder it is for the normal fluid to flow. In the limit of very narrow superleaks we approach the ideal superleak which was invoked in order to treat the fountain effect as an equilibrium state.

Notes p. 83

In order to explain the constancy of the chemical potential across the superleak in the steady state ($\boldsymbol{v}_s = 0$) and in the dynamical approach to the steady state ($\boldsymbol{v}_s =$ constant in the superleak) Landau postulates that the chemical potential is the driving force for the superfluid:

$$\frac{\mathrm{D}_s \boldsymbol{v}_s}{\mathrm{D}t} \equiv \frac{\partial \boldsymbol{v}_s}{\partial t} + (\boldsymbol{v}_s \cdot \nabla)\boldsymbol{v}_s = -\nabla \mu. \tag{2-11}$$

Thus a pressure gradient is not sufficient to accelerate the superfluid. Instead it responds to a gradient in the chemical potential. And when its acceleration can be neglected Eq. (2-11) implies that the chemical potential must be constant.

For He II one has a law of conservation of momentum just as with an Euler fluid:

$$\frac{\partial J_i}{\partial t} + \frac{\partial P_{i\alpha}}{\partial r_\alpha} = 0. \tag{2-12}$$

Except now since there are two velocity fields one takes for the stress tensor

$$P_{ij} = p\delta_{ij} + \rho_n v_{n,i} v_{n,j} + \rho_s v_{s,i} v_{s,j}. \tag{2-13}$$

The Landau two fluid equations (2-8,9,11,12) are eight independent equations for the time development of the eight independent variables ρ, s, $\boldsymbol{v}_n$, $\boldsymbol{v}_s$ which describe the flow of He II. When supplemented with equations of state for ρ_n, p, μ in terms of these variables, the equations form a complete closed description of the flow on the reversible level. There is an important difference between the form of the equations of state of He II and those of an ordinary fluid, which we mention. In a classical fluid $p = p(\rho, s)$ but for He II:

$$p = p[\rho, s, (\boldsymbol{v}_n - \boldsymbol{v}_s)^2].$$

The quantity $(\boldsymbol{v}_n - \boldsymbol{v}_s)^2$ is scalar with respect to rotations and invariant with respect to a Galilean transformation of the reference system. Thus it has the same general properties as the usual internal variables ρ, s, and can in general appear with them in the equations of state. Similarly

$$\rho_n = \rho_n[\rho, s, (\boldsymbol{v}_n - \boldsymbol{v}_s)^2],$$

$$\mu = \mu[\rho, s, (\boldsymbol{v}_n - \boldsymbol{v}_s)^2].$$

We put off until § 6 a discussion of the boundary conditions.

Notes p. 83

When $\boldsymbol{v}_n = \boldsymbol{v}_s$ and variations in the temperature can be neglected, $d\mu = dp/\rho$ and Eqs. (2-12) and (2-11) become identical with each other and with the Euler equation (1-3). For flows which satisfy this requirement (e.g., Torricelli and sound propagation) the behavior of He II will be like that of an Euler fluid.

In situations where the variations of ρ_s, ρ, s can be neglected, the two fluid equations become

$$\nabla \cdot \boldsymbol{v}_n = 0,$$

$$\nabla \cdot \boldsymbol{v}_s = 0,$$

$$\rho_n \frac{D_n \boldsymbol{v}_n}{Dt} = -\nabla p_n, \tag{2-14}$$

$$\rho_s \frac{D_s \boldsymbol{v}_s}{Dt} = -\nabla p_s, \tag{2-15}$$

where $p_s = \rho_s \mu$, $p_n + p_s = p$ and $D_n/Dt \equiv \partial/\partial t + \boldsymbol{v}_n \cdot \nabla$. In this case the basic equations separate into two independent Euler type equations for the normal and super components.

One might argue that in order to explain a few experiments one has introduced a few extra parameters. Confidence in the Landau two fluid equations can come only from an investigation of their consequences in many diverse situations. When we do this we will see that they do indeed provide the basic description of the flow of He II.

In this section we have followed the historical development of the two fluid concept. However, in our historical coarse graining, the important qualitative insights of Tisza [12] have not been mentioned.

The two fluid idea was first presented by Tisza in 1938 [12]. He was completely aware of the need to introduce an extra velocity field in order to describe the unusual properties of He II, but nowhere in his early work do any of the two fluid equations (2-8,9,11,12) correctly appear. Tisza demonstrated a remarkable qualitative insight into the behavior of He II, but his contributions prior to the Landau papers of 1941, did not constitute a workable theory. Nevertheless based on his intuitive understanding Tisza was the first to predict that He II would possess an additional collective propagating mode, that would involve thermal disturbances. This so called second sound is discussed in § 7, where the dispersion law is derived based on the Landau two fluid theory. This result which is in agreement with experiment is different from the dispersion law presented by Tisza.

Notes p. 83

3 *Derivation of the Landau Two Fluid Equations*

In § 2 we showed how various experimental results inductively led to the Landau two fluid equations for He II which are a generalization of the Euler equations of motion. However, there are several questions concerning these equations which are as yet unanswered. For instance: are these equations consistent with each other and with the principles of energy conservation, thermodynamics and Galilean relativity? Also what are the minimum number of assumptions which must be made in order to uniquely arrive at these equations? The answer to this last question from the phenomenological point of view is important since in the ultimate attempt to understand the behavior of He II from the microscopic approach one must know, which are the properties that must be derived and which are the properties that will follow from general symmetry requirements.

In order to describe the flow of He II the basic assumption which must be made from the phenomenological point of view is that knowledge of two independent velocity fields is required. Thus, whereas a classical fluid is described by five variables, He II is characterized by eight. One can take these variables as ρ, s, $\boldsymbol{v}_n$, $\boldsymbol{v}_s$, *but for the purpose of this exposition we take the eight basic variables as* ρ, s, $\boldsymbol{v}_s$ *and the mass current* $\boldsymbol{J}$, unless otherwise specified.

A complete description of the motion will then involve eight dynamical equations. Five of these must describe the conservation of mass, energy, and momentum:

$$\frac{\partial \rho}{\partial t} + \nabla \cdot \boldsymbol{J} = 0, \tag{3-1}$$

$$\frac{\partial U}{\partial t} + \nabla \cdot \boldsymbol{Q} = 0, \tag{3-2}$$

$$\frac{\partial \mathscr{J}_i}{\partial t} + \frac{\partial P_{i\alpha}}{\partial r_\alpha} = 0, \tag{3-3}$$

where U is the total energy (kinetic plus internal) density, $\boldsymbol{Q}$ is the energy flux density, P_{ij} is the stress tensor and $\mathscr{J}_i$ the momentum density. For a classical fluid, and in fact for He II, $\boldsymbol{\mathscr{J}} = \boldsymbol{J}$ but from the macroscopic point of view there is no first principle which forces us to take these quantities as being equal [44]. For this exposition we take $\boldsymbol{\mathscr{J}} = \boldsymbol{J}$ and defer to Appendix I a discussion of the proof that this is in fact the case.

Notes p. 83

The last three equations are a consequence of the assumption that on the ideal level the superfluid velocity obeys a Kelvin circulation theorem (1-13). This forces the equation to be of the form

$$\frac{D_s \boldsymbol{v}_s}{Dt} = -\nabla\psi, \tag{3-4}$$

where ψ is an unknown driving force. The Eqs. (3-1,2,3,4) constitute a complete set but are an empty frame since we have no explicit relationships for the fluxes (i.e., $\boldsymbol{Q}$, P_{ij}, ψ) in terms of the basic variables. However, since we focus our attention in this chapter on non-dissipative processes we have at our disposal an additional thermodynamic restriction expressing the conservation of entropy:

$$\frac{\partial \rho s}{\partial t} + \nabla \cdot \boldsymbol{f} = 0, \tag{3-5}$$

where $\boldsymbol{f}$ is the entropy flux density.

Now we argue that (3-1,2,3,4,5) constitute *nine* equations for *eight* unknowns and hence must be redundant. We formulate this redundancy condition as follows: for a classical fluid we noticed that the equations of mass, entropy and momentum conservation implied the equation of energy conservation; similarly we say here that (3-1,3,4,5) must imply the energy conservation equation (3-2).

We next show following Landau [3] that when this redundancy condition is combined with the principles of Galilean covariance and thermodynamics these equations become identical with the Landau two fluid equations [in particular $\psi = \mu$ and P_{ij} is given by (2-13)] *and there are no other possibilities.* In addition expressions for U and $\boldsymbol{Q}$ will follow.

Thus we will show that the Landau two fluid equations are a unique consequence of the assumptions, that eight variables form a complete set and that the additional velocity field $\boldsymbol{v}_s$ obeys a Kelvin circulation theorem. In parallel with the classical fluid Pascal's law is also assumed.

We were in § 1 able to derive the Euler equations of motion without appealing to the Galilean transformation. This resulted from the existence in classical hydrodynamics of a preferred rest system. This reference frame (the one in which $\boldsymbol{v} = 0$) is clearly preferred since in it, the mass flow, entropy flow and energy current all vanish. Quantities such as the temperature are defined with respect to an observer in this

Notes p. 83

reference frame. Also it is possible by a Galilean transformation to bring any element of fluid to rest. In He II there are two independent velocity fields and by a Galilean transformation it is impossible to bring both fluids to rest. Thus for He II there is no preferred reference system! The reference frame in which the entropy flux $\boldsymbol{f}$ vanishes is in principle just as good, as the (generally different) reference frame in which the mass flow $\boldsymbol{J}$ vanishes, as far as describing the flow and defining such quantities as the temperature. In the electromagnetic theory of the vacuum the Lorentz transformation plays an especially important role since there is no rest system for the electromagnetic phenomena. In the same manner the Galilean transformation plays a crucial role in the behavior of He II since it also has no rest system. This and the macroscopic quantum effects are the two most important properties of superfluid helium.

We take for the Galilean transformation of U and $\boldsymbol{J}$ the same formulas as are obeyed by the Euler fluid. From the classical expressions for U and $\boldsymbol{J}$ we find that the relationship between the values of U and $\boldsymbol{J}$ measured in two different Galilean systems (denoted by subscripts 1 and 2) in relative motion with relative velocity $\boldsymbol{v}_R$ is

$$U_2 = U_1 + \boldsymbol{v}_R \cdot \boldsymbol{J}_1 + \tfrac{1}{2}\rho v_R^2, \tag{3-6}$$

$$\boldsymbol{J}_2 = \boldsymbol{J}_1 + \rho \boldsymbol{v}_R, \tag{3-7}$$

where we have used $\boldsymbol{v}_2 = \boldsymbol{v}_1 + \boldsymbol{v}_R$. It is not obvious (especially in view of the above comments) that when one introduces an additional internal velocity (such as in He II) the Galilean transformations remain unchanged. The extent to which it can be proven that (3-6) and (3-7) are valid for He II is commented upon in Appendix II.

As an example of the usefulness of the Galilean transformation we consider (3-7) and temporarily remark upon the case where the eight independent variables are taken to be ρ, s, $\boldsymbol{v}_n$, $\boldsymbol{v}_s$. Since $\boldsymbol{J}$ must be a vector with respect to rotation of the coordinate axis, the most general expression for $\boldsymbol{J}$ in terms of the basic variables is

$$\boldsymbol{J} = \rho_n \boldsymbol{v}_n + \rho_s \boldsymbol{v}_s, \tag{3-8}$$

where ρ_n and ρ_s are so far only restricted to be scalars with respect to rotation. One might ask why there isn't a term $\alpha \nabla \rho$ on the right hand side of (3-8) since it also is a vector (provided that α is a scalar). Such a term would violate the assumption of Pascal's law since then the equations would be at least second order in the gradients and the fluxes,

Notes p. 83

$\boldsymbol{J}$, P_{ij}, $\boldsymbol{f}$, ψ would then depend on the deformation (i.e., gradients) on the reversible level. Thus terms like $\alpha\nabla\rho$ can be omitted from present considerations. We next show that the Galilean transformation (3-7) further restricts ρ_n and ρ_s in (3-8) to be Galilean invariants whose sum is ρ (i.e., $\rho_n + \rho_s = \rho$). First from (3-8) and (3-7) we find

$$\rho_{n,2}\boldsymbol{v}_{n,2} + \rho_{s,2}\boldsymbol{v}_{s,2} = \rho_{n,1}\boldsymbol{v}_{n,1} + \rho_{s,1}\boldsymbol{v}_{s,1} + \rho\boldsymbol{v}_R. \tag{3-9}$$

But since $\boldsymbol{v}_{n,2} = \boldsymbol{v}_{n,1} + \boldsymbol{v}_R$ and similarly for $\boldsymbol{v}_s$, we have

$$\rho_{n,2}\boldsymbol{v}_{n,1} + \rho_{s,2}\boldsymbol{v}_{s,1} + (\rho_{n,2} + \rho_{s,2})\boldsymbol{v}_R = \rho_{n,1}\boldsymbol{v}_{n,1} + \rho_{s,1}\boldsymbol{v}_{s,1} + \rho\boldsymbol{v}_R. \tag{3-10}$$

As (3-10) must be an identity and since $\boldsymbol{v}_n$, $\boldsymbol{v}_s$ and $\boldsymbol{v}_R$ are mutually independent we conclude: $\rho_{n,2} = \rho_{n,1}$, $\rho_{s,2} = \rho_{s,1}$ and $\rho_n + \rho_s = \rho$, which is what we wanted to show. Thus in the case where the eight basic variables are taken to be ρ, s, $\boldsymbol{v}_n$, $\boldsymbol{v}_s$, the mass current is given by (3-8) where ρ_n and ρ_s are scalar Galilean invariants [which are to be considered as functions of ρ, s, $(\boldsymbol{v}_n - \boldsymbol{v}_s)^2$] whose sum is the total fluid density ρ.

We now return to our general attempts to derive the two fluid equations. An expression for the energy density U which fulfils the transformation (3-6) is

$$U = U_0 + \boldsymbol{v}_s \cdot (\boldsymbol{J} - \rho\boldsymbol{v}_s) + \tfrac{1}{2}\rho v_s^2, \tag{3-11}$$

where U_0 must be a Galilean invariant. As two quantities which obey identical Galilean transformations can differ at most by an invariant (3-11) with U_0 an undetermined invariant can be taken to be the expression for the energy density.

As U_0 is a Galilean invariant it must depend only on ρ, s and $\boldsymbol{J} - \rho\boldsymbol{v}_s$ (although $\boldsymbol{J} - \rho\boldsymbol{v}_s$ is a vector it is a Galilean invariant because it depends on the difference of two quantities which obey the same Galilean transformation). Hence we can set

$$\mathrm{d}U_0 = \mu\,\mathrm{d}\rho + T\,\mathrm{d}\rho s + \boldsymbol{w}\,\mathrm{d}(\boldsymbol{J} - \rho\boldsymbol{v}_s), \tag{3-12}$$

where for the moment μ, T, $\boldsymbol{w}$ are only formally defined as the conjugate intensive variables to ρ, ρs, and $J - \rho\boldsymbol{v}_s$:

$$\mu = \left(\frac{\partial U_0}{\partial \rho}\right)_{\rho s, \boldsymbol{J}-\rho\boldsymbol{v}_s}, \quad T = \left(\frac{\partial U_0}{\partial \rho s}\right)_{\rho, \boldsymbol{J}-\rho\boldsymbol{v}_s},$$

$$\boldsymbol{w} = \left(\frac{\partial U_0}{\partial(\boldsymbol{J} - \rho\boldsymbol{v}_s)}\right)_{\rho, \rho s}.$$

Notes p. 83

Equation (3-12) is the first and second law of thermodynamics for He II. Because of isotropy (i.e., U_0 is a scalar) $\boldsymbol{w}$ must be parallel to $\boldsymbol{J} - \rho \boldsymbol{v}_s$. The energy density does not depend on the deformation (e.g., $\nabla \rho$) by again invoking Pascal's law.

From (3-11) and (3-12) we find

$$\mathrm{d}U = [\mu + \tfrac{1}{2}v_s^2 - (\boldsymbol{v}_s + \boldsymbol{w}) \cdot \boldsymbol{v}_s]\,\mathrm{d}\rho + T\,\mathrm{d}\rho s + (\boldsymbol{v}_s + \boldsymbol{w}) \cdot \mathrm{d}\boldsymbol{J} + [\boldsymbol{J} - \rho(\boldsymbol{v}_s + \boldsymbol{w})] \cdot \mathrm{d}\boldsymbol{v}_s. \quad (3\text{-}13)$$

Forming the time derivative $\partial U/\partial t$ yields

$$\frac{\partial U}{\partial t} = [\mu + \tfrac{1}{2}v_s^2 - (\boldsymbol{v}_s + \boldsymbol{w}) \cdot \boldsymbol{v}_s] \frac{\partial \rho}{\partial t} + T \frac{\partial \rho s}{\partial t} + (\boldsymbol{v}_s + \boldsymbol{w}) \cdot \frac{\partial \boldsymbol{J}}{\partial t} + [\boldsymbol{J} - \rho(\boldsymbol{v}_s + \boldsymbol{w})] \cdot \frac{\partial \boldsymbol{v}_s}{\partial t}. \quad (3\text{-}14)$$

Using (3-1,3,4,5) to eliminate the time derivatives on the right hand side of (3-14) in favor of space derivatives we find

$$\frac{\partial U}{\partial t} = -[\mu + \tfrac{1}{2}v_s^2 - (\boldsymbol{v}_s + \boldsymbol{w}) \cdot \boldsymbol{v}_s]\nabla \cdot \boldsymbol{J} - T\nabla \cdot \boldsymbol{f} - (\boldsymbol{v}_s + \boldsymbol{w}) \cdot \nabla p - (v_s + w)_i \frac{\partial \Pi_{ij}}{\partial r_j} - [J - \rho(v_s + w)]_i \left(\frac{\partial \psi}{\partial r_i} + v_{s,k} \frac{\partial v_{s,i}}{\partial r_k} \right), \quad (3\text{-}15)$$

where we have put $P_{ij} = p\delta_{ij} + \Pi_{ij}$. This decomposition of P_{ij} is accomplished as follows. By Pascal's law it does not depend on the gradients thus the only quantities at our disposal for forming a tensor of rank two are δ_{ij} and the vectors $v_{s,i}$, J_i. Thus P_{ij} can in general be decomposed into a superposition of scalars multiplying δ_{ij} and scalars multiplying quadratic combinations of the velocity vectors. This last or kinetic contribution to P_{ij} we denote by Π_{ij}.

Writing $-T\nabla \cdot \boldsymbol{f} \equiv -\nabla \cdot (\boldsymbol{f}T) + \boldsymbol{f} \cdot \nabla T$ and similarly flipping around the derivatives of the other terms which are also in the form of a coefficient multiplying a divergence yields

$$\frac{\partial U}{\partial t} = -\frac{\partial}{\partial r_\alpha}\{[\mu + \tfrac{1}{2}v_s^2 - (\boldsymbol{v}_s + \boldsymbol{w}) \cdot \boldsymbol{v}_s]J_\alpha + f_\alpha T + (v_s + w)_i \Pi_{i\alpha}\} - (\boldsymbol{v}_s + \boldsymbol{w}) \cdot \nabla p + \Pi_{ik} \frac{\partial (v_s + w)_i}{\partial r_k} + \boldsymbol{J} \cdot \nabla[\mu + \tfrac{1}{2}v_s^2 - (\boldsymbol{v}_s + \boldsymbol{w}) \cdot \boldsymbol{v}_s] +$$

Notes p. 83

$$- [\boldsymbol{J} - \rho(\boldsymbol{v}_\mathrm{s} + \boldsymbol{w})] \cdot \nabla\psi + \boldsymbol{f} \cdot \nabla T - [J - \rho(v_\mathrm{s} + w)]_i \, v_{\mathrm{s},k} \frac{\partial v_{\mathrm{s},i}}{\partial r_k}. \quad (3\text{-}16)$$

To proceed further we need an expression for p in terms of the other variables. We first show that p is in fact the pressure in that a change in volume requires $p\,\mathrm{d}V$ work. Integrate the momentum conservation equation over a closed volume and assume that the velocities perpendicular to a wall bounding this volume vanish. From the above decomposition of P_{ij} we find that the components of Π_{ij} perpendicular to the wall also vanish. Thus the change in total momentum in the volume is given by $\int p\,\mathrm{d}\boldsymbol{S}$ over a wall containing the volume. Therefore $\int p\,\mathrm{d}\boldsymbol{S}$ is the force on the fluid, p being the force per unit area and when the volume changes there must be a $p\,\mathrm{d}V$ work which in turn leads to a change in the total energy of the fluid. Since the velocities can be taken independent of p one is permitted to consider the special case where their perpendicular components vanish at the boundary. In general this component (and the corresponding components of Π_{ij}) will not vanish and this will lead to other contributions to the work performed in changing the volume. All that we can conclude then, is that the pressure is the derivative of the total energy with respect to the volume where certain quantities must be kept constant. We now elucidate which variables these are.

In a classical fluid the variables to be kept constant are M, S, $\boldsymbol{I}$ or

$$p = -\left(\frac{\partial E}{\partial V}\right)_{M,S,\boldsymbol{I}}, \quad (3\text{-}17)$$

where E is the total energy, V the volume, S the total entropy and $\boldsymbol{I}$ the total momentum. The dynamics of He II should be a generalization of the dynamics of an Euler fluid. More exactly, when the dependence on the extra variable $\boldsymbol{v}_\mathrm{s}$ identically vanishes [from (3-13) we see that this happens when $\boldsymbol{J} = \rho(\boldsymbol{v}_\mathrm{s} + \boldsymbol{w})$] the number of independent variables is reduced to five. In this limit the results which we obtain must be consistent with the Euler equations as none of the basic assumptions which we have made are in this limit inconsistent with the Euler hydrodynamics, which are a unique consequence of the fact that five variables are a complete set. Therefore in He II the pressure is also taken to be the derivative of the energy with respect to the volume, at constant M, S, $\boldsymbol{I}$. But because of the existence of three extra variables p is not yet uniquely determined until we specify which three additional variables are to be

Notes p. 83

held constant. The answer to this question cannot follow from the classical limit. Instead it follows from the Galilean transformation. From (3-13) we find

$$\mathrm{d}E = [\mu + \tfrac{1}{2}v_s^2 - (\boldsymbol{v}_s + \boldsymbol{w}) \cdot \boldsymbol{v}_s]\,\mathrm{d}M + T\,\mathrm{d}S + (\boldsymbol{v}_s + \boldsymbol{w}) \cdot \mathrm{d}\boldsymbol{I}$$
$$+ V[\boldsymbol{J} - \rho(\boldsymbol{v}_s + \boldsymbol{w})] \cdot \mathrm{d}\boldsymbol{v}_s + \{U - \rho[\mu + \tfrac{1}{2}v_s^2 - (\boldsymbol{v}_s + \boldsymbol{w}) \cdot \boldsymbol{v}_s]$$
$$- \rho s T - (\boldsymbol{v}_s + \boldsymbol{w}) \cdot \boldsymbol{J}\}\,\mathrm{d}V, \tag{3-18}$$

where $E = UV$, $M = \rho V$, $S = \rho s V$, $\boldsymbol{I} = \boldsymbol{J}V$. Thus one possibility for the pressure is

$$p = -\left(\frac{\partial E}{\partial V}\right)_{M,S,\boldsymbol{I},\boldsymbol{v}_s} \tag{3-19}$$

and by writing $V\,\mathrm{d}\boldsymbol{v}_s = \mathrm{d}(V\,\boldsymbol{v}_s) - \boldsymbol{v}_s\,\mathrm{d}V$ we obtain the only other possible independent choice [45]:

$$p = -\left(\frac{\partial E}{\partial V}\right)_{M,S,\boldsymbol{I},\boldsymbol{v}_s V} \tag{3-20}$$

which differs from (3-19) by the quantity $\boldsymbol{v}_s \cdot [\boldsymbol{J} - \rho(\boldsymbol{v}_s + \boldsymbol{w})]$. The pressure must be a Galilean invariant. From the transformation of energy, velocity and momentum one verifies that (3-19) is invariant whereas (3-20) is not. Thus (3-19) is the desired expression. From (3-18,19,11,12) we then find the very important relation

$$\mathrm{d}p = \rho\,\mathrm{d}\mu + \rho s\,\mathrm{d}T + (\boldsymbol{J} - \rho\boldsymbol{v}_s) \cdot \mathrm{d}\boldsymbol{w}, \tag{3-21}$$

which in the limit that $\boldsymbol{J} = \rho(\boldsymbol{v}_s + \boldsymbol{w})$ reduces to the classical expression [note: since $\boldsymbol{w}$ is parallel to $\boldsymbol{J} - \rho(\boldsymbol{v}_s + \boldsymbol{w})$ when this quantity vanishes $\boldsymbol{w}$ vanishes and thus so also does $\boldsymbol{J} - \rho\boldsymbol{v}_s$].

Substituting Eq. (3-21) into Eq. (3-16) yields

$$\frac{\partial U}{\partial t} = -\frac{\partial}{\partial r_k}\{[\mu + \tfrac{1}{2}v_s^2 - (\boldsymbol{v}_s + \boldsymbol{w}) \cdot \boldsymbol{v}_s]J_k + Tf_k + (v_s + w)_i \Pi_{ik}\}$$
$$+ [\boldsymbol{f} - \rho s(\boldsymbol{v}_s + \boldsymbol{w})] \cdot \nabla T + [\boldsymbol{J} - \rho(\boldsymbol{v}_s + \boldsymbol{w})] \cdot \nabla(\mu - \psi)$$
$$+ (\Pi_{ik} - v_{s,i}J_k)\frac{\partial(v_s + w)_i}{\partial r_k} - \{w_i J_k + [J - \rho(v_s + w)]_i\, v_{s,k}\}\frac{\partial v_{s,i}}{\partial r_k}$$
$$- (v_s + w)_k (J - \rho v_s)_i \frac{\partial w_i}{\partial r_k}. \tag{3-22}$$

Notes p. 83

As $\boldsymbol{w}$ and $\boldsymbol{J} - \rho \boldsymbol{v}_s$ are parallel the combination $w_i J_k - \rho(v_s + w)_i v_{s,k}$ is symmetric in the indices. By switching the indices (3-22) is simplified to

$$\frac{\partial U}{\partial t} + \frac{\partial}{\partial r_k}\{[\mu + \tfrac{1}{2}v_s^2 - (\boldsymbol{v}_s + \boldsymbol{w})\cdot \boldsymbol{v}_s] J_k + Tf_k + (v_s + w)_i \Pi_{ik}\}$$

$$= [\boldsymbol{f} - \rho s(\boldsymbol{v}_s + \boldsymbol{w})]\cdot \nabla T + [\boldsymbol{J} - \rho(\boldsymbol{v}_s + \boldsymbol{w})]\cdot \nabla(\mu - \psi)$$

$$+ [\Pi_{ik} - v_{s,i}J_k - (J - \rho v_s)_i (v_s + w)_k] \frac{\partial(v_s + w)_i}{\partial r_k}. \quad (3\text{-}23)$$

Since by the redundancy condition (3-1,3,4,5) must imply the energy conservation law (3-2) the right hand side of (3-23) must vanish. The simplest way of achieving this is to require that each term separately vanish. We follow this procedure below. In Appendix III we discuss application of the rigorous requirement that only the coefficients of the independent gradients $[\nabla T, \nabla\mu, \partial(v_s + w)_i/\partial r_k]$ need vanish separately.

Two cases can be discerned:

(A) $\boldsymbol{J} = \rho(\boldsymbol{v}_s + \boldsymbol{w})$. In this case $\boldsymbol{v}_s + \boldsymbol{w} = \boldsymbol{v}$, since $\boldsymbol{v} \equiv \boldsymbol{J}/\rho$ is the definition of $\boldsymbol{v}$, and $\boldsymbol{f}, \Pi_{ik}, U$, take on their values for an Euler fluid. The superfluid equation (3-4) is uncoupled from the others as there is no restriction on ψ. This is the limit in which the number of independent variables required to describe the flow becomes five instead of eight thus leaving us with the Euler hydrodynamics.

(B) $\boldsymbol{J} \neq \rho(\boldsymbol{v}_s + \boldsymbol{w})$. This is the more interesting case since now eight independent variables describe the fluid and all the equations are coupled. From the restriction that each of the terms on the right hand side of (3-23) vanish we find

$$\boldsymbol{f} = \rho s(\boldsymbol{v}_s + \boldsymbol{w}), \quad (3\text{-}24)$$

$$\psi = \mu, \quad (3\text{-}25)$$

$$\Pi_{ik} = v_{s,i}J_k + (J - \rho v_s)_i (v_s + w)_k. \quad (3\text{-}26)$$

Using the relations (3-24,25,26) the Eqs. (3-1,3,4,5) become eight equations for the eight basic variables ρ, s, $\boldsymbol{J}$, $\boldsymbol{v}_s$ provided that equations of state are given in terms of these variables for the three quantities μ, p and $\boldsymbol{v}_s + \boldsymbol{w}$. *Until this point* $\boldsymbol{v}_n$ *appears nowhere in these equations.* If we introduce it by the definition $\boldsymbol{v}_n \equiv \boldsymbol{v}_s + \boldsymbol{w}$ then from general arguments we have already shown that $\boldsymbol{J}$ is related to $\boldsymbol{v}_n$ and $\boldsymbol{v}_s$ by (3-8). Furthermore (3-24,25,26) when substituted into (3-1,3,4,5) now yield the two fluid

Notes p. 83

equations in the form first presented in § 2. In this case one can take as the eight basic variables ρ, s, $\boldsymbol{v}_{\mathrm{n}}$, $\boldsymbol{v}_{\mathrm{s}}$, and equations of state must be given for the three quantities μ, p, ρ_{n}.

Finally we remark that having introduced $\boldsymbol{v}_{\mathrm{n}}$ through the above definition, $\boldsymbol{J} - \rho(\boldsymbol{v}_{\mathrm{s}} + \boldsymbol{w}) = \rho_{\mathrm{s}}(\boldsymbol{v}_{\mathrm{s}} - \boldsymbol{v}_{\mathrm{n}})$. Thus the terms involving $\nabla\mu$ in (3-23) can also vanish if $\rho_{\mathrm{s}} = 0$. In order to allow that ρ_{s} might vanish at some points in the fluid we mention that the superfluid equation can be more precisely written as

$$\rho_{\mathrm{s}} \frac{\mathrm{D}_{\mathrm{s}} \boldsymbol{v}_{\mathrm{s}}}{\mathrm{D}t} = -\rho_{\mathrm{s}} \nabla \mu, \tag{3-27}$$

which clearly reduces to the usual form (2-11) when $\rho_{\mathrm{s}} \neq 0$. We will have use for (3-27) in § 17.

4 *General Consequences of the Landau Two Fluid Equations: The Doubling of the Classical Hydrodynamic Theorems*

In the last section we have shown that the Landau two fluid equations are a unique consequence of the assumptions that eight variables (which we now take as ρ, s, $\boldsymbol{v}_{\mathrm{n}}$, $\boldsymbol{v}_{\mathrm{s}}$) are a complete set, and that $\boldsymbol{v}_{\mathrm{s}}$ obeys a Kelvin circulation theorem. The equations which we obtained are

$$\frac{\partial \rho}{\partial t} + \nabla \cdot (\rho_{\mathrm{n}} \boldsymbol{v}_{\mathrm{n}} + \rho_{\mathrm{s}} \boldsymbol{v}_{\mathrm{s}}) = 0, \tag{4-1}$$

$$\frac{\partial \rho s}{\partial t} + \nabla \cdot (\rho s \boldsymbol{v}_{\mathrm{n}}) = 0, \tag{4-2}$$

$$\frac{\mathrm{D}_{\mathrm{s}} \boldsymbol{v}_{\mathrm{s}}}{\mathrm{D}t} = -\nabla \mu, \tag{4-3}$$

$$\frac{\partial}{\partial t}(\rho_{\mathrm{n}} v_{\mathrm{n}} + \rho_{\mathrm{s}} v_{\mathrm{s}})_i + \frac{\partial}{\partial r_\alpha}(p\delta_{i\alpha} + \rho_{\mathrm{n}} v_{\mathrm{n},i} v_{\mathrm{n},\alpha} + \rho_{\mathrm{s}} v_{\mathrm{s},i} v_{\mathrm{s},\alpha}) = 0, \tag{4-4}$$

where $\rho_{\mathrm{n}} + \rho_{\mathrm{s}} = \rho$.

We found for the first and second laws of thermodynamics [(3-12) with $\boldsymbol{w} \equiv \boldsymbol{v}_{\mathrm{n}} - \boldsymbol{v}_{\mathrm{s}}$ and $\boldsymbol{J}$ given by (3-8)]

$$\mathrm{d}U_0 = \mu\,\mathrm{d}\rho + T\,\mathrm{d}\rho s + (\boldsymbol{v}_{\mathrm{n}} - \boldsymbol{v}_{\mathrm{s}}) \cdot \mathrm{d}\rho_{\mathrm{n}}(\boldsymbol{v}_{\mathrm{n}} - \boldsymbol{v}_{\mathrm{s}}), \tag{4-5}$$

Notes p. 83

where the total energy density is

$$U = U_0 + \boldsymbol{v}_s \cdot \rho_n(\boldsymbol{v}_n - \boldsymbol{v}_s) + \tfrac{1}{2}\rho v_s^2. \tag{4-6}$$

Since (4-1,2,3,4) are a complete set of equations [provided that equations of state are given for ρ_n, p, μ in terms of ρ, s, $(\boldsymbol{v}_n - \boldsymbol{v}_s)^2$] the law of conservation of energy is a consequence of them and was shown to be (3-23) or

$$\frac{\partial U}{\partial t} + \nabla \cdot \{(\mu + \tfrac{1}{2}v_s^2)(\rho_n \boldsymbol{v}_n + \rho_s \boldsymbol{v}_s) + \rho s T \boldsymbol{v}_n + \rho_n \boldsymbol{v}_n[\boldsymbol{v}_n \cdot (\boldsymbol{v}_n - \boldsymbol{v}_s)]\} = 0. \tag{4-7}$$

Finally we have derived the very basic relation between the pressure and the other quantities

$$\mathrm{d}p = \rho\, \mathrm{d}\mu + \rho s\, \mathrm{d}T + \tfrac{1}{2}\rho_n\, \mathrm{d}(\boldsymbol{v}_n - \boldsymbol{v}_s)^2. \tag{4-8}$$

In the presence of an external force per unit mass, $\boldsymbol{K} = -\nabla\Omega$ one must add $\rho\boldsymbol{K}$, $\boldsymbol{K}$, $\rho\Omega$ to the right hand side of (4-4,3,6) respectively. If $\partial\Omega/\partial t = 0$ then energy is conserved and one obtains (4-7) with μ replaced by $\mu + \Omega$.

While (4-1) through (4-8) summarize our theoretical results they are quite formal so far in that we have not shown for instance that T can be interpreted as the temperature in the usual sense. We postpone the operational definitions of the quantities appearing in the two fluid theory until § 6. Here we concentrate on some general consequences of these equations which are important for interpreting and utilizing the theory.

Following the discussion of the Euler fluid in § 1 we will especially discuss the Kelvin, Lagrange, and Bernoulli laws which follow from the two fluid theory. It will be seen that the existence of an extra velocity field leads to a doubling of the classical hydrodynamical theorems. There are for He II *two* Kelvin, Lagrange and Bernoulli laws.

The form of the superfluid equation (4-3) was chosen, as a basic assumption, to satisfy a Kelvin circulation theorem:

$$\frac{\mathrm{D}_s}{\mathrm{D}t}\oint \boldsymbol{v}_s \cdot \mathrm{d}\boldsymbol{\ell} = 0, \tag{4-9}$$

or that the circulation is unchanged as one follows the motion of the superfluid particles. From (4-9) by Stokes' law one sees that if $\nabla \times \boldsymbol{v}_s = 0$ everywhere at $t = 0$ its time derivative is zero and hence it stays zero.

Notes p. 83

This shows us that it is possible to consider special cases of flow for which $\nabla \times \boldsymbol{v}_s = 0$. In fact Landau always supplemented his equations with the requirement that the superfluid motion be *restricted* to this irrotational behavior:

$$\nabla \times \boldsymbol{v}_s = 0. \tag{4-11}$$

Also from (4-3) (with an external field) it follows that for stationary flow $\mu + \Omega + \frac{1}{2}v_s^2$ is constant along streamlines of the superfluid. But when condition (4-11) holds one finds the Bernoulli law

$$\frac{\partial \phi}{\partial t} + \mu + \tfrac{1}{2}v_s^2 + \Omega = \text{constant everywhere}, \tag{4-12}$$

where $\boldsymbol{v}_s \equiv \nabla\phi$.

We now show that when $\nabla \times \boldsymbol{v}_s = 0$, the Landau equations can be transformed into

$$\frac{\partial A_i}{\partial t} + (\boldsymbol{v}_n \cdot \nabla)A_i = -\frac{\partial T}{\partial r_i} - A_j\frac{\partial v_{n,j}}{\partial r_i}, \tag{4-13}$$

with

$$\boldsymbol{A} = \frac{\rho_n}{s\rho}(\boldsymbol{v}_n - \boldsymbol{v}_s), \tag{4-14}$$

from which a second Kelvin, Lagrange and Bernoulli theorem will follow.

Using (4-8) and the identity

$$\frac{\partial}{\partial r_j}[\rho_n v_{n,j}(v_n - v_s)_i] + \rho v_{s,j}\frac{\partial v_{s,i}}{\partial r_j} + v_{s,i}\frac{\partial}{\partial r_j}(\rho_s v_{s,j} + \rho_n v_{n,j})$$
$$\equiv \frac{\partial}{\partial r_j}(\rho_n v_{n,i}v_{n,j} + \rho_s v_{s,i}v_{s,j}) - \rho_n(v_n - v_s)_j\frac{\partial v_{s,i}}{\partial r_j},$$

the equation of motion (4-4) becomes

$$\frac{\partial}{\partial t}(\rho_n v_n + \rho_s v_s)_i + \frac{\partial}{\partial r_j}[\rho_n v_{n,j}(v_n - v_s)_i] + \rho v_{s,j}\frac{\partial v_{s,i}}{\partial r_j} + v_{s,i}\frac{\partial}{\partial r_j}(\rho_n v_n + \rho_s v_s)_j$$
$$= -\rho\frac{\partial \mu}{\partial r_j} - \rho s\frac{\partial T}{\partial r_j} - \rho_n(v_n - v_s)_j\frac{\partial v_{n,j}}{\partial r_i} + \rho_n(v_n - v_s)_j\left(\frac{\partial v_{s,j}}{\partial r_i} - \frac{\partial v_{s,i}}{\partial r_j}\right). \tag{4-15}$$

Notes p. 83

From the definition of $\boldsymbol{A}$ (4-14) we note the identity

$$\frac{\partial}{\partial r_j}\left[\rho_n v_{n,j}(v_n - v_s)_i\right] \equiv A_i \frac{\partial \rho s v_{n,j}}{\partial r_j} + \rho s v_{n,j}\frac{\partial A_i}{\partial r_j}. \tag{4-16}$$

Multiplying (4-3) by ρ transforms it into

$$\frac{\partial \rho \boldsymbol{v}_s}{\partial t} - \boldsymbol{v}_s \frac{\partial \rho}{\partial t} + \rho(\boldsymbol{v}_s \cdot \nabla)\boldsymbol{v}_s = -\rho \nabla \mu. \tag{4-17}$$

Subtracting (4-17) from (4-15) and introducing (4-16) we find

$$\frac{\partial}{\partial t}\rho_n(v_n - v_s)_i - A_i \frac{\partial \rho s}{\partial t} + \rho s v_{n,j}\frac{\partial A_i}{\partial r_j}$$

$$= -\rho s \frac{\partial T}{\partial r_i} - \rho_n(v_n - v_s)_j \frac{\partial v_{n,j}}{\partial r_i} + \rho_n(v_n - v_s)_j\left(\frac{\partial v_{s,j}}{\partial r_i} - \frac{\partial v_{s,i}}{\partial r_j}\right), \tag{4-18}$$

where we have also used (4-1,2). Division of (4-18) by ρs yields

$$\frac{\partial A_i}{\partial t} + (\boldsymbol{v}_n \cdot \nabla)A_i = -\frac{\partial T}{\partial r_i} - A_j \frac{\partial v_{n,j}}{\partial r_i} + [\boldsymbol{A} \times (\nabla \times \boldsymbol{v}_s)]_i, \tag{4-19}$$

where we have used the vector identity

$$B_j\left(\frac{\partial C_j}{\partial r_i} - \frac{\partial C_i}{\partial r_j}\right) \equiv [\boldsymbol{B} \times (\nabla \times \boldsymbol{C})]_i. \tag{4-20}$$

When $\nabla \times \boldsymbol{v}_s$ vanishes (4-19) becomes (4-13) as asserted. It is interesting to note that in the presence of an external field (4-19) or (4-13) are unchanged.

From (4-13) one obtains the second Kelvin circulation theorem expressing the conservation of the circulation of $\boldsymbol{A}$ as one follows the motion of the normal fluid [13]. In fact from (4-13) follows

$$\frac{\mathrm{D_n}}{\mathrm{D}t}\oint \boldsymbol{A}\cdot \mathrm{d}\ell = \oint \frac{\mathrm{D_n}\boldsymbol{A}}{\mathrm{D}t}\cdot \mathrm{d}\ell + \oint \boldsymbol{A}\cdot \frac{\mathrm{D_n d}\ell}{\mathrm{D}t}$$

$$= \oint(-\nabla T - A_j \nabla v_{n,j})\cdot \mathrm{d}\ell + \oint \boldsymbol{A}\cdot\frac{\mathrm{D_n d}\ell}{\mathrm{D}t}, \tag{4-21}$$

where $\mathrm{D_n/D}t \equiv \partial/\partial t + (\boldsymbol{v}_n \cdot \nabla)$ is the substantial derivative for the motion of the normal fluid and determines the change in a quantity as one follows the motion of the normal fluid particles. As the contour

Notes p. 83

of integration is composed of normal fluid particles the difference in the velocities of contour elements separated by a distance $d\ell$ is $d\boldsymbol{v}_n$ or: $D_n d\ell/Dt = d\boldsymbol{v}_n$. With this expression the right hand side of (4-21) now vanishes because it is the integral around a closed contour of the gradient of a single valued function; thus when $\nabla \times \boldsymbol{v}_s = 0$

$$\frac{D_n}{Dt}\oint \boldsymbol{A} \cdot d\ell = 0. \tag{4-22}$$

By Stokes' law (4-22) tells us that if $\nabla \times \boldsymbol{A} = 0$ everywhere at $t = 0$ it remains zero for all time (second Lagrange theorem). This can also be seen directly from (4-13) which by use of (4-20) can be written as

$$\frac{\partial \boldsymbol{A}}{\partial t} = -\nabla(T + \boldsymbol{v}_n \cdot \boldsymbol{A}) + \boldsymbol{v}_n \times (\nabla \times \boldsymbol{A}). \tag{4-23}$$

Taking the curl of (4-23) yields

$$\frac{\partial}{\partial t}(\nabla \times \boldsymbol{A}) = \nabla \times [\boldsymbol{v}_n \times (\nabla \times \boldsymbol{A})], \tag{4-24}$$

from which the second Lagrange theorem for $\boldsymbol{A}$ also follows. In the stationary state (4-23) implies the second Bernoulli theorem [14]:

$$T + \boldsymbol{v}_n \cdot \boldsymbol{A} = \text{constant along normal fluid streamlines.} \tag{4-25}$$

When $\nabla \times \boldsymbol{A}$ can be taken zero everywhere we find that $T + \boldsymbol{v}_n \cdot \boldsymbol{A}$ is everywhere the same constant.

In an Euler fluid we had to make an assumption concerning the thermodynamic variables (e.g., isentropic flow) in order to obtain the Kelvin, Lagrange and Bernoulli laws. For He II such an assumption is not necessary for the superfluid since that is how we chose the form of its equation of motion. But also for the second Kelvin, Lagrange and Bernoulli laws, no thermodynamic assumption was needed, instead we had to take $\nabla \times \boldsymbol{v}_s = 0$.

Corresponding hydrodynamic theorems for the normal fluid velocity $\boldsymbol{v}_n$ can be obtained if one makes the thermodynamic assumption that $\rho s/\rho_n$ is constant for the flow. In this event one need *not* assume $\nabla \times \boldsymbol{v}_s = 0$ to obtain the Kelvin, Lagrange and Bernoulli theorems. With this assumption the two fluid equations become greatly simplified. Eqs. (4-1,2) become

$$\frac{\partial \rho_s}{\partial t} + \nabla \cdot \rho_s \boldsymbol{v}_s = 0, \tag{4-26}$$

Notes p. 83

$$\frac{\partial \rho_n}{\partial t} + \nabla \cdot \rho_n \boldsymbol{v}_n = 0, \tag{4-27}$$

where we have used $\rho_n + \rho_s = \rho$. So when $\rho s/\rho_n$ is constant the normal and superfluid densities are separately conserved. The superfluid equation (4-3) is unchanged whereas (4-4) can be immediately transformed into

$$\frac{D_n \boldsymbol{v}_n}{Dt} = -\nabla[\mu + \tfrac{1}{2}(\boldsymbol{v}_n - \boldsymbol{v}_s)^2 + \rho s T/\rho_n]. \tag{4-28}$$

From (4-28) follow the Kelvin and Lagrange theorems for the normal fluid velocity v_n. In addition one has the Bernoulli law that $\mu + \frac{1}{2}(\boldsymbol{v}_n - \boldsymbol{v}_s)^2 + \frac{1}{2}v_n^2 + \rho s T/\rho_n$ is constant along normal fluid streamlines (or constant everywhere when $\nabla \times \boldsymbol{v}_n = 0$) when the flow is steady. If one introduces the entropy per gram of normal fluid 's_n' by the definition $\rho_n s_n \equiv \rho s$, then the condition that s_n be constant is clearly a generalization of the concept of isentropic flow which played an important role for the Euler fluid. Our consideration of the consequences of taking s_n constant are hardly academic as is indicated by the fact that although s changes by a factor of four between T_λ and 1.7 °K, s_n changes by less than 10%. Below 1 °K, however, serious errors can be introduced by taking s_n constant.

5 *The Thermal and Superfluid Vortices*

In the last section we have seen that there are two Lagrange theorems for He II. As a consequence it is consistent with the equations of motion to consider two special cases of flow: $\nabla \times \boldsymbol{v}_s = 0$, and $\nabla \times \boldsymbol{v}_s = 0$ and $\nabla \times \boldsymbol{A} = 0$, everywhere within the fluid. Thus in contrast with the classical fluid there can exist two kinds of vortices in He II. According to the Kelvin theorems the $\boldsymbol{A}$ vortex lines must move with the local velocity of the normal fluid and the superfluid vortices must move with the local velocity of the superfluid. Thus there are two Helmholtz theorems. Also the $\boldsymbol{v}_s$ and $\boldsymbol{A}$ vortices cannot terminate in the fluid, they must end on the boundaries or close into themselves (vortex rings). The proof of the above fact follows from the hydrodynamic theorems in the same manner as the proof of the corresponding facts for a classical fluid given in § 1.

Notes p. 83

In the cylindrically symmetric geometry where a vortex lies on the z axis of an infinite fluid, the velocity fields of the $\boldsymbol{v}_s$ and $\boldsymbol{A}$ vortices are

$$\boldsymbol{v}_s = (\gamma/r)\hat{\boldsymbol{e}}_\theta, \tag{5-1}$$

$$\boldsymbol{A} = (\gamma_A/r)\hat{\boldsymbol{e}}_\theta. \tag{5-2}$$

Focusing our attention on special cases of vortex motion we first consider a situation in which $\boldsymbol{v}_n = 0$ and there is a stationary superfluid vortex. We find from (4-19) that (note that in this case $\nabla \times \boldsymbol{A} = 0$)

$$T = \text{constant}, \tag{5-3}$$

and from (5-1,3) and (4-8,12)

$$\nabla p = -\tfrac{1}{2}\rho_s \nabla v_s^2.$$

Thus the pressure drops near the core of the superfluid vortex in just the same way as for a vortex in a classical fluid (1-19).

Next consider the case that $\boldsymbol{v}_s = 0$ and there is a single $\boldsymbol{A}$ vortex line. We find from (5-2) and (4-14,23)

$$T = T_\infty - (\gamma_A^2/r^2)\rho s/\rho_n, \tag{5-4}$$

where T_∞ is the constant value of T at large r. Near the core (i.e., close to $r = 0$) the temperature is reduced from its value at infinity and one can therefore speak of this as a thermal vortex line. From (4-3) we see that $\nabla\mu = 0$ so that from (5-4) and (4-8) we find that the pressure distribution is determined by

$$\nabla p = -\tfrac{1}{2}[(\rho s)^2/\rho_n]\nabla A^2.$$

In the situation where a combined $\boldsymbol{v}_s$ and $\boldsymbol{A}$ vortex are present we find from (5-1,2) and the thermal ($\boldsymbol{A}$) Bernoulli law

$$T = T_\infty - [\gamma + (\rho s/\rho_n)\gamma_A]\gamma_A/r^2.$$

The pressure distribution is determined by (4-8,12) and is

$$\nabla p = -\tfrac{1}{2}\rho\nabla v_s^2 - \tfrac{1}{2}[(\rho s)^2/\rho_n]\nabla A^2 - \rho s\nabla(\boldsymbol{v}_s \cdot \boldsymbol{A}).$$

When a superfluid vortex is present and $\boldsymbol{v}_n = 0$ the angular momentum is

$$\boldsymbol{L} = \int \boldsymbol{r} \times \boldsymbol{J}\,\mathrm{d}V = \gamma M_s \hat{\boldsymbol{e}}_z,$$

where $M_s = \int \rho_s\,\mathrm{d}V$ is the total mass of the supercomponent. When a thermal vortex is present and $\boldsymbol{v}_s = 0$ the angular momentum is $\gamma_A S \hat{\boldsymbol{e}}_z$

Notes p. 83

(where S is the total entropy). Finally when both thermal and superfluid vortices are present the angular momentum is

$$\boldsymbol{L} = \gamma M \hat{\boldsymbol{e}}_z + \gamma_{\mathrm{A}} S \hat{\boldsymbol{e}}_z. \tag{5-5}$$

6 *Operational Definitions and Boundary Conditions for Quantities Appearing in the Two Fluid Equations*

In order to complete the equations of motion one must, as with the Euler fluid, supplement them with boundary conditions for the velocity fields. Since in the two fluid picture there are two velocities: $\boldsymbol{v}_{\mathrm{n}}$ and $\boldsymbol{v}_{\mathrm{s}}$, we expect that there will be two boundary conditions.

The boundary conditions are a consequence of the conservation laws. From the continuity equation for mass (4-1), we find that at a stationary solid boundary the perpendicular component of mass flow must vanish: $J_\perp = 0$ or (at the boundary)

$$\rho_{\mathrm{n}} v_{\mathrm{n}\perp} + \rho_{\mathrm{s}} v_{\mathrm{s}\perp} = 0. \tag{6-1}$$

From the conservation law for energy (4-7) we find that the energy per unit area per second, $\dot{W}$ to leave the boundary into the fluid must be given (at the boundary) by

$$\dot{W} = \rho s (T + \boldsymbol{v}_{\mathrm{n}} \cdot \boldsymbol{A}) v_{\mathrm{n}\perp}, \tag{6-2}$$

where we have made use of (6-1) and have again set

$$\boldsymbol{A} \equiv (\rho_{\mathrm{n}}/s\rho)(\boldsymbol{v}_{\mathrm{n}} - \boldsymbol{v}_{\mathrm{s}}). \tag{6-3}$$

In most experiments in He II the velocities are below 10 cm/sec. The reason for this is related to the existence of critical velocities above which the flow becomes turbulent, or perhaps the two fluid theory breaks down. We don't discuss this question here but only remark that for velocities of the order of 10 cm/sec $\boldsymbol{v}_{\mathrm{n}} \cdot \boldsymbol{A} \approx 10^{-5}$ °K which is quite small. Thus to a good approximation (6-2) becomes

$$\dot{W} \approx \rho s T v_{\mathrm{n}\perp}. \tag{6-4}$$

Equations (6-1,2) are two equations for the perpendicular components of $\boldsymbol{v}_{\mathrm{n}}$ and $\boldsymbol{v}_{\mathrm{s}}$. As with the Euler fluid the tangential components are unrestricted.

Notes p. 83

In an Euler fluid the boundary condition $v_{\perp} = 0$ precludes the possibility of an energy flux from a stationary wall to the fluid [see (1-11)]. Also when the center of mass is at rest a heat flow cannot take place in a classical fluid on the level where dissipative effects are ignored. In a classical fluid heat flow (with $\boldsymbol{v} = 0$) is a dissipative process involving the thermal conductivity. In He II because of the existence of two velocity fields the energy flux is independent of the mass flux and we find that even when the fluid is at 'rest' there can on the ideal level be a heat flow. This process where the normal fluid carries the heat away from a stationary boundary and the superfluid flows in the opposite direction [see (6-1)] is called internal convection.

On the level where dissipative effects are ignored one has for He II also a law of conservation of entropy (4-2), which when applied to the boundary yields the condition that the entropy to leave a unit area of boundary per second must equal $\rho s v_{n\perp}$ at the boundary. If we let T_B be the temperature of the boundary this condition becomes

$$\dot{W}/T_B = \rho s v_{n\perp}, \tag{6-5}$$

where we have interpreted $\dot{W}$ as the heat per second per unit area to leave the boundary since a stationary boundary can do no work and all the energy to leave must thus be heat.

Equations (6-5) and (6-2) must be consistent since they both follow from the basic two fluid equations. This results in the existence of a thermal discontinuity at a stationary boundary where heat is put into He II or

$$T_B - T = \boldsymbol{v}_n \cdot \boldsymbol{A}. \tag{6-6}$$

Again we comment that for ordinary arrangements $\boldsymbol{v}_n \cdot \boldsymbol{A}$ and hence the size of the discontinuity is quite small, though definitely not unmeasurable with present techniques.

One can object to our derivation of (6-6) from the point of view that when discontinuities are present one cannot use the law of conservation of entropy. Classically, for instance, in the presence of shock waves one cannot use the entropy conservation law, since dissipative effects within the thin discontinuity become important. One can also note that in order to derive the entropy conservation law (4-2) from the eight equations (4-1,3,4,7) use must be made of the first and second laws of thermodynamics for reversible processes (4-5). This relation is valid only when variations from point to point in the thermodynamic quantities can be

Notes p. 83

taken infinitesimally small. When variations are finite, higher order terms (i.e., terms in $(d\rho)^2$, etc.) must be included in the expression for dU_0 and the conservation of entropy no longer follows from the other equations.

However, there must be a discontinuity at the boundary since if none were present we would be completely justified in using the entropy conservation law and would be led to a contradiction. The above remarks only emphasize that for a complete understanding of this non-classical discontinuity we must investigate the two fluid equations modified to include dissipative effects. At that time (§ 28) we will see that as with the classical liquid the mistake in using the entropy conservation law is third order in the small quantities. Thus to second order (and $\boldsymbol{v}_n \cdot \boldsymbol{A}$ is a second order term, being quadratic in the velocities) Eq. (6-6) is correct.

This boundary discontinuity is a unique shock wave in that it is at rest in the rest frame of the boundary and there is fluid on only one side of the shock (it is so to speak half of a shock wave). The physical reason for the discontinuity in temperature is as follows. In He II the heat flow involves a *convection* or internal mass flow and hence has *inertia*. In order to have a heat flow one must supply in addition to the heat, the kinetic energy for the convection of the normal and superfluids. Since at a stationary boundary we do no work on the system, the work necessary for supplying the ordered kinetic energy of the internal convection comes from the transfer of heat from the temperature of the boundary to the lower temperature of the fluid. From (6-6) and (6-1) we notice that $T_B > T$ consistent with this interpretation, and from (6-2) we see that $\rho s(\boldsymbol{v}_n \cdot \boldsymbol{A}) v_{n\perp}$ is the kinetic energy flux density of the heat flow.

Another paradox arises if we consider the spherically symmetric heat flow between two concentric spheres. Let heat (and thus normal fluid) flow from the outer sphere to the inner sphere, the motion of $\boldsymbol{v}_s$ being in the opposite direction. As the entropy per second to arrive at the inner sphere must equal the entropy per second to leave the outer sphere we find [by integrating (4-2) over the entire region and applying Gauss' law] that the normal fluid velocity at the inner sphere is greater than the normal fluid velocity at the outer sphere. Therefore by (6-6) the temperature drop (from boundary to fluid) at the outer sphere is less than the temperature increase (from fluid to boundary) at the inner sphere and one might wonder if we have succeeded in transporting heat reversible from a lower to a higher temperature. If the temperature within the He II were constant this would indeed be the case but according to the

Notes p. 83

thermal Bernoulli law (4-25) we see that for this simplified geometry $T + \boldsymbol{v}_n \cdot \boldsymbol{A}$ and not T is constant within the fluid. This variation of temperature within the fluid precisely accounts for the difference in the two discontinuities, so that indeed the temperatures of the two spheres are equal on the ideal level.

Finally one might object to the thermal discontinuity on the grounds that perhaps T is not the temperature of the He II. After all we have seen that it is $T + \boldsymbol{v}_n \cdot \boldsymbol{A}$ that is constant in the He II, and it is $T + \boldsymbol{v}_n \cdot \boldsymbol{A}$ that equals the temperature of the boundary, so maybe $T + \boldsymbol{v}_n \cdot \boldsymbol{A}$ and not T is the temperature of He II (such as, for instance, would be registered by a thermometer).

To show that what we have designated formally by the symbol T [see discussion following Eq. (3-12)] is indeed the temperature requires us to consider the operational definitions of the quantities appearing in the two fluid equations.

The *extensive* variables, such as U, ρ, ρs, $\boldsymbol{J}$ can be operationally defined in the same way as for a classical fluid. The trouble comes in interpreting the *intensive* variables (e.g., T, μ). To elicit the interpretations of the intensive variables we must consider a situation in which He II variables are related to the variables of a well defined system. Since the vapor of He II is an Euler 'fluid' obeying the usual thermodynamics we will look at a case in which energy is exchanged between He II and its vapor under equilibrium conditions.

We denote the vapor quantities by the subscript g. The change δE in the total energy, $E = UV$ of the liquid phase (occupying volume V) follows from (4-5,6,8) or equivalently from (3-18) and is

$$\delta E = (\mu + \tfrac{1}{2}v_s^2 - \boldsymbol{v}_n \cdot \boldsymbol{v}_s)\,\delta M + T\,\delta S + \boldsymbol{v}_n \cdot \delta \boldsymbol{I} + \rho_s V(\boldsymbol{v}_s - \boldsymbol{v}_n) \cdot \delta \boldsymbol{v}_s - p\,\delta V, \quad (6\text{-}7)$$

where $M = \rho V$ is total mass, $S = \rho s V$ is total entropy, $\boldsymbol{I} = \boldsymbol{J}V$ is total momentum. A similar expression follows from (1-8,9,10) for the vapor

$$\delta E_g = (\mu_g - \tfrac{1}{2}v_g^2)\,\delta M_g + T_g\,\delta S_g + \boldsymbol{v}_g \cdot \delta \boldsymbol{I}_g - p_g\,\delta V_g, \quad (6\text{-}8)$$

where $\boldsymbol{v}_g$ is the local velocity of the gas. An exchange of energy which takes place under equilibrium conditions for a closed system involves no net change of total entropy:

$$\delta S + \delta S_g = 0. \quad (6\text{-}9)$$

This must be supplemented by the conditions that the total change in energy, mass, momentum must vanish since we look at a closed system:

Notes p. 83

$$\begin{aligned} \delta E + \delta E_g &= 0, \\ \delta M + \delta M_g &= 0, \\ \delta \boldsymbol{I} + \delta \boldsymbol{I}_g &= 0, \\ \delta V + \delta V_g &= 0. \end{aligned} \tag{6-10}$$

Inserting (6-9) and (6-10) into (6-7,8) we find

$$\begin{aligned} &[(\mu + \tfrac{1}{2}v_s^2 - \boldsymbol{v}_n \cdot \boldsymbol{v}_s) - (\mu_g - \tfrac{1}{2}v_g^2)]\,\delta M + (T - T_g)\,\delta S \\ &\qquad + (\boldsymbol{v}_n - \boldsymbol{v}_g) \cdot \delta \boldsymbol{I} - (p - p_g)\,\delta V + \rho_s V(\boldsymbol{v}_s - \boldsymbol{v}_n) \cdot \delta \boldsymbol{v}_s = 0. \end{aligned} \tag{6-11}$$

Since δM, δS, $\delta \boldsymbol{I}$, δV are all independent and different from zero we conclude the following operational definitions for the intensive variables:

$$\mu + \tfrac{1}{2}v_s^2 - \boldsymbol{v}_n \cdot \boldsymbol{v}_s = \mu_g - \tfrac{1}{2}v_g^2, \tag{6-12}$$

$$T = T_g, \tag{6-13}$$

$$\boldsymbol{v}_n = \boldsymbol{v}_g, \tag{6-14}$$

$$p = p_g. \tag{6-15}$$

Since the vapor lacks an extra internal variable corresponding to $\boldsymbol{v}_s$ there can be no exchange of energy between liquid and vapor corresponding to a $\delta \boldsymbol{v}_s$ and in the variation considered above we must take $\delta \boldsymbol{v}_s = 0$. The Eqs. (6-12,13,14,15) relate the thermodynamic quantities in He II to the unambiguously defined quantities in the vapor. We see, for instance, that T has the same interpretation as the temperature in a classical fluid, but the chemical potential μ is modified by the presence of kinetic terms. The only quantity appearing in the two fluid equations which has not been directly operationally defined by this procedure is $\boldsymbol{v}_s$. One can say that (6-7) yields this definition since all the other quantities appearing in it have been operationally defined.

We have found that when we measure the temperature of He II with an ideal gas thermometer it is the quantity T that we observe and thus the discontinuity which exists in the presence of a heat flow (6-6) is a bonafide thermal discontinuity.

Neither this discontinuity, nor the thermal Bernoulli law (4-25), nor the thermal vortices (§ 5) have ever been looked for. An experimental observation of the stationary thermal discontinuity will be complicated by the Kapitza resistance [15]. It is found that in heat flow in liquid helium (both above and below T_λ) and in other liquids there is a thermal

Notes p. 83

discontinuity at a boundary where heat enters or leaves the fluid. This effect is a property of the fluid and the physical chemistry of the boundary. The thermal discontinuity (6-6) is entirely a property of superfluid helium and can in principle be distinguished from the Kapitza resistance since the He II effect is quadratic in the heat flow whereas the Kapitza effect is linear in the heat current.

When $\boldsymbol{v}_n = \boldsymbol{v}_s$ the relations (6-12,13,14,15) obviously reduce to those for a classical liquid and its vapor. The new and interesting properties of He II are always manifest in situations where $\boldsymbol{v}_n \neq \boldsymbol{v}_s$. A clever check of the consistency of (6-4) with (6-14), which expresses the fact that the vapor above He II moves with the normal fluid velocity in equilibrium, when $\boldsymbol{v}_n \neq \boldsymbol{v}_s$, has been provided by Osborne [16].

In his experiment (Fig. 5) a disc D was suspended on a torsion wire

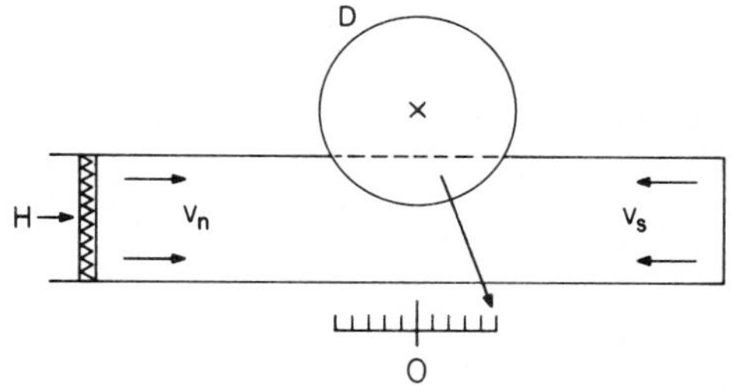

Fig. 5. The apparatus used by Osborne to investigate the interaction of moving He II with its vapor.

(which is indicated by the cross and points towards the reader) in the vapor above a vessel containing He II (we are looking down on the free surface of the vessel). When a heat flow is established by means of the heater H one expects according to (6-1,4) that the normal fluid flows away from the heater and the superfluid flows towards it. Osborne reasoned that if (6-14) were correct then the vapor would be dragged along by the normal fluid (since we naturally assume that there exist processes which drive a system to its equilibrium state) and would also flow in the direction of the heat current. Since the vapor is a classical 'fluid' one knows how it will behave when it flows past the disc. In particular, it will exert a drag on it which, for his geometry, amounts to a torque on the torsion wire and an angular displacement of the disc from its equilibrium position. The equilibrium position, no heat flow, is realized when the arrow points to the zero.

Notes p. 83

Osborne found that consistent with (6-14), the disc was always deflected in the direction of the heat current and furthermore he could qualitatively verify that stronger heat flows led to greater deflections.

From the momentum conservation law (4-4) we can obtain a boundary condition relating the force exerted on the boundary by the fluid to the flow of momentum at the boundary. First note that from the form of the momentum conservation law we can as with the Euler fluid interpret the stress tensor P_{ij} as the momentum in the ith direction to flow per second across a unit area perpendicular to the jth direction. The momentum to flow per second across a surface element $\mathrm{d}\boldsymbol{S}$ forming the boundary between the fluid and a solid wall must be the negative of the force exerted by the fluid on the wall. We thus find that this force is $P_{ij}\,\mathrm{d}S_j$ or

$$p\,\mathrm{d}\boldsymbol{S} + \rho_n \boldsymbol{v}_n(\boldsymbol{v}_n \cdot \mathrm{d}\boldsymbol{S}) + \rho_s \boldsymbol{v}_s(\boldsymbol{v}_s \cdot \mathrm{d}\boldsymbol{S}). \tag{6-16}$$

When $v_{n\perp} = v_{s\perp}$ then by (6-1) both vanish and we find that the force on the boundary is $p\,\mathrm{d}\boldsymbol{S}$ as in a classical fluid. However, when there is a heat flow and $v_{n\perp} \neq v_{s\perp}$ there is present an additional 'reaction' force on the boundary due to the momentum (inertia) of the heat flow in He II. Perpendicular to a unit area of boundary the total force is now

$$p + \rho_n v_{n\perp}^2 + \rho_s v_{s\perp}^2, \tag{6-17}$$

or by use of (6-1)

$$p + (\rho_n \rho/\rho_s) v_{n\perp}^2.$$

Introducing the heat flux from the boundary by (6-4) and thus ignoring $\boldsymbol{v}_n \cdot \boldsymbol{A}$ effects we find for the force per unit area perpendicular to the boundary

$$p + \rho_n \dot{W}^2/\rho_s \rho s^2 T^2. \tag{6-18}$$

In total contrast with the classical *Euler* fluid there can in He II be a force *parallel* to the boundary [3]. When there is a heat flow in He II one can say that the superfluid which flows to the boundary receives entropy and is thereby converted into normal fluid which flows away from the boundary. If the super and normal fluids have different tangential velocities (denoted by $v_{s\parallel}$ and $v_{n\parallel}$) at the boundary then there must during this conversion be a force supplied by the boundary to provide for the 'change' in the tangential component of momentum of the fluid. The tangential momentum per second to flow into the boundary along with the superfluid is $\rho_s v_{s\parallel}(\boldsymbol{v}_s \cdot \mathrm{d}\boldsymbol{S})$ and the tangential momentum

Notes p. 83

to flow away as normal fluid is $-\rho_n v_{n\parallel}(\boldsymbol{v}_n \cdot d\boldsymbol{S})$ and hence the change in momentum per second, or force exerted on the boundary, is

$$\rho_n v_{n\parallel}(\boldsymbol{v}_n \cdot d\boldsymbol{S}) + \rho_s v_{s\parallel}(\boldsymbol{v}_s \cdot d\boldsymbol{S}).$$

This force also follows directly from (6-16) by taking the tangential component.

By (6-1) this force becomes

$$(v_{n\parallel} - v_{s\parallel})\rho_n(\boldsymbol{v}_n \cdot d\boldsymbol{S}),$$

or in terms of the heat flow per unit area $\dot{W}$ from the boundary the force is per unit area

$$(v_{s\parallel} - v_{n\parallel})\rho_n \dot{W}/\rho s T \tag{6-19}$$

and has the same direction as the parallel component of $\boldsymbol{v}_s - \boldsymbol{v}_n$.

The boundary condition (6-17) or equivalently (6-18) was investigated by Hall [17]. In his apparatus (see Fig. 6) a glass plate G was suspended

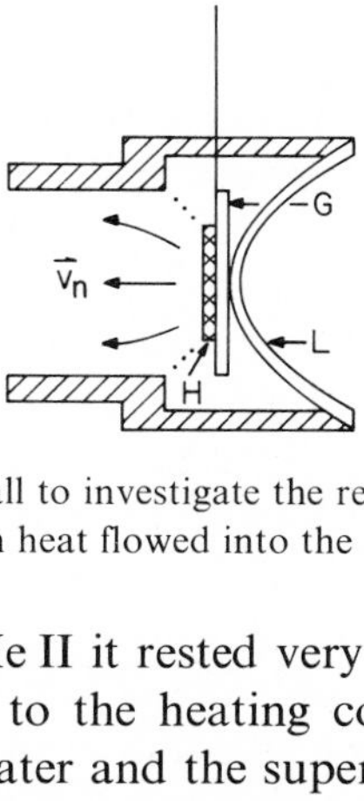

Fig. 6. The apparatus used by Hall to investigate the reaction stress on a boundary from which heat flowed into the He II.

so that in the stationary He II it rested very close to a polished lens L. When current is supplied to the heating coil H, normal fluid carries the heat away from the heater and the superfluid flows towards it. The resulting reaction force on the plate, displaces it against the suspension and leads to a change in thickness of the He II between the plate and lens. This causes a displacement of the Newton interference rings formed between them from which the reaction force can be determined if the apparatus has been calibrated.

For a given heating rate $\dot{W}$ Hall found that the net force per unit area of the heater had as a function of temperature a behavior qualitatively consistent with (6-18). A typical result is shown in Fig. 7. It is seen for

Notes p. 83

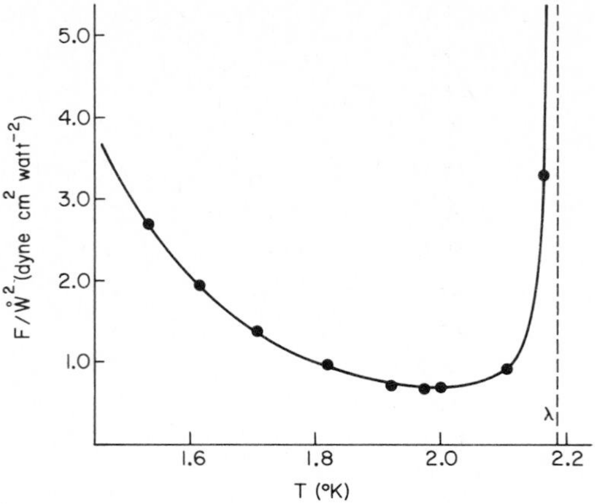

Fig. 7. The reaction force F per unit area of the heater versus temperature for a given heating rate $\dot{W}$ in an experiment of Hall. The solid line represents $\beta\rho_n/\rho_s\rho s^2T^2$ for $\beta=0.28$.

instance that at T_λ where one expects the superfluid density ρ_s to vanish the force indeed diverges. It was also found that the reaction force was quadratic in the heating rate $\dot{W}$ again as predicted by (6-18). One might expect that from a comparison of these results with (6-18) one could determine the basic parameter ρ_n/ρ of the two fluid theory. However the interpretation of the results is hindered by the fact that as a consequence of the counterflow the pressure p might also change. Thus the force exerted on the plate might have also a contribution from the difference in pressures on the two sides as well as from the reaction force. For instance, in the case where the flow is everywhere curl free ($\nabla \times \boldsymbol{v}_s = \nabla \times \boldsymbol{A} = 0$) then one finds from (4-8), (4-3) and (4-23) that

$$\nabla p = -\tfrac{1}{2}\rho\nabla v_s^2 - \rho s\nabla(\boldsymbol{v}_n \cdot \boldsymbol{A}) + \tfrac{1}{2}\rho_n\nabla(\boldsymbol{v}_n - \boldsymbol{v}_s)^2. \qquad (6\text{-}20)$$

If the velocities are negligible compared to the sound velocity then we can neglect the dependence of ρ, ρs, ρ_n on the velocities and integrate (6-20) to obtain

$$p + \tfrac{1}{2}\rho_n v_n^2 + \tfrac{1}{2}\rho_s v_s^2 = \text{constant}. \qquad (6\text{-}21)$$

Thus in this case one might expect that there will be a pressure difference of $\tfrac{1}{2}(\rho_n v_n^2 + \rho_s v_s^2)$ between front and back of the plate so that the net force in the presence of a heat flow is

$$\tfrac{1}{2}\rho_n \dot{W}^2/\rho_s\rho s^2 T^2. \qquad (6\text{-}22)$$

Notes p. 83

In the case where the fluid behind the plate is separated from the fluid in front by a vortex sheet, which is a surface (indicated say by the dotted lines in Fig. 6) where the tangential component of velocity is discontinuous the pressures will be equal and the net reaction force will be *twice* (6-22). This result follows from the fact that pressure is continuous across a vortex sheet. To see this note that from (6-16) the force exerted perpendicular to a surface element $\mathrm{d}\boldsymbol{S}$ of vortex sheet by the fluid on a given side of the vortex sheet is just $p\,\mathrm{d}\boldsymbol{S}$ since the velocity at the sheet is parallel to it. As the vortex sheet is arbitrarily thin, the forces must balance and hence p is continuous across it.

Neither Bernoulli flow or tangential discontinuities will be realized in practice. These examples only indicate the limitations of this particular experiment *where p is not directly measured.* However, these two 'limiting' cases do suggest that the reaction force will always be of the form:

$$\beta \rho_n \dot{W}^2 / \rho_s \rho s^2 T^2,$$

where β is a scaling factor determined by the particular experimental geometry. Hall could verify that for various heaters and geometries there always existed a value of β which scaled all results to Fig. 7.

The boundary condition (6-19) was investigated by Hunt [18]. In this experiment (Fig. 8) the heater was a cylindrical glass bar G painted black. When radiated it would heat up and send heat into the He II, in which it was suspended via a quartz torsion wire Q. From (6-19) we see that the glass bar should experience a total torque equal to

$$(\ell \pi d^2 \rho_n \dot{W} / 2\rho s T)(v_{s\|} - v_{n\|}) \tag{6-23}$$

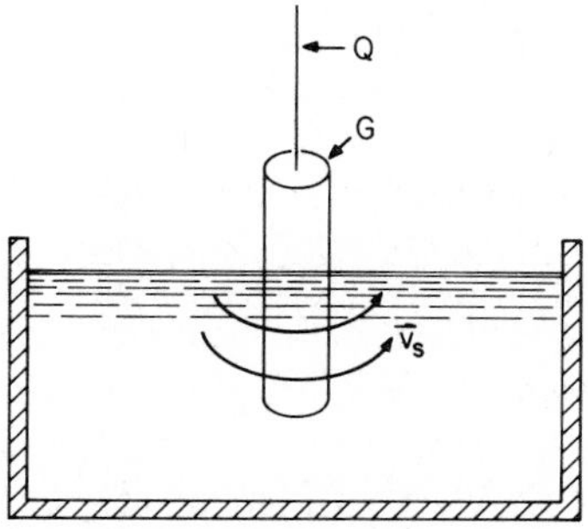

Fig. 8. The apparatus used by Hunt to observe the heat torque effect. When the glass cylinder G is heated it experiences a torque in the same direction as the superflow (assuming $v_n = 0$).

Notes p. 83

where we have assumed symmetry along that part (length ℓ) of the bar immersed in the He II; $\frac{1}{2}d$ is the radius of the bar.

Hunt found that there was a torque and also verified as given by (6-23) that the torque was linear in the heating rate $\dot{W}$. He also found that for a given flow field and given heating rate $\dot{W}$ the temperature dependence followed $\rho_n/\rho sT$ within experimental accuracy (we will discuss in § 7 the means by which ρ_n/ρ is accurately measured). The dependence of the torque on $v_{s\|} - v_{n\|}$ could not be checked since there was no independent way in which $v_{s\|} - v_{n\|}$ could be measured.

The experiments could be interpreted as indicating that the torque was in the appropriate direction as follows. In a typical experimental run the vessel containing the liquid helium was brought into rotation at a temperature above T_λ, so that the entire fluid would be rotating. Next the rotating fluid and container were cooled to a He II temperature and the vessel subsequently brought to rest. The net effect is to have a situation where the normal fluid is at rest whereas the superfluid may be in motion. This happens because the normal fluid like a classical fluid is viscous and tries to assume the velocity of the boundary. This property, and the boundary condition $v_{n\|} = 0$, will be discussed in Chapter II where we take up the question of dissipative effects. But already (6-14) suggests that only the normal fluid senses the boundary. Due to the basic property of frictionless flow the superfluid does not viscously interact with the boundary and hence continues to circulate while $\boldsymbol{v}_n = 0$.

One clearly expects $\boldsymbol{v}_s$ to rotate in the same sense as the originally imposed rotation and according to (6-23) the torque should also be in this direction as was verified by Hunt.

7 *Propagation of Sound in Superfluid Helium*

The Landau two fluid equations were in large part motivated by the results of Kapitza's experiments. However, the real test of a theory is its ability to predict new phenomena. In the last section we have already discussed some qualitative experimental checks of predictions of the two fluid equations. Historically the prediction of Landau and Tisza that He II could support two different propagating wave (i.e., sound) modes and the subsequent experimental confirmations of Peshkov [19]

Notes p. 83

in 1944 provided the first striking support for the two fluid idea, and a quantitative means of measuring the basic parameters ρ_s and ρ_n.

Following the approach of § 1 we discuss the propagation of sound in He II by investigating its response to a small disturbance from a steady state in which $\boldsymbol{v}_n = \boldsymbol{v}_s = 0$ and the thermodynamic variables are constants. Denoting the disturbance from equilibrium by δ and the constant equilibrium values by the subscript zero, we have

$$\begin{aligned} \rho &= \rho_0 + \delta\rho(\boldsymbol{r}, t), & s &= s_0 + \delta s(\boldsymbol{r}, t), \\ p &= p_0 + \delta p(\boldsymbol{r}, t), & T &= T_0 + \delta T(\boldsymbol{r}, t), \\ \boldsymbol{v}_n &= \delta\boldsymbol{v}_n(\boldsymbol{r}, t), & \boldsymbol{v}_s &= \delta\boldsymbol{v}_s(\boldsymbol{r}, t). \end{aligned} \tag{7-1}$$

We assume that $\delta\rho/\rho_0$, $\delta s/s_0$, etc., are much less than unity and further that $\boldsymbol{v}_n$, $\boldsymbol{v}_s$ are much less than the sound velocity. Then as with the classical fluid we will be justified in linearizing the two fluid equations. So neglecting all terms quadratic in the small quantities (4-1,2,3,4) supplemented by (4-8) become

$$\frac{\partial\delta\rho}{\partial t} + \rho_{n,0}\nabla\cdot\delta\boldsymbol{v}_n + \rho_{s,0}\nabla\cdot\delta\boldsymbol{v}_s = 0, \tag{7-2}$$

$$\rho_0\frac{\partial\delta s}{\partial t} + s_0\frac{\partial\delta\rho}{\partial t} + \rho_0 s_0\nabla\cdot\delta\boldsymbol{v}_n = 0, \tag{7-3}$$

$$\frac{\partial\delta\boldsymbol{v}_s}{\partial t} - s_0\nabla\delta T + \frac{1}{\rho_0}\nabla\delta p = 0, \tag{7-4}$$

$$\rho_{n,0}\frac{\partial\delta\boldsymbol{v}_n}{\partial t} + \rho_{s,0}\frac{\partial\delta\boldsymbol{v}_s}{\partial t} = -\nabla\delta p. \tag{7-5}$$

When we use equations of state for say ρ, s, in terms of p, T these become eight equations for eight unknowns as should be the case. The dependence in the equations of state on $(\boldsymbol{v}_n - \boldsymbol{v}_s)^2$ can be ignored since that leads to terms quadratic in the velocities.

We look for solutions to these equations in the form of longitudinal travelling waves with frequency ω and wave number k_0. Thus we set

$$T = T_0 + T' \exp(ik_0 x - i\omega t), \tag{7-6}$$

$$p = p_0 + p' \exp(ik_0 x - i\omega t), \tag{7-7}$$

$$\boldsymbol{v}_n = v_n' \exp(ik_0 x - i\omega t)\hat{\boldsymbol{e}}_x, \tag{7-8}$$

Notes p. 83

$$\boldsymbol{v}_s = v_s' \exp(ik_0x - i\omega t)\hat{\boldsymbol{e}}_x, \tag{7-9}$$

where T', p', v_n', v_s' are the amplitude of deviation of the temperature, pressure, $\boldsymbol{v}_n$, $\boldsymbol{v}_s$ from equilibrium and $\hat{\boldsymbol{e}}_x$ is a unit vector in the x direction.

Substituting (7-6,7,8,9) into (7-2,3,4,5) along with equations of state for ρ, s, in terms of p, T we find the set of equations

$$-i\omega\frac{\partial\rho}{\partial p}p' - i\omega\frac{\partial\rho}{\partial T}T' + ik_0\rho_{n,0}v_n' + ik_0\rho_{s,0}v_s' = 0, \tag{7-10}$$

$$-i\omega\frac{\partial\rho s}{\partial p}p' - i\omega\frac{\partial\rho s}{\partial T}T' + ik_0\rho_0 s_0 v_n' = 0, \tag{7-11}$$

$$-i\omega v_s' - ik_0 s_0 T' + i\frac{k_0}{\rho_0}p' = 0, \tag{7-12}$$

$$-i\omega\rho_{s,0}v_s' - i\omega\rho_{n,0}v_n' + ik_0 p' = 0. \tag{7-13}$$

As (7-5,6,7,8) are four homogeneous equations in four unknowns (p', T', v_n', v_s') the determinant must vanish in order for there to exist a non-trivial solution. This yields a dispersion law relating ω and k_0:

$$(1 - u^2/u_1^2)(1 - u^2/u_2^2) = 1 - C_V/C_p, \tag{7-14}$$

where we have set

$$C_V = T(\partial s/\partial T)_\rho, \tag{7-15}$$

$$C_p = T(\partial s/\partial T)_p, \tag{7-16}$$

$$u^2 = \omega^2/k_0^2, \tag{7-17}$$

$$u_1^2 = (\partial p/\partial\rho)_s, \tag{7-18}$$

$$u_2^2 = \rho_s s^2 T/\rho_n C_V, \tag{7-19}$$

and the subscript zero has been dropped from the equilibrium quantities.

In order to derive the dispersion law (7-14) use must be made of the following thermodynamic identities

$$\left(\frac{\partial p}{\partial\rho}\right)_s \equiv \left(\frac{\partial s}{\partial T}\right)_p\left[\left(\frac{\partial s}{\partial T}\right)_p\left(\frac{\partial\rho}{\partial p}\right)_T - \left(\frac{\partial s}{\partial p}\right)_T\left(\frac{\partial\rho}{\partial T}\right)_p\right]^{-1}, \tag{7-20}$$

$$\left(\frac{\partial s}{\partial T}\right)_p\left(\frac{\partial\rho}{\partial p}\right)_T^{-1} \equiv \left(\frac{\partial s}{\partial T}\right)_\rho\left(\frac{\partial p}{\partial\rho}\right)_s. \tag{7-21}$$

Notes p. 83

The dispersion law is quadratic in u^2. Hence, in general, there exist two solutions to the dispersion law (7-14), each of which corresponds to a disturbance which can propagate in the plus or minus x direction. In He II at most temperatures and pressures $1 - C_V/C_p \ll 1$, (e.g., at 2 °K it equals 10^{-3}). For these cases the right hand side of (7-14) can be neglected and the two solutions to the dispersion law (i.e., the speeds of propagation of the two sound modes) are given simply by $u^2 = u_1^2$ and $u^2 = u_2^2$.

To determine the nature of the two different sound modes let us investigate the relationships between the variables that follow from the linearized equations (7-10,11,12,13). In some cases, it will be necessary to include terms first order in $1 - C_V/C_p$. For instance very near the lambda transition and under high pressure this term can become much larger than at the lower temperatures. Also in discussing the generation of sound these corrections are important. To have a consistent description to first order in $1 - C_V/C_p$ the dispersion law must also be solved to this accuracy. From (7-14) one finds the two solutions

$$u^2 = u_1^2 + \frac{u_1^2 u_2^2}{u_1^2 - u_2^2}\left(1 - \frac{C_V}{C_p}\right), \tag{7-22}$$

$$u^2 = u_2^2 - \frac{u_1^2 u_2^2}{u_1^2 - u_2^2}\left(1 - \frac{C_V}{C_p}\right) = \frac{C_V}{C_p}u_2^2 - \frac{u_2^4}{u_1^2 - u_2^2}\left(1 - \frac{C_V}{C_p}\right). \tag{7-23}$$

There is never any trouble with the denominator on the right hand side of (7-22,23) since it is always found that $u_1^2 > 3u_2^2$.

From (7-10) and (7-13) follows a relation between T' and p' when a sound wave propagates. Substituting that expression into (7-12) yields a relation between T' and v_s':

$$T' = \frac{\rho u[1 - u^2(\partial\rho/\partial p)_T]v_s'}{u^2(\partial\rho/\partial T)_p - \rho s[1 - u^2(\partial\rho/\partial p)_T]}. \tag{7-24}$$

From (7-24) and (7-12) one now finds a relation between p' and v_s'

$$p' = \frac{\rho u^3(\partial\rho/\partial T)_p v_s'}{u^2(\partial\rho/\partial T)_p - \rho s[1 - u^2(\partial\rho/\partial p)_T]}. \tag{7-25}$$

And finally from (7-24,25) and (7-10) one obtains the variation in v_n which results from a given variation in v_s:

$$v_n' = -\frac{\rho_s}{\rho_n}v_s' + \frac{u^2(\rho/\rho_n)(\partial\rho/\partial T)_p v_s'}{u^2(\partial\rho/\partial T)_p - \rho s[1 - u^2(\partial\rho/\partial p)_T]}. \tag{7-26}$$

Notes p. 83

In these relations u must of course be set equal to either u_1 or u_2 or if greater accuracy is desired it must be set equal to the u determined by (7-22,23).

When first or 'ordinary' sound propagates [i.e., when u is given by (7-22)] its speed is to an excellent approximation equal to the speed of sound in a classical Euler fluid (1-31). From (7-22) and (7-26) we find to first order in $1 - C_V/C_p$ the relation between v_n' and v_s' in first sound:

$$v_n' = v_s' - \frac{\rho^2 s(1 - C_V/C_p)v_s'}{\rho_n(\partial\rho/\partial T)_p(u_1^2 - u_2^2)}. \tag{7-27}$$

Or using (7-18,19) and the identity

$$1 - \frac{C_p}{C_V} \equiv -\left[\frac{1}{\rho}\left(\frac{\partial\rho}{\partial T}\right)_p\right]^2\left(\frac{\partial p}{\partial\rho}\right)_s \frac{T}{C_p} \tag{7-28}$$

Eq. (7-27) becomes

$$v_n' = v_s' - \frac{(\partial\rho/\partial T)_p\, u_1^2 u_2^2}{\rho_s s(u_1^2 - u_2^2)} v_s'. \tag{7-29}$$

This expansion is valid to high accuracy at all temperatures and pressures. Since at most temperatures (i.e., $T > 0.8$ °K) and all pressures, the second term on the right hand side of (7-29) is much smaller than the first we find that when first sound propagates one has to good accuracy

$$v_n' = v_s' = v', \tag{7-30}$$

or the two fluids move together in phase with a velocity equal to the center of mass velocity v':

$$v' \equiv (\rho_n/\rho)v_n' + (\rho_s/\rho)v_s'.$$

From (7-13) we then see that to lowest order $p' = \rho u_1 v'$ which is again just like the behavior of classical sound. It should be remarked the first sound in He II is similar to ordinary sound in an Euler fluid only when $1 - C_V/C_p$ or equivalently $(\partial\rho/\partial T)_p$ are so small that they can be neglected. For experiments where this is not the case the first sound mode is just as unique as the second wave mode which we discuss below. Careful measurements of these effects have not yet been performed. The speed of first sound is found to be within ten per cent of 2.3×10^4 cm/sec at all temperatures [20], at the saturated vapor pressure.

Notes p. 83

Whereas first sound in lowest order involves a center of mass motion with no relative motion of the super and normal components, second sound [i.e., u given by (7-23)] involves at this order a relative motion of the two fluids with no center of mass motion. To see this first use (7-23,26) to obtain a relation between v'_n and v'_s valid when second sound propagates:

$$\rho_s v'_s + \rho_n v'_n = \frac{\rho(\partial\rho/\partial T)_p v'_s}{(\partial\rho/\partial T)_p - \rho s(u_1^2 - u_2^2)/u_1^2 u_2^2 + (\rho s/u_1^2)(1 - C_V/C_p)}.$$

The reason that $1 - C_V/C_p$ is so small is that $(\partial\rho/\partial T)_p$ is small (see 7-28). Keeping terms now to lowest non-vanishing order in $(\partial\rho/\partial T)_p$ the above relation becomes

$$\rho v' = -\frac{(\partial\rho/\partial T)_p u_1^2 u_2^2 v'_s}{s(u_1^2 - u_2^2)}. \tag{7-31}$$

Although $(\partial\rho/\partial T)_p$ is small, so is s at low temperature. In fact the approximation which must be made to obtain (7-31):

$$\left(\frac{\partial\rho}{\partial T}\right)_p \ll \frac{\rho s(u_1^2 - u_2^2)}{u_1^2 u_2^2}$$

is valid only above 0.8 °K. Below this temperature one must use the exact relation given above. For $T > 0.8$ °K we find that the right hand side of (7-31) is small compared with $\rho_s v'_s$ and thus second sound to a good approximation satisfies $\rho_n v'_n + \rho_s v'_s = 0$ at these temperatures.

The thermal fluctuations that accompany second sound follow from (7-19,24) and are at lowest order

$$T' = -u_2 v'_s/s. \tag{7-32}$$

As v' is small so also is p' and we conclude that second sound is basically a thermal or entropy wave. This fact is made especially clear by considering the manner in which the various modes must be excited.

First we note that when the disturbance is generated by an oscillating plate which puts no heat into the He II we must have that at the surface of the plate,

$$\boldsymbol{v}_n = \boldsymbol{v}_s = \boldsymbol{v}_0. \tag{7-33}$$

Relation (7-33) can be derived by a Galilean transformation of (6-1,2) from the reference frame in which the boundary is at rest to the laboratory

Notes p. 83

reference frame in which it has velocity $\boldsymbol{v}_0$. In the disturbance generated $\boldsymbol{v}_\mathrm{n}$ and $\boldsymbol{v}_\mathrm{s}$ will be equal to the sum of their respective velocities in the two sound modes generated or

$$\begin{aligned}\boldsymbol{v}_\mathrm{n} &= \boldsymbol{v}_{\mathrm{n},1} + \boldsymbol{v}_{\mathrm{n},2},\\ \boldsymbol{v}_\mathrm{s} &= \boldsymbol{v}_{\mathrm{s},1} + \boldsymbol{v}_{\mathrm{s},2},\end{aligned} \tag{7-34}$$

where here $\boldsymbol{v}_{\mathrm{n},1}$ and $\boldsymbol{v}_{\mathrm{n},2}$ are the normal fluid velocities in the first and second sound modes generated by the plate, etc., for $\boldsymbol{v}_{\mathrm{s},1}$ and $\boldsymbol{v}_{\mathrm{s},2}$. Substituting (7-34) into (7-33) yields

$$\boldsymbol{v}_{\mathrm{n},1} + \boldsymbol{v}_{\mathrm{n},2} = \boldsymbol{v}_{\mathrm{s},1} + \boldsymbol{v}_{\mathrm{s},2}. \tag{7-35}$$

If we ignore the small terms proportional to $(\partial\rho/\partial T)_p$ in (7-29) and (7-31) we have $\boldsymbol{v}_{\mathrm{n},1} = \boldsymbol{v}_{\mathrm{s},1}$; $\rho_\mathrm{n}\boldsymbol{v}_{\mathrm{n},2} = -\rho_\mathrm{s}\boldsymbol{v}_{\mathrm{s},2}$, which when placed into (7-35) yields $\boldsymbol{v}_{\mathrm{n},2} = \boldsymbol{v}_{\mathrm{s},2} = 0$ or in other words no second sound is generated by the oscillating plate when the small terms depending on $(\partial\rho/\partial T)_p$ or equivalently $1 - C_V/C_p$ are ignored.

In a similar manner if one considers a stationary plate which generates a disturbance by an oscillatory heating and cooling of the fluid then from (6-1)

$$\rho_\mathrm{n}\boldsymbol{v}_\mathrm{n} + \rho_\mathrm{s}\boldsymbol{v}_\mathrm{s} = 0. \tag{7-36}$$

Equation (7-34) is of course still valid and we find

$$\rho_\mathrm{n}\boldsymbol{v}_{\mathrm{n},1} + \rho_\mathrm{n}\boldsymbol{v}_{\mathrm{n},2} + \rho_\mathrm{s}\boldsymbol{v}_{\mathrm{s},1} + \rho_\mathrm{s}\boldsymbol{v}_{\mathrm{s},2} = 0. \tag{7-37}$$

Again if we ignore the small terms brought in by $(\partial\rho/\partial T)_p$ in (7-29,31) we find from (7-37) that $\boldsymbol{v}_{\mathrm{n},1} = \boldsymbol{v}_{\mathrm{s},1} = 0$ or that no first sound is generated in this approximation. We conclude that all the energy put into the fluid by the stationary heat source must be in the form of second sound disturbances, thus showing that second sound is basically a thermal wave.

We now discuss the generation of second sound by an oscillating plate and the generation of first sound by a stationary heat source when terms first order in the small thermodynamic quantities proportional to $(\partial\rho/\partial T)_p$ are included [21].

One could proceed as above and calculate the relative amplitudes of the first and second sound waves in this approximation. Instead we choose to calculate the relative intensities of the two modes for the various boundary conditions. The intensity of a sound mode is determined by the energy flux density $\boldsymbol{Q}$ of the mode. Our objective is to

Notes p. 83

calculate the relationship between $\boldsymbol{Q}_1$ and $\boldsymbol{Q}_2$, which are the energy flux densities of first and second sound.

First we calculate the energy density of the sound mode by expanding U to second order in the deviation from its constant equilibrium value U_{eq}:

$$U = U_{\mathrm{eq}} + \left(\frac{\partial U_0}{\partial \rho}\right)_{\rho s} \delta\rho + \left(\frac{\partial U_0}{\partial \rho s}\right)_{\rho} \delta\rho s + \rho_{\mathrm{n},0} \frac{(v_{\mathrm{n}} - v_{\mathrm{s}})^2}{2} + \rho_{\mathrm{n},0}(v_{\mathrm{n}} - v_{\mathrm{s}})v_{\mathrm{s}}$$
$$+ \tfrac{1}{2}\rho_0 v_{\mathrm{s}}^2 + \left(\frac{\partial^2 U_0}{\partial \rho^2}\right)_{\rho s} \frac{(\delta\rho)^2}{2} + \left(\frac{\partial^2 U_0}{\partial (\rho s)^2}\right)_{\rho} \frac{(\delta\rho s)^2}{2} + \frac{\partial^2 U_0}{\partial\rho\partial\rho s} \delta\rho\, \delta\rho s, \quad (7\text{-}38)$$

where we have used (4-5) and (4-6), and to second order have written

$$(v_{\mathrm{n}} - v_{\mathrm{s}})\, \mathrm{d}[\rho_{\mathrm{n}}(v_{\mathrm{n}} - v_{\mathrm{s}})] = \rho_{\mathrm{n},0}\, \mathrm{d}[(v_{\mathrm{n}} - v_{\mathrm{s}})^2/2] = \mathrm{d}[\rho_{\mathrm{n},0}(v_{\mathrm{n}} - v_{\mathrm{s}})^2/2];$$

for all the thermodynamic derivatives it is understood that $\rho_{\mathrm{n}}(\boldsymbol{v}_{\mathrm{n}} - \boldsymbol{v}_{\mathrm{s}})$ is also kept fixed. From further use of (4-5) we reduce (7-38) to

$$U = U_{\mathrm{eq}} + \mu_0\, \delta\rho + T_0\, \delta\rho s + \left(\frac{\partial \mu}{\partial \rho}\right)_{\rho s} \frac{(\delta\rho)^2}{2} + \left(\frac{\partial T}{\partial \rho s}\right)_{\rho} \frac{(\delta\rho s)^2}{2}$$
$$+ \left(\frac{\partial \mu}{\partial \rho s}\right)_{\rho} \delta\rho\, \delta\rho s + \tfrac{1}{2}\rho_{\mathrm{n},0} v_{\mathrm{n}}^2 + \tfrac{1}{2}\rho_{\mathrm{s},0} v_{\mathrm{s}}^2, \quad (7\text{-}39)$$

where all derivatives are of course to be evaluated in the equilibrium state. On integrating (7-39) over the entire volume of fluid the term $\mu_0\, \delta\rho$ contributes nothing, since we can consider the sound waves as propagating in a system of fixed total mass ($\int \delta\rho\, \mathrm{d}V = 0$) [46]. The term $T_0\, \delta\rho s$ will not, however, vanish on integration since when second sound propagates, entropy flows to and from the fluid via the boundary. What can be said is that the change in total entropy of the fluid is due *only* to the entropy to flow into the fluid from the boundary, since entropy is conserved on the ideal level. In this (reversible) approximation one also has that the time average of the change in total entropy can be taken to be zero for a periodic disturbance. The contribution to the energy density due to the disturbance, which does not vanish on integrating and time averaging is taken to be the energy density of the sound wave and is at second order

$$\left(\frac{\partial \mu}{\partial \rho}\right)_{\rho s} \frac{(\delta\rho)^2}{2} + \left(\frac{\partial T}{\partial \rho s}\right)_{\rho} \frac{(\delta\rho s)^2}{2} + \left(\frac{\partial \mu}{\partial \rho s}\right)_{\rho} \delta\rho\, \delta\rho s + \tfrac{1}{2}\rho_{\mathrm{n},0} v_{\mathrm{n}}^2 + \tfrac{1}{2}\rho_{\mathrm{s},0} v_{\mathrm{s}}^2 . \quad (7\text{-}40)$$

Notes p. 83

The energy density will still be accurate to second order if we set $\delta\rho s = \rho_0\delta s + s_0\delta\rho$ and use

$$\left(\frac{\partial\mu}{\partial\rho}\right)_{\rho s} = -s_0\left(\frac{\partial T}{\partial\rho}\right)_{\rho s} + \frac{1}{\rho_0}\left(\frac{\partial p}{\partial\rho}\right)_{\rho s},$$

the dependence of μ on $(v_n - v_s)^2$ leading to terms of higher order. Making these substitutions in (7-40) we find for the energy density of sound in He II

$$\frac{1}{\rho_0}\left(\frac{\partial p}{\partial\rho}\right)_s\frac{(\delta\rho)^2}{2} + \rho_0\left(\frac{\partial T}{\partial s}\right)_\rho\frac{(\delta s)^2}{2} + \frac{1}{\rho_0}\left(\frac{\partial p}{\partial s}\right)_\rho\delta\rho\,\delta s + \tfrac{1}{2}\rho_{n,0}v_n^2 + \tfrac{1}{2}\rho_{s,0}v_s^2, \tag{7-41}$$

where we have also used the identity

$$\left(\frac{\partial p}{\partial\rho}\right)_s \equiv \left(\frac{\partial p}{\partial\rho}\right)_{\rho s} + \frac{s}{\rho}\left(\frac{\partial p}{\partial s}\right)_\rho.$$

When a monochromatic wave propagates we have to first order

$$\delta\rho = \frac{\rho_{n,0}v_n + \rho_{s,0}v_s}{u}, \tag{7-42}$$

$$\delta s = \frac{\rho_{s,0}s_0}{\rho_0 u}(v_n - v_s), \tag{7-43}$$

where we have used (7-2,3). As (7-41) is already second order it will still be accurate to this order if we substitute (7-42,43) for $\delta\rho$ and δs and find

$$\frac{1}{\rho}\left(\frac{\partial p}{\partial\rho}\right)_s\frac{(\rho_n v_n + \rho_s v_s)^2}{2u^2} + \left(\frac{\partial T}{\partial s}\right)_\rho\frac{\rho_s^2 s^2(v_n - v_s)^2}{2\rho u^2}$$
$$+ \left(\frac{\partial p}{\partial s}\right)_\rho\frac{(\rho_n v_n + \rho_s v_s)\rho_s s(v_n - v_s)}{\rho^2 u^2} + \tfrac{1}{2}\rho_n v_n^2 + \tfrac{1}{2}\rho_s v_s^2, \tag{7-44}$$

where we have dropped the subscript zero.

When first sound propagates we have to lowest order in $(\partial\rho/\partial T)_p$ that $v_n = v_s$ and $\delta s = 0$. Hence the energy density of first sound in lowest approximation is

$$U_1 = \rho_n v_{n,1}^2 + \rho_s v_{s,1}^2, \tag{7-45}$$

where we remember that to this order $u^2 = (\partial p/\partial\rho)_s$ for first sound.

Notes p. 83

When second sound propagates $\rho_n v_n + \rho_s v_s = 0$ and to lowest order in $(\partial\rho/\partial T)_p$ we find the energy density

$$U_2 = \rho_n v_{n,2}^2 + \rho_s v_{s,2}^2. \tag{7-46}$$

The energy flux density $\boldsymbol{Q}_1$ of first sound is determined by the conservation law

$$\frac{\partial U_1}{\partial t} + \nabla \cdot \boldsymbol{Q}_1 = 0$$

and similarly for second sound. We thus find to second order in the deviation from equilibrium

$$\begin{aligned} Q_1 &= (\rho_n v_{n,1}^2 + \rho_s v_{s,1}^2)u_1, \\ Q_2 &= (\rho_n v_{n,2}^2 + \rho_s v_{s,2}^2)u_2. \end{aligned} \tag{7-47}$$

If one considers a wave which is not monochromatic then as with the classical fluid (7-45,46,47) are still valid if one interprets all the quantities as being time averages. Also the total energy density is the sum of the energy densities at each frequency.

Returning to the question of the relative intensities of the two waves we first consider the oscillating boundary. Substituting (7-29,31) into (7-35) and now keeping terms to first order in $(\partial\rho/\partial T)_p$ we find that an oscillating boundary which puts no heat into the fluid generates waves of first and second sound where the ratio of the superfluid velocities is

$$\frac{v_{s,2}}{v_{s,1}} = -\frac{\rho_n}{\rho_s \rho s}\left(\frac{\partial\rho}{\partial T}\right)_p \frac{u_1^2 u_2^2}{u_1^2 - u_2^2}. \tag{7-48}$$

From (7-48) and (7-29,31) we find that the ratio of the magnitudes of the intensities of the sound so generated is to lowest non-vanishing order in $(\partial\rho/\partial T)_p$

$$\frac{Q_2}{Q_1} = \frac{\rho_n}{\rho_s \rho^2 s^2}\left(\frac{\partial\rho}{\partial T}\right)_p^2 \left(\frac{u_1^2 u_2^2}{u_1^2 - u_2^2}\right)^2 \frac{u_2}{u_1}, \tag{7-49}$$

which is extremely small (less than 10^{-7}). We conclude that the pressure transducer which is the accepted means of generating ordinary sound is an extremely inefficient producer of second sound.

By the same procedure we find that the ratio of the intensities of first to second sound generated by a stationary heat source is

$$\frac{Q_1}{Q_2} = \frac{\rho_n}{\rho_s \rho^2 s^2}\left(\frac{\partial\rho}{\partial T}\right)_p^2 \left(\frac{u_1^2 u_2^2}{u_1^2 - u_2^2}\right)^2 \frac{u_1}{u_2}, \tag{7-50}$$

Notes p. 83

where we have used (7-29,31,37). Thus a stationary heat source is an extremely inefficient generator of first sound (Q_1/Q_2 being less than 10^{-6}), as almost all the energy goes into the second sound waves.

According to Peshkov the first attempts to see second sound were made before the war and were based on the predictions of Landau. Is this a suggestion that perhaps the Landau two fluid theory was completed well before its publication in 1941? In any case Peshkov in these original experiments tried to excite second sound by the oscillating plate method. As we have seen above this technique is doomed to failure and indeed Peshkov's first results were negative. It was in 1944 that Lifshitz produced essentially the above calculation [21] showing that second sound is best generated by a periodic heating and cooling of the liquid. Based on the results of Lifshitz, Kapitza then encouraged Peshkov to look for second sound with this new technique. This time his efforts met with immediate success.

That thermal disturbances propagate reversibly as waves rather than irreversibly by conduction as in classical materials, is unique to superfluid helium. Although there is no compression of the center of mass for second sound, there is a compression of the normal and super components. As the superfluid carries no entropy the compressions and rarefactions of superfluid correspond to reversible decreases and increases of temperature. The restoring force which resists these variations comes from the chemical potential. A change in temperature with no change in pressure such as occurs in second sound leads to a gradient in the chemical potential which according to the basic equation (4-3) causes an acceleration of superfluid which always acts to oppose the compression or rarefaction. In Fig. 9 the speed of second sound is indicated as a function of temperature at the vapor pressure [22]. It quickly rises from zero at T_λ to its typical value of 1.9×10^3 cm/sec. Below 1 °K the speed increases again. Most important is that from measurements of the speed of second sound [see Eq. (7-19)] and equilibrium measurements of s, T, ρ, C_V one can determine the superfluid fraction ρ_s/ρ (or equivalently $\rho_n/\rho = 1 - \rho_s/\rho$) which is the basic new parameter of the two fluid theory. In Fig. 10 is a graph of ρ_s/ρ versus temperature at the vapor pressure. As one might expect ρ_s/ρ vanishes at the lambda point where superfluidity disappears, and at absolute zero where the entropy must vanish ρ_s/ρ goes to 100%.

A striking feature of second sound that we have emphasized is that although the center of mass is at rest the normal and superfluids are in

Notes p. 83

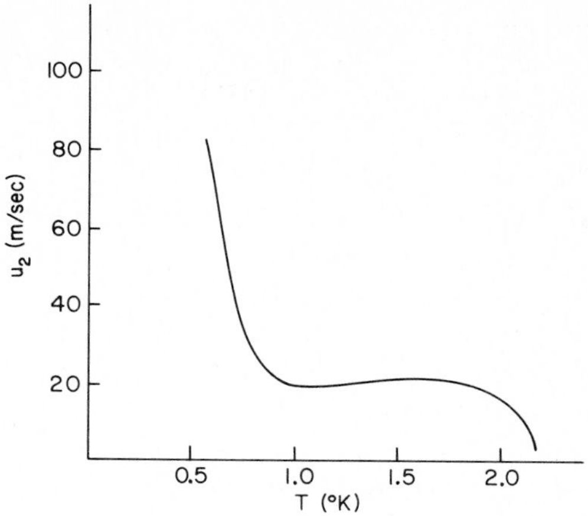

Fig. 9. Speed of second sound versus temperature for He II under its own vapor pressure.

motion. One might wonder if there is a direct means by which this internal convection can be observed. Pellam and Hanson [23] attacked this problem and were able to experimentally demonstrate this motion by use of a Rayleigh disc.

An object immersed in potential flow ($\nabla \times \boldsymbol{v} = 0$) in a classical fluid does not experience a drag force, but can feel a torque. For a thin disc

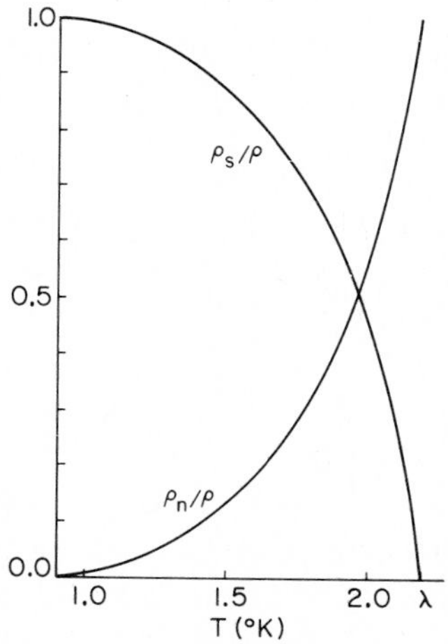

Fig. 10. The normal and super component fractions in He II, at the vapor pressure.

Notes p. 83

(Rayleigh disc) of diameter d the torque τ is proportional to the square of the streaming velocity $\boldsymbol{U}$ at infinity and acts to align the disc perpendicular to the flow [24]:

$$\tau = \tfrac{1}{6}\rho d^3 U^2 \sin 2\theta, \tag{7-51}$$

where θ is the angle a normal to the disc makes with the direction of flow. Such a disc was used by Rayleigh to demonstrate the fluid motion in sound in a classical liquid.

As with the classical fluid one expects that when sound propagates in He II the flow will to a good approximation be potential flow ($\nabla \times \boldsymbol{v}_s = 0$ and $\nabla \times \boldsymbol{A} = 0$ or to first order $\nabla \times \boldsymbol{v}_n = 0$) since, in equilibrium the velocities vanish (and hence $\nabla \times \boldsymbol{v}_n = \nabla \times \boldsymbol{v}_s = 0$ everywhere in equilibrium) and in addition one has a Lagrange theorem for the change in vorticity with time: Pellam and Hanson then reasoned that although the total momentum vanishes for second sound, the sum of the squares of the momenta of the super and normal fluids does not, and one should expect that the total torque would be the sum of the torques exerted by the two fluids separately or based on (7-51):

$$\tau = \tfrac{1}{6}d^3(\rho_n U_n^2 + \rho_s U_s^2) \sin 2\theta, \tag{7-52}$$

where U_s, U_n are the streaming velocities of the super and normal fluids far from the disc.

The justification for adding the torques of the two fluids comes from investigating the two fluid hydrodynamics when variations in ρ_n, ρ, s are ignored: Eqs. (2-14,15). In this approximation each fluid behaves like a classical fluid and the total stress tensor

$$P_{ij} = p_n\delta_{ij} + \rho_n v_{n,i} v_{n,j} + p_s\delta_{ij} + \rho_s v_{s,i} v_{s,j} \tag{7-53}$$

is the *sum* of the stress tensors of the two fluids, where we remember that the total pressure $p = p_s + p_n$ ($p_s = \rho_s\mu$) in this approximation. First we look at steady flow around the disc, then since we do not heat or cool the disc from outside the perpendicular components of $\boldsymbol{v}_s$, $\boldsymbol{v}_n$ will vanish at the surface and the force on an area $\mathrm{d}\boldsymbol{S}$ will be $(p_s + p_n)\,\mathrm{d}\boldsymbol{S}$. The torque on the disc will then be $\int \boldsymbol{r} \times p_s \mathrm{d}\boldsymbol{S} + \int \boldsymbol{r} \times p_n \mathrm{d}\boldsymbol{S}$ over the entire surface of the disc. As a consequence of the stresses adding we see that the total torque is the sum of the torques exerted by the two fluids as though each were an Euler fluid and obeyed boundary conditions like those imposed on an Euler fluid. Thus (7-51) is valid for each fluid and the total torque is given by (7-52).

Notes p. 83

When sound propagates, however, we cannot consider the flow as steady or take ρ_n, ρ, s constant. But as far as the *disc* is concerned this will be a good approximation if the wavelength of the sound is much greater than d and if the time constant of the disc's response (which is determined by the torsion wire upon which it is suspended) is much longer than the period of the second sound, as was the case in this experiment.

As second sound involves no net mass flux $\rho_n \boldsymbol{U}_n + \rho_s \boldsymbol{U}_s = 0$ so (7-52) becomes

$$\tau = \tfrac{1}{6} d^3 (\rho_n \rho / \rho_s) U_n^2 \sin 2\theta. \tag{7-54}$$

By (6-4) we can relate U_n to the heat input $\dot{W}$ at the wall which is used to drive the second sound and obtain

$$\tau = \tfrac{1}{6} d^3 (\rho_n \dot{W}^2 / \rho_s \rho s^2 T^2) \sin 2\theta. \tag{7-55}$$

Finally since the disc responds slowly to changes in U_n what is really measured is the time average of the torque on the disc or

$$\langle \tau \rangle = \tfrac{1}{6} d^3 (\rho_n \langle \dot{W}^2 \rangle / \rho_s \rho s^2 T^2) \sin 2\theta. \tag{7-56}$$

A rough schematic of the apparatus is given in Fig. 11. By appropriate

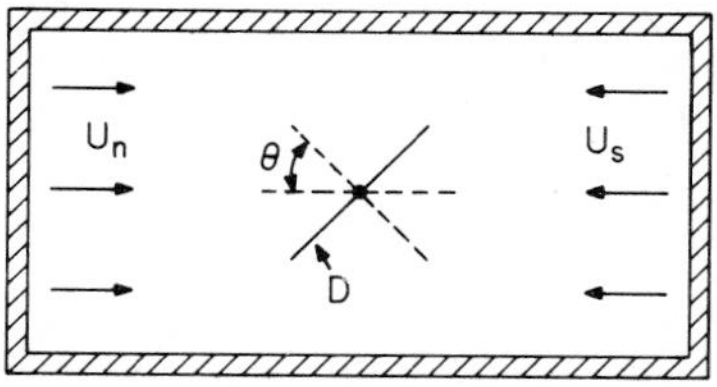

Fig. 11. The experimental arrangement used by Hanson and Pellam for the investigation of the torque on a Rayleigh disc D suspended in a second sound field.

periodic heating and cooling the walls of a cavity filled with He II a second sound resonance can be set up. The torque on the Rayleigh disc D can be determined by comparing its equilibrium position (no sound) with its orientation when second sound propagates. The torsion wire whose properties are assumed known is indicated by the dot and points towards the reader.

All quantities in (7-56) could be independently measured by Pellam and Hanson and the agreement between the two fluid theory and

Notes p. 83

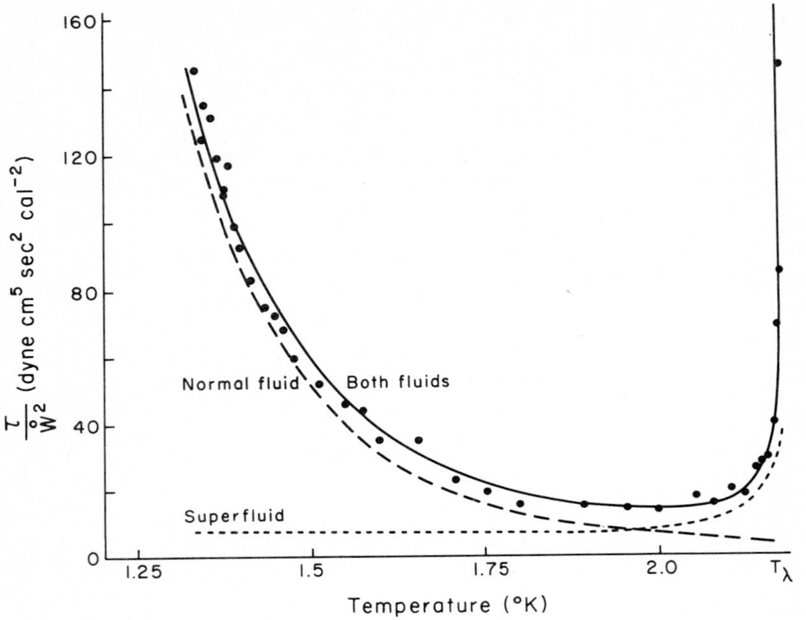

Fig. 12. Torque τ on a Rayleigh disc ($d = 1.26$ cm, $\theta = 45°$) due to a heat flux $\dot{W}$, as a function of temperature. Points are experimentally determined and the solid curve represents theoretical predictions based on (7-56). Dashed lines represent the separate contributions to the torque of the normal and super fluids.

experiment for this non-linear application was excellent. In Fig. 12 is a graph of their results for τ for a given heating rate $\dot{W}$ as a function of T. It is interesting to note that near T_λ the superfluid contributes most of the torque although its density is very small. This happens because the torque depends on U_s^2 and as $\rho_s \to 0$, U_s gets large because of the condition of no net mass flow and more than compensates for the small ρ_s. Near $T = 0$ °K the torque also gets large. In this case it is due to the fact that for a given heating rate U_n must get large since s goes to zero.

In this section we have considered the propagation of sound relative to a homogeneous (no external fields) steady state where $\boldsymbol{v}_n = \boldsymbol{v}_s = 0$. As with a classical fluid this is not the only homogeneous steady state. One can, for instance, consider the state obtained by a Galilean transformation of the observer so that $\boldsymbol{v}_n = \boldsymbol{v}_s \neq 0$. Sound propagated relative

Notes p. 83

to this moving fluid is Doppler shifted as with the Euler fluid and we do not go into the straightforward calculations here.

In complete contrast with the Euler fluid there are in He II uniform steady states possible which are *not* Galilean transformations of the simplest state $\boldsymbol{v}_n = \boldsymbol{v}_s = 0$. Such a state is, for instance, obtained by a steady heat flow. Then one has $\boldsymbol{v}_n$, $\boldsymbol{v}_s$ both constant but unequal. All the other thermodynamic variables will also be constant. (In § 6 we showed that near the boundary there might be some unusual behavior but we are here concerned with the bulk of the fluid and in any case with linear effects.)

It is clear from these remarks that the most general 'equilibrium' state with respect to which sound can be propagated is that for which $\rho_{n,0}\boldsymbol{v}_{n,0} + \rho_{s,0}\boldsymbol{v}_{s,0} = 0$ and $\boldsymbol{v}_{n,0} \neq 0$. Previously we considered the special case $\boldsymbol{v}_{n,0} = 0$. We now calculate the speed of first and second sound relative to a counterflow to terms linear in the equilibrium velocity [25].

Since in the equilibrium state $\boldsymbol{v}$ is zero it is most practical here to use as a complete set of eight independent variables: $\boldsymbol{v}$, $\boldsymbol{v}_n - \boldsymbol{v}_s$, p, T. For these variables we use as the eight equations of motion: the continuity of mass

$$\frac{\partial \rho}{\partial t} + \nabla \cdot \rho \boldsymbol{v} = 0, \tag{7-57}$$

the entropy law

$$\rho \frac{\partial s}{\partial t} + \rho \boldsymbol{v}_n \cdot \nabla s + s \nabla \cdot \rho_s(\boldsymbol{v}_n - \boldsymbol{v}_s) = 0, \tag{7-58}$$

[which follows from (4-1,2)], the superfluid equation of motion (4-3), and the momentum equation (4-4) in the form

$$\frac{\partial \rho v_i}{\partial t} + \frac{\partial}{\partial r_\alpha}\left[p\delta_{i\alpha} + \rho v_i v_\alpha + \frac{\rho_n \rho_s}{\rho}(v_n - v_s)_i (v_n - v_s)_\alpha\right] = 0. \tag{7-59}$$

Linearizing these equations in the deviation from equilibrium we obtain for a travelling wave

$$-\omega \frac{\partial \rho}{\partial p} p' - \omega \frac{\partial \rho}{\partial T} T' - \omega \frac{\partial \rho}{\partial w^2} 2ww' + \rho k_0 v' = 0, \tag{7-60}$$

Notes p. 83

$$-\omega\rho\frac{\partial s}{\partial p}p' - \omega\rho\frac{\partial s}{\partial T}T' - \omega\rho\frac{\partial s}{\partial w^2}2ww' + \rho v_{\rm n}k_0\left(\frac{\partial s}{\partial p}p' + \frac{\partial s}{\partial T}T'\right)$$
$$+ sk_0\left(\rho_{\rm s}w' + w\frac{\partial \rho_{\rm s}}{\partial p}p' + w\frac{\partial \rho_{\rm s}}{\partial T}T'\right) = 0, \quad (7\text{-}61)$$

$$-\omega v' + \omega\frac{\rho_{\rm n}}{\rho}w' + \omega w\left[\frac{\partial(\rho_{\rm n}/\rho)}{\partial p}p' + \frac{\partial(\rho_{\rm n}/\rho)}{\partial T}T'\right] - \frac{\rho_{\rm n}}{\rho}k_0 wv'$$
$$+ \frac{\rho_{\rm n}\rho_{\rm s}}{\rho^2}k_0 ww' - sk_0 T' + \frac{1}{\rho}k_0 p' = 0, \quad (7\text{-}62)$$

$$-\omega\rho v' + k_0 p' + \frac{\rho_{\rm n}\rho_{\rm s}}{\rho}2k_0 ww' = 0, \quad (7\text{-}63)$$

where we have dropped the subscript nought from equilibrium quantities and have kept terms which are at most linear in the equilibrium velocities. Also

$$\boldsymbol{w} \equiv \boldsymbol{v}_{\rm n} - \boldsymbol{v}_{\rm s}, \quad (7\text{-}64)$$

and we have used the identity

$$\boldsymbol{v}_{\rm s} \equiv \boldsymbol{v} - (\rho_{\rm n}/\rho)\boldsymbol{w}. \quad (7\text{-}65)$$

Equations (7-60,61,62,63) are four homogeneous equations in the four unknowns v', w', p', T'. In order for a non-trivial solution to exist the determinant must vanish, thus yielding the dispersion law

$$(u^2 - u_1^2)(u^2 - u_2^2) + u^3 w\left[-\frac{4\rho_{\rm s}}{\rho} + \frac{2s}{\rho_{\rm n}}\frac{\partial\rho_{\rm n}}{\partial T}\left(\frac{\partial s}{\partial T}\right)^{-1}\right]$$
$$+ uw\left[\frac{4\rho_{\rm s}}{\rho}\left(\frac{\partial\rho}{\partial p}\right)^{-1} - \frac{2s}{\rho_{\rm n}}\frac{\partial\rho_{\rm n}}{\partial T}\left(\frac{\partial\rho}{\partial p}\right)^{-1}\left(\frac{\partial s}{\partial T}\right)^{-1}\right] = 0, \quad (7\text{-}66)$$

where we have also neglected the small terms involving $(\partial\rho/\partial T)_p$. To derive (7-66) we made use of the Maxwell relations

$$\frac{1}{\rho^2}\frac{\partial\rho}{\partial w^2} = \frac{1}{2}\frac{\partial(\rho_{\rm n}/\rho)}{\partial p},$$
$$\frac{\partial s}{\partial w^2} = \frac{1}{2}\frac{\partial(\rho_{\rm n}/\rho)}{\partial T}, \quad (7\text{-}67)$$

Notes p. 83

which follow from (4-8). To terms linear in the equilibrium counterflow velocity w we find from (7-66) that the speed of first sound is unaffected but that the speed of the sound mode which reduces to second sound when $w = 0$ (or so to speak, the generalized second sound mode) is

$$u = \pm u_2 + \left[\frac{2\rho_s}{\rho} - \frac{s}{\rho_n}\frac{\partial \rho_n}{\partial T}\left(\frac{\partial s}{\partial T}\right)^{-1}\right] w. \tag{7-68}$$

In the next section we will see that the speed of large amplitude second sound waves [which has a strong resemblance with (7-68)] has been experimentally measured and is in agreement with (7-68).

8 *Shock Waves in Superfluid Helium*

The expressions (7-18,19) for the speeds of first and second sound apply only when the amplitude of the disturbance is so small that the linearized equations provide an accurate description of the flow. In that approximation the speed with which a disturbance travels is independent of its size. In general, however, different points of the profile of a disturbance (i.e., points of different amplitude) travel with different velocities.

These effects are best investigated by solving the hydrodynamical equations to *second* order in the deviation from equilibrium [26]. To do this we focus our attention on the speed u with which a point, on a one dimensional disturbance, corresponding to a fixed deviation δT from the equilibrium temperature T, moves through the fluid. Since in a one dimensional disturbance any quantity can be written as a function of any other single quantity, all the parameters obey

$$\partial/\partial t = -u(\partial/\partial x) \tag{8-1}$$

for the motion of a point of constant amplitude.

Keeping terms as far as second order of smallness in the deviation from the equilibrium state where $\boldsymbol{v}_n = \boldsymbol{v}_s = 0$, the Landau two fluid equations (7-57,58,59) and (4-3) become

$$-u\frac{\partial \rho}{\partial p}\frac{\partial p}{\partial x} - u\frac{\partial \rho}{\partial T}\frac{\partial T}{\partial x} - 2uw\frac{\partial \rho}{\partial w^2}\frac{\partial w}{\partial x} + \rho\frac{\partial v}{\partial x} + v\frac{\partial \rho}{\partial x} = 0, \tag{8-2}$$

Notes p. 83

$$\left[(-u\rho + \rho v_n)\frac{\partial s}{\partial p} + ws\frac{\partial \rho_s}{\partial p}\right]\frac{\partial p}{\partial x} + \left[(-u\rho + \rho v_n)\frac{\partial s}{\partial T} + ws\frac{\partial \rho_s}{\partial T}\right]\frac{\partial T}{\partial x}$$
$$+ \left[-2uw\rho\frac{\partial s}{\partial w^2} + \rho_s s\right]\frac{\partial w}{\partial x} = 0, \quad (8\text{-}3)$$

$$\left[v - \left(u + \frac{\rho_n}{\rho}w\right)\right]\frac{\partial v}{\partial x} + \left[\frac{\rho_n}{\rho}u - \frac{\rho_n\rho_s}{\rho^2}w - \frac{\rho_n}{\rho}v\right]\frac{\partial w}{\partial x}$$
$$+ \left[uw\frac{\partial(\rho_n/\rho)}{\partial p} + \frac{1}{\rho}\right]\frac{\partial p}{\partial x} + \left[u\frac{\partial(\rho_n/\rho)}{\partial T} - s\right]\frac{\partial T}{\partial x} = 0, \quad (8\text{-}4)$$

$$(-u\rho + \rho v)\frac{\partial v}{\partial x} + \frac{\partial p}{\partial x} + \frac{2\rho_n\rho_s}{\rho}w\frac{\partial w}{\partial x} = 0, \quad (8\text{-}5)$$

where $w \equiv v_n - v_s$ and we have used (8-1). Since these equations are to be considered as valid up to second order the coefficients are not to be evaluated in the equilibrium state. For instance in (8-2) the coefficient $\partial\rho/\partial p$ of $\partial p/\partial x$ is to be taken as accurate to first order in the deviation from equilibrium. The coefficient $\partial\rho/\partial w^2$ of $w\,\partial w/\partial x$ is, however, to be evaluated in the equilibrium configuration since $w\,\partial w/\partial x$ is already second order small.

Equations (8-2,3,4,5) describe the behavior of both first and second sound waves of the large amplitude. In the approximation where the small quantities proportional to $\partial\rho/\partial T$ are neglected the behavior of large amplitude first sound waves is just like that in a classical Euler fluid. We now focus our attention on the second sound unique to He II.

When second sound propagates we take $v \approx 0$ (again since $1 - C_V/C_p$ is small) and then (8-2,3,4,5) take the same form as (7-60,61,62,63) which is not surprising since at a point of given amplitude of deviation from equilibrium there is a given v_n and v_s (not equal to zero) which satisfy $\rho_n v_n + \rho_s v_s = 0$. The consistency requirement for the above equations is thus contained in (7-68) or

$$u = \pm u_2 + \left[\frac{2\rho_s}{\rho} - \frac{s}{\rho_n}\frac{\partial\rho_n}{\partial T}\left(\frac{\partial s}{\partial T}\right)^{-1}\right]w, \quad (8\text{-}6)$$

where u is the speed of propagation of a point in the disturbance with amplitude w of deviation from equilibrium. To the approximation where we keep terms in the two fluid equations quadratic in the deviation from

Notes p. 83

equilibrium, one easily verifies that we obtain corrections to the sound velocity linear in the deviation from equilibrium. Thus in (8-6) the coefficient of w is to be evaluated in the equilibrium state whereas u_2 must be interpreted as the ordinary speed of second sound [i.e., Eq. (7-19)] evaluated at the given disturbance or to first order (and again neglecting pressure variations)

$$u = u_{2,0} + \frac{\partial u_2}{\partial T}\frac{\mathrm{d}T}{\mathrm{d}w} w, \tag{8-7}$$

where $u_{2,0}$ is the speed of second sound relative to the equilibrium state and we now investigate propagation in the $+x$ direction. To first order (8-7) will be still valid if we use (7-32) for $\mathrm{d}T/\mathrm{d}w$. Then combining (8-6,7) we have

$$u = u_{2,0} + \left[\frac{\rho_n u_2}{\rho s}\frac{\partial u_2}{\partial T} + \frac{2\rho_s}{\rho} - \frac{s}{\rho_n}\frac{\partial \rho_n}{\partial T}\left(\frac{\partial s}{\partial T}\right)^{-1}\right] w, \tag{8-8}$$

where all terms except w are to be evaluated in the equilibrium state. By ignoring small terms involving $\partial\rho/\partial T$ (8-8) becomes

$$u = u_{2,0} + \frac{sT}{C_V}\left\{\frac{\partial}{\partial T}\log\left[u_2^3\left(\frac{\partial s}{\partial T}\right)_\rho\right]\right\} v_n. \tag{8-9}$$

A graph of the coefficient of v_n in (8-9) versus T is given in Fig. 13.

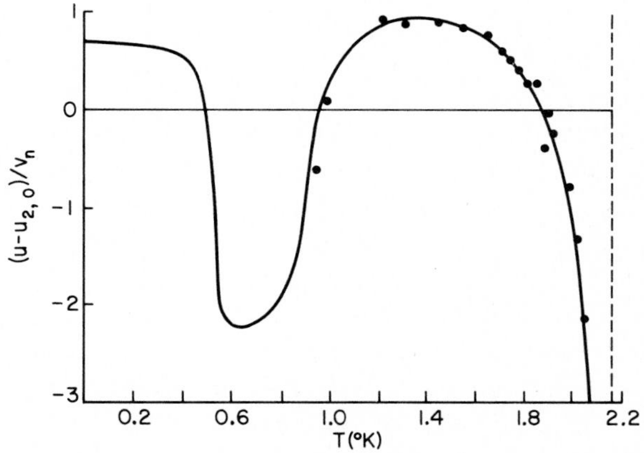

Fig. 13. The speed of a second sound wave of large amplitude versus temperature. The solid line is determined by (8-9) and the points represent the experimental data of Dessler and Fairbank.

Notes p. 83

Equation (8-9) has been verified by Dessler and Fairbanks [27] who measured the speed of a second sound pulse of small amplitude that was superimposed on a large amplitude pulse.

From Eq. (8-9) we see that the coefficient of $\boldsymbol{v}_n$ can be both positive and negative depending upon the temperature. This has the following interesting consequence. When a large amplitude wave propagates the faster moving points on the profile eventually overtake the slower moving points resulting in the formation of a shock wave or discontinuity in the parameters that describe the disturbance. In a classical fluid it turns out that the peaks always travel faster than the troughs and hence the shock always forms at the front of the travelling wave: Fig. 14a.

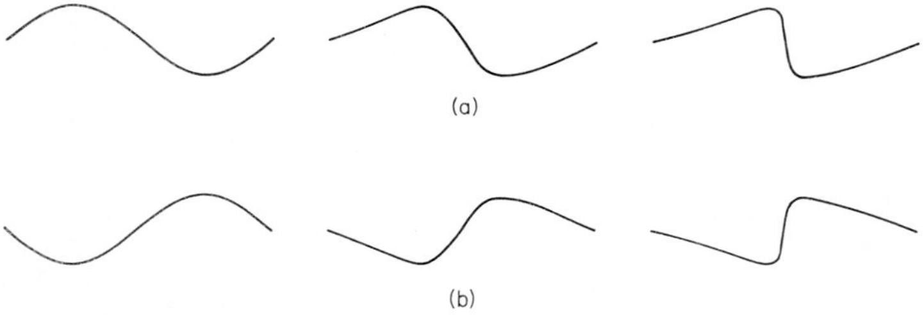

Fig. 14. The deformation of a second sound wave due to non-linear effects. In (a) the temperature is such that points of large amplitude move faster than those of low amplitude and hence the shock forms at the front. In (b) the temperature is such that the troughs travel faster than the peaks and thus the shock forms at the back.

In second sound this is also the case for $1.0\ ^\circ\mathrm{K} < T < 1.95\ ^\circ\mathrm{K}$ and $T < 0.5\ ^\circ\mathrm{K}$, but for all other $T < T_\lambda$ we see from Fig. 13 that the troughs travel faster than the peaks and hence in this case the discontinuity should form at the back of the wave (Fig. 14b). This behavior has been observed by Osborne [28].

Once a discontinuity forms the non-dissipative equations no longer give an accurate description of the region near the discontinuity since the gradients are large and the viscous terms (which are ignored on the Euler ideal level) become important. But the ideal equations are still valid at a large enough distance away from the shock front and can be used to related quantities on the two sides.

The relationship between thermohydrodynamic quantities on the two sides of a shock wave follow from the conservation laws. From the

Notes p. 83

law of conservation of mass (4-1) we find that in the rest frame of the discontinuity the continuity of mass flow is expressed by

$$[\rho v_\perp] = 0, \tag{8-10}$$

where the brackets denote taking the difference between the given quantity on the two sides of the shock, and $v_\perp$ is the velocity of fluid perpendicular to the shock front. In the presence of dissipative effects such as occur at the shock front, energy is still conserved. By integrating the energy conservation law $\partial U/\partial t + \nabla \cdot \boldsymbol{Q} = 0$ across the shock and choosing the end points far enough from the shock so that the (ideal) Landau two fluid expression for $\boldsymbol{Q}$ can be used we find from (4-7)

$$[(\mu + \tfrac{1}{2}v_s^2)\rho v_\perp + \rho s T v_{n\perp} + \rho_n v_{n\perp} \boldsymbol{v}_n \cdot (\boldsymbol{v}_n - \boldsymbol{v}_s)] = 0, \tag{8-11}$$

which is valid in the rest frame of the shock. Similarly from the momentum conservation law we find using (4-4)

$$[p\delta_{i\perp} + \rho_n v_{n,i} v_{n\perp} + \rho_s v_{s,i} v_{s\perp}] = 0. \tag{8-12}$$

Equations (8-10,11,12) are five relations which follow from the five conservation laws obeyed by the fluid. Due to the dissipation near a shock wave we could not make use of an entropy conservation law. In a classical fluid, five variables give a complete description of its state and hence five relations are a complete set. But for superfluid helium eight variables are a complete set and thus (8-10,11,12) do not uniquely relate the behavior of the fluid on the two sides of the shock. Three more relations are needed.

Landau always supplemented his equations with the restriction $\nabla \times \boldsymbol{v}_s = 0$, see § 4. If one assumes that even in the presence of dissipation $\nabla \times \boldsymbol{v}_s = 0$, then the general form of the superfluid equation must be

$$\frac{\partial \boldsymbol{v}_s}{\partial t} + \nabla(\mu + \tfrac{1}{2}v_s^2 + H) = 0, \tag{8-13}$$

where H is some term that depends on the dissipative effects. By integrating (8-13) across the shock and evaluating it at end points far from the shock (i.e., where H is negligible) we find

$$[\mu + \tfrac{1}{2}v_s^2] = 0, \tag{8-14}$$

which when combined with

$$\nabla \times \boldsymbol{v}_s = 0 \tag{8-15}$$

Notes p. 83

yields the three extra conditions needed to completely relate the behavior of the fluid on the two sides of the shock.

It is a big assumption to say that the fluid behind the shock is irrotational since in classical fluids it is already well known that the shock can be a source of vorticity [29]. This raises the following questions which have not been investigated. Is He II unique in that in general the passage of a shock wave leaves the fluid irrotational? If the shock can be a source of vorticity then one no longer has a complete set of relations for the fluid on the two sides of the shock and one is thus forced to ask if a closed (i.e., deterministic) description of the fluid flow is possible.

We remark that (8-14) and (8-10) enable one to simplify (8-11) down to

$$[\rho s T v_{\mathrm{n}\perp} + \rho_{\mathrm{n}} v_{\mathrm{n}\perp} \boldsymbol{v}_{\mathrm{n}} \cdot (\boldsymbol{v}_{\mathrm{n}} - \boldsymbol{v}_{\mathrm{s}})] = 0. \tag{8-16}$$

Also the thermal boundary shock wave discussed in § 6 is not described by (8-10,12,14,16) since in that case there is fluid on only one side of the shock. A description of this situation must wait for a discussion of the dissipative phenomena.

We now focus our attention on one dimensional flow where the question of vorticity does not arise classically or in He II. In this situation (8-10,12,14,16) become four relations between fluid parameters on the two sides of the shock and yield a complete description. In the laboratory reference frame the shock will move with velocity u and the relationship between quantities on the two sides becomes

$$[\rho(v - u)] = 0, \tag{8-17}$$

$$[p + \rho_{\mathrm{n}}(v_{\mathrm{n}} - u)^2 + \rho_{\mathrm{s}}(v_{\mathrm{s}} - u)^2] = 0, \tag{8-18}$$

$$[\mu + \tfrac{1}{2}(v_{\mathrm{s}} - u)^2] = 0, \tag{8-19}$$

$$[\rho s T(v_{\mathrm{n}} - u) + \rho_{\mathrm{n}}(v_{\mathrm{n}} - u)^2(v_{\mathrm{n}} - v_{\mathrm{s}})] = 0, \tag{8-20}$$

where now all quantities are referred to the laboratory reference frame. Denoting the values of the thermodynamic quantities on the two sides of the shock by indices '1' and '2' we can set

$$p_2 = p_1 + \Delta p,$$

$$T_2 = T_1 + \Delta T,$$

$$v_2 = v_1 + \Delta v, \tag{8-21}$$

$$w_2 = w_1 + \Delta w. \tag{8-22}$$

Notes p. 83

Placing these relations in (8-17,18,19,20) yields an expression for the speed of the shock in terms of the discontinuity. If the shock wave is weak then $\Delta p/p_1$ and $\Delta T/T_1$ are much less than unity and we can expand the equations in powers of the discontinuity. Keeping terms in (8-17, 18,19,20) to first order in the discontinuity and the velocities combined we find that the pressure discontinuities travel with the speed of first sound (7-18) and the thermal discontinuities travel with the speed of second sound (7-19). The separation into thermal and pressure discontinuities is only accurate insofar as $1 - C_V/C_p$ is negligible.

To second order in the discontinuity and velocities combined the speed of the shock depends on the strength of the discontinuity and is from (8-17,18,19,20) found to be one half the sum of the speeds of sound (to the quadratic hydrodynamic approximation) on the two sides of the shock. For second sound we then find that the speed of the shock is

$$u = u_{2,0} + \frac{sT}{2C_V}\left\{\frac{\partial}{\partial T}\log\left[u_2^3\left(\frac{\partial s}{\partial T}\right)_\rho\right]\right\}(v_{n,1} + v_{n,2}). \qquad (8\text{-}23)$$

9 The Equations of Motion for the Normal Fluid and the Center of Mass

An explicit equation of motion for the superfluid velocity $\boldsymbol{v}_s$ is given by (4-3). Until now we have not discussed the equation for the acceleration of the normal fluid. This follows directly from (4-1,3,4) and is

$$\rho_n \frac{D_n \boldsymbol{v}_n}{Dt} = -\nabla p + \rho_s \nabla \mu + (\boldsymbol{v}_s - \boldsymbol{v}_n)\left(\frac{\partial \rho_n}{\partial t} + \nabla \cdot \rho_n \boldsymbol{v}_n\right). \qquad (9\text{-}1)$$

The last term on the right side of (9-1) is of special interest in that it represents an 'interaction' between the two fluids. The quantity $\partial\rho_n/\partial t + \nabla \cdot \rho_n \boldsymbol{v}_n$ determines the rate at which normal fluid is converted to superfluid, for instance, as would happen when the He II is uniformly heated. The last term on the right side of (9-1) then represents the contribution to the momentum change due to this conversion. Clearly since the total momentum of the fluid is conserved there can be no net momentum change within the fluid and Eq. (9-1) states that there is an acceleration of the normal fluid in response to this transition such that the total momentum is conserved.

Notes p. 83

Thus when superfluid in motion is converted to normal fluid it delivers its momentum to the normal fluid which then experiences a kick. What is especially interesting is that even when normal fluid is converted to superfluid the momentum change of the superfluid is provided for by the acceleration of the normal fluid. The normal fluid always experiences the reaction force as, for instance, we note that there is no term like

$$(\boldsymbol{v}_n - \boldsymbol{v}_s)\left(\frac{\partial \rho_n}{\partial t} + \nabla \cdot \rho_n \boldsymbol{v}_n\right) \tag{9-2}$$

on the right hand side of (4-3). We interpret this as meaning that in a transition from super to normal fluid the new superfluid is created with the velocity which the superfluid already had before the transition and the momentum change of the superfluid is provided by the acceleration of the normal fluid.

An experiment where these considerations play a role was performed by Mehl and Zimmermann [30]. They made use of the fact that in a narrow channel the normal fluid is clamped, $\boldsymbol{v}_n = 0$, and the superfluid is free to flow. This was suggested by Kapitza's experiment, and we will also see in the next chapter that when dissipative effects are included one must modify the two fluid theory so that the normal fluid flows with friction (i.e., is viscous) whereas the superfluid is frictionless. By dealing with narrow channels (which were formed by packing a container with very fine powder) that formed closed paths they were able to set up a persistent current which is flow with a relative velocity between the superfluid and the container that persists on account of the frictionless flow.

Such a persistent current was observed through the angular momentum associated with it. For instance a displacement of the container in general would result in a procession from which one could determine the angular momentum.

Mehl and Zimmermann could then show that the dependence of the angular momentum of the persistent current on temperature was the same as that of ρ_s or

$$\boldsymbol{L} = \boldsymbol{C}\rho_s,$$

where $\boldsymbol{C}$ is a constant that is temperature independent but which can depend on the geometry of the apparatus. Thus as the temperature of the stationary container was varied the change in angular momentum was entirely accounted for by the change in mass taking part in the persistent current. They concluded that the transition of normal fluid

Notes p. 83

to superfluid or vice versa did not produce a change in $\boldsymbol{v}_s$. This is a consequence of (4-3) which, as we commented above implies that in superfluid–normal fluid conversion there is no acceleration of the superfluid [i.e., no effect like (9-2)] provided of course that the heating or cooling is slow and uniform so that we can neglect the accelerations due to a chemical potential gradient.

A change in angular momentum of the superfluid implies a change in angular momentum of the entire fluid (since all measurements are made with $\boldsymbol{v}_n = 0$) and this is provided by the torque necessary to keep the container at rest as the temperature is changed. This happens as follows. From (9-1) we see that as the temperature is changed, the normal fluid experiences a reaction torque. But the normal fluid is locked to the powder and, hence to the container, by its viscosity. Thus the normal fluid plus container will, as the result of a temperature change, try to spin in the opposite direction to the change in angular momentum of the superfluid. The torque necessary to bring $\boldsymbol{v}_n$ back to rest accounts for the net change in angular momentum of the fluid.

In addition to $\boldsymbol{v}_n$, $\boldsymbol{v}_s$ another velocity of interest in He II is the center of mass velocity

$$\boldsymbol{v} = (\rho_n \boldsymbol{v}_n + \rho_s \boldsymbol{v}_s)/\rho.$$

Its equation of motion follows from (4-1,4) and is

$$\rho \frac{\mathrm{D}\boldsymbol{v}}{\mathrm{D}t} = -\nabla p - \frac{\partial}{\partial r_j}\left[\frac{\rho_n \rho_s}{\rho}(v_n - v_s)_i (v_n - v_s)_j\right], \tag{9-3}$$

where

$$\frac{\mathrm{D}\boldsymbol{v}}{\mathrm{D}t} \equiv \frac{\partial \boldsymbol{v}}{\partial t} + (\boldsymbol{v}\cdot\nabla)\boldsymbol{v}.$$

This equation is to be contrasted with the classical equation of motion (1-3). The simple form of (1-3) results from the existence of a preferred rest frame for the fluid. In He II due to the existence of two independent velocity fields there is no preferred rest system and terms which depend on the Galilean invariant $\boldsymbol{v}_n - \boldsymbol{v}_s$ enter the equations as in (9-3).

10 The Macroscopic Quantum Effects

A question that always arises in physics is that of deriving the phenomenological or macroscopic equations (e.g., the Euler or Landau two

Notes p. 83

fluid equations) from the first principle microscopic laws of physics. It is well known that for a simple (one component) fluid the classical Euler equations (see § 1) can be demonstrated to be a consequence of the interacting molecules moving according to Newton's laws. This can of course be shown only for simplified situations such as from the Boltzmann equation for a dilute gas. Superfluid helium is a 'simple' fluid; as far as interhelium forces are concerned He^4 is the 'simplest' element. Yet the Landau two fluid equations which describe its dynamics are *not* the Euler equations. Thus the two fluid theory does not follow from Newton's laws! This leaves only the possibility that, in order to understand He II from a *microscopic* or molecular approach the quantum theory may be essential; this view is especially supported by the fact that at these low temperatures the thermal de Broglie wavelength $h/(mk_B T)^{1/2}$, where h is Planck's constant, m the mass of a helium atom and k_B Boltzmann's constant, becomes comparable with the distance between atoms and as a result the requirement that He^4 atoms obey Bose statistics becomes of crucial importance. We see that in He II the first principles of the quantum theory should become important for understanding the macroscopic description and for this reason He II is called a quantum fluid.

The main reason that He II has aroused so much interest lies in its unusual *macroscopic* properties and from the strictly macroscopic point of view one might well ask if there is any reason to call He II a quantum fluid. As we have seen in this chapter He II certainly behaves quite differently from an ordinary fluid like water or air, but we also saw how Landau, by introducing an extra macroscopic variable $\boldsymbol{v}_s$, was able to derive a closed set of equations which fulfil all the a priori macroscopic requirements and which describe the dynamical properties of He II in excellent agreement with experiment. *These equations, which form the theoretical foundation of our understanding of He II do not contain Planck's constant*, and in this sense the Landau two fluid equations are just as 'classical' as the Euler equations.

Of course $\hbar$ implicitly appears in the two fluid equations in that a theoretical calculation based on the microscopic theory will certainly show that the equation of state for ρ_s as a function of T, p, $(\boldsymbol{v}_n - \boldsymbol{v}_s)^2$ involves Planck's constant. But based on the two fluid equations there is no experiment which can be performed on He II that will measure Planck's constant! So from the macroscopic point of view there is at this stage no reason to call He II a quantum fluid.

Notes p. 83

This situation was changed in 1948 as a result of the landmark work of Onsager [31]. Feynman (1955) also presented the same results [32]. They proposed that the quantum of action would enter directly into the macroscopic two fluid theory through the quantization of the superfluid circulation

$$\oint \boldsymbol{v}_s \cdot d\boldsymbol{\ell} \equiv \Gamma_s = nh/m, \tag{10-1}$$

where n is an integer. This has the consequence that vorticity is quantized. For instance consider a vortex line (see § 5) in the superfluid. Its velocity field according to (10-1) must be

$$\boldsymbol{v}_s = n(\hbar/mr)\hat{\boldsymbol{e}}_\theta \tag{10-2}$$

so that only vortices of a certain quantized strength (circulation) can exist in the superfluid. In this way one sees that Planck's constant limits the number of allowed *fluid* states! Or from a careful measurement of $\boldsymbol{v}_s$, h/m can be determined. Note, $h/m \approx 10^{-3}$ cm^2/sec so that for macroscopic distances the steps in $\boldsymbol{v}_s$ are quite small. Also since in the two fluid theory there is a Kelvin conservation of circulation theorem (see § 4) for $\boldsymbol{v}_s$, it is *consistent* with the two fluid equations to impose the condition (10-1) on the motion.

The quantum condition (10-1) is similar to the Bohr–Sommerfeld quantum conditions of the old quantum theory. In that case, the adiabatic invariants of the classical (deterministic) motion were restricted to a discrete set of states or

$$\oint \boldsymbol{p}\, d\boldsymbol{q} = nh, \tag{10-3}$$

where $\boldsymbol{p}$, $\boldsymbol{q}$ are the canonical coordinates and the integral is over a period of the motion. In § 4 we have seen that the circulation of the superfluid is an invariant of the Landau two fluid theory, which is an adiabatic approximation in that dissipation is ignored. Thus (10-1) is also a quantization of the adiabatic invariants of the motion as was remarked by Onsager. But now one uses the quantization to limit the *macroscopically* allowed states!

For the Landau two fluid theory we saw in § 4 that the thermal circulation

$$\oint \boldsymbol{A} \cdot d\boldsymbol{\ell} \equiv \oint (\rho_n/s\rho)(\boldsymbol{v}_n - \boldsymbol{v}_s) \cdot d\boldsymbol{\ell} \tag{10-4}$$

is also a constant of the motion. Thus it is consistent with these equations, to impose on this adiabatic invariant a second quantum condition

$$\oint \boldsymbol{A} \cdot d\boldsymbol{\ell} \equiv \Gamma_A = n'(h/k_B), \tag{10-5}$$

Notes p. 83

where k_B is Boltzmann's constant, $h/k_B \approx 10^{-11}$ degree/sec, and n' again an integer. One might say that h/k_B is the natural unit for Γ_A just as h/m is for Γ_s.

Broer [33] has emphasized that the expression adiabatic invariant is used in two contexts. On the one hand there are thermodynamic adiabatic invariants which are quantities that do not change when the processes are so slow (quasi-static) that entropy production can be neglected. On the other hand there are Ehrenfest adiabatic invariants which are quantities whose exact equations are *time reversible* and which are unchanged under a variation of the constraints that takes place slow compared to *all* the natural frequencies of the system.

It is the Ehrenfest and not the thermodynamic adiabatic invariants which are quantized according to the old quantum theory. While the two kinds of invariants are related, the two circulations Γ_s, Γ_A are clearly at this point to be considered as thermodynamic adiabatic invariants. Whether a thermodynamic adiabatic invariant is also an Ehrenfest adiabatic invariant depends crucially upon how the theory must be modified to include dissipative effects. Since these quantum conditions are imposed and not derived their validity can only be decided by experiment. In 1961 Vinen [34] provided the first experimental evidence that the superfluid circulation Γ_s is quantized. This was further confirmed by the fundamental experiments of Rayfield and Reif [35]. There is no evidence for the second quantum condition (10-5) and one must expect therefore that the dissipative effects do not affect the conservation of Γ_s while they destroy the conservation of Γ_A. We return to this in § 22 and now discuss the important experimental checks of (10-1).

Vortex lines in the superfluid play a crucial role in our understanding of the behavior of He II, because through them Planck's constant enters directly into the macroscopic dynamics. The pioneering work of Vinen in observing this macroscopic quantum effect has been repeated in a more elaborate form by Whitmore and Zimmermann [36] whose work we now discuss.

In these experiments the Magnus force on a vibrating thin wire around which there is a circulation of He II is observed. In an Euler fluid a cylindrical object immersed in a flow field with circulation $\boldsymbol{\Gamma}$ (for convenience we assign the circulation a sign with the right hand rule) experiences a force $\rho \boldsymbol{U} \times \boldsymbol{\Gamma}$, where $\boldsymbol{U}$ is the relative velocity of the object

Notes p. 83

and flow at infinity. In He II the Magnus force is (in the incompressible approximation where ρ, ρ_s, s are constant)

$$\rho \boldsymbol{U} \times \boldsymbol{\Gamma}_s + \rho s \boldsymbol{U}_n \times \boldsymbol{\Gamma}_A = \rho_s \boldsymbol{U}_s \times \boldsymbol{\Gamma}_s + \rho_n \boldsymbol{U}_n \times \boldsymbol{\Gamma}_n, \qquad (10\text{-}6)$$

where $\rho \boldsymbol{U} = \rho_n \boldsymbol{U}_n + \rho_s \boldsymbol{U}_s$, $\boldsymbol{\Gamma}_n$ is the circulation of the normal fluid and $\boldsymbol{U}_s$, $\boldsymbol{U}_n$ are the relative streaming velocities between the object and super, normal fluids at infinity. We should emphasize at this point that a Magnus force acts only on a body immersed in a fluid. It is improper to speak of a Magnus force on a vortex line, as the motion of a vortex line is entirely determined by Kelvin's circulation theorem. A derivation of (10-6) and a discussion of the approximations which limit its validity (i.e., the restriction that v_n, v_s be much less than the sound velocities) are given in Appendix IV.

With their apparatus (Fig. 15) Whitmore and Zimmermann were able

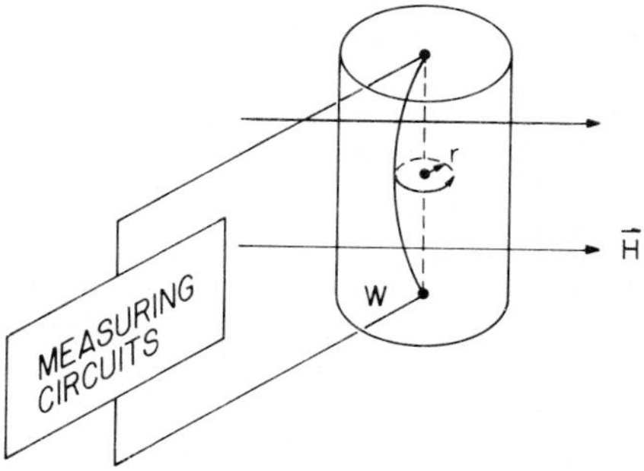

Fig. 15. The experimental arrangement of Whitmore and Zimmermann.

to observe continuously the plane of vibration of a stretched wire W near the axis of a cylindrical vessel containing He II by measuring the E.M.F. its vibrations induced as it cut across the lines of force of an externally applied magnetic field $\boldsymbol{H}$. A circulation around the wire (which was found to be present whether or not the vessel was rotated) leads to a Magnus force which causes the plane of vibration to rotate at a rate measured by the above technique.

More precisely: the angular frequencies of the two fundamental circularly polarized modes of a stretched wire will be degenerate when tension is the only force driving the small oscillations. If F is the restoring force per unit length of wire and ρ_W the mass per unit length of wire,

Notes p. 83

the angular velocity ω of the circularly polarized mode is determined by

$$\rho_W \omega^2 r = F,$$

where r is the amplitude of oscillation as shown in Fig. 15. A circulation around the wire leads to an additional central force (Magnus force) which acts oppositely on the two modes and thus removes the degeneracy. The splitting in the frequency ($d\omega$) of the two fundamental circularly polarized modes is then

$$d\omega = dF/2\omega r \rho_W = (\rho_s \Gamma_s + \rho_n \Gamma_n)/\rho_W, \tag{10-7}$$

where dF is the difference in central force for the two modes. We have also used the fact that for this experimental arrangment $\boldsymbol{U}_n = \boldsymbol{U}_s$ is determined by the known velocity ωr of the vibrating wire relative to the boundary. Due to the external field a splitting in the frequency of the circularly polarized modes shows up as a splitting in the frequency of the induced E.M.F. In this way their apparatus could continuously measure $\rho_s \boldsymbol{\Gamma}_s + \rho_n \boldsymbol{\Gamma}_n$ or equivalently

$$\boldsymbol{\Gamma}_s + (\rho_n/\rho_s)/\boldsymbol{\Gamma}_n \equiv \rho \boldsymbol{\Gamma}/\rho_s$$

since ρ_s is known.

The experimental results for $\rho\boldsymbol{\Gamma}/\rho_s$ versus time, Fig. 16, show that most of the time it is quantized. This can be interpreted by saying that

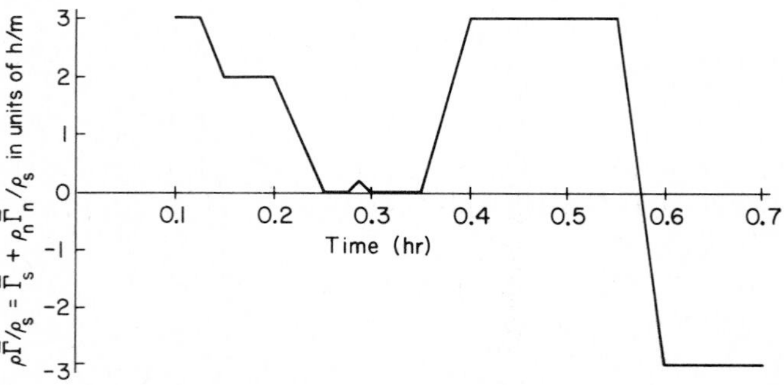

Fig. 16. A schematic of the results of Whitmore and Zimmermann for the effective circulation, $\boldsymbol{\Gamma}_s + (\rho_n/\rho_s)\boldsymbol{\Gamma}_n$, around a wire as deduced from the Magnus force exerted on it when vibrating. Note that states with a circulation equal to an in.ger multiplying h/m are the only stable states observed. These can perhaps be interpreted as states with $\Gamma_n = 0$ and Γ_s quantized according to (10-1).

Notes p. 83

most of the time $\boldsymbol{\Gamma}_n = 0$ and $\boldsymbol{\Gamma}_s$ is quantized according to (10-1). The observed states in which $\rho\boldsymbol{\Gamma}/\rho_s$ is not quantized can perhaps be understood as being made up of a quantized $\boldsymbol{\Gamma}_s$ and, a $\boldsymbol{\Gamma}_n$ circulation which is in the process of decaying to zero as a result of viscous forces in the normal fluid. Consistent with this note that states in which $\rho\boldsymbol{\Gamma}/\rho_s$ is not quantized, are not stable. Of course the mechanism by which a quantum of $\boldsymbol{\Gamma}_s$ circulation is converted to $\boldsymbol{\Gamma}_n$ circulation (which then decays) is at the moment an unsolved problem.

The most convincing evidence for the quantization of circulation is provided by the work of Rayfield and Reif [35]. While investigating the motion of ions in superfluid helium Meyer and Reif [37] found that as the temperature is lowered at high accelerating electric fields, the resistance to ion motion suddenly diminished and they were able to drift through the liquid with apparantly no resistance. That is, after being accelerated from the source S (see Fig. 17) by a potential Φ they were

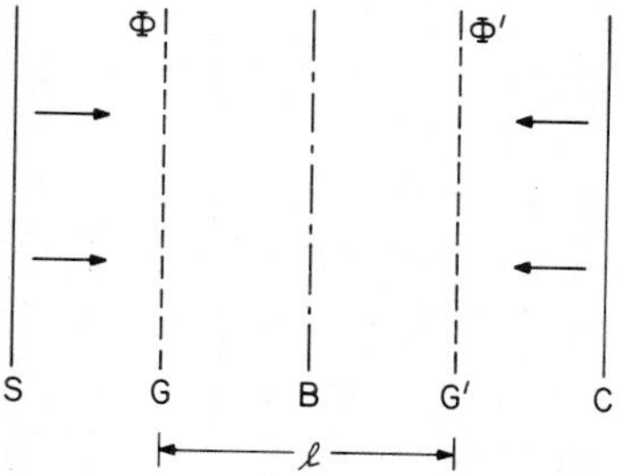

Fig. 17. The apparatus used by Rayfield and Reif to measure the time of flight of ions in He II at low temperatures. The arrows indicate the direction of the accelerating or decelerating electric fields.

able to overcome a repulsive potential Φ' of almost the same magnitude (and be recorded at collector C) after drifting through a field free region (region G to G′). They named the phenomenon 'runaway' and did not understand it. Rayfield and Reif measured the velocity of the ions in the field free region by applying a small alternating square wave boosting potential of angular frequency ω at B. If the velocity v_0 of the ions was in phase with the potential ($\ell/v_0 = \pi/\omega$) they would receive an extra kick and be able to overcome a retarding potential slightly greater than the accelerating potential. Since ℓ is known from the geometry and ω is measured, v_0 is determined by the above relation. The accelerating

Notes p. 83

potential determines the energy E and the graph of E versus v_0 is given in Fig. 18. It seemed that the greater the accelerating potential the slower the ion moved!

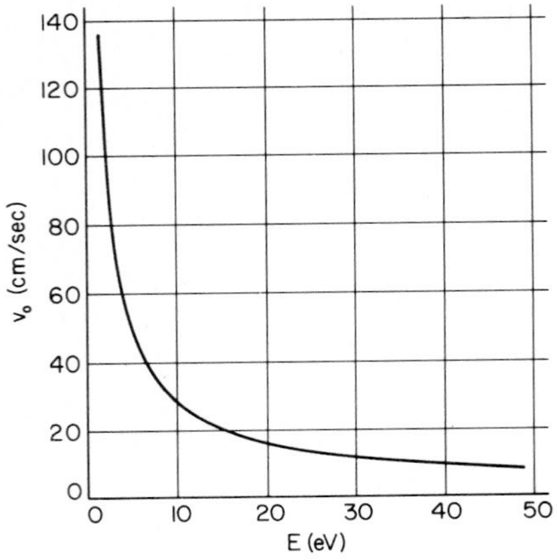

Fig. 18. Energy in electronvolt versus velocity, v_0, for ions in the field free region of the experiment of Rayfield and Reif.

It was not too long before they realized that in a classical fluid vortex rings display such a paradoxical behavior. The kinetic energy and velocity of classical vortex rings in an infinite incompressible medium are given by

$$\int \tfrac{1}{2}\rho v^2 \mathrm{d}V = \mathrm{K.E.}_{\mathrm{R}} = 2\pi^2\rho\gamma^2 R[\log(8R/a) - 2], \tag{10-8}$$

$$v_{\mathrm{R}} = (\gamma/2R)\left[\log(8R/a) - \tfrac{1}{2}\right], \tag{10-9}$$

where $2\pi\gamma$ is the circulation of any contour that encircles the hollow core of radius a and R is the radius of the ring. A diagram of the flow around a vortex ring is given in Fig. 19. In an otherwise quiescent fluid a vortex ring moves under its own power since at each point of the core the net velocity induced by the other elements of the ring is non-vanishing and by the Kelvin theorem the ring (core) must then move with that velocity. By symmetry each element of core moves with the same velocity which is given by (10-9) and is perpendicular to the plane of the ring. We see that $v_{\mathrm{R}} \sim 1/\mathrm{K.E.}_{\mathrm{R}}$ and observe that when a vortex ring of given circulation receives energy rather than accelerate, it increases its size (note $\mathrm{K.E.}_{\mathrm{R}} \sim R$) and slows down. A derivation of (10-8,9) is given in Appendix V.

Notes p. 83

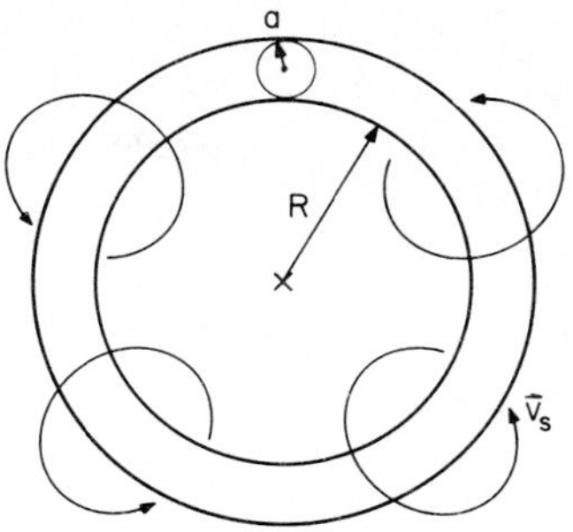

Fig. 19. The flow of fluid around a vortex ring of radius R and core radius a. The fluid circulates the core as indicated and the vortex ring moves towards the reader at velocity given by (10-9).

If Rayfield and Reif assumed that in their experiments the ions became coupled to superfluid vortex rings [38] then their data could be used to determine the circulation of the rings. To the accuracy of their experiment they found $\gamma = \hbar/m$ (thus they only observed states with one quantum of circulation) and $a \approx 10^{-8}$ cm. We remark that the kinetic energy of a superfluid vortex ring is $\int \frac{1}{2}\rho_s v_s^2 \, dV$ and is obtained in the incompressible (ρ_s = constant) approximation by replacing ρ with ρ_s in (10-8).

A basic objection to interpreting the results in terms of the macroscopic two fluid theory is that the value of a so determined is less than the average spacing between atoms. In a classical fluid the macroscopic variables are averages over the motion of the individual atoms as for instance the velocity field of a vortex ring is due to the average over the many excited translational velocities of the atoms comprising the fluid. As the variables are averaged one would not dream of applying classical hydrodynamics to distances of the order of an atomic spacing. But for He II we will always have to keep in mind the fundamental idea of London (see directly below) that the superfluid is a single coherent quantum state. With this view the superfluid velocity is not an average over the superfluid atoms but is a common property of all the superfluid. If this is the case the limits of applicability of the macroscopic superfluid theory may depend upon criteria which are quite different from classical fluids. Thus as long as we can successfully describe the experiments we will not hesitate to substitute microscopic parameters into the superfluid equation.

We now know that in the experiments of Reif the 'runaway' was

Notes p. 83

accompanied by the formation of a quantized vortex ring attached to the ion. But the question as to why such a system should lose less energy than a 'free' ion in transit through the field free region will be discussed in § 32 where the motion of quantized vortices according to the Landau two fluid theory modified to include dissipative effects will be discussed.

The advances made possible by Onsager's remarks did not occur out of a vacuum and we now discuss in somewhat more detail the history behind the macroscopic quantization.

The macroscopic quantum nature of liquid helium was first (1938) and continually emphasized by F. London [39]. He drew attention to the fact that the behavior of He II could be at least qualitatively understood in terms of the Bose–Einstein condensation [40] which takes place in an ideal *quantum* gas obeying Bose statistics.

In Chapter VIII we will discuss in detail the behavior of the condensed ideal Bose gas since it forms the qualitative basis for understanding superfluid hydrodynamics. But for the purpose of this discussion we mention that below a critical temperature (which for an ideal Bose gas of the density of He^4 turns out to be very close to T_λ) a *macroscopic* fraction of the particles drop or 'condense' into the same single particle quantum state (the ground state). This fraction is 100% at $T = 0$ °K and vanishes at the critical temperature. This behavior is usually referred to as condensation in momentum space, though the single particle quantum states become momentum eigenstates only with periodic boundary conditions. London always had in mind that the Bose condensed particles were analogous to the supercomponent and the other (excited) particles were similar to the normal fluid. Thus the superfluid was to be viewed as a *single coherent quantum state* whose occupation is a function of temperature. As a pure state has no entropy one is led in this manner to a microscopic understanding of the unusual thermal effects discussed in § 2 and in particular Eq. (4-2).

Based on these qualitative ideas physicists at about 1940 fully accepted the fact that He II was a quantum fluid. But as we remarked Planck's constant still did not enter the macroscopic dynamics.

The next step in this direction was hinted at in a remarkable paper by Bijl et al. [41] that appeared in 1941. They discussed the experiments of Daunt and Mendelssohn [42] and Allen and Misener [5] on the flow properties of He II in narrow geometries. As we have mentioned He II can flow through narrow constrictions without any friction or alternatively without a pressure difference necessary to drive the flow.

Notes p. 83

According to the two fluid model this is interpreted as a frictionless flow of the superfluid with the normal fluid held at rest due to its viscous interaction with the walls. The precise details of how the normal fluid viscosity is incorporated into the two fluid model will be discussed in the next chapter on dissipative effects.

In any case the experiments on flow indicate that there exists a so called critical velocity of superfluid relative to the walls, $v_{s,c}$, above which the superflow breaks down quite abruptly. Bijl noticed that for these experiments on steady flow the critical velocity was approximately

$$v_{s,c} = \hbar/md, \tag{10-10}$$

where d is the width of the channel. That a formula like (10-10) described the experimental situation was also observed by F. and H. London [43], but the theoretical understanding of (10-10) was provided by Bijl as follows. A single atom at rest with respect to the walls of the channel has zero angular momentum with respect to them. In motion the atom has angular momentum but unless its angular momentum is of order $\hbar$ there is no possibility for an exchange of angular momentum (say by a collision) with the channel. Equation (10-10) then becomes a measure of the velocity which the atom must exceed in order to exchange angular momentum or energy with the walls. To go from the behavior of the atom to that of the superfluid, Bijl simply appealed to the London picture of all the superfluid atoms being in the same quantum state. Hence when one atom can exchange energy with the wall they all can and in this way one is led to the critical velocity (10-10) above which energy and momentum are required in order to maintain the flow of superfluid. Bijl did not describe the nature of the flow that results for $v_s > v_{s,c}$. In fact realizing that this argument is not the last word on critical velocities [though even today (10-10) is the best simple description of $v_{s,c}$ in channel] it was suggested by Bijl that the important problem posed by this work was that of unifying these microscopically motivated ideas with the macroscopic two fluid theory of Landau.

This was the step carried out by Onsager as represented by the macroscopic quantization (10-1). In terms of the quantization principle one can now say that as v_s increases past $v_{s,c}$ the superfluid has a transition from a state of potential flow with v_s constant to a quantum turbulent flow with quantized vortices. The formation of these vortices results from interaction with the walls and thus results in a loss of frictionless flow. A suggestive means of calculated $v_{s,c}$ from this picture was provided

Notes p. 83

by Onsager and Feynman as follows. Consider flow in a capillary for which above a critical velocity quantized vortex rings will form and flow down the capillary at a rate ν per second. Let us calculate the minimum velocity v_s at which the energy and momentum of potential flow can get entirely transformed into the quantized vortex rings. We thus want the minimum v_s such that

$$\rho_s v_s[\pi(d^2/4)v_s] = \nu I_R, \tag{10-11}$$

$$\tfrac{1}{2}\rho_s v_s^2[\pi(d^2/4)v_s] = \nu \text{K.E.}_R \tag{10-12}$$

where d is the diameter of the capillary and K.E.$_R$ and I_R are the kinetic energy and momentum (it is better to speak of impulse) of a vortex ring in the capillary. Assuming that this minimum v_s will be roughly $v_{s,c}$ we have

$$v_{s,c} = \min(2\text{K.E.}_R/I_R). \tag{10-13}$$

We evaluate (10-13) approximately by using the K.E.$_R$ and I_R of a vortex in an infinite fluid. As we show in Appendix V

$$I_R = 2\pi^2 \rho_s \gamma R^2, \tag{10-14}$$

so that

$$v_{s,c} = \min\{(2\gamma/R)[\log(8R/a) - 2]\}.$$

The minimum is achieved for the largest R, which is $\frac{1}{2}d$, so that roughly

$$v_{s,c} = (4\hbar/md)[\log(4d/a) - 2]. \tag{10-15}$$

As with Bijl this result is essentially a consequence of dimensional analysis since still no explanation as to why the quantum turbulent flow should take place for $v_s > v_{s,c}$ has been presented. The only advance has been to present a picture of the macroscopic flow for $v_s > v_{s,c}$, but the complete connection with the Landau two fluid theory plus quantization is lacking. It is interesting that the first motivation for introducing Planck's constant into the macroscopic theory, namely the problem of the critical velocities, is still not understood today. We return to this question in Chapter VI.

The main result of this section is that the basic macroscopic or phenomenological description of He II consists of the Landau two fluid equations plus the macroscopic quantization rule (10-1). In any situation one should first investigate the consequences of this theory since when modi-

Notes p. 83

fied to include dissipation (Chapter II) it forms the most complete theory of He II we have as yet. Also we have especially emphasized the superfluid vortices since it is only through them that $\hbar$ clearly enters the macroscopic fluid behavior, a property of central importance in understanding the unusual nature of superfluid helium.

Finally we must note that the two fluid theory plus quantization bears a striking similarity to the old quantum theory. Just as the old quantum theory had to be modified in light of the wave particle duality, one must expect that our deterministic two fluid theory of He II will be modified by a *macroscopic wave particle duality*.

While the old quantum theory could explain the stationary levels it could not explain the transitions or quantum jumping. Similarly the two fluid theory plus quantization can explain the stationary circulation levels but apparently cannot explain the macroscopic quantum jumps such as for instance take place for $v_s > v_{s,c}$ and in the experiments of Vinen, etc.

One of the most important problems for the future is that of finding the complete self-consistent macroscopic quantum theory of He II. We try to develop it further in Chapter VII where we discuss the shortcomings of the two fluid theory plus quantization.

11 The Landau Two Fluid Equations at Absolute Zero

In deriving the Landau two fluid equations we have tried to carefully elucidate their connection with such macroscopic principles as the first and second laws of thermodynamics. Since He II is a macroscopic system in which quantum effects become important and since the third law of thermodynamics has a quantum-mechanical foundation we discuss in this section implications of the third law for the two fluid thermohydrodynamics.

According to the third law of thermodynamics the entropy s vanishes at $T = 0$ °K. Making this substitution into the two fluid equations (4-1,2,3,4) they become seven equations for the seven variables ρ, $\boldsymbol{v}_n$, $\boldsymbol{v}_s$ which are

$$\frac{\partial \rho}{\partial t} + \nabla \cdot (\rho_n \boldsymbol{v}_n + \rho_s \boldsymbol{v}_s) = 0, \tag{11-1}$$

Notes p. 83

$$\frac{\mathrm{D_s}\boldsymbol{v}_\mathrm{s}}{\mathrm{D}t} = -\nabla\mu, \tag{11-2}$$

$$\frac{\partial}{\partial t}(\rho_\mathrm{n}v_\mathrm{n} + \rho_\mathrm{s}v_\mathrm{s})_i + \frac{\partial}{\partial r_\alpha}(p\delta_{i\alpha} + \rho_\mathrm{n}v_{\mathrm{n},i}v_{\mathrm{n},\alpha} + \rho_\mathrm{s}v_{\mathrm{s},i}v_{\mathrm{s},\alpha}) = 0, \tag{11-3}$$

supplemented by the thermodynamic relations

$$\mathrm{d}\mu = \frac{1}{\rho}\,\mathrm{d}p - \frac{\rho_\mathrm{n}}{2\rho}\,\mathrm{d}(\boldsymbol{v}_\mathrm{n} - \boldsymbol{v}_\mathrm{s})^2, \tag{11-4}$$

$$U = U_0 + \boldsymbol{v}_\mathrm{s}\cdot\rho_\mathrm{n}(\boldsymbol{v}_\mathrm{n} - \boldsymbol{v}_\mathrm{s}) + \tfrac{1}{2}\rho v_\mathrm{s}^2, \tag{11-5}$$

where

$$\mathrm{d}U_0 = \mu\,\mathrm{d}\rho + (\boldsymbol{v}_\mathrm{n} - \boldsymbol{v}_\mathrm{s})\cdot\mathrm{d}\rho_\mathrm{n}(\boldsymbol{v}_\mathrm{n} - \boldsymbol{v}_\mathrm{s}). \tag{11-6}$$

Note that we have not taken $\rho_\mathrm{n} = 0$ at $T = 0$ °K because this does not follow from the third law of thermodynamics. Although the framework in which the Landau two fluid equations were motivated (i.e., Kapitza's experiments), and the experiments on second sound, certainly suggest $\rho_\mathrm{n} = 0$ at $T = 0$ °K there is no general principle from which this follows. One might wonder for instance if in the presence of vortex lines near which $(\boldsymbol{v}_\mathrm{n} - \boldsymbol{v}_\mathrm{s})^2$ gets large there might be some normal fluid even at $T = 0$ °K.

From the third law we can obtain relations for the thermodynamic derivatives of ρ_n at $T = 0$ °K. For instance from (4-8) we find

$$\left(\frac{\partial(\rho_\mathrm{n}/\rho)}{\partial T}\right)_{p,w^2} = 0. \tag{11-7}$$

Also from (4-8) follows the well known relation

$$\left(\frac{\partial\rho}{\partial T}\right)_{p,w^2} = 0. \tag{11-8}$$

If we now make the additional assumption that $\rho_\mathrm{n} = 0$ at $T = 0$ °K then $\rho_\mathrm{s} = \rho$ and the dependence on $\boldsymbol{v}_\mathrm{n}$ identically vanishes leaving us with four equations for the four unknowns ρ, $\boldsymbol{v}_\mathrm{s}$. From (11-1,2,3,4,5,6) we find

$$\frac{\partial\rho}{\partial t} + \nabla\cdot\rho\boldsymbol{v}_\mathrm{s} = 0, \tag{11-9}$$

Notes p. 83

$$\frac{\partial \boldsymbol{v}_s}{\partial t} + (\boldsymbol{v}_s \cdot \nabla)\boldsymbol{v}_s = -\nabla\mu, \tag{11-10}$$

supplemented by the thermodynamic relations

$$\mathrm{d}\mu = (1/\rho)\,\mathrm{d}p, \tag{11-11}$$

$$\mathrm{d}U = (\mu + \tfrac{1}{2}v_s^2)\,\mathrm{d}\rho + \rho\boldsymbol{v}_s \cdot \mathrm{d}\boldsymbol{v}_s. \tag{11-12}$$

Equations (11-9,10,11,12) are those which are generally used to describe the flow of He II at $T = 0$ °K.

Notes

[1] J. F. Allen and A. D. Misener, Nature **141**(1938)75.
[2] P. Kapitza, Nature **141**(1938)74.
[3] L. D. Landau, Zh. Eksp. Teor. Fiz. **11**(1941)592; J. Phys. USSR **5**(1941)71; L. D. Landau and E. M. Lifshitz, *Fluid Mechanics* (Pergamon, London, 1959) Chap. 16.
[4] Actually the initial valve problem for the Euler equations does not have a unique solution if certain unstable discontinuities are admitted; see Landau and Lifshitz (Ref. [3] Chap. 1). For the classical fluid this difficulty is academic since the introduction of viscosity is expected to lead to a unique solution. For He II the corresponding difficulty may be fundamental, and is discussed in § 21.
[5] J. F. Allen and A. D. Misener, Proc. Roy. Soc. **A172**(1939)467.
[6] J. C. Findlay, A. Pitt, H. Grayson-Smith and J. D. Wilhelm, Phys. Rev. **54**(1938)506.
[7] J. F. Allen and J. Jones, Nature **141** (1938)243.
[8] J. G. Daunt and K. Mendelssohn, Nature **143**(1939)719.
[9] P. Kapitza, J. Phys. USSR **5**(1941)59; Phys. Rev. **60**(1941)354. For more recent work on these phenomena see D. F. Brewer and D. O. Edwards, Proc. Phys. Soc. (London) **71**(1958)117; W. E. Keller and E. F. Hammel, Phys. Rev. **124**(1961)1641.
[10] H. London, Proc. Roy. Soc. **A171**(1939)484; F. London, *Superfluids* (Wiley, New York, 1954) Vol. 2, p. 70.
[11] Explanations of the fountain effect according to the thermodynamics of irreversible processes are thus incorrect. The fountain effect is analogous with the osmotic pressure effect and not with the thermoelectric effects. For an attempt to understand the fountain effect according to irreversible processes see S. R. de Groot, L. Jansen and P. Mazur, Physica **16**(1950)421,691.
[12] L. Tisza, Nature **141**(1938)913; Compt. Rend. **207**(1938)1035,1186; J. Phys. Radium **1**(1940)164,350.
[13] The second Kelvin, Lagrange and Bernoulli laws for the vector $\boldsymbol{A}$ were first published by P. G. Saffman, Phys. Fluids **11**(1968)2505.
[14] L. D. Landau [3] derived this Bernoulli law in the overly simplified case where ρ_n, ρ, s are all constant.
[15] For a review paper on the Kapitza resistance see G. L. Pollack, Rev. Mod. Phys. **41**(1969)48; and L. J. Challis, J. Phys. **7C**(1974)481.

[16] D. V. Osborne, Proc. Phys. Soc. (London) **80**(1962)103,1343.
[17] H. E. Hall, Proc. Phys. Soc. (London) **A67**(1954)485.
[18] T. K. Hunt, Phys. Rev. **170**(1968)245.
[19] V. P. Peshkov, Dokl. Akad. Nauk SSSR **45**(1944)365; J. Phys. USSR **8**(1944)381; J. Phys. USSR **10**(1946)389.
[20] Some more recent experiments on the speed of sound are given in: C. E. Chase, Proc. Roy. Soc. **A220**(1953)116; K. R. Atkins and R. A. Stasior, Can. J. Phys. **31**(1953)1156.
[21] E. M. Lifshitz, J. Phys. USSR **8**(1944)110.
[22] Some other experiments on the speed of second sound are given in: J. R. Pellam, Phys. Rev. **75**(1949)1183.
[23] J. R. Pellam and W. B. Hanson, Phys. Rev. **85**(1952)216.
[24] W. König, Wiedemann Ann. **43**(1891)51.
[25] I. M. Khalatnikov, Zh. Eksp. Teor. Fiz. **30**(1956)617 [Sov. Phys. JETP **3**(1956)649].
[26] I. M. Khalatnikov, Zh. Eksp. Teor. Fiz. **23**(1952)253; *Introduction to the Theory of Superfluidity* (Benjamin, New York, 1965) Chap. 13.
[27] A. J. Dessler and W. M. Fairbank, Phys. Rev. **104**(1956)6.
[28] D. V. Osborne, Proc. Phys. Soc. (London) **A64**(1951)114.
[29] See L. D. Landau and E. M. Lifshitz (Ref. [3] p. 422).
[30] J. B. Mehl and W. Zimmermann, Jr., Phys. Rev. **167**(1968)214.
[31] L. Onsager, unpublished remark at a Low Temperature Physics Conference at Shelter Island, 1948 (see footnote 10, p. 151 in *Superfluids*: Ref. [10]). See also L. Onsager, Nuovo Cimento Suppl. no. 2 to Vol. **6** (1949)249.
[32] R. P. Feynman, in: *Progress in Low Temperature Physics*, Vol. 1, ed. C. J. Gorter (North-Holland, Amsterdam, 1955) p. 36.
[33] L. J. F. Broer, Physica **17**(1951)531.
[34] W. F. Vinen, Proc. Roy. Soc. **A260**(1961)218.
[35] G. W. Rayfield and F. Reif, Phys. Rev. Letters **11**(1963)305; Phys. Rev. **136**(1964) A1194.
[36] S. C. Whitmore and W. Zimmermann, Jr., Phys. Rev. **166**(1968)181.
[37] F. Reif and L. Meyer, Phys. Rev. **119**(1960)1164.
[38] It is not understood how an ion can create and, or become coupled to a vortex ring especially since the rings in these experiments have a radius of about 10^{-5} cm which is large compared to the ion. Perhaps the ions create a small vortex ring of the same size which then expands to a radius appropriate to the bound state.
[39] F. London, Nature **141**(1938)643; Phys. Rev. **54**(1938)947; *Superfluids* (Wiley, New York, 1954) Vol. 2, p. 59.
[40] A. Einstein, Sitzber. Preuss. Akad. Wiss. (1924)261; (1925)3.
[41] A. Bijl, J. de Boer and A. Michels, Physica **8**(1941)655. During the war Bijl perished in a concentration camp and a further discussion of his work was published by J. de Boer, Conference Report, Phys. Soc. Cambridge (1947) p. 32.
[42] J. G. Daunt and K. Mendelssohn, Proc. Roy. Soc. **A170**(1939)423.
[43] F. London, Rev. Mod. Phys. **17**(1945)310. H. London, in: *Report on a Low Temperature Conference*, 1946 (Phys. Soc., London, 1947) p. 48.
[44] T. D. Lee and C. N. Yang, Phys. Rev. **113**(1959)1406, present equations where the mass flow and momentum density need not be taken equal.

[45] One can in general hold constant some vector function $\boldsymbol{G}$ of $\boldsymbol{v}_s$, V. This leads to corrections to p which are proportional to $\partial \boldsymbol{G}/\partial V$ multiplied by the difference between (3-19) and (3-20). Thus these are also not Galilean covariant unless $\boldsymbol{G}$ is independent of V as is the case with (3-19).

[46] We have also assumed that the total volume is fixed. If not then this integral vanishes only upon time averaging for a periodic disturbance.

CHAPTER II

Hydrodynamics of He II when Modified to Include Dissipation

12 Introduction: The Navier–Stokes Equations of Classical Hydrodynamics

The Euler equations in § 1 are only a first approximation to the description of the motion of a classical fluid, in that they ignore friction and any effects which might lead to dissipation or entropy production. The Navier–Stokes equations are the next approximation in that they include the effects of dissipation but only insofar as the viscous stresses τ_{ij} and heat conduction $\boldsymbol{q}$ are linear in the spatial derivatives of the basic variables. For a classical fluid the Navier–Stokes equations are (to be derived in § 15):

$$\frac{\partial \rho}{\partial t} + \nabla \cdot \rho \boldsymbol{v} = 0, \tag{12-1}$$

$$\frac{\partial \rho s}{\partial t} + \nabla \cdot \left(\rho s \boldsymbol{v} + \frac{\boldsymbol{q}}{T} \right) = \frac{\Sigma}{T}, \tag{12-2}$$

$$\rho \frac{\mathrm{D} v_i}{\mathrm{D} t} = -\frac{\partial p}{\partial r_i} - \frac{\partial \tau_{ij}}{\partial r_j}, \tag{12-3}$$

where

$$\boldsymbol{q} = -\kappa \nabla T, \tag{12-4}$$

and

$$\tau_{ij} = -\eta \left(\frac{\partial v_i}{\partial r_j} + \frac{\partial v_j}{\partial r_i} - \tfrac{2}{3} \delta_{ij} \nabla \cdot \boldsymbol{v} \right) - \zeta \delta_{ij} \nabla \cdot \boldsymbol{v}, \tag{12-5}$$

and the entropy production is Σ / T, where

$$\Sigma = -\frac{\boldsymbol{q} \cdot \nabla T}{T} - \tau_{\alpha\beta} \frac{\partial v_\alpha}{\partial r_\beta}. \tag{12-6}$$

Notes p. 133

Since the second law of thermodynamics for irreversible processes tells us that Σ must be positive definite the bulk viscosity ζ, thermal conductivity κ and viscosity η are all positive. Together with the boundary condition that the fluid sticks at a stationary solid boundary, so that both the perpendicular and tangential components of $\boldsymbol{v}$ vanish, these equations describe the time development of the five basic variables provided that the dissipative coefficients κ, η, ζ and the appropriate equations of state are known.

An equation expressing the law of conservation of momentum follows from (12-1,3) and is

$$\frac{\partial \rho v_i}{\partial t} + \frac{\partial}{\partial r_\alpha}(P_{i\alpha} + \tau_{i\alpha}) = 0, \tag{12-7}$$

where P_{ij} is the Euler stress tensor. The energy conservation law implied by (12-1,2,3) and (1-8,9) is (no external field, so $\Omega = 0$)

$$\frac{\partial}{\partial t}(\rho\varepsilon + \tfrac{1}{2}\rho v^2) + \nabla\cdot[\rho\boldsymbol{v}(\tfrac{1}{2}v^2 + \varepsilon + p/\rho) + \boldsymbol{Q}'] = 0, \tag{12-8}$$

where the dissipative contribution $\boldsymbol{Q}'$ to the energy flux density is given by

$$Q_i' = q_i + \tau_{i\alpha}v_\alpha. \tag{12-9}$$

In the case of incompressible flow so that $\nabla\cdot\boldsymbol{v} = 0$ the dynamical equation (12-3) is greatly simplified to

$$\rho\frac{\mathrm{D}\boldsymbol{v}}{\mathrm{D}t} = -\nabla p + \eta\nabla^2\boldsymbol{v}. \tag{12-10}$$

A representative application of the Navier–Stokes equations is the flow of fluid in a pipe under the influence of a pressure gradient. In the steady state the velocity will depend only on the distance r from the axis of the capillary. So if the flow is in the x direction

$$\boldsymbol{v} = v(r)\hat{\boldsymbol{e}}_x \tag{12-11}$$

and therefore

$$\nabla\cdot\boldsymbol{v} = 0; \qquad (\boldsymbol{v}\cdot\nabla)\boldsymbol{v} = 0. \tag{12-12}$$

Then the equation (12-10) implies

$$\nabla p = \eta\nabla^2\boldsymbol{v}. \tag{12-13}$$

Notes p. 133

As the pressure gradient which drives the flow is in the x direction:

$$p = p(x). \tag{12-14}$$

The solution to (12-13) must then be of the form

$$\frac{\partial p}{\partial x} = \text{constant}, \qquad \nabla^2 \boldsymbol{v} = \text{constant}. \tag{12-15}$$

The requirement that the velocity vanish at the boundary:

$$v(\tfrac{1}{2}d) = 0, \tag{12-16}$$

yields a solution to (12-15):

$$\boldsymbol{v} = C(\tfrac{1}{4}d^2 - r^2)\hat{\boldsymbol{e}}_x. \tag{12-17}$$

The corresponding pressure gradient is

$$\nabla p = -4C\eta\hat{\boldsymbol{e}}_x. \tag{12-18}$$

Combining (12-17) yields an expression for the velocity in terms of the pressure head Δp

$$\boldsymbol{v} = -(\Delta p/4\ell\eta)(\tfrac{1}{4}d^2 - r^2)\hat{\boldsymbol{e}}_x, \tag{12-19}$$

where ℓ is the length of the pipe. The larger the viscosity the slower the fluid flows in response to a given pressure head.

Another application consists of calculating the torque exerted on a cylindrical bucket when a concentric vessel is rotated at a different angular velocity and fluid fills the angular region between them. We look for a steady state solution to (12-10) with

$$\boldsymbol{v} = v(r)\hat{\boldsymbol{e}}_\theta, \tag{12-20}$$

where r is the distance from the axis. As the pressure p will also depend on the distance from the axis we find

$$\nabla^2 \boldsymbol{v} = 0,$$

or

$$\boldsymbol{v} = (ar + b/r)\hat{\boldsymbol{e}}_\theta. \tag{12-21}$$

The boundary condition is that the fluid stick to the walls, i.e., no relative motion, hence

Notes p. 133

$$v(\tfrac{1}{2}d) = \tfrac{1}{2}\omega d, \tag{12-22}$$

$$v(\tfrac{1}{2}d_1) = \tfrac{1}{2}\omega_1 d_1, \tag{12-23}$$

where d_1, d are the diameters of the inner and outer buckets and ω_1, ω the respective angular velocities. Equations (12-21,22,23) imply

$$a = (\omega d^2 - \omega_1 d_1^2)/(d^2 - d_1^2), \tag{12-24}$$

$$4b = (\omega - \omega_1)\, d_1^2 d^2/(d_1^2 - d^2). \tag{12-25}$$

The pressure variation follows from (12-10). The stress tensor

$$P_{ij} + \tau_{ij}$$

yields the force in the ith direction on a unit area perpendicular to the jth direction. Therefore the torque exerted on a surface is

$$\boldsymbol{\tau} = \int \boldsymbol{r} \times [P_{ij} + \tau_{ij}]\, \mathrm{d}S_j, \tag{12-26}$$

where the notation means take the cross product of $\boldsymbol{r}$ with the vector formed from the inner product of $\mathrm{d}\boldsymbol{S}$ and the stress tensor. Due to the boundary condition on $\boldsymbol{v}$ and the radial dependence of pressure

$$\boldsymbol{\tau} = \int \boldsymbol{r} \times [\tau_{ij}\, \mathrm{d}S_j], \tag{12-27}$$

whose precise value can be calculated from (12-21,25). When $\omega = 0$ one finds

$$\tau = \pi\eta\omega_1 d_1^2 d^2/(d^2 - d_1^2). \tag{12-28}$$

The Euler equations introduced in § 1 are time reversible, hence any solution with time dependence must be periodic and cannot display dissipation. For this reason, the Euler equations lead to no sound absorption. The Navier–Stokes equations in contrast are time irreversible as required by the second law of thermodynamics for irreversible processes. From them the absorption of sound to first order in the deviation from equilibrium can be calculated.

Linearizing these equations as in § 1 and looking for a plane wave solution yields

$$-i\omega\rho' + ik\rho v' = 0, \tag{12-29}$$

$$-i\omega(\rho s)' + ik\rho s v' + \kappa k^2 T'/T = 0, \tag{12-30}$$

$$-i\omega\rho v' + ikp' + (\tfrac{4}{3}\eta + \zeta)k^2 v' = 0. \tag{12-31}$$

Notes p. 133

The requirement that the determinant of these homogeneous equations vanish yields

$$k = k_0 + i\alpha, \tag{12-32}$$

where α is the absorption of sound since it yields the exponential decay of the travelling wave. To first order in the dissipative coefficients k_0 is given by (1-31) and

$$\alpha = \frac{\omega^2}{2\rho u^3}\left[\tfrac{4}{3}\eta + \zeta + \kappa\left(\frac{1}{C_V} - \frac{1}{C_p}\right)\right]. \tag{12-33}$$

13 *The Viscosity Paradox*

For a classical fluid the dissipative coefficients must be determined experimentally and of course if the Navier–Stokes equations are a valid description, different experimental methods should give the same values for the dissipative coefficients. Much of the early work on He II was stimulated by the fact that if one applied the Navier–Stokes equations to the flow of He II different experimental methods seemed to lead to quite different dissipative constants. An example is the so called viscosity paradox.

From the Navier–Stokes equations the volume flow rate $\dot{V}$ through a capillary of radius $\frac{1}{2}d$ is given in terms of the pressure difference Δp by the Poiseuille formula (12-19)

$$\dot{V} = \pi d^4 \Delta p / 2^7 \eta \ell, \tag{13-1}$$

where ℓ is the length of the capillary [1]. Comparison of (13-1) with experiment [2] suggested that $\eta = 0$ (frictionless flow) in that flow rates were observed with arbitrarily small pressure heads. Actually for the early experiments the upper bound on η was 10^{-11} (c.g.s.) to be compared with the viscosity of 10^{-4} (c.g.s.) in He I for $T > T_\lambda$. From the Navier–Stokes equations the torque τ transmitted to a stationary cylinder of radius $\frac{1}{2}d$ when an inner concentric cylinder of radius $\frac{1}{2}d_1$ rotates at angular velocity ω_1 is, see Eqs. (12-27,28) and Ref. [3],

$$\tau = \pi\eta\omega_1 d_1^2 d^2/(d^2 - d_1^2). \tag{13-2}$$

Measurements of η with this rotating cylinder viscometer yielded, in conflict with the frictionless flow, a finite value of η which at T_λ

Notes p. 133

connected smoothly with the viscosity of He I [4]. Finally a measurement of the damping of the amplitude of oscillation of a disc immersed in He II also yielded a finite viscosity, but with a strikingly different temperature dependence than that determined from the rotating cylinder viscometer [5].

The origin of the paradox is clearly the use of the Navier–Stokes equations, which are a generalization of the Euler equations, while the flow of He II should be described by a generalization of the Landau two fluid equations, which include dissipative effects. The viscosity paradox can already be resolved if one assumes that on the dissipative level the superfluid still flows without friction, while the normal fluid behaves like a classical viscous fluid. This can be incorporated in the two fluid equations (for the incompressible case) by adding the viscous stress term $\eta\nabla^2\boldsymbol{v}_n$ to the right side of (2-14) and leaving (2-15) unchanged so that

$$\rho_n \frac{D_n \boldsymbol{v}_n}{Dt} = -\nabla p_n + \eta\nabla^2\boldsymbol{v}_n, \tag{13-3}$$

$$\rho_s \frac{D_s \boldsymbol{v}_s}{Dt} = -\nabla p_s, \tag{13-4}$$

where as before $p_s \equiv \rho_s\mu$ and $p_s + p_n = p$.

In this approximation one can picture He II as being a 'mixture' of an Euler fluid for $\boldsymbol{v}_s$ and a Navier–Stokes fluid for $\boldsymbol{v}_n$ [compare (13-3) with (12-10)]. These fluids interpenetrate each other, the relative amounts present in each volume element being determined by an equation of state giving ρ_s/ρ as a function of p, T, $(\boldsymbol{v}_n - \boldsymbol{v}_s)^2$.

In the flow of He II in a narrow capillary one must now say that although the normal fluid is held back by its viscous interaction with the walls and itself, the super-component can run right through without any friction and that it is its flow rate which was measured. On the other hand in the oscillating disc method the normal fluid sticks to the disc and produces the damping. The same is true for the rotating cylinder viscometer.

The different temperature dependence for these methods is explained as follows. From the Navier–Stokes equation (12-10) the torque τ exerted by the frictional stresses on a disc of radius $d/2$ oscillating as $\theta = \theta_0 \cos \omega t$ where θ is the angle of displacement is [6]

$$\tau = \pi\omega\theta_0(\omega\rho\eta)^{1/2}(d/2)^4 \cos(\omega t - \pi/4). \tag{13-5}$$

Notes p. 133

According to the two fluid model presented above one must calculate for He II the torque with (13-3) and this amounts to substituting ρ_n for ρ in (13-5) so that for He II

$$\tau = \pi\omega\theta_0(\omega\rho_n\eta)^{1/2}(d/2)^4 \cos(\omega t - \pi/4). \tag{13-6}$$

In the same way (13-2) is *unchanged* for a rotating cylinder viscometer in He II. Thus the application of (13-2) to a rotating cylinder viscometer in He II does indeed yield η, but in comparing their oscillating disc results with (13-5) as opposed to (13-6) the experimenters were really measuring $\eta\rho_n/\rho$ instead of what they thought was η. In fact, from the different temperature dependence of these two methods one can determine ρ_n/ρ as a function of T which is in agreement with what one finds for instance from the velocity of second sound.

From Eqs. (13-3,4) one can also discuss the approximations involved in treating the fountain effect from the point of view of reversible thermodynamics (see § 2). Since in principle the normal fluid can, according to (13-3) flow in narrow capillaries, an arrangement with a pressure and temperature difference such as pictured in Fig. 3, is only approximately an equilibrium state. Carrying over the solution (13-1) of the Navier–Stokes equation (12-10) to the normal fluid flow, we obtain that the volume flow rate of normal fluid through the superleak is

$$\dot{V}_n = \pi\Delta p_n(d/2)^4/8\eta\ell, \tag{13-7}$$

where $d/2$ is the radius of the superleak of length ℓ. In the steady state $\nabla\mu = 0$, hence

$$\Delta p_n/\ell \equiv |\nabla p_n| = |\nabla p| = \rho s\,|\nabla T|. \tag{13-8}$$

The normal fluid carries the entropy (4-2) so that the entropy flow which is irreversibly trying to even out the temperature difference is

$$\rho s\dot{V}_n = \pi(\rho s)^2\,|\nabla T|\,d^4/2^7\eta. \tag{13-9}$$

For a given temperature difference the fountain effect can be regarded as reversible only in the limit where d is so small that the entropy flow given by (13-9) leads to negligible temperature changes over the experimental time. The important fact is that according to (13-9) this limit can in principle be achieved to desired accuracy thus justifying H. London's treatment of the fountain effect as reversible to lowest order. If the narrow capillary connects containers of volume $\sim 1\ \text{cm}^3$ and supports a temperature gradient of $10^{-2}\ {}^\circ\text{K/cm}$ the time required for the normal

Notes p. 133

flow to even out the temperature difference will be 10^8 sec if $d \approx 10^{-4}$ cm and only 1 sec if $d \approx 10^{-2}$ cm.

An estimate of the time over which a normal fluid vortex decays due to viscous effects can be obtained from (13-3). Taking the curl of both sides and neglecting non-linear terms yields

$$\frac{\partial}{\partial t}(\nabla \times \boldsymbol{v}_n) = \frac{\eta}{\rho_n} \nabla^2(\nabla \times \boldsymbol{v}_n), \tag{13-10}$$

which is a diffusion equation for normal fluid vorticity.

If we consider a cylindrical vessel of diameter d with a normal fluid vortex on the axis at $t = 0$ then (13-10) yields a description of its decay. For simplicity approximate the initial state by a delta function in vorticity centered at the origin. From (13-10) the characteristic decay time turns out to be

$$\rho_n d^2/\eta. \tag{13-11}$$

When $d = 0.3$ cm and $T = 1.2\,°\text{K}$ so that $\rho_n = 4 \times 10^{-3}$ g/cm^3, $\eta = 1.7 \times 10^{-5}$ poise, one finds that the decay time of a normal fluid vortex is about 25 sec. This is roughly on the order of the time required for the superfluid circulation to complete a transition, as in the experiment of Whitmore and Zimmermann (see § 10). Perhaps this is evidence that the change in superfluid circulation around the wire proceeds, first through a transformation of super to normal circulation, which next decays as given by (13-10). However, the mechanism for such a transformation is completely dark.

14 *The Rotation Paradox*

For an Euler fluid we saw that from (1-3) one can derive a law of conservation of circulation if s = constant. Hence according to these equations a classical fluid initially at rest in a cylindrical vessel (circulation zero) *cannot* be brought into rotation as the vessel is rotated. In the Navier–Stokes regime, however, circulation is no longer conserved and in fact the viscous forces in (12-3) will drive the fluid to the observed state of solid body rotation ($\boldsymbol{v} = \boldsymbol{\omega} \times \boldsymbol{r}$, where $\boldsymbol{\omega}$ is the angular velocity of the walls).

In order to explain the viscosity paradox we assumed that only the normal component of He II experienced viscous forces which implies

Notes p. 133

that the circulation of $\boldsymbol{v}_s$ is still conserved on the dissipative level. Therefore one would expect that only the normal fluid could be brought from rest into solid body rotation. This implication of the dissipative two fluid equations was experimentally tested by Reppy et al. [7] who measured the total angular momentum of He II contained in a rotating bucket of known angular velocity. Their results indicated that the supercomponent took part in the rotation! Thus we are confronted with a 'rotation paradox': how can the frictionless flow of the supercomponent be made consistent with its twisting into rotation? This is the main problem of this chapter.

Andronikashvili [8] suggested that a possible solution to the paradox might be that the rotation destroyed the superfluid character of He II. However, he showed that this was not the case since he found that the Kapitza experiment was unaffected by rotation.

The paradox therefore remains. Since the rotating fluid is in some sense in an equilibrium state one should, to analyze the paradox further, first inquire about the limitations thermodynamics imposes on the equilibrium of a rotating fluid and then investigate the relation between the thermodynamic equilibrium conditions and the hydrodynamical equations of motion without and with dissipation.

For a classical fluid the answer to these questions is known and not surprising. In a rotating cylindrical vessel a classical fluid can be in thermodynamic equilibrium if it is in solid body rotation, if the temperature is constant and if the pressure provides for the centripetal acceleration. It can now be argued that in thermal equilibrium the dissipation must vanish and hence:

(a) the Euler equations must be consistent with the above equilibrium conditions,

(b) the general hydrodynamic dissipative fluxes must have the property that they vanish in this particular state.

Furthermore the dissipative fluxes must drive any other fluid motion to equilibrium. These special properties (and some other general restrictions such as conservation of mass, energy, momentum, Galilean covariance, and a linear dependence of the fluxes on the gradients) enable one to derive uniquely the dissipative equations on the Navier–Stokes level [i.e., (12-1,2,3) supplemented with (12-4,5,6)]. In § 15 we present the details of this argument.

In §§ 16 and 17 we turn our attention to the thermodynamic equilibrium state of rotating He II and the consistency of this state with the

Notes p. 133

ideal two fluid equations [9]. We especially find that in thermal equilibrium $\boldsymbol{v}_n = \boldsymbol{\omega} \times \boldsymbol{r}$, the motion is stationary as viewed by an observer rotating with the normal fluid and $\nabla \times \boldsymbol{v}_s = 0$ in the superfluid. While $\nabla \times \boldsymbol{v}_s = 0$ precludes the possibility of solid body rotation, the superfluid can rotate if, for instance, one dimensional regions are excluded from the superfluid; i.e., $\rho_s = 0$ at one dimensional regions. A solution with $\nabla \times \boldsymbol{v}_s = 0$ except at these one dimensional regions corresponds to motion about vortex lines. In order for the equilibrium state to be stationary for the rotating observer these vortex lines must rotate with the normal fluid. If there are many vortex lines then it will appear as if the superfluid is rotating with the normal fluid. This is a partial explanation of the rotation paradox. But now one can say more. In § 18 we show that under reasonable approximations the equilibrium distribution of vortex lines must satisfy the condition:

$$\int \left[\tfrac{1}{2}\rho_s v_s^2 - \boldsymbol{\omega} \cdot (\boldsymbol{r} \times \rho_s \boldsymbol{v}_s)\right] \mathrm{d}V = \text{minimum}, \tag{14-1}$$

if the equilibrium state is to be *stable*. If the strength (i.e., circulation) of the vortex lines can be arbitrarily weak then one can show that the minimum of (14-1) is realized for a uniform distribution of very many and very weak vortex lines which approximate solid body rotation as closely as desired. However, if one supplements the theory with the Onsager quantization hypothesis (10-1) then for each value of ω there is a *discrete* array of quantized vortex lines which satisfy (14-1). In particular it follows that below a certain critical angular velocity $\boldsymbol{v}_s = 0$ and this is confirmed by the experiment of Hess and Fairbank [10] which will be discussed in § 19.

In § 20 we summarize in detail the resolution of the rotation paradox and at that time emphasize that since the rotation of the superfluid is due to vortex singularities there need be no conflict between the Kelvin circulation theorem and the twisting into rotation of $\boldsymbol{v}_s$.

In § 21 we consider what modifications of the Landau two fluid equations must be made in order to take the dissipation into account. If the state in which vortex lines move in solid body rotation with the normal fluid is a thermodynamic equilibrium state one must require that in this state there is no dissipation. In addition one must require that the dissipative forces drive the fluid for given ω to the thermodynamic equilibrium state in which the normal fluid is in solid body rotation, and the vortex lines present are rotating with the normal fluid at the *positions* which follow from (14-1).

Notes p. 133

Since the *number* of vortices or the total circulation in the superfluid follows from thermodynamic stability it *may* be that the hydrodynamics with dissipation do not explain the change in number of vortices. In one view the changes in the number of vortex lines as ω varies must be looked upon as a quantum phase transition. The appearance of new vortex lines must then occur through a kind of nucleation process [11] similar to the formation of drops when a vapor condenses. In this approach interphase *fluctuations* play a crucial role and thus the *deterministic* hydrodynamics cannot possibly account for the change in number of vortex lines. We return to this picture in Chapters IV and VI. In another view [12] modeled after the behavior of the condensed ideal Bose gas (see Chapter VIII) the number of vortex lines can change in an *adiabatic* manner and thus might follow from the equations of motion. The problem of the change in number of vortex lines is still unsolved, but in any case one expects to observe metastability since the number present is a stability property of the fluid. The observations of Reppy and Lane [7], Packard and Sanders [13] and Whitmore and Zimmermann [16] are consistent with this view.

When the above special restrictions on the dissipative forces are combined with the general requirements of mass, momentum and energy conservation, Galilean covariance and the simplifying assumption that the dissipative fluxes are linear in the deviation from equilibrium, one is led to the equations first presented by Clark [14]. If it is further assumed that the dissipative fluxes are linear in $\boldsymbol{v}_n - \boldsymbol{v}_s$ as well as the deviation from equilibrium (for which there is no good reason) then one is led to the dissipative equations of Khalatnikov [15].

Although the dissipative equations derived in § 21 have been motivated by the behavior of He II in the special case of rotation, they are general and thus applicable to all phenomena involving dissipation. In Chapter III we discuss application of these equations to various situations.

15 The Equilibrium of a Rotating Classical Fluid

If $s(\varepsilon, \rho)$ is the entropy per unit mass as a function of the internal energy ε per unit mass, and the mass density ρ, the fluid in a rotating bucket of fixed volume will be in stable thermodynamic equilibrium when

$$\int \rho s(\varepsilon, \rho)\, \mathrm{d}V = \text{maximum}, \tag{15-1}$$

Notes p. 133

subject to the condition that we deal with a closed system so that the total energy, angular momentum and mass are given. Thus one has the three subsidiary conditions

$$\int \rho \, \mathrm{d}V = \text{constant}, \tag{15-2}$$

$$\int \rho(\varepsilon + \tfrac{1}{2}v^2) \, \mathrm{d}V = \text{constant}, \tag{15-3}$$

$$\int (\boldsymbol{r} \times \rho \boldsymbol{v}) \, \mathrm{d}V = \text{constant}. \tag{15-4}$$

The solution of (15-1) subject to the subsidiary conditions (15-2,3,4) is solved by the method of Lagrange multipliers. Multiplying (15-2,3,4) with Lagrange multipliers C_a, C_b, $\boldsymbol{C}_c$ and adding to (15-1) we find

$$\int [\rho s + C_a \rho + C_b \rho(\varepsilon + \tfrac{1}{2}v^2) + \boldsymbol{C}_c \cdot (\boldsymbol{r} \times \rho \boldsymbol{v})] \, \mathrm{d}V = \text{maximum}. \tag{15-5}$$

The equilibrium conditions follow from the restriction that the first variation δ from equilibrium must vanish. Expressing all the variations in (15-5) in terms of $\delta\rho$, $\delta\varepsilon$, $\delta\boldsymbol{v}$ we find that in order for the first variation to vanish the coefficients of $\delta\rho$, $\delta\varepsilon$, $\delta\boldsymbol{v}$ must vanish, or

$$\varepsilon + p/\rho - sT - \tfrac{1}{2}v^2 \equiv \mu - \tfrac{1}{2}v^2 = -C_a/C_b, \tag{15-6}$$

$$T = -1/C_b, \tag{15-7}$$

$$\boldsymbol{v} = -(\boldsymbol{C}_c \times \boldsymbol{r})/C_b, \tag{15-8}$$

where we have used Eqs. (1-10a,10b).

The equilibrium conditions are therefore, that the temperature is constant, the fluid is in solid body rotation with angular velocity $\boldsymbol{\omega} = -\boldsymbol{C}_c/C_b$ (which must be determined from the given total angular momentum) and the chemical potential minus the kinetic energy per unit mass is constant.

It is easy to show that these five conditions are consistent with the five Euler hydrodynamical equations. First note that the equilibrium state is stationary as (15-6,7,8) are five relations for five variables (a complete set for a classical fluid) which are all time independent. From the thermodynamic identity

$$\mathrm{d}\mu = -s \, \mathrm{d}T + (1/\rho) \, \mathrm{d}p$$

one gets by taking the gradient of (15-6)

$$(1/\rho)\nabla p = \nabla(\tfrac{1}{2}v^2), \tag{15-9}$$

Notes p. 133

since T is constant. Now for $\boldsymbol{v} = \boldsymbol{\omega} \times \boldsymbol{r}$: $\nabla \times \boldsymbol{v} = 2\,\boldsymbol{\omega}$ and $\nabla(\frac{1}{2}v^2) = -(\boldsymbol{v} \cdot \nabla)\boldsymbol{v}$ so that one has

$$(\boldsymbol{v} \cdot \nabla)\boldsymbol{v} = -(1/\rho)\nabla p,$$

which is just the Euler equation (1-3) in the stationary state. The dependence of ρ on the distance to the axis of rotation follows from (15-9) and an equation of state for p as a function of ρ, T. The continuity equation (1-1) is then also satisfied since with $\boldsymbol{v} = \boldsymbol{\omega} \times \boldsymbol{r}$ (therefore $\nabla \cdot \boldsymbol{v} = 0$) it becomes

$$\frac{\partial \rho}{\partial t} + \boldsymbol{v} \cdot \nabla \rho = 0,$$

which implies that ρ must be stationary with respect to a coordinate system rotating with the fluid. This is clearly the case as ρ depends only on the distance to the axis of rotation. A similar argument shows that the entropy distribution is consistent with the entropy conservation law (1-5).

For the extremum which we have found to be a maximum, and for the above equilibrium state to be stable, one must require that the quadratic form in $\delta\rho$, $\delta\varepsilon$, $\delta\boldsymbol{v}$ expressing the variation of the total entropy subject to the subsidiary conditions, to second order be negative definite or

$$\iint\left[\left(\rho\frac{\partial^2 s}{\partial \rho^2} + 2\frac{\partial s}{\partial \rho}\right)\frac{(\delta\rho)^2}{2} + \rho\frac{\partial^2 s}{\partial \rho\,\partial \varepsilon}\delta\rho\,\delta\varepsilon + \rho\frac{\partial^2 s}{\partial \varepsilon^2}\frac{(\delta\varepsilon)^2}{2} + C_{\mathrm{b}}\rho\frac{(\delta\boldsymbol{v})^2}{2}\right]\mathrm{d}V < 0, \tag{15-10}$$

where we have used (15-7,8) and

$$(\delta\boldsymbol{v})^2 \equiv (\delta v_x)^2 + (\delta v_y)^2 + (\delta v_z)^2.$$

One finds that (15-10) is negative definite if

$$\rho > 0, \qquad C_V > 0, \qquad \left(\frac{\partial p}{\partial \rho}\right)_T > 0, \tag{15-11}$$

where we have assumed $T > 0$.

For the proof of (15-11) the following identities are useful

$$\frac{\partial^2 s}{\partial \varepsilon^2} \equiv -1/C_V T^2, \tag{15-12}$$

Notes p. 133

$$-\frac{1}{T}\left(\frac{\partial p}{\partial \rho}\right)_T \frac{\partial^2 s}{\partial \varepsilon^2} \equiv \rho\frac{\partial^2 s}{\partial \varepsilon^2}\left(2\frac{\partial s}{\partial \rho} + \rho\frac{\partial^2 s}{\partial \rho^2}\right) - \rho^2\left(\frac{\partial^2 s}{\partial \varepsilon\, \partial \rho}\right)^2. \quad (15\text{-}13)$$

In order to discuss the approach to equilibrium (and derive the Navier–Stokes equations) one must consider the dissipative effects. According to the second law of thermodynamics for irreversible processes the entropy is not conserved off equilibrium. The most general entropy equation then takes the form (12-2) where now the dissipative entropy flow $\boldsymbol{q}/T$ and the entropy production Σ are as yet undetermined. However, one requires that the general dissipative terms induce equilibrium in the sense that Σ is positive definite off equilibrium. Off equilibrium momentum and mass must still be conserved. Thus the most general modification of (1-6) is (12-7) and the most general modification of (1-1) is

$$\frac{\partial \rho}{\partial t} + \nabla\cdot(\rho \boldsymbol{v} + \boldsymbol{D}) = 0. \quad (15\text{-}14)$$

Equations (12-2,7) and (15-14) form five equations for the five variables ρ, s, $\boldsymbol{v}$ which are, however, empty since $\boldsymbol{D}$, Σ, $\boldsymbol{q}$, τ_{ij} are undetermined.

There is one more piece of information, namely, since these constitute a complete set of equations they must imply energy conservation. From (1-8,9) the time derivative of the energy density is (with no external field)

$$\frac{\partial U}{\partial t} = (\mu - \tfrac{1}{2}v^2)\,\frac{\partial \rho}{\partial t} + T\frac{\partial \rho s}{\partial t} + \boldsymbol{v}\cdot\frac{\partial \boldsymbol{J}}{\partial t}. \quad (15\text{-}15)$$

The time derivatives on the right hand side of (15-15) can be eliminated in favor of space derivatives by use of (15-14) and (12-2,7). Since energy is conserved these space derivatives must combine to form a perfect divergence. The most general fashion in which this can happen is if $\partial U/\partial t$ is given by (12-8) with $\boldsymbol{Q}'$ and Σ also restricted to

$$Q_i' = q_i + v_\alpha \tau_{\alpha i} + D_i(\mu - \tfrac{1}{2}v^2), \quad (15\text{-}16)$$

$$\Sigma = -\frac{\boldsymbol{q}\cdot\nabla T}{T} - \tau_{\alpha\beta}\frac{\partial v_\alpha}{\partial r_\beta} - \boldsymbol{D}\cdot\nabla(\mu - \tfrac{1}{2}v^2). \quad (15\text{-}17)$$

In equilibrium ∇T, $\nabla(\mu - \frac{1}{2}v^2)$, $(\partial v_i/\partial r_j + \partial v_j/\partial r_i)$ are all zero. Off but close to equilibrium they can be considered small. Since $\boldsymbol{q}$, τ_{ij}, $\boldsymbol{D}$ are dissipative effects they must vanish in equilibrium. Thus as a first approximation (the Navier–Stokes approximation) one takes $\boldsymbol{q}$, τ_{ij}, $\boldsymbol{D}$

Notes p. 133

as linear in the deviation from equilibrium or linear in the above gradients. We note that the dissipative effects cannot depend on the combination $(\partial v_i/\partial r_j - \partial v_j/\partial r_i)$ since it does not vanish in the rotational equilibrium state.

As the dissipative effects are linear in the gradients the entropy production Σ will be a positive definite quadratic form in the gradients. We now look for the most general expressions for $\boldsymbol{q}$, τ_{ij}, $\boldsymbol{D}$ which make Σ positive definite and which also satisfy the Galilean transformation.

From the methods of Appendix II one verifies that Σ, $\boldsymbol{q}$, τ_{ij}, $\boldsymbol{D}$ must be Galilean invariants. Since the temperature gradient and the velocity gradient are invariant we conclude from (15-17) that $\nabla(\mu - \frac{1}{2}v^2)$ had better be invariant. This is not the case, hence we must take,

$$\boldsymbol{D} = 0,$$

so that Σ is given by (12-6) and $\boldsymbol{Q}$ by (12-9). Now the most general expressions for $\boldsymbol{q}$ and τ_{ij} which make Σ positive definite and are linear in

$$\nabla T \qquad \text{and} \qquad \frac{\partial v_i}{\partial r_j} + \frac{\partial v_j}{\partial r_i}$$

are given by (12-4,5). One must still invoke the Galilean transformation to forbid a dependence of $\boldsymbol{q}$, τ_{ij} on the velocity field v_i, otherwise terms of the form $v_i v_j \, \partial T/\partial r_j$ would appear in q_i.

16 The Thermodynamic Equilibrium of Rotating He II

The essential difference between He II and a classical fluid is the existence of an additional velocity field. Thus there is an additional scalar Galilean invariant upon which the internal variables might depend. In fact from (4-5,8) we see that we can write for the entropy

$$T\,\mathrm{d}s = \mathrm{d}\varepsilon_0 - (p/\rho^2)\,\mathrm{d}\rho - (\boldsymbol{v}_\mathrm{n} - \boldsymbol{v}_\mathrm{s}) \cdot \mathrm{d}\boldsymbol{k}, \tag{16-1}$$

where

$$\rho\varepsilon_0 = U_0, \qquad \boldsymbol{k} = (\rho_\mathrm{n}/\rho)(\boldsymbol{v}_\mathrm{n} - \boldsymbol{v}_\mathrm{s}). \tag{16-2}$$

Generalizing the argument of the previous section we claim that He II contained in a rotating bucket of fixed volume will be in stable thermodynamic equilibrium if

$$\int \rho s(\varepsilon_0, \rho, \boldsymbol{k})\,\mathrm{d}V = \text{maximum} \tag{16-3}$$

Notes p. 133

subject to the conditions that the mass, energy and angular momentum are given constants for the closed system:

$$\int \rho \, \mathrm{d}V = \text{constant}, \tag{16-4}$$

$$\int U \, \mathrm{d}V \equiv \int \rho(\varepsilon_0 + \boldsymbol{k} \cdot \boldsymbol{v}_\mathrm{s} + \tfrac{1}{2}v_\mathrm{s}^2) \, \mathrm{d}V = \text{constant}, \tag{16-5}$$

$$\int (\boldsymbol{r} \times \boldsymbol{J}) \, \mathrm{d}V \equiv \int \boldsymbol{r} \times \rho(\boldsymbol{k} + \boldsymbol{v}_\mathrm{s}) \, \mathrm{d}V = \text{constant}. \tag{16-6}$$

For the solution of (16-3) with subsidiary conditions (16-4,5,6) again multiply (16-4,5,6) with Lagrange constant multipliers C_a, C_b, $\boldsymbol{C}_\mathrm{c}$ and incorporate in (16-3) to obtain

$$\int \{\rho s + C_\mathrm{a}\rho + C_\mathrm{b}\rho(\varepsilon_0 + \boldsymbol{k} \cdot \boldsymbol{v}_\mathrm{s} + \tfrac{1}{2}v_\mathrm{s}^2) + \boldsymbol{C}_\mathrm{c} \cdot [\boldsymbol{r} \times \rho(\boldsymbol{k} + \boldsymbol{v}_\mathrm{s})]\} \, \mathrm{d}V = \text{maximum}. \tag{16-7}$$

First we look for those conditions which follow from the fact that in order for the integral (16-7) to be a maximum it must be an extremum. Thus its first variation from equilibrium must vanish. Since eight independent variables (which are here taken to be ρ, ε_0, $\boldsymbol{k}$, $\boldsymbol{v}_\mathrm{s}$) are required to describe the state of He II its first variation would ordinarily involve the first variation of the eight independent variables. However, in anticipation of the fact that there is a macroscopic coherence which prevents $\boldsymbol{v}_\mathrm{s}$ from being varied independently and by an arbitrarily small amount in each volume element we do not perform the variation of $\boldsymbol{v}_\mathrm{s}$ (i.e., $\delta \boldsymbol{v}_\mathrm{s} = 0$) and thus investigate the extremum conditions implied by (16-7) for a given superfluid velocity $\boldsymbol{v}_\mathrm{s}$. Our objective is of course to ascertain which restrictions on $\boldsymbol{v}_\mathrm{s}$ are consistent with thermal equilibrium.

Performing the first variation of (16-7) we find from the vanishing of the coefficients of $\delta\varepsilon_0$, $\delta\boldsymbol{k}$, $\delta\rho$:

$$T = -1/C_\mathrm{b}, \tag{16-8}$$

$$\boldsymbol{v}_\mathrm{n} = -(\boldsymbol{C}_\mathrm{c} \times \boldsymbol{r})/C_\mathrm{b}, \tag{16-9}$$

$$\mu + \tfrac{1}{2}v_\mathrm{s}^2 - \boldsymbol{v}_\mathrm{n} \cdot \boldsymbol{v}_\mathrm{s} = -C_\mathrm{a}/C_\mathrm{b}, \tag{16-10}$$

where in deriving (16-9) one must use (16-1,8) and in deriving (16-10) use was made of (16-1,8,9) and (4-8). So in equilibrium the temperature is constant, the normal fluid is in solid body rotation at a frequency $\boldsymbol{\omega} = -\boldsymbol{C}_\mathrm{c}/C_\mathrm{b}$ and the chemical potential obeys (16-10).

One must now investigate the consistency of these results with the equations of motion without dissipation.

Notes p. 133

17 *Consistency of the Thermodynamic Equilibrium Conditions with the Ideal Two Fluid Hydrodynamics*

As with the classical fluid we expect that in equilibrium the dissipation vanishes and that therefore the equilibrium conditions (16-8,9,10) should be consistent with the ideal Landau two fluid equations. Note that in contrast to the case of a classical fluid where the number of equilibrium conditions was equal to the number of dynamical equations, for He II, since we have not varied the $\boldsymbol{v}_s$ field, one still has only five equilibrium conditions for the eight dynamical variables. As a result for the classical fluid the equilibrium conditions fulfilled the Euler equations identically, while for He II the Landau equations should lead to non-trivial consistency conditions, especially for the superfluid velocity field $\boldsymbol{v}_s$ which was left undetermined by the equilibrium conditions. This is also the reason why in (3-4) or equivalently (4-3) we have *not* assumed $\nabla \times \boldsymbol{v}_s = 0$ since we are especially interested in the consistency of the irrotational motion of the superfluid with the rotation of the fluid as a whole.

First consider the superfluid equation of motion (4-3) or more exactly (3-27). By transforming to a coordinate system rotating with angular velocity $\boldsymbol{\omega}$ and in this system denoting all quantities by primes (3-27) becomes

$$\rho_s \frac{\partial \boldsymbol{v}'_s}{\partial t'} + \rho_s \nabla'[\tfrac{1}{2}(v'_s)^2 + \mu - \tfrac{1}{2}\omega^2 r^2] - \rho_s \boldsymbol{v}'_s \times (2\boldsymbol{\omega} + \nabla' \times \boldsymbol{v}'_s) = 0. \quad (17\text{-}1)$$

Since $\boldsymbol{v}'_s = \boldsymbol{v}_s - \boldsymbol{\omega} \times \boldsymbol{r}$ and $\boldsymbol{v}_n = \boldsymbol{\omega} \times \boldsymbol{r}$ it follows from the equilibrium condition (16-10) that the second term is zero so that $\boldsymbol{v}'_s$ must fulfil the equation

$$\rho_s \frac{\partial \boldsymbol{v}'_s}{\partial t'} = \rho_s \boldsymbol{v}'_s \times (2\boldsymbol{\omega} + \nabla' \times \boldsymbol{v}'_s). \quad (17\text{-}2)$$

By a scalar multiplication with $\boldsymbol{v}'_s$ one sees that this implies

$$\rho_s \partial(v'_s)^2/\partial t' = 0 \quad (17\text{-}3)$$

so that v_s^2 is stationary for the *rotating* observer. From (17-2,3) one now finds by use of the boundary condition that the perpendicular component of $\boldsymbol{v}'_s$ vanishes at the walls of the bucket, that $\boldsymbol{v}'_s$ is independent of t' or in other words, that the superfluid velocity field must be stationary in the coordinate system rotating with the normal fluid. To see this,

Notes p. 133

note that at the boundary where $v'_{s\perp} = 0$ (17-3) implies that $\partial v'_{s\parallel}/\partial t' = 0$ or at the boundary $\partial \boldsymbol{v}'_s/\partial t' = 0$. Since (17-2) is a first order differential equation, if the boundary condition is independent of time the solution is also independent of time, as the system is closed.

From (17-2) one now concludes

$$\rho_s \boldsymbol{v}'_s \times (2\boldsymbol{\omega} + \nabla' \times \boldsymbol{v}'_s) = 0,$$

or in terms of the quantities in the inertial system

$$\rho_s(\boldsymbol{v}_s - \boldsymbol{\omega} \times \boldsymbol{r}) \times (\nabla \times \boldsymbol{v}_s) = 0, \tag{17-4}$$

since $\nabla \times \boldsymbol{v}_n = 2\boldsymbol{\omega}$.

Thus by application of the restriction that the equilibrium conditions be consistent with the ideal two fluid equations we obtain that in equilibrium $\boldsymbol{v}_s$ must satisfy *either* $\boldsymbol{v}_s = \boldsymbol{v}_n$ or $\nabla \times \boldsymbol{v}_s = 0$. If $\boldsymbol{v}_s = \boldsymbol{v}_n$ then (16-8,9,10) become identical with (15-6,7,8) and the behavior of He II in equilibrium is identical with that of a classical fluid. But if we want to allow the possibility that the behavior of He II be different from a classical fluid then the only other possibility is $\nabla \times \boldsymbol{v}_s = 0$ in the super-component in equilibrium. Various ways in which this can be realized are:

(1) If $\boldsymbol{v}_s$ is regular everywhere then from $\nabla \times \boldsymbol{v}_s = 0$ and the cylindrical symmetry it follows that $\boldsymbol{v}_s = 0$. This was the original prediction about the behavior of He II which led to the rotation paradox.

(2) The superfluid velocity $\boldsymbol{v}_s$ is due to a distribution of vortices in the fluid. In this case $\boldsymbol{v}_s$ is singular on a set of one dimensional regions (vortex lines). Since $\nabla \times \boldsymbol{v}_s$ is also singular at the vortex line it follows from (17-4) that in order to have consistency of thermodynamics with the hydrodynamics that

$$\rho_s = 0 \text{ at the vortex line.} \tag{17-5}$$

In general one approximates this behavior of ρ_s by saying that ρ_s is zero within a core of radius a around the vortex line, where a is a measure of the distance over which ρ_s drops to zero. Thus for this situation $\nabla \times \boldsymbol{v}_s$ is zero throughout the superfluid except at the vortex lines where, however, $\rho_s = 0$. In order for $\boldsymbol{v}_s$ to be stationary in the rotating system one must require that the vortex line move with the normal fluid. Note that in this case one has a thermodynamic equilibrium state which in general is not stationary in the inertial system.

(3) If $\boldsymbol{v}_s$ is singular on a set of two dimensional regions (vortex sheets),

Notes p. 133

then $\nabla \times \boldsymbol{v}_s$ is still zero if one excludes the thin transition regions, but the fluid region is now disconnected. For instance in the model of rotating He II considered by London [17] and Landau [18] the fluid is divided by cylindrical vortex sheets into a series of concentric cylinders in each of which the superfluid rotates with a velocity inversely proportional to the distance from the axis. The velocity is discontinuous if one crosses a vortex sheet and in order to fulfil (17-4) one must require that the jump in velocity be symmetric about the value of ωr at the crossing point.

Turning now to the consistency with the remaining Landau equations we first note that (16-8,9,10) are five conditions for the five variables, T, $\mu + \frac{1}{2}(\boldsymbol{v}_n - \boldsymbol{v}_s)^2$, $\boldsymbol{v}_n$, which imply that these quantities are stationary for *both* the rotating and inertial observer. However, since $\boldsymbol{v}_s$ is stationary only for the rotating observer we have that eight variables, and hence the state of the fluid, are stationary as viewed in the rotating frame of reference. This implies that

$$\frac{D_n\mu}{Dt} = \frac{D_n p}{Dt} = \frac{D_n\rho}{Dt} = \frac{D_n\rho s}{Dt} = \frac{D_n\rho_n}{Dt} = 0, \tag{17-6}$$

since $D_n/Dt = \partial/\partial t'$.

One now sees that the entropy equation (4-2) is identically satisfied since with $\nabla \cdot \boldsymbol{v}_n = 0$ it becomes $D_n\rho s/Dt = 0$. Also the momentum conservation law (4-4) is identically satisfied. This can be seen most readily by using it in the form (9-1). Eliminating ∇p with (4-8), taking T constant and $\boldsymbol{v}_n = \boldsymbol{\omega} \times \boldsymbol{r}$ transforms it to

$$(\boldsymbol{v}_s - \boldsymbol{v}_n)\frac{D_n\rho_n}{Dt} = 0,$$

which because of (17-6) is also satisfied.

There remains the continuity equation which is *not* identically satisfied, since with $\nabla \cdot \boldsymbol{v}_n = 0$ and $\rho_n = \rho - \rho_s$, (4-1) can be transformed into

$$\frac{D_n\rho}{Dt} = \nabla \cdot \rho_s(\boldsymbol{v}_n - \boldsymbol{v}_s). \tag{17-7}$$

Hence from (17-6) one obtains the additional consistency requirement

$$\nabla \cdot \rho_s(\boldsymbol{v}_n - \boldsymbol{v}_s) = 0. \tag{17-8}$$

Notes p. 133

Equation (17-8) and the restriction $\nabla \times \boldsymbol{v}_s = 0$ determine the $\boldsymbol{v}_s$ field in equilibrium (as together they determine the divergence and curl of $\boldsymbol{v}_s$) provided that the location and strength of any singularities are known. For example, in the usual case where one approximates ρ_s as constant, Eq. (17-8) implies $\nabla \cdot \boldsymbol{v}_s = 0$ or $\nabla^2 \phi = 0$ where $\boldsymbol{v}_s = \nabla \phi$.

To understand the location and strength of the singularities one must investigate the stability conditions which we do in the next section.

Finally we note that the restriction $\nabla \times \boldsymbol{v}_s = 0$ is one which would prevent a variation of $\boldsymbol{v}_s$ by an independent amount $\delta \boldsymbol{v}_s$ in each volume element of the fluid. This restriction justifies a posteriori our not performing the variation of $\boldsymbol{v}_s$ in § 16.

18 Stability Conditions and the Quantization Hypothesis

We saw in § 16 that the total entropy of He II in a rotating bucket is, for any superfluid velocity $\boldsymbol{v}_s$ an extremum if the conditions (16-8,9,10) are fulfilled. One must now ask (still with given $\boldsymbol{v}_s$) whether this extremum is actually a maximum. This involves investigating whether the variation from equilibrium of the entropy with subsidiary conditions [i.e., (16-7)] to second order in the independent variations $\delta\rho$, $\delta\varepsilon_0$, $\delta\boldsymbol{k}$ is a negative definite quadratic form.

To second order in these quantities one obtains from (16-7)

$$\int \Bigg[\left(\rho \frac{\partial^2 s}{\partial \rho^2} + 2 \frac{\partial s}{\partial \rho} \right) \frac{(\delta\rho)^2}{2} + \rho \frac{\partial^2 s}{\partial \varepsilon_0^2} \frac{(\delta\varepsilon_0)^2}{2} + \rho \frac{\partial^2 s}{\partial \rho\, \partial \varepsilon_0} \delta\rho\, \delta\varepsilon_0 + \rho \frac{\partial^2 s}{\partial k_i\, \partial k_j} \frac{\delta k_i\, \delta k_j}{2}$$

$$+ \rho \frac{\partial^2 s}{\partial \varepsilon_0\, \partial k_i} \delta\varepsilon_0\, \delta k_i + \rho \frac{\partial^2 s}{\partial \rho\, \partial k_i} \delta\rho\, \delta k_i \Bigg] \mathrm{d}V < 0. \quad (18\text{-}1)$$

From the submatrix formed by $\delta\rho$, $\delta\varepsilon_0$ one immediately obtains the generalization of the classical conditions which are (we assume $T > 0$)

$$\left(\frac{\partial s}{\partial T} \right)_{\rho, k} > 0, \qquad \left(\frac{\partial p}{\partial \rho} \right)_{T, k} > 0. \quad (18\text{-}2)$$

In order to obtain the additional stability conditions which follow from the second order variations that involve $\delta\boldsymbol{k}$ we first write (18-1) in a more transparent form by introducing the variable $\upsilon \equiv 1/\rho$ and rotating the coordinate system so that $k = k_z$. Then (18-1) becomes

Notes p. 133

$$\int \frac{1}{v}\left\{\frac{\partial^2 s}{\partial v^2}\frac{(\delta v)^2}{2} + \frac{\partial^2 s}{\partial \varepsilon_0^2}\frac{(\delta\varepsilon_0)^2}{2} + \frac{\partial^2 s}{\partial v\,\partial\varepsilon_0}\delta v\,\delta\varepsilon_0 + \frac{\partial^2 s}{\partial k_z^2}\frac{(\delta k_z)^2}{2} \right.$$
$$\left. - \frac{\rho}{\rho_n T}\left[\frac{(\delta k_x)^2}{2} + \frac{(\delta k_y)^2}{2}\right] + \frac{\partial^2 s}{\partial\varepsilon_0\,\partial k_z}\delta\varepsilon_0\,\delta k_z + \frac{\partial^2 s}{\partial v\,\partial k_z}\delta v\,\delta k_z\right\} \mathrm{d}V < 0, \tag{18-3}$$

where we have used

$$\frac{\partial s}{\partial k_i} = -(\rho/\rho_n T)k_i,$$

which follows from (16-1,2). From the coefficient of $(\delta k_x)^2$ and $(\delta k_y)^2$ we obtain the stability requirement

$$\rho_n > 0. \tag{18-4}$$

There still remains the stability requirement which follows from the restriction that the 3×3 matrix involving δv, $\delta\varepsilon_0$, δk_z, be negative definite. This condition can be obtained by diagonalizing the matrix by means of completing the square and using standard thermodynamic manipulations and is found to be

$$\left[\frac{\partial(\rho_n/\rho)(v_n - v_s)_z}{\partial(v_n - v_s)_z}\right]_{p,T} > 0. \tag{18-5}$$

A direct derivation of the stability requirements is obtained from the following theorem (e.g., see Ref. [19]) concerning the requirement that the second order variation of a function s of variables $x_1 \ldots x_n$ be negative definite. Namely for

$$\mathrm{d}^2 s = \frac{1}{2}\sum_{i,j=1}^{n} \frac{\partial^2 s}{\partial x_i\,\partial x_j}\delta x_i\,\delta x_j < 0 \tag{18-6}$$

it is necessary and sufficient that

$$\left[\frac{\partial}{\partial x_1}\left(\frac{\partial s}{\partial x_1}\right)_{x_i}\right]_{x_2\ldots x_n} < 0, \qquad \left[\frac{\partial}{\partial x_2}\left(\frac{\partial s}{\partial x_2}\right)_{x_i}\right]_{\left(\frac{\partial s}{\partial x_1}\right)_{x_i}, x_3,\ldots x_n} < 0,$$

and so on; or in general

$$\left[\frac{\partial}{\partial x_k}\left(\frac{\partial s}{\partial x_k}\right)_{x_i}\right]_{\left(\frac{\partial s}{\partial x_1}\right)_{x_i},\ldots,\left(\frac{\partial s}{\partial x_{k-1}}\right)_{x_i}, x_{k+1},\ldots x_n} < 0, \tag{18-7}$$

Notes p. 133

for $k = 1$ through n. Clearly Eq. (18-3) is of the form (18-6) and applying (18-7) we find the restrictions (18-2,5). To derive (18-5) we have had to assume $\rho > 0$. However $\rho > 0$ will be seen to follow from the stability requirements associated with the variation in $\boldsymbol{v}_s$. The stability conditions which we have so far derived can be written as

$$\left(\frac{\partial s}{\partial T}\right)_{\rho,k} > 0, \quad \left(\frac{\partial p}{\partial \rho}\right)_{T,k} > 0, \quad \frac{\rho_n}{\rho} > 0, \quad \frac{\rho_n}{\rho} + w^2\left[\frac{\partial(\rho_n/\rho)}{\partial(w^2/2)}\right]_{p,T} > 0; \tag{18-8}$$

where $\boldsymbol{w} \equiv \boldsymbol{v}_n - \boldsymbol{v}_s$. Relations (18-8) comprise the necessary and sufficient conditions for the equilibrium state with a given $\boldsymbol{v}_s$ to be stable with respect to the variations $\delta\rho$, $\delta\varepsilon_0$, $\delta\boldsymbol{k}$.

We now turn our attention to the more interesting question of how the stability depends on the superfluid velocity field $\boldsymbol{v}_s$. We saw in § 17 that in order for there to be consistency of the equilibrium conditions (16-8,9,10) with the two fluid hydrodynamics $\boldsymbol{v}_s$ must be stationary in the reference frame rotating with the normal fluid and $\nabla \times \boldsymbol{v}_s$ can be taken to be zero except on sets of vortex lines or vortex sheets provided that (17-8) is also satisfied. This still leaves many possible $\boldsymbol{v}_s$ fields and one may ask whether there is a most stable $\boldsymbol{v}_s$ configuration.

First we remark that in § 16 where we obtained the equilibrium conditions (16-8,9,10) from the vanishing of the variations in entropy associated with $\delta\rho$, $\delta\varepsilon_0$, $\delta\boldsymbol{k}$, we did not vary $\boldsymbol{v}_s$ in anticipation of a condition which restricts such a variation. In § 17 this restriction was found to be $\nabla \times \boldsymbol{v}_s = 0$. Although $\nabla \times \boldsymbol{v}_s = 0$ certainly restricts any variation of the superfluid velocity field there are still many ways in which $\boldsymbol{v}_s$ can be varied maintaining $\nabla \times \boldsymbol{v}_s = 0$. For instance, setting $\boldsymbol{v}_s = \nabla\phi$, the restriction $\nabla \times \boldsymbol{v}_s = 0$ can be maintained everywhere if ϕ is varied in each volume element by an arbitrary amount. Thus one must first ask if the entropy (16-7) is an *extremum* with respect to those variations in $\boldsymbol{v}_s$ which maintain $\nabla \times \boldsymbol{v}_s = 0$.

We investigate this by substituting $\phi = \phi_0 + \delta\phi$ into (16-7) where ϕ_0 is the equilibrium value of ϕ. Keeping ρ, ε_0, $\boldsymbol{k}$, fixed at their equilibrium values we find

$$\int \{(C_b\rho\boldsymbol{k} + \rho\boldsymbol{C}_c \times \boldsymbol{r}) \cdot \nabla\delta\phi + C_b\rho[\tfrac{1}{2}(\nabla\delta\phi)^2 + \nabla\phi_0 \cdot \nabla\delta\phi]\}\, \mathrm{d}V < 0. \tag{18-9}$$

Notes p. 133

Rearranging terms we find

$$\int\{\nabla\cdot\delta\phi[C_b\rho(\boldsymbol{k}+\nabla\phi_0)+\rho\boldsymbol{C}_c\times\boldsymbol{r}]-\delta\phi\nabla\cdot[C_b\rho(\boldsymbol{k}+\nabla\phi_0)+\rho\boldsymbol{C}_c\times\boldsymbol{r}]$$
$$+\tfrac{1}{2}C_b\rho(\nabla\delta\phi)^2\}\,\mathrm{d}V<0. \quad (18\text{-}10)$$

The term in the form of a divergence vanishes since $\boldsymbol{v}_n$ and $\boldsymbol{v}_s$ have zero components perpendicular to the wall bounding the fluid. To satisfy (18-10) for all $\delta\phi$, the coefficient of $\delta\phi$ must vanish (extremum condition) and also $C_b\rho$ must be negative (stability requirement). This will be satisfied if

$$\nabla\cdot\rho[(\boldsymbol{k}+\nabla\phi_0)+\boldsymbol{C}_c\times\boldsymbol{r}/C_b]=0, \quad (18\text{-}11)$$

and

$$\rho>0. \quad (18\text{-}12)$$

From (16-2) and (16-9) we see that (18-11) is just the condition

$$\nabla\cdot\rho_s(\boldsymbol{v}_n-\boldsymbol{v}_s)=0,$$

which was derived in § 17 from the requirements of consistency of thermodynamics and hydrodynamics.

Thus for $\rho>0$ any superfluid velocity field which is stationary in the rotating reference frame, and satisfies $\nabla\times\boldsymbol{v}_s=0$, $\nabla\cdot\rho_s(\boldsymbol{v}_n-\boldsymbol{v}_s)=0$, is stable against small displacements from equilibrium *if the deviations of* $\boldsymbol{v}_s$ *from equilibrium take place at constant* ρ, ε_0, $\boldsymbol{k}$. That this is in general a valid assumption can be questioned from considering a case where the deviation of $\boldsymbol{v}_s$ from equilibrium corresponds to the small displacement of a vortex line. Then one finds that the term quadratic in $\delta\phi$ makes the integral in (18-10) negative infinity which is unphysical since it implies that a vortex can be neither formed or destroyed. The physical reason for this result is two-fold. First, in keeping ρ, ε_0, $\boldsymbol{k}$ fixed we have kept ρ_s fixed in the displacement, since $\rho_s=\rho_s(\rho,\varepsilon_0,k^2)$. Thus at the displaced location of the vortex line $\rho_s\neq 0$, in contradiction with (17-5). Second, in order to keep $\boldsymbol{k}$ fixed in this variation, there must appear singular changes in the circulation of $\boldsymbol{v}_n$ at the displaced and equilibrium locations of the vortex. Since $\boldsymbol{v}_n$ is regular in the equilibrium state the small displacement of a vortex at given ρ, ε_0, $\boldsymbol{k}$ cannot be regarded as a small deviation from equilibrium as was already suggested by the existence of the divergence of the entropy integral. Finally the Landau two fluid equations, which should be an excellent approximation to the behavior of the fluid in the region of equilibrium imply that $\boldsymbol{k}$ should

Notes p. 133

not remain invariant when a $\boldsymbol{v}_s$ vortex moves. For instance, in § 4 we saw that the circulation of $\boldsymbol{A} \equiv \boldsymbol{k}/s$ is *not* conserved when $\nabla \times \boldsymbol{v}_s \neq 0$ such as when a vortex is present. On the right hand side of (4-19) the term involving $\nabla \times \boldsymbol{v}_s$ leads to changes in the circulation of $\boldsymbol{A}$ which account for the flow of superfluid vortices.

Since in equilibrium $\boldsymbol{v}_n = \boldsymbol{\omega} \times \boldsymbol{r}$ has a definite value independent of $\boldsymbol{v}_s$ it is better to consider the dependence of the stability on $\boldsymbol{v}_s$, for $\boldsymbol{v}_n$ rather than $\boldsymbol{k}$ held fixed in the variation. The interplay between hydrodynamics and thermodynamics which led us to this conclusion is unique to He II and happens because the relative velocity $\boldsymbol{v}_n - \boldsymbol{v}_s$ is a thermodynamic as well as dynamic variable.

To investigate the stability for given $\boldsymbol{v}_n$, it is convenient to also take $\mu + \frac{1}{2}v_s^2 - \boldsymbol{v}_n \cdot \boldsymbol{v}_s$ and T as given. Differentiating and integrating the integrand of (16-7) and using (4-5,6) we obtain

$$\int \left[\int C_b \rho_s(\boldsymbol{v}_s - \boldsymbol{v}_n) \cdot \mathrm{d}\boldsymbol{v}_s\right] \mathrm{d}V = \text{maximum}, \tag{18-13}$$

where we have also made use of the equilibrium conditions (16-8,9,10). The inner integral in (18-13) is indefinite but in principle is well defined since with $T =$ constant, $\boldsymbol{v}_n = \boldsymbol{\omega} \times \boldsymbol{r}$ and μ determined by (16-10), ρ_s becomes a function of $\boldsymbol{v}_s$ alone. As $C_b < 0$, (18-13) becomes

$$\int \left[\int \rho_s \, \mathrm{d}(\tfrac{1}{2}v_s^2 - \boldsymbol{v}_n \cdot \boldsymbol{v}_s)\right] \mathrm{d}V = \text{minimum}. \tag{18-14}$$

The left hand side of (18-14) is often loosely called the free energy of the superfluid in a rotating bucket. If ρ_s can be taken as exactly incompressible then (18-14) can be written in the more transparent form

$$\int \left[\tfrac{1}{2}\rho_s v_s^2 - \boldsymbol{\omega} \cdot (\boldsymbol{r} \times \rho_s \boldsymbol{v}_s)\right] \mathrm{d}V = \text{minimum}, \tag{18-15}$$

however, as we will see (18-14,15) are not equivalent when one takes into account the requirement (17-5) that $\rho_s \to 0$ at the vortex line.

The region of integration in (18-14) is the *entire* volume of fluid. The vortex line itself is part of the fluid and will not make a divergent contribution. As we have seen the equation of state for ρ_s is such that it vanishes at the line.

Let us first consider variations in the free energy where the singularities stay fixed. In this case by varying ϕ ($\boldsymbol{v}_s = \nabla\phi$) by an arbitrary small amount $\delta\phi$ in each volume element, one finds again the extremum condition $\nabla \cdot \rho_s(\boldsymbol{v}_n - \boldsymbol{v}_s) = 0$.

For the more important case where the *locations* of the vortex singularities are varied let us write the 'free energy' F as a function of the

Notes p. 133

locations r_i of the ith vortex line (specializing here to the case of vortex lines parallel to the axis), then

$$F(r_i) = \int \{ \int \rho_s(r_i)\, \mathrm{d}\{\tfrac{1}{2}[v_s(r_i)]^2 - \boldsymbol{v}_n \cdot \boldsymbol{v}_s(r_i)\} \}\, \mathrm{d}V = \text{minimum}. \tag{18-16}$$

To satisfy (18-16) one must have for each vortex line

$$\frac{\partial F}{\partial \boldsymbol{r}_i} = 0, \qquad \text{or} \qquad \frac{\partial F}{\partial x_i} = \frac{\partial F}{\partial y_i} = 0, \tag{18-17}$$

so that the change in free energy with respect to a displacement of the line as a whole must vanish.

From (18-16) we find

$$\frac{\partial F}{\partial r_{i\alpha}} = \int \rho_s(\boldsymbol{v}_s - \boldsymbol{v}_n) \frac{\partial \boldsymbol{v}_s}{\partial r_{i\alpha}}\, \mathrm{d}V, \tag{18-18}$$

where the subscript α denotes the x, y components of r_i. By using $\boldsymbol{v}_s = \nabla\phi$, (18-18) becomes

$$\frac{\partial F}{\partial r_{i\alpha}} = \int \left\{ \nabla \cdot \left[\rho_s(\boldsymbol{v}_s - \boldsymbol{v}_n) \frac{\partial \phi}{\partial r_{i\alpha}} \right] - \frac{\partial \phi}{\partial r_{i\alpha}} \nabla \cdot \rho_s(\boldsymbol{v}_s - \boldsymbol{v}_n) \right\} \mathrm{d}V. \tag{18-19}$$

The first term on the right can be converted to an integral over the surface bounding the fluid for which it vanishes. Thus

$$\frac{\partial F}{\partial r_{i\alpha}} = -\int \frac{\partial \phi}{\partial r_{i\alpha}} \nabla \cdot \rho_s(\boldsymbol{v}_s - \boldsymbol{v}_n)\, \mathrm{d}V \tag{18-20}$$

and for the free energy to be an extremum with respect to variations in the location of the vortex line it is sufficient for $\boldsymbol{v}_s$ to obey the already derived restriction $\nabla \cdot \rho_s(\boldsymbol{v}_n - \boldsymbol{v}_s) = 0$, throughout the fluid. Since the volume of integration is the entire fluid one must satisfy this restriction even in the region of depleted ρ_s near the vortex lines.

In order for the free energy to be a minimum with respect to the location of the vortex line one must have

$$\frac{\partial^2 F}{\partial r_{i\alpha}\, \partial r_{i\beta}} \delta r_{i\alpha}\, \delta r_{i\beta} > 0 \tag{18-21}$$

for all displacements δr_i. From (18-20) we find that the second derivative of F is

$$\frac{\partial^2 F}{\partial r_{i\alpha}\, \partial r_{i\beta}} = -\int \frac{\partial \phi}{\partial r_{i\alpha}} \nabla \cdot \left[\frac{\partial}{\partial r_{i\beta}} \rho_s(\boldsymbol{v}_s - \boldsymbol{v}_n) \right] \mathrm{d}V, \tag{18-22}$$

Notes p. 133

where after taking the derivatives all quantities are to be evaluated in the equilibrium state. As we will see (18-22) is finite and well defined so that under the above conditions a small displacement of the vortex does lead to a small change in the entropy integral (16-7). Equation (18-22) should be compared with the second derivative of F for given ρ, ε_0, $\boldsymbol{k}$:

$$\left(\frac{\partial^2 F}{\partial r_{i\alpha}\,\partial r_{i\beta}}\right)_{\rho,\varepsilon_0,k} = -\int \frac{\partial \phi}{\partial r_{i\alpha}} \nabla \cdot \rho \frac{\partial \boldsymbol{v}_s}{\partial r_{i\beta}} \mathrm{d}V, \tag{18-23}$$

which follows from (18-10) or (16-7) and which we have remarked is divergent since ρ need not vanish at the vortex.

For a given number of vortex lines located so that they rotate with the normal fluid (18-21) provides an additional constraint on the equilibrium state expressing that it will be stable against *small* perturbations of the vortices. In general, stable configurations will exist for different numbers of vortex lines in the rotating fluid. In this case the number appropriate to the stable equilibrium state must be determined from a comparison of the value of F as given by (18-14) for the different configurations.

However, in applying (18-14) to find the most stable number of vortex lines it is important to realize that *additional* constraints on $\boldsymbol{v}_s$ are necessary because otherwise one always finds that solid body rotation is the most stable configuration. To illustrate this first consider the case where there are a number of parallel vortex lines in the superfluid. If one would vary the strength (circulation) of the vortices as well as their number then since the lines move with the normal fluid it is easy to see that a dense uniform distribution of very weak vortex lines (which induce a velocity field arbitrarily close to solid body rotation) will minimize the integral in (18-14). So at this point we again introduce the quantization hypothesis of Onsager (see § 10) as a restriction on the circulation of any vortex lines present. Since $\nabla \times \boldsymbol{v}_s = 0$ in equilibrium it is consistent with the two fluid equations and thermodynamics to impose the quantization condition. Had it not been possible to have $\nabla \times \boldsymbol{v}_s = 0$ in equilibrium, then there would be no room to impose a quantization condition on the two fluid equations. These remarks are a consequence of Stokes' theorem which says that $\nabla \times \boldsymbol{v}_s$ must be zero in a region where $\oint \boldsymbol{v}_s \cdot \mathrm{d}\ell$ is independent of path as occurs when it is quantized.

In the case of a number of cylindrical vortex sheets as envisaged by London [17] and Landau [18] one also finds that solid body rotation is most stable unless an additional restriction on $\boldsymbol{v}_s$ is imposed. To escape

Notes p. 133

this conclusion, London proposed that the circulation of the superfluid in the nth cylinder is nh/m consistent with the Onsager quantization. By varying the number and positions of the vortex sheets he finds a critical value of ω equal to $2\hbar/md^2$ below which $\boldsymbol{v}_s = 0$ and for increasing ω an approach to solid body rotation. Landau on the other hand introduces a surface energy per unit area for each sheet which must be added to the integral in (18-14) and which is kept fixed. For increasing ω he finds a gradual change of the motion of the superfluid from rest to solid body rotation.

There is no conclusive *experimental* evidence as to whether the equilibrium state of rotating He II has vortex lines or vortex sheets. However, since various microscopic models suggest vortex lines, and since in superconductors in an external field (which is mathematically analogous to rotation) one definitely observes flux lines, we will from here on consider only the vortex line solution.

To each value of $\boldsymbol{\omega}$ there is now a unique and discrete distribution of quantized vortex lines satisfying (18-14). The arrangements have been worked out by Vinen [20], Fetter [21] and Hess [22], who for simplicity assume that each vortex has one quantum h/m of circulation. The most striking result is that there exists a critical angular velocity

$$\omega_{cr} = (4\hbar/md^2)\log(d\sqrt{e}/2a) \tag{18-24}$$

below which the most stable configuration is $\boldsymbol{v}_s = 0$. In Eq. (18-24) d is the diameter of the rotating bucket and again a is a measure of the radius of the region, near the vortex line, in which ρ_s is depleted.

To derive (18-24) we must calculate the free energy of a quantized vortex in He II. The angular velocity at which it becomes less than the free energy of no vortex is ω_{cr}.

To calculate the free energy one first assumes a simple form for the equation of state for ρ_s. Since $\mu + \frac{1}{2}(\boldsymbol{v}_n - \boldsymbol{v}_s)^2$, T, $\boldsymbol{v}_n$ are given, ρ_s becomes a function of $\frac{1}{2}v_s^2 - \boldsymbol{v}_n \cdot \boldsymbol{v}_s$. We chose this function so that it vanishes when the velocity is too large and is otherwise a constant $\rho_{s,0}$:

$$\rho_s = \rho_{s,0}\,\theta[\gamma^2/2a^2 - (\tfrac{1}{2}v_s^2 - \boldsymbol{v}_n \cdot \boldsymbol{v}_s)], \tag{18-25}$$

where θ is the step function. According to (18-25) the core is a line of constant $\frac{1}{2}v_s^2 - \boldsymbol{v}_n \cdot \boldsymbol{v}_s$ and thus strictly speaking will not be circular, so a is to be interpreted as the mean core radius. When one makes the generally valid approximation that $\boldsymbol{v}_n \cdot \boldsymbol{v}_s$ is negligible compared to $\frac{1}{2}v_s^2$

Notes p. 133

at the core then (18-25) simply says that $\rho_s = 0$ for $|\boldsymbol{r} - \boldsymbol{r}_1| < a$ which is what is meant by the core radius a.

In the spirit of the two fluid theory Eq. (18-25) can be written without any reference to γ^2/a^2. By making the substitution $\gamma^2/a^2 = \frac{1}{2}u_1^2$ (which is valid when $a \approx 1$ Å) in (18-25) one would obtain ρ_s entirely as a function of the thermohydrodynamic properties of the superfluid. Indeed it seems reasonable that the compressibility depends upon the sound velocity.

Substituting (18-25) into (18-14) we find

$$F = \rho_{s,0} \int (\tfrac{1}{2}v_s^2 - \boldsymbol{v}_n \cdot \boldsymbol{v}_s - \gamma^2/2a^2)\, \theta[\gamma^2/2a^2 - (\tfrac{1}{2}v_s^2 - \boldsymbol{v}_n \cdot \boldsymbol{v}_s)]\, \mathrm{d}V + C, \tag{18-26}$$

where C is a constant of integration which we chose so that the free energy of no vortex (i.e., $\boldsymbol{v}_s = 0$) vanishes:

$$C = \rho_{s,0}(\gamma^2/2a^2)V, \tag{18-27}$$

where $V = \frac{1}{4}\pi \ell d^2$ is the total volume, ℓ being the height of the bucket. For one vortex (18-26) with (18-27) yields

$$F = \rho_{s,0} \int (\tfrac{1}{2}v_s^2 - \boldsymbol{v}_n \cdot \boldsymbol{v}_s)\, \theta[\gamma^2/2a^2 - (\tfrac{1}{2}v_s^2 - \boldsymbol{v}_n \cdot \boldsymbol{v}_s)]\, \mathrm{d}V + \tfrac{1}{2}\rho_{s,0}\gamma^2\pi\ell, \tag{18-28}$$

where we have used $\pi a^2 \ell$ for the volume of the core. Since the core is not strictly circular this brings in an error of order

$$a/(\tfrac{1}{2}d - r_1), \tag{18-29}$$

which is very small. The superfluid velocity $\boldsymbol{v}_s$ will not simply be inversely proportional to the distance from the vortex line since for an off-center vortex this would violate the boundary condition that the perpendicular component of $\boldsymbol{v}_s$ vanish at the boundary. The appropriate velocity (assuming $\nabla \cdot \boldsymbol{v}_s = 0$) is obtained by superimposing on the vortex of strength γ located at $\boldsymbol{r}_i = (r_i, \theta_i)$, an 'image' of strength $-\gamma$ located at $(d^2/4r_i, \theta_i) \equiv \boldsymbol{r}_i'$, where we use polar coordinates so that r_i is the distance of vortex i from the axis of rotation and θ_i its angle as measured from the x axis. In this way the velocity field of an off-center vortex is

$$\boldsymbol{v}_s = \frac{\gamma}{|\boldsymbol{r} - \boldsymbol{r}_1|}\,\hat{\boldsymbol{e}}_{\Theta_1} - \frac{\gamma}{|\boldsymbol{r} - \boldsymbol{r}_1'|}\,\hat{\boldsymbol{e}}_{\Theta_1'}, \tag{18-30}$$

where $\hat{\boldsymbol{e}}_{\Theta_1}$ and $\hat{\boldsymbol{e}}_{\Theta_1'}$ are unit vectors circulating the vortex and its image respectively. In Cartesian coordinates (18-30) becomes

Notes p. 133

$$\boldsymbol{v}_{\mathrm{s}} = \frac{\gamma\{(x-x_1)\hat{\boldsymbol{e}}_y-(y-y_1)\hat{\boldsymbol{e}}_x\}}{|\boldsymbol{r}-\boldsymbol{r}_1|^2} - \frac{\gamma\{[x-(d^2x_1/4r_1^2)]\hat{\boldsymbol{e}}_y-[y-(d^2y_1/4r_1^2)]\hat{\boldsymbol{e}}_x\}}{|\boldsymbol{r}-\boldsymbol{r}_1'|^2}. \tag{18-31}$$

One easily verifies that (18-31) satisfies $\oint \boldsymbol{v}_{\mathrm{s}} \cdot \mathrm{d}\boldsymbol{\ell} = 2\pi\gamma$ and $\nabla \cdot \boldsymbol{v}_{\mathrm{s}} = 0$ for $r < \frac{1}{2}d$ and that the perpendicular component of $\boldsymbol{v}_{\mathrm{s}}$ vanishes at $r = \frac{1}{2}d$.

Due to the Kelvin circulation theorem (§ 4) the vortex line at $\boldsymbol{r}_i$ must move with the local velocity of the superfluid at the core. For one vortex off center the only contribution to a velocity perpendicular to the core comes from its image and from (18-30) is given by

$$\gamma r_1/(\tfrac{1}{4}d^2 - r_1^2) \tag{18-32}$$

and is normal to the line joining the vortex and its image. The Kelvin theorem does not apply to the image since it is outside the fluid. From (18-32) we see that an off-center vortex rotates about the axis of the bucket at an angular velocity

$$\gamma/(\tfrac{1}{4}d^2 - r_1^2). \tag{18-33}$$

Writing $v_{\mathrm{s}}^2 = \nabla \cdot (\phi \nabla \phi)$ since $\nabla^2 \phi = 0$ when $\nabla \cdot \boldsymbol{v}_{\mathrm{s}} = 0$, which we assume, we find

$$F = \rho_{\mathrm{s},0} \int \theta[\gamma^2/2a^2 - (\tfrac{1}{2}v_{\mathrm{s}}^2 - \boldsymbol{v}_{\mathrm{n}} \cdot \boldsymbol{v}_{\mathrm{s}})] \nabla \cdot (\tfrac{1}{2}\phi\nabla\phi - \phi\boldsymbol{\omega} \times \boldsymbol{r})\,\mathrm{d}V + \tfrac{1}{2}\rho_{\mathrm{s},0}\gamma^2\pi\ell. \tag{18-34}$$

The volume integral of a divergence multiplied by the step function can be converted to an integral over the surface bounding the fluid plus core; but the surface must include a branch cut, as is indicated in Fig. 20, since ϕ is not single valued. As the components of $\nabla\phi$ and $\boldsymbol{\omega} \times \boldsymbol{r}$ perpendicular to the physical boundary vanish the only contribution to the surface integral comes from the branch cut. Denoting the values of ϕ on the upper and lower part of the cut by ϕ_+, ϕ_- (18-34) becomes

$$F = \rho_{\mathrm{s},0}\ell \int_{r_1+a}^{\frac{1}{2}d} (\phi_+ - \phi_-)(\tfrac{1}{2}\boldsymbol{v}_{\mathrm{s}} - \boldsymbol{\omega} \times \boldsymbol{r}) \cdot \hat{\boldsymbol{e}}_y\,\mathrm{d}r + \tfrac{1}{2}\rho_{\mathrm{s},0}\gamma^2\pi\ell, \tag{18-35}$$

where we have oriented the branch cut so that it is parallel to the x axis and have used the fact that $\nabla\phi$ and $\boldsymbol{v}_{\mathrm{n}}$ are single valued. Furthermore the contribution from the integral around the core has been neglected. For a circular core this is easily verified; due to the small non-circularity of the core the error is again of order (18-29). The phase ϕ will have a

Notes p. 133

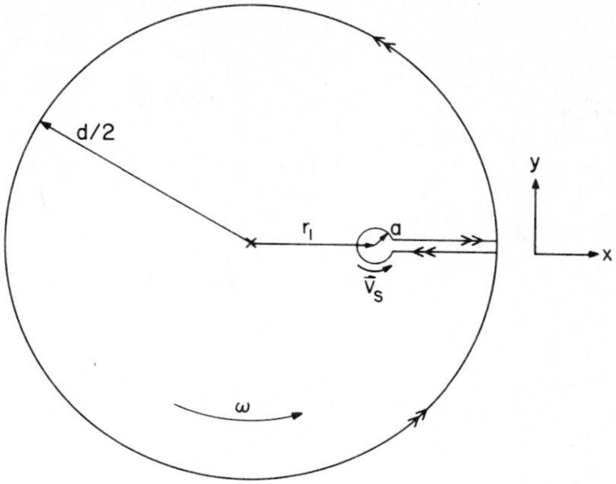

Fig. 20. The contour of integration used for evaluating the free energy is indicated by the double arrows. The direction of rotation $\boldsymbol{\omega}$ and the velocity $\boldsymbol{v}_s$ of the superfluid near the core are indicated.

contribution from the image and the real vortex. That of the image is single valued. Hence $\phi_+ - \phi_-$ is determined only by the real vortex. The velocity potential of the real vortex is $\phi = \gamma\Theta_1$ where Θ_1 is the angle as measured about a coordinate system located at the core. As we have chosen the branch cut to lie on a line of constant Θ_1 we find

$$\phi_+ - \phi_- = 2\pi\gamma \tag{18-36}$$

and substituting (18-30) for $\boldsymbol{v}_s$ we find

$$F = \pi\gamma^2\rho_{s,0}\ell\left\{\log\left[\frac{\frac{1}{4}d^2 - r_1^2}{(d/2\sqrt{\mathrm{e}})a}\right] - \frac{\omega}{\gamma}(\tfrac{1}{4}d^2 - r_1^2)\right\}, \tag{18-37}$$

where the $\sqrt{\mathrm{e}}$ accounts for the last term on the right side of (18-35) and in (18-37) we have neglected small terms of order a/d.

When the vortex is on the order of a core radius from the wall F as given by (18-37) goes to zero (which is the free energy of $\boldsymbol{v}_s = 0$) as one would expect, since as the vortex approaches the wall it is cancelled by its image. For $\frac{1}{2}d - a < r_1 < \frac{1}{2}d$, F as given by (18-37) becomes negative. This is of no concern since our entire derivation of (18-37) hinged on the validity of (18-29) being small, and the core being almost circular.

Except for the unimportant $\sqrt{\mathrm{e}}$ in the denominator (18-37) is in

Notes p. 133

agreement with the literature [22]. This is surprising since if one takes a strictly circular core

$$\rho_s = \rho_{s,0}\,\theta(|\boldsymbol{r} - \boldsymbol{r}_1| - a) \tag{18-38}$$

as is always assumed, one would find that the free energy is one-half of that given by (18-37)! As a discussion of this point yields an insight into some of the fine points in the thermohydrodynamics of quantized vortices we elaborate below.

First note that with ρ_s given by (18-38) one cannot perform directly the indefinite integration in (18-14), so we will rather demonstrate that $\partial F/\partial \boldsymbol{r}_1$ for (18-38) is half of $\partial F/\partial \boldsymbol{r}_1$ for (18-25). From (18-20) and $\nabla \cdot \boldsymbol{v}_s = 0$ we find

$$\frac{\partial F}{\partial \boldsymbol{r}_1} = -\int \frac{\partial \phi}{\partial \boldsymbol{r}_1}\,[(\boldsymbol{v}_s - \boldsymbol{v}_n)\cdot \nabla \rho_s]\,\mathrm{d}V. \tag{18-39}$$

From (18-38) we find

$$\nabla \rho_s = \rho_{s,0}\delta(|\boldsymbol{r} - \boldsymbol{r}_1| - a)(\boldsymbol{r} - \boldsymbol{r}_1)/|\boldsymbol{r} - \boldsymbol{r}_1|, \tag{18-40}$$

so that $\boldsymbol{v}_s \cdot \nabla \rho_s$ will have a contribution only from the image. The delta function enables one to transform the volume integral into one over the surface $|\boldsymbol{r} - \boldsymbol{r}_1| = a$. At this surface the dominant contribution to $\partial \phi/\partial \boldsymbol{r}_1$ will come from ignoring the image [provided (18-29) is small] so that

$$\partial \phi/\partial \boldsymbol{r}_1 = -\partial \phi/\partial \boldsymbol{r} = -(\gamma/|\boldsymbol{r} - \boldsymbol{r}_1|)\hat{\boldsymbol{e}}_{\Theta_1}, \tag{18-41}$$

where $\hat{\boldsymbol{e}}_{\Theta_1}$ is a unit vector circling the core. Using the relations

$$\int_{x_0-\varepsilon}^{x_0+\varepsilon} \delta[f(x) - f(x_0)]\,\mathrm{d}x = |f'(x_0)|^{-1}, \qquad \varepsilon > 0, \tag{18-42}$$

$$\begin{aligned} \hat{\boldsymbol{e}}_{r_1} &= (\boldsymbol{r} - \boldsymbol{r}_1)/|\boldsymbol{r} - \boldsymbol{r}_1| = \hat{\boldsymbol{e}}_x \cos\Theta_1 + \hat{\boldsymbol{e}}_y \sin\Theta_1, \\ \hat{\boldsymbol{e}}_{\Theta_1} &= -\hat{\boldsymbol{e}}_x \sin\Theta_1 + \hat{\boldsymbol{e}}_y \cos\Theta_1, \end{aligned} \tag{18-43}$$

one is led to an expression for $\partial F/\partial \boldsymbol{r}_1$ which is half what follows from (18-37).

The origin of this factor can be understood immediately by a partial integration of (18-16) to obtain (ignoring an integration constant)

$$F = \int \rho_s(\tfrac{1}{2}v_s^2 - \boldsymbol{v}_n\cdot\boldsymbol{v}_s)\,\mathrm{d}V - \int\left[\int(\tfrac{1}{2}v_s^2 - \boldsymbol{v}_n\cdot\boldsymbol{v}_s)\,\mathrm{d}\rho_s\right]\mathrm{d}V \tag{18-44}$$

Notes p. 133

whether one uses (18-38) or (18-25) for ρ_s the first term on the right side of (18-44) will have the same value. But the other contribution to F will be crucially affected. This happens because $d\rho_s$ is enormous at just those points where $\boldsymbol{v}_s$ is largest. If following (18-25) one says that the core is a line of constant $\frac{1}{2}v_s^2 - \boldsymbol{v}_n \cdot \boldsymbol{v}_s$ then by integrating around the core the second term on the right side of (18-44) vanishes. If, however, the core is strictly circular then $\frac{1}{2}v_s^2 - \boldsymbol{v}_n \cdot \boldsymbol{v}_s$ will not be constant at the core and the term in question will be equal to precisely half of the first term. Previous calculations using circular cores have agreed with (18-37) since in addition they always ignored the second term on the right side of (18-44).

This term represents the free energy required to make ρ_s drop to zero at the vortex line. Based on the two fluid theory the core should be a line of constant $\frac{1}{2}v_s^2 - \boldsymbol{v}_n \cdot \boldsymbol{v}_s$ and thus the factor of $\frac{1}{2}$ resulting from a strictly circular core would seem to be out of place. However, one could in principle investigate this question by experiments on the critical velocity in geometries consisting of both free (unpinned), and pinned (wrapped around a wire), vortex lines.

Taking the core to be a line of constant $\frac{1}{2}v_s^2 - \boldsymbol{v}_n \cdot \boldsymbol{v}_s$ we are thus led to (14-1) an expression fundamental to the resolution of the rotation paradox.

From (18-37) we see that a single vortex will be located at an extremum of the entropy (free energy) and hence its motion will be stationary in the rotating system if

$$\partial F/\partial r_1 = 2\pi\gamma\rho_{s,0}\ell[\omega r_1 - \gamma r_1/(\tfrac{1}{4}d^2 - r_1^2)] = 0, \qquad (18\text{-}45)$$

which is just the condition that the normal fluid velocity at the core equal the velocity of the vortex as is given in (18-32). Equation (18-45) has the two solutions

$$r_1^2 = \tfrac{1}{4}d^2 - \gamma/\omega, \qquad (18\text{-}46)$$

$$r_1 = 0. \qquad (18\text{-}47)$$

In order for (18-46) to make sense ω must be larger than $4\hbar/md^2$, but if this is the case we find by differentiating (18-37) again that this extremum is a maximum and hence unstable. Although a vortex located at (18-46) will be rotating with the normal fluid and hence an extremum of F, it will be unstable. The solution (18-47) corresponds to a local minimum of F only if the bucket rotates faster than $4\hbar/md^2$. Thus a

Notes p. 133

single vortex can be stable against small perturbations only when it is on the axis of a bucket rotating faster than $4\hbar/md^2$. These comments are made clear by Fig. 21. In this case its free energy is

$$F_1 = \pi\gamma^2 \ell \rho_{s,0} [\log(d\sqrt{e}/2a) - \omega d^2/4\gamma]. \tag{18-48}$$

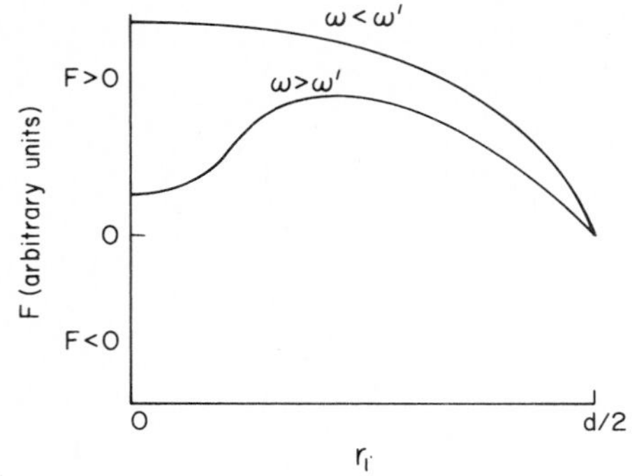

Fig. 21. The free energy of one quantized vortex as a function of its distance r_1 from the axis of rotation; $\omega' \equiv 4\hbar/md^2$ is the minimum angular velocity so that a vortex on the axis will be stable against small perturbations.

Next we consider the problem as to when one vortex will be stable compared with no vortices. As no vortices imply $F = 0$ one finds that one vortex at the center has a lower value of the free energy than no vortex if

$$\omega > \omega_{cr} = (4\hbar/md^2)\log(d\sqrt{e}/2a). \tag{18-49}$$

For $d = 0.2$ cm and $a \approx 1.2$ Å one finds $\omega_{cr} \approx 0.25\ \text{sec}^{-1}$. In Fig. 22 are graphed the free energies F_0, F_1, F_2 of zero, one, and two vortex lines at their stable locations as a function of ω. Of course one and two vortex lines can be stable against small perturbations only for high enough ω and this stable region is indicated schematically by the solid lines. For the lowest ω we see that $\boldsymbol{v}_s = 0$ has the lowest free energy and is the stable equilibrium state. At ω_{cr} the states with a vortex at the axis and $\boldsymbol{v}_s = 0$ become degenerate and for higher ω the state with a vortex at the center is most stable. For still higher ω another transition is reached at which two vortices, located symmetrically about the center, become most stable and so on. In this way one arrives at a relation between the number of vortex lines and speed of rotation which obeys

Notes p. 133

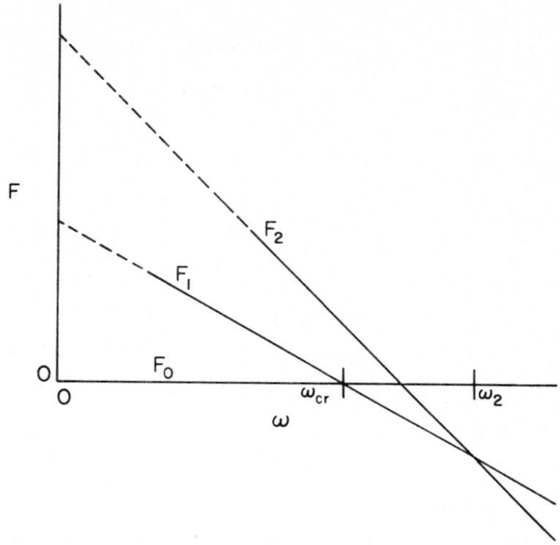

Fig. 22. The free energies F_0, F_1, F_2 of zero, one and two quantized vortices located in the stable positions, as a function of ω. The dotted lines indicate the extrapolation of F to small angular velocities where the vortices are still located so that they move with the normal fluid but are unstable.

a quantum step structure such as is represented in Fig. 23. Thus the macroscopic properties of the system show quantum jumps which perhaps can be called quantum phase transitions.

Before discussing the experiment which verifies the quantum step structure we wish to discuss the curious situation in which $\boldsymbol{v}_s = 0$ ($\omega < \omega_{cr}$). As all the velocities and accelerations appearing in the

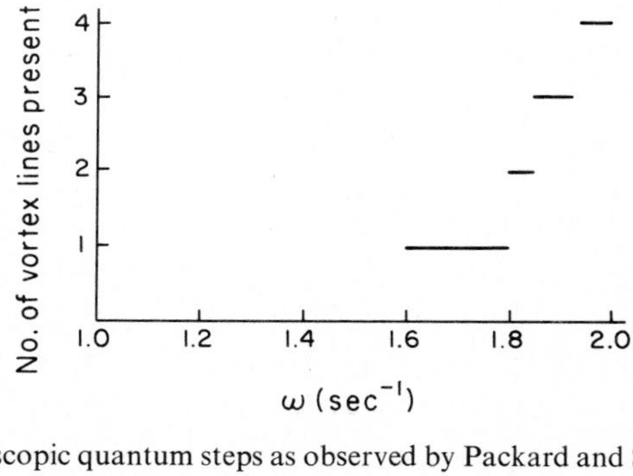

Fig. 23. The macroscopic quantum steps as observed by Packard and Sanders; $d = 0.1$ cm.

Notes p. 133

equations of motion are naturally written with respect to an observer situated in an absolute inertial system our consistency condition $\nabla \times \boldsymbol{v}_s = 0$ must be interpreted as requiring that the curl of the superfluid velocity field vanish with respect to an absolute inertial system. Thus when $\boldsymbol{v}_s = 0$ is most stable, the superfluid will in this state be at rest with respect to an absolute inertial system. In this way one can consider the following thought experiment which uses the irrotationality of the superfluid to demonstrate that the Earth is not an inertial system. Imagine a bucket of liquid helium situated at the north pole for simplicity and initially in the normal state, $T > T_\lambda$, so that the entire fluid is at rest with respect to the Earth but of course in solid body rotation with respect to an inertial system. If the bucket is cooled to $T < T_\lambda$ the supercomponent comes to rest with respect to the inertial system because the angular velocity of the Earth is less than ω_{cr} if $d \lesssim 20$ cm. In doing this it must, by conservation of angular momentum, give up angular momentum to the walls of the bucket which will cause it to rotate with respect to the Earth demonstrating that the Earth is not an inertial system. One might thus refer to He II as a *quantum* Foucault pendulum, and the condition $\nabla \times \boldsymbol{v}_s = 0$ is a *quantum* Mach paradox since it is a quantum preference for the inertial system. No experiments have yet had the sensitivity to see these effects.

The quantum step structure of rotation was observed by Packard and Sanders [13] who made use of the fact that free electrons in He II are in bubbles (of radius 15 Å) which are attracted to and captured by vortex cores. This happens because the Bernoulli effect reduces the pressure (see § 5) at the vortex core. Assuming that each vortex line goes from the bottom to the top of the rotating bucket and hence captures the same number of electrons (which were first provided by exposure to a radioactive source) they determined the number of vortices present at a given ω by discharging the trapped electrons in a manner that enabled them to be counted. Their results are shown in Fig. 23. They are in qualitative agreement with the predictions based on (18-15) plus quantization but in general strong metastability was observed. In the experiments of Reppy and Lane [7], which demonstrated that the superfluid participated in the rotations, effects of metastability were also observed. For instance at speeds of rotation where a hundred vortices should be present, they found (though rarely) $\boldsymbol{v}_s = 0$.

These metastability effects are to be expected since the number of vortex lines present is a property of the He II that follows from thermo-

Notes p. 133

dynamic stability. If the entrance of the vortex lines is to be viewed as a quantum phase transition then perhaps the metastability is to be viewed as the quantum analogue of the supercooling of a saturated vapor.

Evidence that the quantized vortex lines extend from the bottom to the top of the rotating bucket is provided by the experiment of Donnelly et al. [23]. They measured the time of flight of a pulse of ions, from the bottom to the top of a bucket of rotating helium, under the influence of an electric field parallel to the axis of rotation. In response to a single pulse at the bottom two pulses were observed at the top. One of these was interpreted as being due to free ions which were not influenced by the vortex cores and in fact had transit times consistent with other experiments [24] on the motion of ions in stationary He II. The flight times of both pulses were proportional to the height of the bucket, and independent of ω. Thus the second pulse was interpreted as being due to ions trapped to and travelling along quantized vortex lines that extended from the bottom to the top of the bucket, a distance of over 5 cm. The difference in flight times might for instance be due to a variation of the effective mobility with p and $(\boldsymbol{v}_n - \boldsymbol{v}_s)^2$.

In this section we have first investigated the stability conditions relating to the variations in the internal variables ρ, ε_0, $\boldsymbol{k}$ for given $\boldsymbol{v}_s$ and then the stability of flow as $\boldsymbol{v}_s$ is varied for given other variables. In general there can exist cross terms between variations of $\boldsymbol{v}_s$ and the other variables which we now take into account.

First we must decide which will be the complete independent set of variables. We saw before that when vortex singularities are considered, in order for a small displacement of a vortex to lead to a small change in 'entropy' (16-7) one cannot work with the variables, ρ, ε_0, $\boldsymbol{k}$, $\boldsymbol{v}_s$. We found that by formulating the stability condition in terms of $\mu + \frac{1}{2}v_s^2 - \boldsymbol{v}_n \cdot \boldsymbol{v}_s$, T, $\boldsymbol{v}_n$, $\boldsymbol{v}_s$, one could arrive at a well behaved variation of the entropy as the vortex location is changed. This would seem to suggest that our discussion of the cross terms be based upon the second set of variables. However, we will here consider the stability requirements associated with variations, where $\delta \boldsymbol{v}_s$ is small (and thus the singularities are fixed). Then all variations of the entropy are well defined and it is mathematically immaterial which set of variables is used.

The second order variation of the 'entropy' (16-7) is

$$\int \frac{1}{v}\left[\frac{\partial^2 s}{\partial v^2}\frac{(\delta v)^2}{2} + \frac{\partial^2 s}{\partial \varepsilon_0^2}\frac{(\delta \varepsilon_0)^2}{2} + \frac{\partial^2 s}{\partial v\, \partial \varepsilon_0}\delta v\, \delta \varepsilon_0 + \frac{\partial^2 s}{\partial k_i\, \partial k_j}\frac{\delta k_i\, \delta k_j}{2} + \right.$$

Notes p. 133

$$+ \frac{\partial^2 s}{\partial \varepsilon_0 \, \partial k_i} \delta \varepsilon_0 \, \delta k_i + \frac{\partial^2 s}{\partial v \, \partial k_i} \delta v \, \delta k_i + C_\mathrm{b} \frac{\delta \boldsymbol{v}_\mathrm{s} \cdot \delta \boldsymbol{v}_\mathrm{s}}{2}$$

$$+ C_\mathrm{b} \delta \boldsymbol{k} \cdot \delta \boldsymbol{v}_\mathrm{s} - \frac{C_\mathrm{b}}{v} \left(\boldsymbol{v}_\mathrm{s} + \boldsymbol{k} + \frac{\boldsymbol{C}_\mathrm{c} \times \boldsymbol{r}}{C_\mathrm{b}} \right) \delta v \, \delta \boldsymbol{v}_\mathrm{s} \Bigg] \mathrm{d}V < 0. \quad (18\text{-}50)$$

As we have emphasized $\delta \boldsymbol{v}_\mathrm{s}$ is not free to vary by an arbitrary amount in each volume element. Since $\nabla \times \boldsymbol{v}_\mathrm{s} = 0$, it is proper to say that ϕ, ($\boldsymbol{v}_\mathrm{s} = \nabla \phi$) is free to vary in each volume element. Thus although $\boldsymbol{v}_\mathrm{s}$ is a vector it is characterized by one and not three independent variables. Now $\delta \boldsymbol{v}_\mathrm{s} \cdot \delta \boldsymbol{v}_\mathrm{s}$ is a scalar and therefore while $\delta \boldsymbol{v}_\mathrm{s}$ cannot assume arbitrary values one expects that $\delta \boldsymbol{v}_\mathrm{s} \cdot \delta \boldsymbol{v}_\mathrm{s}$ can vary independently throughout the fluid. For this reason we require that the integrand in (18-50) be a negative definite quadratic form, for stability.

Setting

$$s'(\varepsilon_0, v, \boldsymbol{k}, \boldsymbol{v}_\mathrm{s}) = s(\varepsilon_0, v, \boldsymbol{k}) + \tfrac{1}{2} C_\mathrm{b} v_\mathrm{s}^2 + C_\mathrm{b} \boldsymbol{k} \cdot \boldsymbol{v}_\mathrm{s} + C_\mathrm{b} v [\rho_\mathrm{s} (\boldsymbol{v}_\mathrm{n} - \boldsymbol{v}_\mathrm{s})]_0 \cdot \boldsymbol{v}_\mathrm{s}, \quad (18\text{-}51)$$

where $[\,]_0$ denotes the equilibrium value, (18-50) becomes

$$\int \delta^2 s' \, \mathrm{d}V < 0, \quad (18\text{-}52)$$

where $\delta^2 s'$ denotes the variation of s' to second order in the deviation from equilibrium. Equation (18-52) is in the form for which theorem (18-7) can be applied. It is found in a straightforward manner that in addition to (18-8,12) one must have for stability

$$\frac{\rho_\mathrm{s}}{\rho} + 2\rho_\mathrm{s} w^2 \left[\frac{\partial(\rho_\mathrm{n}/\rho)}{\partial p} \right]_{w^2, T} - w^2 \left[\frac{\partial(\rho_\mathrm{n}/\rho)}{\partial(w^2/2)} \right]_{p,T} + (\rho_\mathrm{s} w)^2 \left[\frac{\partial v}{\partial p} \right]_{w^2, T} > 0, \quad (18\text{-}53)$$

$$\frac{\rho_\mathrm{n}}{\rho} < 1, \quad (18\text{-}54)$$

where $\boldsymbol{w} \equiv \boldsymbol{v}_\mathrm{n} - \boldsymbol{v}_\mathrm{s}$.

By thermodynamic manipulations (18-53) can be shown to *imply* the more transparent stability requirements

$$\frac{\rho_\mathrm{n}}{\rho} + w^2 \left[\frac{\partial(\rho_\mathrm{n}/\rho)}{\partial(w^2/2)} \right]_{p,T} < 1, \quad (18\text{-}55)$$

$$\left[\frac{\rho_\mathrm{s}}{\rho} (\boldsymbol{v}_\mathrm{n} - \boldsymbol{v}_\mathrm{s}) \right]^2 < \left[\frac{\partial p}{\partial \rho} \right]_{w^2, T}. \quad (18\text{-}56)$$

Notes p. 133

In fact (18-55), (18-56) can be derived directly from the necessary but not sufficient requirements that the separate submatrices formed by $\delta \boldsymbol{k}$, $\delta \boldsymbol{v}_s$ and $\delta v\, \delta \boldsymbol{v}_s$ in (18-50) be negative definite.

The condition (18-56) can be used to obtain an idea of the minimum radius of the core of a vortex. Since $v_n - v_s$ increases without limit near the line ρ_s must drop to zero to satisfy (18-56). This is a more precise statement of the requirement already discussed in § 17. If we use the speed of first sound squared for $\partial p / \partial \rho$ we find that the minimum core radius is that at which the superfluid velocity is on the order of the speed of sound, and for a quantized vortex this turns out to be about 1 Å which is very close to the measured core size in say the vortex ring experiments.

Finally we comment that a consideration of the cross terms that result from variations of $\mu + \frac{1}{2}v_s^2 - \boldsymbol{v}_n \cdot \boldsymbol{v}_s$, T, $\boldsymbol{v}_n$ and a displacement of a singularity lead to no new stability requirements in addition to those presented above.

19 Is the Superfluid Flow Merely Flow at Zero Viscosity?

As F. London [17] has always emphasized the restriction $\nabla \times \boldsymbol{v}_s = 0$ is much more stringent than the stipulation that the super component flow without friction. To see this consider two different means by which the state with He II contained in a rotating bucket can be reached. In one way liquid helium with $T > T_\lambda$ can be cooled to $T < T_\lambda$ while rotating. In the other way liquid helium at rest is cooled to $T < T_\lambda$ and then the vessel is rotated.

If the flow of superfluid were simply characterized by the absence of viscosity then one finds that for the first procedure the supercomponent holds onto its solid body rotation, whereas by the second procedure it would remain at rest (for simplicity we take $\omega < \omega_{cr}$). So for a superfluid characterized only by zero viscosity one finds that the final state depends upon the state of the system when T_λ is crossed.

In the course of this chapter we have found that the two fluid thermo-hydrodynamics lead to a unique stable state for He II contained in a rotating bucket. In particular we have found that $\nabla \times \boldsymbol{v}_s = 0$ which rules out the possibility of the supercomponent holding onto the solid body rotation.

Notes p. 133

That the rotating liquid helium drops into a state with $\nabla \times \boldsymbol{v}_s = 0$ on cooling through T_λ was verified by the experiment of Hess and Fairbank [10] who actually measured the angular momentum of He II contained in a small bucket rotating at $\omega \lesssim \omega_{cr}$. Their results determined an ω_{cr} in agreement with (18-24) above which the angular momentum of the superfluid was non-zero, but their measurements were not accurate enough to resolve a step structure.

20 *Resolution of the Rotation Paradox*

In order to understand the flow of the superfluid in narrow capillaries one says that the superfluid experiences no shear stresses. This results in conservation of superfluid circulation yet experiments do show that the superfluid comes into rotation. This is the 'rotation paradox' which motivated the discussion in this chapter.

A partial resolution of the rotation paradox is already provided by the observation in § 18 that the rotation of the super component in equilibrium is not like that which would follow from viscous stresses (i.e., solid body rotation) but instead is a more complicated rotation about vortex singularities. Furthermore the early experiments which found that the superfluid rotated were performed at angular velocities much greater than ω_{cr}. In this case the minimum of the 'free energy' will be achieved by a uniform distribution of quantized vortex lines which will approximate solid body rotation. The density (number per unit area) n_0 of vortex lines in this case can be calculated by equating the circulation of the vortex lines to the circulation of the solid body rotation which they approximate, or for a contour at distance r from the axis of rotation:

$$\pi r^2 n_0 h/m = 2\pi r^2 \omega,$$

so that

$$n_0 = 2\omega m/h. \tag{20-1}$$

But even if this is the means by which the superfluid component rotates one can well ask again how its twisting into rotation and acquiring circulation can be consistent with the conservation of circulation of the superfluid velocity. By a careful application of the Kelvin theorem one finds that it need not be violated when a fluid acquires circulation due

Notes p. 133

to vortex lines. This can happen because the Kelvin theorem says that the circulation of a *given* fluid contour is unchanged as the contour moves. Thus as a vortex say enters from the wall there is no fluid contour for which the theorem is violated. If one focuses attention at $t = 0$ on a given fluid contour with zero circulation it is found that as a vortex enters from the wall this contour is repelled by the vortex and can never encircle it, although there will appear *new* contours for which the circulation is non-zero.

In this manner there are other means by which vortices can enter and not violate the Kelvin theorem; such as if a vortex dipole consisting of two vortices of equal but opposite circulation forms out of nothing in the middle of the fluid.

Although the rotation of the superfluid can be consistent with the Kelvin theorem one can wonder if the Landau two fluid equations modified to include dissipation will drive the fluid to the state with the appropriate number of vortex lines. As we have said the change in number of vortex lines is perhaps like a phase transition, which is not explained by hydrodynamics.

21 *Generalization of the Landau Two Fluid Equations to Include Dissipative Effects*

In this section we generalize to He II the arguments which in § 15 led to the Navier–Stokes equations for a classical fluid. Our goal is to ascertain the most general dissipative equations consistent with

(a) mass, energy, and momentum conservation;

(b) Galilean covariance;

(c) the requirements imposed by the thermodynamic equilibrium conditions in the special case of rotation;

(d) a mathematic approximation that we admit dissipative fluxes that are at most linear in deviation from equilibrium.

We will have especially in mind the case of a small number of quantized vortex lines rotating with the normal fluid so that the equilibrium conditions (16-8,9,10) are satisfied. Since this is a thermodynamic equilibrium state one must require that in this state the dissipation vanishes and that the dissipative effects lead to a positive definite entropy production which would drive the system to this state.

Notes p. 133

On the dissipative level the entropy equation must thus assume the form

$$\frac{\partial \rho s}{\partial t} + \nabla \cdot \left(\rho s \boldsymbol{v}_{\mathrm{n}} + \frac{\boldsymbol{q}}{T} \right) = \frac{\Sigma}{T}, \tag{21-1}$$

where in accord with the requirements imposed by the thermodynamic equilibrium conditions the dissipative contribution to the entropy flux, $\boldsymbol{q}/T$ and the entropy production Σ must vanish in equilibrium. Furthermore Σ must be positive definite off equilibrium.

Since in the equilibrium state the normal fluid is in solid body rotation, it is natural to expect dissipative stresses of the Navier–Stokes type for $\boldsymbol{v}_{\mathrm{n}}$. However, for the superfluid velocity $\boldsymbol{v}_{\mathrm{s}}$ the form of the dissipative effects must be quite different. This is because the motion of the superfluid in and near equilibrium satisfies $\nabla \times \boldsymbol{v}_{\mathrm{s}} = 0$, except at an array of quantized vortex lines (where $\rho_{\mathrm{s}} = 0$). To be consistent with these solutions the dissipative stresses must conserve the superfluid circulation and the form of the superfluid equation of motion must then be [25]:

$$\rho_{\mathrm{s}} \frac{\mathrm{D}_{\mathrm{s}} \boldsymbol{v}_{\mathrm{s}}}{\mathrm{D}t} = -\rho_{\mathrm{s}} \nabla \mu - \rho_{\mathrm{s}} \nabla H, \tag{21-2}$$

where the off-equilibrium correction to the chemical potential is denoted by H.

In the presence of dissipation there must still be laws of mass, energy and momentum conservation, or

$$\frac{\partial \rho}{\partial t} + \nabla \cdot \boldsymbol{J} = 0, \tag{21-3}$$

$$\frac{\partial J_i}{\partial t} + \frac{\partial}{\partial r_\alpha} (P_{i\alpha} + \tau_{i\alpha}) = 0, \tag{21-4}$$

$$\frac{\partial U}{\partial t} + \nabla \cdot (\boldsymbol{Q} + \boldsymbol{Q}') = 0, \tag{21-5}$$

where τ_{ik} is the viscous stress tensor and $\boldsymbol{Q}'$ is the dissipative contribution to the energy flux density; P_{ij} and $\boldsymbol{Q}$ are given by (4-4) and (4-7).

Equations (21-1,2,3,4,5) constitute nine equations for the eight basic variables which describe the state of He II. Since eight equations form a complete set the energy equation for instance must be implied by the other eight. To apply this restriction we form the time derivative of the energy from (4-5,6)

Notes p. 133

$$\frac{\partial U}{\partial t} = (\mu + \tfrac{1}{2}v_s^2 - \boldsymbol{v}_n \cdot \boldsymbol{v}_s)\frac{\partial \rho}{\partial t} + T\frac{\partial \rho s}{\partial t} + \boldsymbol{v}_n \cdot \frac{\partial \boldsymbol{J}}{\partial t} + \rho_s(\boldsymbol{v}_s - \boldsymbol{v}_n) \cdot \frac{\partial \boldsymbol{v}_s}{\partial t}. \quad (21\text{-}6)$$

Next eliminate the time derivatives on the right hand side of (21-6) in favor of space derivatives by means of (21-1,2,3,4) to obtain

$$\frac{\partial U}{\partial t} = -\nabla \cdot \boldsymbol{Q} + \Sigma - T\nabla \cdot \frac{\boldsymbol{q}}{T} - v_{n,\alpha}\frac{\partial \tau_{\alpha\beta}}{\partial r_\beta} - \rho_s(\boldsymbol{v}_s - \boldsymbol{v}_n) \cdot \nabla H, \quad (21\text{-}7)$$

where we have also used the fact that the non-dissipative fluxes combine to form $-\nabla \cdot \boldsymbol{Q}$ as we saw in § 3. Writing $T\nabla \cdot (\boldsymbol{q}/T) = \nabla \cdot \boldsymbol{q} - (\boldsymbol{q}/T) \cdot \nabla T$ and similarly flipping the derivative around for the other terms not in the form of a divergence yields

$$\frac{\partial U}{\partial t} + \nabla \cdot (\boldsymbol{Q} + \boldsymbol{Q}') = \Sigma + \frac{\boldsymbol{q}}{T} \cdot \nabla T + \tau_{\alpha\beta}\frac{\partial v_{n,\alpha}}{\partial r_\beta} + H\nabla \cdot \rho_s(\boldsymbol{v}_s - \boldsymbol{v}_n), \quad (21\text{-}8)$$

where

$$Q_i' = q_i + \tau_{\alpha i}v_{n,i} + H\rho_s(v_s - v_n)_i. \quad (21\text{-}9)$$

In order for there to be energy conservation (21-8) implies

$$\Sigma = -\frac{\boldsymbol{q} \cdot \nabla T}{T} - \tau_{\alpha\beta}\frac{\partial v_{n,\alpha}}{\partial r_\beta} - H\nabla \cdot \rho_s(\boldsymbol{v}_s - \boldsymbol{v}_n). \quad (21\text{-}10)$$

The most general expressions for $\boldsymbol{q}$, τ_{ij}, H, which vanish in equilibrium, satisfy Galilean covariance, are first order in the deviation from equilibrium and lead to $\Sigma > 0$ off equilibrium are derived in Appendix VI. The equations on this level involve *thirteen* independent dissipative coefficients, and were first presented by Clark [14].

If we further restrict the dissipative fluxes by requiring that they be first order in the deviation from equilibrium and internal velocity $\boldsymbol{v}_n - \boldsymbol{v}_s$, combined, then the most general fluxes involve five independent dissipative coefficients and are given by

$$\boldsymbol{q} = -\kappa\nabla T, \quad (21\text{-}11)$$

$$H = -\zeta_3\nabla \cdot \rho_s(\boldsymbol{v}_s - \boldsymbol{v}_n) - \zeta_4\nabla \cdot \boldsymbol{v}_n, \quad (21\text{-}12)$$

$$\tau_{ij} = -\eta\left(\frac{\partial v_{n,i}}{\partial r_j} + \frac{\partial v_{n,j}}{\partial r_i} - \tfrac{2}{3}\delta_{ij}\nabla \cdot \boldsymbol{v}_n\right) - \delta_{ij}[\zeta_1\nabla \cdot \rho_s(\boldsymbol{v}_s - \boldsymbol{v}_n) + \zeta_2\nabla \cdot \boldsymbol{v}_n], \quad (21\text{-}13)$$

Notes p. 133

where in order for Σ to be positive definite

$$\kappa, \eta, \zeta_2, \zeta_3 > 0 \tag{21-14}$$

and

$$(\zeta_1 + \zeta_4)^2 \leqslant 4\zeta_2\zeta_3, \tag{21-15}$$

and by the Onsager symmetry principle we must set

$$\zeta_1 = \zeta_4. \tag{21-16}$$

Relations (21-11,12,13) are the dissipative fluxes presented by Khalatnikov [15]. In equilibrium ∇T, $\nabla \cdot \boldsymbol{v}_n$, $\nabla \cdot \rho_s(\boldsymbol{v}_n - \boldsymbol{v}_s)$, and $(\partial v_{n,\alpha}/\partial r_\beta + \partial v_{n,\beta}/\partial r_\alpha)$ all vanish. Thus as with the classical fluid when He II is off but close to equilibrium these quantities are small and in first approximation it is natural to consider dissipative corrections which are linear in these derivatives. As we have seen $\boldsymbol{v}_n - \boldsymbol{v}_s$ does *not* vanish in equilibrium and in fact near the core of a vortex it can be quite large and thus there is no good reason to also expand the dissipative fluxes in powers of $\boldsymbol{v}_n - \boldsymbol{v}_s$. The equations presented by Clark constitute the proper description of He II on the Navier–Stokes level and in § 26 we will discuss a possible application of them.

It is clear from the form of the dissipative terms that they vanish when the fluid in the rotating bucket is in thermodynamic equilibrium. In fact one can show by the following general arguments that these dissipative hydrodynamic equations for He II drive the fluid to the equilibrium state in which $T =$ constant, $\boldsymbol{v}_n = \boldsymbol{\omega} \times \boldsymbol{r}$ and $\mu + \frac{1}{2}v_s^2 - \boldsymbol{v}_n \cdot \boldsymbol{v}_s =$ constant.

The hydrodynamics drive the fluid to an equilibrium state with $\Sigma = 0$, hence $T =$ constant, $\tau_{ij} = 0$ and $\nabla \cdot \rho_s(\boldsymbol{v}_n - \boldsymbol{v}_s) = 0$. The only solutions to $\tau_{ij} = 0$ are $\boldsymbol{v}_n$ equal to a constant or solid body rotation. But the constant can be chosen to be zero by a Galilean transformation, hence the normal fluid is in solid body rotation. The equilibrium condition involving μ is much more difficult to demonstrate. By subtracting (21-2) from (21-4) one finds in hydrodynamic equilibrium

$$\rho_n \nabla(\mu + \tfrac{1}{2}v_s^2 - \boldsymbol{v}_n \cdot \boldsymbol{v}_s) = (\boldsymbol{v}_s - \boldsymbol{v}_n)\frac{\mathrm{D}_n \rho_n}{\mathrm{D}t}. \tag{21-17}$$

Now if one could show that $\mathrm{D}_n\rho_n/\mathrm{D}t = 0$ or that the hydrodynamics drove the fluid to an equilibrium state stationary in the rotating system

Notes p. 133

the proof would be complete. To show the stationarity note that from $\nabla \cdot \boldsymbol{v}_n = 0$ and $\nabla \cdot \rho_s(\boldsymbol{v}_n - \boldsymbol{v}_s) = 0$ and (21-3) one finds

$$\frac{D_n \rho}{Dt} = 0. \tag{21-18}$$

By transforming (21-2) to a rotating system one finds that when $\Sigma = 0$

$$\frac{\partial \boldsymbol{v}'_s}{\partial t'} + \nabla'(\mu + \tfrac{1}{2}v_s^2 - \boldsymbol{v}_n \cdot \boldsymbol{v}_s) = \boldsymbol{v}'_s \times (2\boldsymbol{\omega} + \nabla' \times \boldsymbol{v}'_s), \tag{21-19}$$

where primes denote quantities as seen by the rotating observer; in particular $\boldsymbol{v}'_s = \boldsymbol{v}_s - \boldsymbol{v}_n$. Combining (21-19) with (21-17) leads to

$$\frac{\partial \rho_n \boldsymbol{v}'_s}{\partial t'} = \rho_n \boldsymbol{v}'_s \times (2\boldsymbol{\omega} + \nabla' \times \boldsymbol{v}'_s). \tag{21-20}$$

By taking the dot product of (21-20) with $\rho_n \boldsymbol{v}'_s$ we find that $\rho_n \boldsymbol{v}'_s = \rho_n(\boldsymbol{v}_s - \boldsymbol{v}_n)$ is stationary in the rotating system. Thus eight independent quantities: $\boldsymbol{v}_n$, T, ρ, $\rho_n(\boldsymbol{v}_s - \boldsymbol{v}_n)$ are driven to stationarity in the rotating system by the hydrodynamics. As eight variables are a complete set we find that $D_n \rho_n / Dt$ also vanishes in equilibrium thus proving that the hydrodynamic equations including dissipation do drive the He II to the thermodynamic equilibrium state.

In order for the superfluid to be in equilibrium the vortex lines which may be present must be moving with the local normal fluid velocity. Thus one expects that these hydrodynamic equations will drive any vortex lines present to locations where they will be moving at the same speed as the normal fluid. In this way the dissipative hydrodynamics lead to an interaction between super and normal components since the vortices move with the local superfluid velocity both in and out of equilibrium. The details of the normal fluid 'drag' on superfluid vortex lines, based on the basic dissipative equations of He II as developed here, are presented in § 32.

There is a deep and not understood difficulty with the hydrodynamic equations derived in this section. It is, that in order to derive an energy conservation law (21-5) from the other equations use was made of the first and second laws of thermodynamics for *reversible* processes (4-5,6). How can one justify using reversible thermodynamics to demonstrate the validity and consistency of irreversible equations?

As this problem also arises in classical hydrodynamics we first show

Notes p. 133

how it is resolved in that instance before turning to He II where a similar resolution is impossible.

For a classical fluid the total energy density U, density ρ, and momentum density $\boldsymbol{J}$, are well defined both in and out of equilibrium since these are the basic conserved quantities. Setting $\boldsymbol{J}/\rho = \boldsymbol{v}$ and $\rho\varepsilon = U - \frac{1}{2}\rho v^2$ defines the off-equilibrium velocity and internal energy ε. The variables p, T appearing in the Navier–Stokes equations are now to be interpreted as being the same functions of ρ, ε, off equilibrium as they are in equilibrium. Thus the quantity s which satisfies

$$\mathrm{d}s = (1/T)\,\mathrm{d}\varepsilon + (p/T)\,\mathrm{d}(1/\rho) \tag{21-21}$$

will similarly be the equilibrium entropy. So the change in s as given by (21-21) will not be the true change in entropy, but the entropy change had the process been reversible. In the Navier–Stokes equation (12-2) however, the quantity s which appears must be interpreted as representing the true entropy and thus cannot be given by (21-21). If we denote the true entropy change by $\mathrm{d}s_{\mathrm{oe}}$ (where oe stands for off equilibrium) then $\mathrm{d}s_{\mathrm{oe}} \neq \mathrm{d}s$ and the difference depends on quantities such as $\nabla \cdot \boldsymbol{v}$, and ∇T which are a measure of the deviation from equilibrium. However, since the entropy is a *maximum* in equilibrium the difference between s and s_{oe} must be at least quadratic in the deviation from equilibrium. In the Navier–Stokes equations terms which lead to quadratic corrections to the fluxes and hence third order derivatives are neglected and hence we can set $s = s_{\mathrm{oe}}$ so that (21-21) is also valid for the true entropy. This explains why we can use irreversible hydrodynamics in conjunction with reversible thermodynamics at the Navier–Stokes level.

For He II U, ρ, $\boldsymbol{J}$ are also well defined both in or out of equilibrium. But unlike a classical fluid for He II one must have three more variables for a complete set; they are the three components of $\boldsymbol{v}_{\mathrm{s}}$; but how is $\boldsymbol{v}_{\mathrm{s}}$ to be defined off equilibrium? For reversible processes we already saw in § 6 that $\boldsymbol{v}_{\mathrm{s}}$ did not have an independent operational definition and at that time we were forced to use the first and second laws of thermodynamics for reversible processes (6-7) in order to arrive at an operational definition of $\boldsymbol{v}_{\mathrm{s}}$. Thus off equilibrium there is no a priori definition of $\boldsymbol{v}_{\mathrm{s}}$ and the entire argument presented above breaks down. For instance there is now no meaning to the statement that p be taken to be the same function of U, ρ, $\boldsymbol{J}$, $\boldsymbol{v}_{\mathrm{s}}$ off equilibrium as it is in equilibrium since $\boldsymbol{v}_{\mathrm{s}}$ is not independently defined off equilibrium.

Notes p. 133

Of course one can determine $\boldsymbol{v}_s$ by means of the solutions to the hydrodynamic equations with dissipation, (and in the absence of a resolution to the problem raised here this will in fact be our procedure) but the purpose of the argument, presented above for classical fluids, was to demonstrate the validity of the hydrodynamics!

This dilemma cannot be escaped by using the first and second laws in the form

$$T\,\mathrm{d}s = \mathrm{d}\varepsilon_0 + p\,\mathrm{d}(1/\rho) - (\boldsymbol{v}_n - \boldsymbol{v}_s)\cdot \mathrm{d}(\rho_n/\rho)(\boldsymbol{v}_n - \boldsymbol{v}_s),$$

since here ε_0 is the energy in the reference frame where $\boldsymbol{v}_s = 0$, which is undefined if $\boldsymbol{v}_s$ is undefined.

As off equilibrium two quantities $\boldsymbol{v}_s$, s are undefined, perhaps it is even possible that *to first order* in the deviation from equilibrium there might be corrections to both s and $\boldsymbol{v}_s$ so that for instance the form of the first and second laws (6-7) is unchanged, but of course the equations of motion would be affected.

Supplemented by the boundary conditions, (21-1,2,3,4) form eight equations for the time development on the dissipative level of the eight independent variables that describe the state of He II.

The boundary conditions for the dissipative equations are discussed in § 28. Here we note that since the viscous stresses experienced by the normal fluid are similar to those of a classical fluid one has to restrict the tangential component of $\boldsymbol{v}_n$ at a boundary in order to obtain a solution to the differential equations. The usual choice is to take this component equal to zero at a stationary boundary. In the absence of a heat flux, $v_{n\perp} = v_{s\perp} = 0$ at a stationary boundary, otherwise the boundary conditions are more complex. As $\boldsymbol{v}_s$ experiences no viscous stresses the superfluid equation would be overdetermined (and $\nabla \times \boldsymbol{v}_s = 0$ violated) if the tangential component of $\boldsymbol{v}_s$ were restricted at boundaries. Thus the tangential component of $\boldsymbol{v}_s$ is left undetermined even on the dissipative level.

This procedure raises the following problem. For classical fluids it is well known that the Euler equations do not have a unique solution for given initial conditions and this is directly related to the lack of specification of the tangential component of velocity on this level. This problem is viewed as academic since on the Navier–Stokes level the tangential component is restricted and thus one is led to expect a unique solution. But as we have seen for the superfluid, even on the dissipative level the tangential component of $\boldsymbol{v}_s$ is unrestricted. Thus the solution of the two

Notes p. 133

fluid equations including dissipation is not unique insofar as $\boldsymbol{v}_s$ is concerned.

We have shown that in the case of rotation there are many solutions of the two fluid equations which are stable against small perturbations and which have $\Sigma = 0$. Each corresponds to different numbers of quantized vortices and thus also to different tangential components of $\boldsymbol{v}_s$ at the boundary. Perhaps the lack of a unique solution is a reflection of the role which quantum theory will play in a more complete macroscopic theory of He II. It may turn out that different arrangements of vortices are all in principle observable but have differing quantum probabilities.

22 *Some General Properties of the Two Fluid Equations Including Dissipation*

The equation of motion for $\boldsymbol{v}_s$ was chosen so that even on the dissipative level the circulation, $\oint \boldsymbol{v}_s \cdot d\boldsymbol{\ell}$, would be a constant of the motion. Thus the superfluid still obeys a Bernoulli law which from (21-2) is

$$\frac{\partial \phi}{\partial t} + \tfrac{1}{2}v_s^2 + \mu + H = \text{constant throughout the fluid,} \qquad (22\text{-}1)$$

where

$$\boldsymbol{v}_s = \nabla \phi. \qquad (22\text{-}2)$$

On the dissipative level the equation of motion for $\boldsymbol{A} = \rho_n(\boldsymbol{v}_n - \boldsymbol{v}_s)/s\rho$ becomes

$$\frac{\partial A_i}{\partial t} + (\boldsymbol{v}_n \cdot \nabla)A_i = -\frac{\partial T}{\partial r_i} - A_j \frac{\partial v_{n,j}}{\partial r_i} + [\boldsymbol{A} \times (\nabla \times \boldsymbol{v}_s)]_i + \frac{1}{s}\frac{\partial H}{\partial r_i} - \frac{1}{\rho s}\frac{\partial \tau_{i\alpha}}{\partial r_\alpha} - A_i \frac{\Sigma}{\rho s T} + \frac{A_i \nabla \cdot (\boldsymbol{q}/T)}{\rho s}. \qquad (22\text{-}3)$$

Although the circulation of $\boldsymbol{A}$ is a constant of the motion on the ideal level this property is destroyed by the dissipative processes.

Including the dissipative effects the equation for the normal fluid becomes from (21-2) and (21-4)

$$\rho_n \frac{\mathrm{D}_n v_{n,i}}{\mathrm{D}t} = \rho_s \frac{\partial \mu}{\partial r_i} - \frac{\partial p}{\partial r_i} + (v_s - v_n)_i \left[\frac{\partial \rho_n}{\partial t} + \nabla \cdot \rho_n \boldsymbol{v}_n\right] + \rho_s \frac{\partial H}{\partial r_i} - \frac{\partial \tau_{i\alpha}}{\partial r_\alpha}. \qquad (22\text{-}4)$$

Notes p. 133

We see that when dissipative effects are included the resulting hydrodynamics yield a thermal circulation which is time irreversible and a superfluid circulation that is time reversible. So the thermal circulation is only a thermal adiabatic invariant whereas the superfluid circulation is an Ehrenfest as well as a thermal adiabatic invariant.

Notes

[1] L. D. Landau and E. M. Lifshitz, *Fluid Mechanics* (Pergamon, London, 1959) p. 57.
[2] J. F. Allen and A. D. Misener, Nature **141**(1938)75; P. Kapitza, Nature **141**(1938)74.
[3] See L. D. Landau and E. M. Lifshitz: Ref. [1], p. 60.
[4] A. D. B. Woods and A. C. Hollis-Hallett; Can. J. Phys. **41**(1963)596.
[5] W. H. Keesom and G. E. MacWood, Physica **5**(1938)737.
[6] See L. D. Landau and E. M. Lifshitz: Ref. [1] p. 94.
[7] J. D. Reppy and C. T. Lane, Phys. Rev. **140**(1965)A106. J. D. Reppy, D. Depatie and C. T. Lane, Phys. Rev. Letters **5**(1960)541.
[8] E. L. Andronikashvili and Yu. G. Mamaladze, Rev. Mod. Phys. **38**(1966)567.
[9] S. J. Putterman and G. E. Uhlenbeck, Phys. Fluids **12**(1969)2229.
[10] G. B. Hess and W. M. Fairbank, Phys. Rev. Letters **19**(1967)216.
[11] This is proposed and investigated by S. V. Iordanskii, Zh. Eksp. Teor. Fiz. **48**(1965) 708 [Sov. Phys. JETP **21**(1965)467]; J. S. Langer and M. E. Fisher, Phys. Rev. Letters **19**(1967)560; R. J. Donnelly and P. H. Roberts, Phil. Trans. Roy. Soc. **A271**(1971)41.
[12] S. J. Putterman, M. Kac and G. E. Uhlenbeck, Phys. Rev. Letters **29**(1972)546.
[13] R. E. Packard and T. M. Sanders, Jr., Phys. Rev. Letters **22**(1969)823.
[14] A. Clark, Jr., Ph. D. Thesis, Massachusetts Institute of Technology (1963).
[15] I. M. Khalatnikov, *An Introduction to the Theory of Superfluidity* (Benjamin, New York, 1965) Chap. 9. I. L. Bekarevitch and I. M. Khalatnikov, Zh. Eksp. Teor. Fiz. **40**(1961)920 [Sov. Phys. JETP **13**(1961)643] have proposed an averaged macroscopic hydrodynamic theory with dissipation that they claim to be valid only in the limit that the He II contains many vortices. Here we are concerned with the 'exact' macroscopic theory valid for any number of vortices.
[16] S. C. Whitmore and W. Zimmermann, Jr., Phys. Rev. **166**(1968)181.
[17] F. London, *Superfluids* (Wiley, New York, 1954) Vol. 2, p. 151.
[18] L. D. Landau, *Collected Works*, ed. D. ter Haar (Gordon and Breach, New York, 1965) p. 650.
[19] H. B. Callen, *Thermodynamics* (Wiley, New York, 1960) Chap. 8.
[20] W. F. Vinen, Proc. Roy. Soc. **A260**(1961)218.
[21] A. L. Fetter, Phys. Rev. **153**(1967)285.
[22] G. B. Hess, Phys. Rev. **161**(1967)189.
[23] W. I. Glaberson, D. M. Strayer and R. J. Donnelly, Phys. Rev. Letters **20**(1968)1428.
[24] F. Reif and L. Meyer, Phys. Rev. **119**(1960)1164.
[25] It has been pointed out by Professor G. W. Ford (private communication) that the most general restriction concerning the circulation of $\boldsymbol{v}_s$ which is consistent with stability and quantization requirements is

$$\left[\frac{\partial}{\partial t} + \boldsymbol{v}_{\rm L} \cdot \nabla\right] \oint \boldsymbol{v}_{\rm s} \cdot {\rm d}\boldsymbol{\ell} = 0,$$

where $\boldsymbol{v}_{\rm L} \neq \boldsymbol{v}_{\rm s}$ except in equilibrium. With this restriction one would obtain instead of (21-2)

$$\rho_{\rm s} \frac{{\rm D}_{\rm s}\boldsymbol{v}_{\rm s}}{{\rm D}t} = -\rho_{\rm s}\nabla(\mu + H) + \rho_{\rm s}(\boldsymbol{v}_{\rm L} - \boldsymbol{v}_{\rm s}) \times (\nabla \times \boldsymbol{v}_{\rm s}).$$

The most general choice for $\boldsymbol{v}_{\rm L}$ which satisfies energy conservation, $\Sigma > 0$ and is linear in the derivatives is

$$\boldsymbol{v}_{\rm L} = \boldsymbol{v}_{\rm s} + \beta(\nabla \times \boldsymbol{v}_{\rm s}) \times (\boldsymbol{v}_{\rm n} - \boldsymbol{v}_{\rm s}),$$

and the additional contribution to Σ is

$$\rho_{\rm s}\beta(\boldsymbol{v}_{\rm n} - \boldsymbol{v}_{\rm s}) \cdot \{[(\nabla \times \boldsymbol{v}_{\rm s}) \times (\boldsymbol{v}_{\rm n} - \boldsymbol{v}_{\rm s})] \times (\nabla \times \boldsymbol{v}_{\rm s})\},$$

where for $\Sigma > 0$, one must have $\beta > 0$.

Note that this contribution to the entropy production vanishes because $\nabla \times \boldsymbol{v}_{\rm s} = 0$ in He II except perhaps at points (vortices) where $\rho_{\rm s} = 0$. Similarly the extra contribution to the superfluid equation involving $\nabla \times \boldsymbol{v}_{\rm s}$ vanishes.

CHAPTER III

Applications of the He II Hydrodynamics Including Dissipation

23 *Introduction: The Completely Incompressible Approximation*

While the dissipative equations of motion were derived and motivated by the properties which they should exhibit in the special case of rotation, they are entirely general and thus form the basis for the description of all dissipative effects in He II. In this chapter we consider these applications and always try to emphasize those aspects of the two fluid equations with dissipation which are different from the classical Navier–Stokes equations.

When the flow of He II on the dissipative level can be approximated by ignoring the variations in ρ_n, ρ, s, and neglecting κ and the quadratic term Σ, the two fluid equations (21-2,4) become the ideal incompressible equations of motion (2-14,15) with the important modification that to the right hand side of the equation of motion of the normal fluid must be added the viscous stress term $\eta\nabla^2\boldsymbol{v}_n$. This was exactly the generalization of the two fluid equations to the dissipative level which enabled us in § 13 to resolve the viscosity paradox.

24 *The Experiment of Andronikashvili*

In § 13 we mentioned that a measurement of the damping of the amplitude of an oscillating disc immersed in He II determines the viscosity. Andronikashvili [1] realized that the interaction of the disc with normal fluid not only affected its amplitude but also changed the period of oscillation. He reasoned that, in the formula for the period of oscillation $\equiv 2\pi/\omega = 2\pi(I/\chi)^{1/2}$ where χ is the known spring constant of the torsion wire upon which the disc is suspended, the moment of inertia I

must in addition to the disc include a contribution from the mass of entrained fluid. As only the normal fluid is viscous only it would be entrained and Andronikashvili used this idea to determine ρ_n from the viscous properties of $\boldsymbol{v}_n$. The agreement of the values of ρ_n found by Andronikashvili and by measurement of the velocity of second sound (a consequence of the ideal equations) provides a strong check on the internal consistency of the generalization of the Landau two fluid equations to the dissipative level.

In order to convert a measurement of I or the entrained mass into knowledge of the density of entrained fluid (i.e., ρ_n) one must know the entrained volume. We shall soon see that from the two fluid equations with dissipation it is a good approximation to expect that all the normal fluid up to a penetration depth

$$\delta = (2\eta/\omega\rho_n)^{1/2} \tag{24-1}$$

moves with the disc. However it was the goal of Andronikashvili to determine ρ_n independent of knowledge of δ. Thus he performed his experiments with a pile of discs such that the spacing between successive and parallel discs was substantially less than δ, and the entrained fluid volume could be taken to be the entire volume enclosed by the discs.

Based upon our discussion of rotating He II in § 18 one might expect that the amplitude of motion of the discs had better be very small so that its angular velocity is less than ω_{cr}. Above ω_{cr} vortices form, and the superfluid receives angular momentum and thus contributes to the moment of inertia.

In 1946 this difficulty was not theoretically understood, but clearly it was empirically encountered. Although the amplitude of motion was not mentioned, it had to be very small since it was observed by reflecting light off a mirror attached to the oscillating assemblage, even for a period of oscillation as long as 30 sec. For his discs $d = 3.5$ cm.

Hollis-Hallett [2] has repeated Andronikashvili's experiment with an eye towards investigating how small the amplitude had to be so that the superfluid did not participate in the motion. For a system of roughly the same diameter and period he found that the amplitude had to be less than 0.1 radian in order to obtain values for the moment of inertia and hence ρ_n in agreement with say second sound work. For this geometry such an amplitude corresponds to an angular velocity equal to roughly $10\omega_{cr}$. We conclude that the validity of the results of these crucial experiments hinged upon the ability of the experimentalists to

Notes p. 176

observe metastable rotation states. Somehow the time of oscillation in each direction was for these motions shorter than the times required for the vortices to form. These experimental results can be turned around to yield a measure of the time required for the vortices to enter the He II. As yet there is no explanation for the origin of the vortices anywhere consistent with these times. In § 44 we will see for instance that a simple thermal fluctuation model yields relaxation times orders of magnitude too long.

We calculate the penetration depth δ for the simplified case of a disc which lies in the x, y plane and oscillates along the y axis. For this geometry all quantities are functions only of z, and furthermore we look for a solution with $\boldsymbol{v}_s = 0$. Then $\boldsymbol{v}_n = v_n(z, t)\hat{\boldsymbol{e}}_y$, $\nabla \cdot \boldsymbol{v}_n = 0$, $(\boldsymbol{v}_n \cdot \nabla)\boldsymbol{v}_n = 0$ so that the two equations of motion (21-2) and (21-4) become

$$\nabla \mu = 0, \tag{24-2}$$

$$\rho_n \frac{\partial \boldsymbol{v}_n}{\partial t} = -\nabla p + \eta \nabla^2 \boldsymbol{v}_n. \tag{24-3}$$

Since p is assumed to depend only on z one obtains from the z component of (24-3)

$$p = \text{constant}, \tag{24-4}$$

and from the y component we find

$$\rho_n \frac{\partial v_{n,y}}{\partial t} = \eta \nabla^2 v_{n,y}. \tag{24-5}$$

The solution of (24-5) satisfying the boundary condition that the normal fluid stick at the surface of the plate is

$$\boldsymbol{v}_n = v_0 \exp\left\{ -\sqrt{\frac{\omega \rho_n}{2\eta}}\, z + i\left[\sqrt{\frac{\omega \rho_n}{2\eta}}\, z - \omega t\right]\right\} \hat{\boldsymbol{e}}_y, \tag{24-6}$$

where $v_0 \exp(-i\omega t)$ is the velocity of the plate. We see from (24-6) that the penetration depth of the plate's motion is just the δ of (24-1). Using the thermodynamic identity (4-8) for μ it also follows from (24-2) that there must be a temperature gradient:

$$\nabla T = (\rho_n / s\rho) \nabla \tfrac{1}{2} v_n^2. \tag{24-7}$$

However, for Andronikashvili's apparatus ($v_n < 1$ cm/sec) these temperature variations are small ($\sim 10^{-7}$ °K).

Notes p. 176

25 *The Absorption of Sound*

When dissipative processes are considered it is found that the amplitude of an incident first or second sound wave diminishes as it travels through the He II. In order to calculate the absorption we linearize the dissipative equations around the equilibrium state where $\boldsymbol{v}_n = \boldsymbol{v}_s = 0$, and look for a solution of the form $\exp(ikx - i\omega t)$. Except as opposed to § 7 we now expect that due to the dissipative processes k will be complex, indicating an absorption. Again setting

$$T = T_0 + T' \exp(ikx - i\omega t), \tag{25-1}$$

$$p = p_0 + p' \exp(ikx - i\omega t), \tag{25-2}$$

$$\boldsymbol{v}_n = v_n' \exp(ikx - i\omega t)\hat{\boldsymbol{e}}_x, \tag{25-3}$$

$$\boldsymbol{v}_s = v_s' \exp(ikx - i\omega t)\hat{\boldsymbol{e}}_x, \tag{25-4}$$

where T', p', v_n', v_s' are the amplitudes of deviation of the temperature, pressure, $\boldsymbol{v}_n$, and $\boldsymbol{v}_s$ from equilibrium, we find that the linearized two fluid equations become, from (21-3)

$$-i\omega \frac{\partial \rho}{\partial p} p' - i\omega \frac{\partial \rho}{\partial T} T' + ik\rho_n v_n' + ik\rho_s v_s' = 0, \tag{25-5}$$

from (21-1) supplemented by (21-11) and (21-10)

$$-i\omega \frac{\partial \rho s}{\partial p} p' - i\omega \frac{\partial \rho s}{\partial T} T' + ik\rho s v_n' + \frac{k^2 \kappa}{T} T' = 0, \tag{25-6}$$

from (21-2) supplemented by (21-12)

$$-i\omega v_s' - iksT' + \frac{ik}{\rho} p' = -\rho_s k^2 \zeta_3 (v_s' - v_n') - k^2 \zeta_4 v_n', \tag{25-7}$$

from (21-4) supplemented by (21-13)

$$-i\omega \rho_n v_n' - i\omega \rho_s v_s' = -ikp' - k^2(\tfrac{4}{3}\eta + \zeta_2 - \rho_s \zeta_1) v_n' - k^2 \rho_s \zeta_1 v_s', \tag{25-8}$$

where the subscript zero has been dropped from the equilibrium quantities.

Equations (25-5,6,7,8) constitute four homogeneous equations in four unknowns. The determinant of the coefficients must vanish in order for

Notes p. 176

there to exist other than the equilibrium solution. We look for a solution in the form

$$k = k_0 + i\alpha, \tag{25-9}$$

where k_0 is the wave number when there is no dissipation and α is the absorption coefficient for sound. As the dissipative equations can be trusted only to linear order in the dissipative coefficients we only keep terms which are linear in α and the dissipative coefficients. Upon substituting (25-9) into (25-5,6,7,8) one finds from the vanishing of the imaginary part of the determinant of the coefficients the two absorptions

$$\alpha_1 = (\omega^2/2\rho u_1^3)(\tfrac{4}{3}\eta + \zeta_2), \tag{25-10}$$

$$\alpha_2 = (\omega^2\rho_s/2\rho u_2^3\rho_n)[\tfrac{4}{3}\eta + \zeta_2 - \rho(\zeta_1 + \zeta_4) + \rho^2\zeta_3 + \rho_n\kappa/\rho_s C_p], \tag{25-11}$$

where in the calculation all terms proportional to the small quantity $(\partial\rho/\partial T)_p$ have been ignored. Very near T_λ these terms are not so small and the absorption coefficients are more complicated. For instance the more accurate expression for first sound (to first order in $1 - C_V/C_p$) is

$$\alpha_{1,\lambda} = \alpha_1 + \frac{\omega^2}{2\rho u_1^3}\left(1 - \frac{C_V}{C_p}\right)\frac{\kappa}{C_p},$$

where now corrections of the order $\rho_s(\partial\rho/\partial T)_p$ are neglected since ρ_s vanishes at T_λ much more quickly than $(\partial\rho/\partial T)_p$ increases.

As η is known from the flow experiments, measurements of the first sound absorption α_1 determine ζ_2. Above 1.2 °K and not too close to T_λ experiments show that ζ_2 is independent of ω and approximately ten times larger than η. For instance at 1.5 °K flow experiments such as discussed in § 13 determine $\eta = 1.4 \times 10^{-5}$ poise and sound absorption yields $\zeta_2 = 1.5 \times 10^{-4}$ poise [3].

Since $\rho_s\omega^2/2\rho_n\rho u_2^3$ and $\frac{4}{3}\eta + \zeta_2$ are known the values of second sound absorption α_2 determine

$$B \equiv \rho^2\zeta_3 - \rho(\zeta_1 + \zeta_4) + \rho_n\kappa/\rho_s C_p. \tag{25-12}$$

As the term depending on κ is positive we can write (as we assume nothing about the value of κ)

$$\rho^2\zeta_3 - \rho(\zeta_1 + \zeta_4) < B, \tag{25-13}$$

but by use of the inequality (21-15) this becomes

$$\sqrt{4\zeta_2\zeta_3} > \zeta_1 + \zeta_4 > \rho\zeta_3 - B/\rho, \tag{25-14}$$

Notes p. 176

which immediately implies the restriction on ζ_3 that

$$\sqrt{\zeta_2\zeta_3} > \tfrac{1}{2}(\rho\zeta_3 - B/\rho). \tag{25-15}$$

As B is experimentally determined and ζ_2 already known (21-15) tells us for instance that at 1.5 °K where $B = -1.2 \times 10^{-4}$ g/cm sec [4]:

$$1.6 \times 10^{-2}\ \text{cm}^5/\text{g sec} > \zeta_3 > 2.0 \times 10^{-3}\ \text{cm}^5/\text{g sec}. \tag{25-16}$$

Using the Onsager relation $\zeta_1 = \zeta_4$ we then find from (25-13) that at 1.5 °K

$$1.5 \times 10^{-3}\ \text{cm}^2/\text{sec} > \zeta_1 > 5.6 \times 10^{-4}\ \text{cm}^2/\text{sec}. \tag{25-17}$$

So that at this temperature the coefficients ζ_1, ζ_3 are only known within about a factor of ten. We observe that $\zeta_1 \approx h/m$.

From (25-12) we find that

$$\rho_n\kappa/\rho_s C_p < B + \zeta_2, \tag{25-18}$$

which at 1.5 °K implies that

$$\kappa < 3 \times 10^4\ \text{erg/sec cm °K}. \tag{25-19}$$

At 2.1 °K experimental data imply

$$1.2 \times 10^{-2}\ \text{cm}^5/\text{g sec} > \zeta_3 > 0, \tag{25-20}$$

$$2.7 \times 10^{-4}\ \text{cm}^2/\text{sec} > \zeta_1 > -2.8 \times 10^{-4}\ \text{cm}^2/\text{sec}, \tag{25-21}$$

$$\kappa < 0.5 \times 10^4\ \text{erg/sec cm °K},$$

$$\eta = 18.6 \times 10^{-6}\ \text{poise};\ \zeta_2 = 7.0 \times 10^{-6}\ \text{poise}. \tag{25-22}$$

No other experiments furnish additional independent information on $\kappa, \zeta_1, \zeta_3, \zeta_4$ and so to date the above constitute the most precise values available.

26 The Absorption of Sound in the Presence of Internal Convection

As mentioned in § 7 one can in He II consider situations where sound propagates with respect to a steady state where $\boldsymbol{v}_n \neq \boldsymbol{v}_s$. In this section we calculate the absorption of such sound modes.

Notes p. 176

For the absorption of sound propagating with respect to quiescent He II the Khalatnikov dissipative fluxes [5] provide the basic description since $\boldsymbol{v}_\mathrm{n} = \boldsymbol{v}_\mathrm{s}$ in the unperturbed state. However, as we emphasized in § 21, when $\boldsymbol{v}_\mathrm{n} \neq \boldsymbol{v}_\mathrm{s}$ in the unperturbed state the dissipative description is provided by the Clark equations [6]. These equations are derived in Appendix VI.

As in § 7 we look for a solution to these equations when linearized. Thus we set

$$T = T_0 + T' \exp(ikx - i\omega t), \tag{26-1}$$

$$p = p_0 + p' \exp(ikx - i\omega t), \tag{26-2}$$

$$\boldsymbol{v} = v' \exp(ikx - i\omega t)\widehat{\boldsymbol{e}}_x, \tag{26-3}$$

$$\boldsymbol{w} = \boldsymbol{w}_0 + w' \exp(ikx - i\omega t)\widehat{\boldsymbol{e}}_x, \tag{26-4}$$

where $\boldsymbol{w}_0$, p_0, T_0 are all constant and

$$\boldsymbol{w} \equiv \boldsymbol{v}_\mathrm{n} - \boldsymbol{v}_\mathrm{s}.$$

From the continuity equation (21-3) we now find

$$-\omega \frac{\partial \rho}{\partial p} p' - \omega \frac{\partial \rho}{\partial T} T' - \omega \frac{\partial \rho}{\partial w^2} 2ww' + \rho k v' = 0. \tag{26-5}$$

From the entropy equation (21-1) and (AVI-11) one obtains by use of (26-5)

$$-i\omega\rho \frac{\partial s}{\partial p} p' - i\omega\rho \frac{\partial s}{\partial T} T' - i\omega\rho \frac{\partial s}{\partial w^2} 2ww'$$
$$+ i\rho_\mathrm{s} k w \left(\frac{\partial s}{\partial p} p' + \frac{\partial s}{\partial T} T' \right) + isk \left(\rho_\mathrm{s} w' + w \frac{\partial \rho_\mathrm{s}}{\partial p} p' + w \frac{\partial \rho_\mathrm{s}}{\partial T} T' \right)$$
$$+ \frac{k^2 \kappa}{T} T' - b_2 k^2 w \left(v' + \frac{\rho_\mathrm{s}}{\rho} w' \right) - b_3 \rho_\mathrm{s} k^2 w w' = 0, \tag{26-6}$$

where we have used

$$\boldsymbol{v}_\mathrm{n} \equiv \boldsymbol{v} + (\rho_\mathrm{s}/\rho)\boldsymbol{w}. \tag{26-7}$$

The subscript zero has been dropped from equilibrium parameters and terms quadratic in w_0 have been neglected. The linearized version of the superfluid equation (21-2) and (AVI-12) is

Notes p. 176

$$-i\omega v' + i\omega \frac{\rho_n}{\rho} w' + i\omega w \left[\frac{\partial(\rho_n/\rho)}{\partial p} p' + \frac{\partial(\rho_n/\rho)}{\partial T} T' \right] - ik \frac{\rho_n}{\rho} w v' - iksT'$$

$$+ \frac{i}{\rho} kp' - ik \frac{\rho_n \rho_s}{\rho^2} ww' + \zeta_4 k^2 \left[v' + \frac{\rho_s}{\rho} w' + w \frac{\partial(\rho_s/\rho)}{\partial T} T' + w \frac{\partial(\rho_s/\rho)}{\partial p} p' \right]$$

$$- \zeta_3 k^2 \left[\rho_s w' + w \frac{\partial \rho_s}{\partial T} T' + w \frac{\partial \rho_s}{\partial p} p' \right] + c_1 k^2 w T' = 0. \quad (26\text{-}8)$$

The momentum equation which follows from (21-4) and (AVI-13,14) is

$$-i\omega\rho v' + ikp' + 2ik \frac{\rho_n \rho_s}{\rho} ww'$$

$$+ k^2(\tfrac{4}{3}\eta + \zeta_2) \left[v' + \frac{\rho_s}{\rho} w' + w \frac{\partial(\rho_s/\rho)}{\partial p} p' + w \frac{\partial(\rho_s/\rho)}{\partial T} T' \right]$$

$$-\zeta_1 k^2 \left[\rho_s w' + w \frac{\partial \rho_s}{\partial p} p' + w \frac{\partial \rho_s}{\partial T} T' \right] - c_2 k^2 w T' = 0. \quad (26\text{-}9)$$

Equations (26-5,6,8,9) are four homogeneous equations in four unknowns and the dispersion law yielding the speed and absorption of sound follows from the requirement that the determinant formed from the coefficients vanish.

Neglecting the small terms in $(\partial\rho/\partial T)_p$ this condition implies

$$(u^2 - u_1^2)(u^2 - u_2^2) + u^3 w R_1 + uwR_2$$
$$+ iku^3 D_1 + iku^2 w D_2 + ikuD_3 + ikwD_4 = 0, \quad (26\text{-}10)$$

where $u = \omega/k$ and u_1, u_2 are the speeds of first and second sound propagating with respect to quiescent He II (7-18,19). In (26-10) the dependence on u, w, k is explicitly demonstrated; the coefficients are given by

$$R_1 = -\frac{4\rho_s}{\rho} + \frac{2s}{\rho_n} \frac{\partial \rho_n}{\partial T} \left(\frac{\partial s}{\partial T} \right)^{-1}, \quad (26\text{-}11)$$

$$R_2 = -R_1 \left(\frac{\partial \rho}{\partial p} \right)^{-1}, \quad (26\text{-}12)$$

$$D_1 = \frac{\kappa}{\rho C_p} + \frac{\frac{4}{3}\eta + \zeta_2}{\rho_n} + \frac{\rho_s}{\rho_n} [\rho\zeta_3 - (\zeta_1 + \zeta_4)], \quad (26\text{-}13)$$

Notes p. 176

$$D_2 = -\frac{3\rho_s\kappa}{\rho^2 C_p} + \frac{\frac{4}{3}\eta + \zeta_2}{\rho_n}\left[2\frac{\partial\rho_s}{\partial p}\left(\frac{\partial\rho}{\partial p}\right)^{-1} - \frac{2}{\rho}\frac{\partial\rho_s s}{\partial T}\left(\frac{\partial s}{\partial T}\right)^{-1} - \frac{\rho_s}{\rho}\right]$$
$$-\frac{\zeta_1 + \zeta_4}{\rho_n}\left[\rho\frac{\partial\rho_s}{\partial p}\left(\frac{\partial\rho}{\partial p}\right)^{-1} - \frac{2\rho_s^2 - \rho_s\rho_n}{\rho}\right]$$
$$-\frac{\rho_s^2}{\rho_n}\zeta_3 - \frac{\rho_s s}{\rho_n}\left(c_1 + \frac{c_2}{\rho} + \frac{b_2}{\rho} + b_3\right)\left(\frac{\partial s}{\partial T}\right)^{-1}, \quad (26\text{-}14)$$

$$D_3 = -D_1\left(\frac{\partial\rho}{\partial p}\right)^{-1} + \frac{\frac{4}{3}\eta + \zeta_2}{\rho}(u_1^2 - u_2^2), \quad (26\text{-}15)$$

$$D_4 = -D_2\left(\frac{\partial\rho}{\partial p}\right)^{-1} - \frac{\zeta_1 + \zeta_4}{\rho_n}\left(\frac{\partial\rho}{\partial p}\right)^{-1}\left[\rho\frac{\partial\rho_s}{\partial p}\left(\frac{\partial\rho}{\partial p}\right)^{-1} - \frac{\rho_s^2 - \rho_s\rho_n}{\rho}\right]$$
$$+(\tfrac{4}{3}\eta + \zeta_2)\left\{\frac{2}{\rho_n}\left(\frac{\partial\rho}{\partial p}\right)^{-1}\left[\frac{\partial\rho_s}{\partial p}\left(\frac{\partial\rho}{\partial p}\right)^{-1} - \frac{1}{\rho}\frac{\partial\rho_s s}{\partial T}\left(\frac{\partial s}{\partial T}\right)^{-1}\right] + \frac{\rho_s}{\rho^2}(u_2^2 - u_1^2)\right\}. \quad (26\text{-}16)$$

In the approximation where dissipation is neglected the dispersion law (26-10) reduces to that derived previously (7-66) for the first order correction to the speed of sound in the presence of internal convection.

To terms linear in the counterflow w the dispersion law now yields the absorption of first and second sound as

$$\alpha_1 = \alpha_{1,0} \pm \{[\omega^2(D_2 + D_4/u_1^2) - 2\alpha_{1,0}u_1^3 R_1]/2u_1^2(u_1^2 - u_2^2)\}\, w, \quad (26\text{-}17)$$

$$\alpha_2 = \alpha_{2,0} \pm \left\{\frac{\omega^2[\frac{1}{2}R_1(D_1 - D_3/u_2^2) - D_2 - D_4/u_2^2] - \alpha_{2,0}u_2(3u_2^2 - u_1^2)R_1}{2u_2^2(u_1^2 - u_2^2)}\right\} w, \quad (26\text{-}18)$$

where $\alpha_{1,0}$ and $\alpha_{2,0}$ are the absorption of first and second sound (25-10,11) propagating in quiescent He II ($w = 0$). The absorption is the decrease in amplitude of the wave as it propagates through the medium. In (26-17,18) the plus and minus sign refer to propagation in the plus or minus x direction. Thus if the correction term leads to an increased absorption for propagation parallel to a given $\boldsymbol{w}$ it will also lead to a decreased absorption for propagation antiparallel to $\boldsymbol{w}$. This property might be useful in experimentally investigating these results. For instance by interfering sound waves travelling with, and opposed to $\boldsymbol{w}$, the resulting amplitude will be determined solely by the coefficients of $\boldsymbol{w}$ in (26-17,18).

Notes p. 176

The correction to the absorption is of order w/u_2; and is proportional to ω^2, as are $\alpha_{1,0}$, $\alpha_{2,0}$. The absorption of first sound does not involve the Clark dissipative fluxes, but the absorption of second sound does. An experimental investigation of (26-17) would uniquely determine the bulk viscosities $\zeta_1, \zeta_2, \zeta_3, \zeta_4$ when compared with existing data. Then a check of (26-18) would demonstrate that the Khalatnikov fluxes did not yield a complete hydrodynamic description of the absorption of second sound to first order in $\boldsymbol{w}$.

As the dispersion law (26-10) is fifth power in k, one might expect that there is a fifth solution; namely

$$\omega = 0, \qquad k = iu_1^2 u_2^2 / D_4 w. \tag{26-19}$$

This non-propagating wave is an erroneous solution as k is inversely proportional to the dissipative coefficients which were presumed small in deriving (26-10). In order to allow for solutions such as (26-19) terms quadratic in the dissipative coefficients cannot be neglected since with k given by (26-19) they lead to terms of the same order as those already included in the dispersion law.

Motivated by the existence of this erroneous solution let us investigate the linearized two fluid equations when $\omega = 0$. From the continuity law we immediately find $v' = 0$. Then (26-6,8,9) become three homogeneous equations in three unknowns (p', T', w') and the desired solution follows from equating their determinant to zero. To terms linear in w but to arbitrary order in the dissipative coefficients this implies

$$u_1^2 u_2^2 + ikwD_4 + k^2 D_5 + ik^3 wD_6 = 0, \tag{26-20}$$

where

$$D_5 = \frac{\rho_s \kappa}{\rho_n \rho^2 C_p} \left[\tfrac{4}{3}\eta + \zeta_2 - \rho(\zeta_1 + \zeta_4) + \rho^2 \zeta_3\right] \left(\frac{\partial \rho}{\partial p}\right)^{-1}, \tag{26-21}$$

$$D_6 = \frac{\rho_s^2 \kappa}{\rho_n \rho^2 C_p} \left[\zeta_3(\tfrac{4}{3}\eta + \zeta_2) - \zeta_1 \zeta_4\right]. \tag{26-22}$$

To lowest order in w, (i.e. zeroth order) we find the solution

$$k = \pm \left(\frac{-u_1^2 u_2^2}{D_5}\right)^{1/2} = \pm\, i \left\{ \frac{s^2 \rho^2 T}{\kappa\left[\tfrac{4}{3}\eta + \zeta_2 - \rho(\zeta_1 + \zeta_4) + \rho^2 \zeta_3\right]} \right\}^{1/2}. \tag{26-23}$$

Notes p. 176

This represents a non-propagating wave which exponentially decays (or increases) over a characteristic distance

$$\delta = \left\{\frac{\kappa[\frac{4}{3}\eta + \zeta_2 - \rho(\zeta_1 + \zeta_4) + \rho^2\zeta_3]}{s^2\rho^2 T}\right\}^{1/2}. \tag{26-24}$$

This solution of the two fluid equations was first presented by Kronig and Thellung [7] and is related to the behavior of He II at a wall where heat is transmitted to the fluid. We return to this solution in § 28. To first order in w, k acquires a small correction so that

$$k = \pm\frac{i}{\delta} + \frac{i}{2}\left(\frac{u_1^2 u_2^2 D_6}{D_5^2} - \frac{D_4}{D_5}\right)w. \tag{26-25}$$

27 *Superfluid Transverse Sound*

In classical fluids it is impossible to propagate waves with a transverse component, with respect to an equilibrium state in which the fluid is uniform. Sometimes this property is taken to be the definition of a liquid. Here we will see that in certain circumstances sound propagating in He II has a transverse component.

The unperturbed state which will be considered, is characterized by $\boldsymbol{v}_n = 0$ and $\boldsymbol{v}_s = \boldsymbol{v}_{s,0} \neq 0$. As is indicated in Fig. 24, $\boldsymbol{v}_{s,0}$ is in the x direction

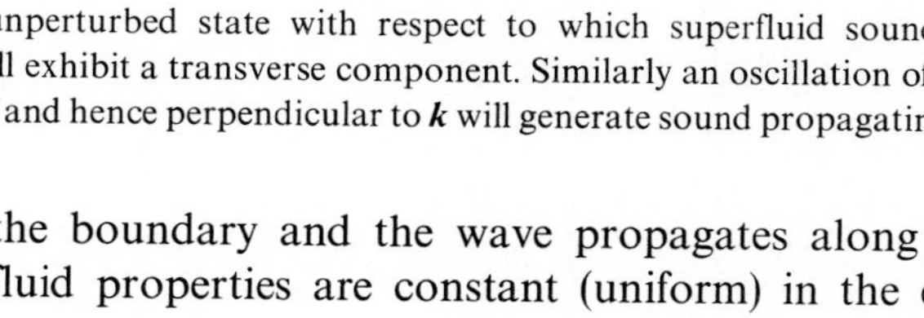

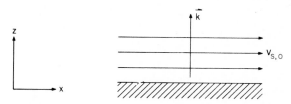

Fig. 24. The unperturbed state with respect to which superfluid sound propagating parallel to $\boldsymbol{k}$ will exhibit a transverse component. Similarly an oscillation of the boundary parallel to itself and hence perpendicular to $\boldsymbol{k}$ will generate sound propagating parallel to $\boldsymbol{k}$.

parallel to the boundary and the wave propagates along the z axis. Clearly all fluid properties are constant (uniform) in the equilibrium state.

The sound wave must satisfy $\nabla \times \boldsymbol{v}_s = 0$, therefore the variations in $\boldsymbol{v}_s$ occur only in the direction of propagation, i.e., $v'_{s,x} = 0$. When dissi-

Notes p. 176

pative effects are ignored the two fluid equations imply that the time change of $\nabla \times \boldsymbol{A}$ depends upon $\nabla \times \boldsymbol{A}$ in such a way that it vanishes when $\nabla \times \boldsymbol{A}$ vanishes, (4-24). Since $\nabla \times \boldsymbol{A} = 0$ for the unperturbed state one can take $\nabla \times \boldsymbol{A} = 0$ at each instant as the sound wave propagates:

$$\nabla \times \frac{\rho_n}{\rho s}(\boldsymbol{v}_n - \boldsymbol{v}_s) = 0, \tag{27-1}$$

or

$$\frac{\rho_n}{s\rho}\nabla \times \boldsymbol{v}_n + \left(\nabla \frac{\rho_n}{s\rho}\right) \times (\boldsymbol{v}_n - \boldsymbol{v}_s) = 0. \tag{27-2}$$

To first order in the deviation from equilibrium (27-2) yields for the amplitude of transverse normal fluid oscillation

$$v'_{n,x} = v_{s,0}\frac{\rho s}{\rho_n}\left(\frac{\rho_n}{s\rho}\right)'. \tag{27-3}$$

Writing $\rho_n/s\rho$ as a function of p, T, $\boldsymbol{w}$ and neglecting terms quadratic in the equilibrium velocity yields

$$v'_{n,x} = v_{s,0}\frac{\rho s}{\rho_n}\left[\frac{\partial(\rho_n/s\rho)}{\partial p}p' + \frac{\partial(\rho_n/s\rho)}{\partial T}T'\right]. \tag{27-4}$$

When second sound propagates with say temperature variations $T' \approx 10^{-2}$ °K one finds that $v'_{n,x} \approx 10^{-3}\, v_{s,0}$ which is small for typical flow values of $v_{s,0} < 10$ cm/sec. However, near the core of a quantized vortex $v_{s,0} \approx 10^4$ cm/sec and thus a second sound wave incident on the vortex core leads to substantial transverse normal fluid oscillations. Since sound leads to transverse oscillations one expects that in the same geometry transverse forced variations of $\boldsymbol{v}_n$ will lead to a propagation of sound. To investigate all these effects in more detail we must consider the linearized two fluid equations which correspond to this case. We set

$$p = p_0 + p' \exp(ikz - i\omega t), \tag{27-5}$$

$$T = T_0 + T' \exp(ikz - i\omega t), \tag{27-6}$$

$$\boldsymbol{v}_s = \boldsymbol{v}_{s,0} + v'_s \exp(ikz - i\omega t)\hat{\boldsymbol{e}}_z, \tag{27-7}$$

$$\boldsymbol{v}_n = (v'_{n,x}\hat{\boldsymbol{e}}_x + v'_{n,z}\hat{\boldsymbol{e}}_z)\exp(ikz - i\omega t). \tag{27-8}$$

Notes p. 176

Substituting these relations into the two fluid equations and keeping terms linear in the equilibrium velocity as well as the deviation from equilibrium we find from (21-3):

$$-\omega \frac{\partial \rho}{\partial p} p' - \omega \frac{\partial \rho}{\partial T} T' + \omega \frac{\partial \rho}{\partial w^2} 2v_s v'_{n,x} + k\rho_n v'_{n,z} + k\rho_s v'_s = 0, \tag{27-9}$$

from (21-1) minus s times (21-3):

$$-i\omega\rho \frac{\partial s}{\partial p} p' - i\omega\rho \frac{\partial s}{\partial T} T' + i\omega\rho \frac{\partial s}{\partial w^2} 2v_s v'_{n,x} + ik\rho_s s(v'_{n,z} - v'_s) + \frac{k^2\kappa}{T} T' = 0, \tag{27-10}$$

from (21-2):

$$-i\omega v'_s - iksT' + \frac{i}{\rho} kp' + k^2\zeta_4 v'_{n,z} - k^2\rho_s\zeta_3(v'_{n,z} - v'_s) + ik\frac{\rho_n}{\rho} v_s v'_{n,x} = 0, \tag{27-11}$$

and from (21-4):

$$-i\omega\rho_n v'_{n,z} - i\omega\rho_s v'_s + ikp' + (\tfrac{4}{3}\eta + \zeta_2 - \rho_s\zeta_1)k^2 v'_{n,z} + \zeta_1\rho_s k^2 v'_s = 0, \tag{27-12}$$

$$-i\omega\rho_n v'_{n,x} - i\omega v_s\left(\frac{\partial \rho_s}{\partial p} p' + \frac{\partial \rho_s}{\partial T} T'\right) + ik\rho_s v_s v'_s + \eta k^2 v'_{n,x} = 0, \tag{27-13}$$

where we note that the Clark and Khalatnikov fluxes yield the same results for this geometry and where we have dropped the subscript zero from the equilibrium quantities.

Equations (27-9,10,11,12,13) form five homogeneous equations in five unknowns and the dispersion laws $\omega(k)$ are obtained from the requirement that the determinant formed from the coefficients vanish. One finds that to terms first order in the equilibrium velocity the speed and absorption of first and second sound (7-14), (25-10), (25-11) are unchanged. There is now also a fifth solution to the determinant which is

$$i\omega = \eta k^2/\rho_n \tag{27-14}$$

and describes the normal fluid shear wave previously discussed in § 24. Although the dispersion laws are unchanged to terms linear in $v_{s,0}$ the propagation of first and second sound does lead to transverse $\boldsymbol{v}_n$ oscillations linear in $v_{s,0}$.

To see this multiply (27-9) by $is\rho_s/\rho_n$ and subtract from (27-10) to find

Notes p. 176

$$i\omega\left(\rho\frac{\partial s}{\partial p} - s\frac{\rho_s}{\rho_n}\frac{\partial \rho}{\partial p}\right)p' + \left[i\omega\left(\rho\frac{\partial s}{\partial T} - s\frac{\rho_s}{\rho_n}\frac{\partial \rho}{\partial T}\right) - \frac{\kappa k^2}{T}\right]T'$$

$$-i\omega\left(\rho\frac{\partial s}{\partial w^2} - s\frac{\rho_s}{\rho_n}\frac{\partial \rho}{\partial w^2}\right)2v_s v'_{n,x} + iks\frac{\rho_s \rho}{\rho_n}v'_s = 0. \quad (27\text{-}15)$$

Solve (27-15) for v'_s and substitute into (27-13) to obtain

$$(-i\omega\rho_n + \eta k^2)v'_{n,x} + i\omega v_s \rho s\left[\frac{\partial(\rho_n/\rho s)}{\partial p}p' + \frac{\partial(\rho_n/\rho s)}{\partial T}T'\right] + v_s\frac{\rho_n}{\rho s}\frac{\kappa k^2}{T}T' = 0, \quad (27\text{-}16)$$

where terms quadratic in v_s have been dropped. For sound frequencies $\omega < 10^7\ \text{sec}^{-1}$ the term involving κ can be neglected in view of (25-19) and its measured value of 10^4 erg/cm sec °K for $T > T_\lambda$. Also for these frequencies we can neglect ηk^2 compared with $\omega\rho_n$ and are led to relation (27-4) which is expected to hold in the limit where dissipation can be neglected.

Perhaps the transverse v_n oscillations can be observed through their effects on little test particles. None of the properties discussed in this section have yet been investigated experimentally and certainly these effects are small.

When (27-14) holds and thus the viscous wave is propagating one finds that it is accompanied by temperature and velocity variations. These can be evaluated by substituting $\eta k^2/\rho_n$ for $i\omega$ in equations (27-9,10,11,12). Then solve for T', p', $v'_{n,z}$, $v'_{s,z}$ in terms of $v'_{n,x}$ ignoring terms quadratic or higher power in the dissipative coefficients in these equations. In this way the variations of the variables in a counterflow viscous wave are

$$T' = \frac{\rho_n}{\rho s}v_s v'_{n,x}, \quad (27\text{-}17)$$

$$p' = 0 \quad (27\text{-}18)$$

$$\rho_n v'_{n,z} + \rho_s v'_s = -2\sqrt{\frac{-i\eta\omega}{\rho_n}}\frac{\partial \rho}{\partial w^2}v_s v'_{n,x}, \quad (27\text{-}19)$$

$$w'_z \equiv v'_{n,z} - v'_s = \left[-\sqrt{\frac{-i\eta\omega}{\rho_n}}\frac{2\rho}{s\rho_s}\frac{\partial s}{\partial w^2} + \frac{\rho_n}{s^2\rho_s\rho}\left(\sqrt{\frac{-i\eta\omega}{\rho_n}}\rho\frac{\partial s}{\partial T} + \frac{\kappa}{T}\sqrt{\frac{-i\omega\rho_n}{\eta}}\right)\right]v_s v'_{n,x}. \quad (27\text{-}20)$$

Notes p. 176

Approximating κ by its value above T_λ it is found that the terms involving κ dominate w'_z and furthermore $\rho w'_z \gg \rho_n v'_{n,z} + \rho_s v'_s$ so that the transverse wave leads to a much larger counterflow than center of mass motion. In fact for $\omega = 10^7\ \text{sec}^{-1}$, $v_{s,0} = 10$ cm/sec, $v'_{n,x} = 1$ cm/sec one finds, $T' = 10^{-6}$ °K and $w'_z \approx 10^{-3}$ cm/sec. But near a vortex core $T' \approx 10^{-3}$ °K which is substantial.

Consider now the excitation of sound by the plate. If it executes transverse oscillations only, then, since it puts no heat into the He II, the perpendicular components of $\boldsymbol{v}_n$ and $\boldsymbol{v}_s$ must vanish at the plate. Since a transverse wave leads to non zero $v'_{n,z}$ and v'_s the only way in which this can happen is if a transverse oscillation generates sound as well as the transverse wave. From these boundary conditions at the oscillating plate and the restriction that the normal fluid stick to the plate oscillating at amplitude v_0 we find

$$v'_{n,x,t} + v'_{n,x,1} + v'_{n,x,2} = v_0, \tag{27-21}$$

$$v'_{n,z,t} + v'_{n,z,1} + v'_{n,z,2} = 0, \tag{27-22}$$

$$v'_{s,t} + v'_{s,1} + v'_{s,2} = 0, \tag{27-23}$$

where the subscripts t, 1, 2 stand for the variations of the given quantity in the transverse, first, and second sound waves that will be generated by the pure transverse oscillations. Since in a sound wave all quantities are related (27-21), (27-22), (27-23) are three equations for three unknowns that determine the relative excitation of various modes at the oscillating plate. Subtracting (27-23) from (27-22) and using that to a high degree of precision $v'_{n,z,1} = v'_{s,1}$ we find

$$w'_{z,t} = -(v'_{n,z,2} - v'_{s,2}). \tag{27-24}$$

But for second sound one has from (7-31) that

$$v'_{n,z,2} = -(\rho_s/\rho_n)v'_{s,2},$$

hence

$$(\rho_n/\rho)w'_{z,t} = v'_{s,2}. \tag{27-25}$$

Also to lowest order the temperature variation in a second sound wave is from (7-32)

$$T' = -u_2 v'_{s,2}/s.$$

Notes p. 176

Therefore the perfect transverse oscillations of a plate in a counterflow establish a second sound wave with a temperature variation

$$T' = -\frac{\rho_n}{s\rho} u_2 w'_{z,t} = \frac{\rho_n}{s\rho} u_2 \left[\sqrt{\frac{-i\eta\omega}{\rho_n}} \frac{2\rho}{s\rho_s} \frac{\partial s}{\partial w^2} \right.$$

$$\left. - \frac{\rho_n}{s^2 \rho_s \rho} \left(\sqrt{\frac{-i\eta\omega}{\rho_n}} \rho \frac{\partial s}{\partial T} + \frac{\kappa}{T} \sqrt{\frac{-i\omega\rho_n}{\eta}} \right) \right] v_s v'_{n,x}, \quad (27\text{-}26)$$

where we have used (27-20). As our calculations are accurate only to linear order in v_s we can in (27-26) substitute v_0 for $v'_{n,x}$, since from (27-21) and (27-4) it follows that $v'_{n,x} - v_0$ is at least first order in v_s. For a frequency $\omega \approx 10^7$ and $v_s = 10$ cm/sec, $v_0 = 1$ cm/sec, one finds that $T' \approx 10^{-7}$ °K which is small.

28 *Boundary Conditions for the Two Fluid Equations when Dissipative Effects are Included*

As a result of dissipative phenomena we have seen that the two fluid equations must be modified to include viscous (shear) stresses that affect the normal fluid. Since these stresses are similar to those encountered in the Navier–Stokes hydrodynamics one must here also restrict the tangential component of the normal fluid velocity at a boundary. In parallel with the classical case we require that this component of the normal fluid velocity vanish at a stationary boundary.

In § 6 it was shown that in the presence of a heat flow from the boundary to the fluid discontinuities existed at the boundary. A description of the thickness and detailed nature of this stationary boundary shock wave can only come from an investigation of the two fluid equations including dissipation.

Here for simplicity we will consider a one dimensional problem as in § 6. Thus four variables, p, T, v_n, v_s are a complete set. First we will derive four equations which relate the properties of the boundary to the properties of the fluid near the boundary. Next we will derive the four equations which relate the properties of the fluid at one point to its behavior at another point. By solving these equations the details of the thermal boundary shock wave will be uncovered.

On the dissipative level the law of conservation of mass is unchanged.

Notes p. 176

Thus at a stationary boundary

$$\rho_n v_{n\perp} + \rho_s v_{s\perp} = 0. \tag{28-1}$$

Although entropy is not conserved, it still follows from an integration of (21-1) over an arbitrarily small volume of finite surface area that the entropy to leave the boundary equals the entropy flow in the He II just at the boundary:

$$\frac{\dot{W}}{T_B} = \rho s v_{n\perp} + \frac{q_\perp}{T}, \tag{28-2}$$

where $\dot{W}$ is the energy flux density from the boundary, of temperature T_B, to the He II. From the energy conservation law (21-5) we find at the boundary

$$\dot{W} = \rho s(T + \boldsymbol{v}_n \cdot \boldsymbol{A})v_{n\perp} + q_\perp - \rho v_{n\perp} H + \tau_{\perp\perp} v_{n\perp}, \tag{28-3}$$

where we have used (28-1) and the fact that $v_{n\parallel} = 0$. As in § 6 the force exerted on the boundary by the fluid is $(P_{ij} + \tau_{ij})\,dS_j$ where dS_j is a surface element forming the boundary of the fluid region. From (21-4) the force exerted on the boundary is then

$$p\,dS_i + \rho_n v_{n,i}(\boldsymbol{v}_n \cdot d\boldsymbol{S}) + \rho_s v_{s,i}(\boldsymbol{v}_s \cdot d\boldsymbol{S}) + \tau_{ij}\,dS_j. \tag{28-4}$$

Equations (28-1,2,3,4) relate directly measurable properties of the boundary to the fluid properties just next to the boundary and are valid without the simplifying assumption of a one dimensional geometry.

Note that we have not assumed $T_B = T$ or that the temperature of the boundary equals that of the fluid just next to the boundary. It is not because we expect there to be a discontinuity present even when dissipation is included. Rather, it is to leave open the possibility that off equilibrium the T which appears in the two fluid equations may not be the real temperature say as measured by a thermometer. A similar difficulty arises in classical hydrodynamics. There the p appearing in the stress tensor (12-7) is for off equilibrium processes not the true pressure (force per unit area) but differs from it by $\zeta\nabla \cdot \boldsymbol{v}$, a term which is a measure of the deviation from equilibrium. So we will leave open the possibility that $T_B - T$ may be proportional to $\nabla \cdot \boldsymbol{v}_n$ or $\nabla \cdot \rho_s(\boldsymbol{v}_n - \boldsymbol{v}_s)$.

For the one dimensional geometry and the Khalatnikov fluxes (the Clark fluxes lead to higher order terms than we wish to consider) Eqs. (28-1,2,3,4) become

$$\rho_n v_n + \rho_s v_s = 0, \tag{28-5}$$

Notes p. 176

$$\frac{\dot{W}}{T_{\mathrm{B}}} = \rho s v_{\mathrm{n}} - \frac{\kappa}{T}\frac{\partial T}{\partial x}, \tag{28-6}$$

$$\dot{W} = \rho s(T + v_{\mathrm{n}}A)v_{\mathrm{n}} - \kappa\frac{\partial T}{\partial x} - \Lambda\frac{\partial v_{\mathrm{n}}}{\partial x}v_{\mathrm{n}} + (\zeta_1 - \rho\zeta_3)v_{\mathrm{n}}^2\frac{\partial \rho}{\partial x}, \tag{28-7}$$

where

$$\Lambda \equiv \tfrac{4}{3}\eta + \zeta_2 - \rho(\zeta_1 + \zeta_4) + \rho^2\zeta_3, \tag{28-8}$$

and the flow is in the x direction; the force per unit area exerted on the boundary is

$$p + \rho_{\mathrm{n}}v_{\mathrm{n}}^2 + \rho_{\mathrm{s}}v_{\mathrm{s}}^2 - (\tfrac{4}{3}\eta + \zeta_2 - \rho\zeta_1)\frac{\partial v_{\mathrm{n}}}{\partial x} + \rho\zeta_1 v_{\mathrm{n}}\frac{\partial \rho}{\partial x} \tag{28-9}$$

and is in the direction of $\mathrm{d}\boldsymbol{S}$. In (28-5,6,7,9) all quantities are to be evaluated in the fluid next to the boundary and we have used the identity

$$\rho_{\mathrm{s}}(\boldsymbol{v}_{\mathrm{s}} - \boldsymbol{v}_{\mathrm{n}}) \equiv \boldsymbol{J} - \rho\boldsymbol{v}_{\mathrm{n}}.$$

The four equations which relate the behavior of the fluid next to the boundary to its behavior at other locations follow from the laws of energy, mass and momentum conservation, and the superfluid equation of motion. The entropy flux does not obey a conservation law when dissipation is included. So we find from (21-2,3,4,5)

$$\mu + \tfrac{1}{2}v_{\mathrm{s}}^2 + (\rho\zeta_3 - \zeta_4)\frac{\partial v_{\mathrm{n}}}{\partial x} + \zeta_3 v_{\mathrm{n}}\frac{\partial \rho}{\partial x} = \text{constant}, \tag{28-10}$$

$$\rho_{\mathrm{n}}v_{\mathrm{n}} + \rho_{\mathrm{s}}v_{\mathrm{s}} = 0, \tag{28-11}$$

$$p + \frac{\rho_{\mathrm{n}}\rho_{\mathrm{s}}}{\rho}(v_{\mathrm{n}} - v_{\mathrm{s}})^2 - (\tfrac{4}{3}\eta + \zeta_2 - \rho\zeta_1)\frac{\partial v_{\mathrm{n}}}{\partial x} + \zeta_1 v_{\mathrm{n}}\frac{\partial \rho}{\partial x} = \text{constant}, \tag{28-12}$$

$$\rho s(T + v_{\mathrm{n}}A)v_{\mathrm{n}} - \kappa\frac{\partial T}{\partial x} - \Lambda\frac{\partial v_{\mathrm{n}}}{\partial x}v_{\mathrm{n}} + (\zeta_1 - \rho\zeta_3)v_{\mathrm{n}}^2\frac{\partial \rho}{\partial x} = \text{constant}. \tag{28-13}$$

We take v_{n} to be first order small. Then the difference Δ between the value of a variable, at a location x, and a location far from the wall will be the same order for all variables. Thus ΔT is on the order of Δv_{n}, etc... The thickness of the shock δ will be found to be zeroth order small;

Notes p. 176

hence $\partial v_{\mathrm{n}}/\partial x$, $\partial T/\partial x$, etc., are all the same order small. Keeping terms in (28-10,12,13) of the lowest order yields

$$-s_\infty \Delta T + \frac{1}{\rho_\infty}\Delta p + (\rho_\infty \zeta_3 - \zeta_4)\frac{\partial \Delta v_{\mathrm{n}}}{\partial x} = 0, \tag{28-14}$$

$$\Delta p - (\tfrac{4}{3}\eta + \zeta_2 - \rho_\infty \zeta_1)\frac{\partial \Delta v_{\mathrm{n}}}{\partial x} = 0, \tag{28-15}$$

$$(\rho s T)_\infty \Delta v_{\mathrm{n}} - \kappa \frac{\partial \Delta T}{\partial x} = 0, \tag{28-16}$$

where the subscript ∞ denotes the value of the quantity far from the boundary and we have used the fact that the constant in (28-10) must be $\mu_\infty + \frac{1}{2}v_{\mathrm{s},\infty}^2$, etc... Eliminate Δp from (28-14) by use of (28-15). Combining this result with (28-16) yields

$$(\rho^2 s^2 T)_\infty \Delta T = \Lambda \kappa \frac{\partial^2 \Delta T}{\partial x^2}. \tag{28-17}$$

Letting the boundary be at $x = 0$ and the fluid at $x > 0$, as in Fig. 25 we find from (28-17) that

$$\Delta T = \Delta T(0)\,\mathrm{e}^{-x/\delta}, \tag{28-18}$$

where $\Delta T(0) \equiv T(0) - T_\infty$ and the thickness δ of the shock is [7]

$$\delta = \sqrt{\Lambda \kappa / \rho^2 s^2 T}, \tag{28-19}$$

where we have dropped the subscript ∞. As we asserted δ is independent of the strength of the shock. This feature is in contrast with the behavior of classical fluids. At 1.5 °K, $\delta \approx 10^{-6}$ cm but at lower temperature it

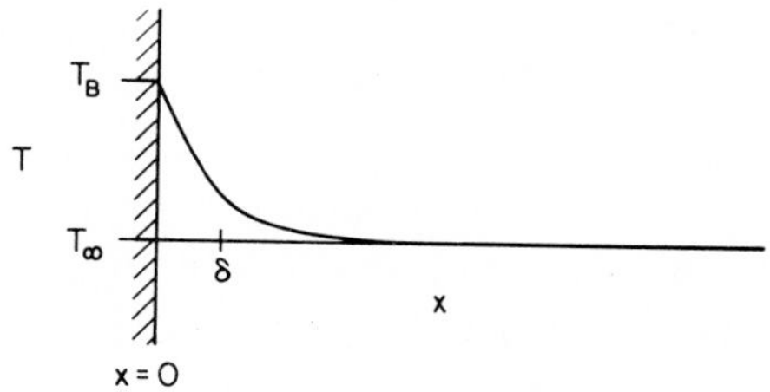

Fig. 25. The behavior of the temperature, according to the two fluid theory, at a boundary where heat enters the He II.

Notes p. 176

increases. This exponential solution is identical with the dispersion law (26-23) for a non-propagating wave found previously.

From (28-16) we find for the normal fluid velocity

$$\Delta v_{\mathrm{n}} = \Delta v_{\mathrm{n}}(0)\, \mathrm{e}^{-x/\delta} = -(\kappa/\rho s T\delta)\Delta T \tag{28-20}$$

verifying that Δv_{n} and ΔT are the same order small.

To complete the solution we need an expression for $\Delta T(0)$. This follows from the boundary conditions (28-5,6,7). For simplicity we first take $T_{\mathrm{B}} = T(0)$ so that the temperature of the boundary equals the temperature of the He II just at the boundary. The qualitative behavior of T is graphed in Fig. 25. Then equating (28-6,7) yields two mutually exclusive solutions:

(1) If $\partial v_{\mathrm{n}}/\partial x$ and hence Δv_{n} is first order small then

$$v_{\mathrm{n}}(0) = 0. \tag{28-21}$$

(2) If $\partial v_{\mathrm{n}}/\partial x$ and hence Δv_{n} is second order small then

$$\Lambda \nabla \cdot \boldsymbol{v}_{\mathrm{n}}(0) = \rho s \boldsymbol{v}_{\mathrm{n}} \cdot \boldsymbol{A} \tag{28-22}$$

evaluated at the wall, and terms of higher (third) order have been neglected. To this order of accuracy (28-22) becomes

$$\Lambda \nabla \cdot \boldsymbol{v}_{\mathrm{n}}(0) = \rho_{\infty} s_{\infty} \boldsymbol{v}_{\mathrm{n},\infty} \cdot \boldsymbol{A}_{\infty}. \tag{28-23}$$

These are the only two solutions possible in the approximation considered here. In the case where the perpendicular component of $\boldsymbol{v}_{\mathrm{n}}$ is restricted one has at lowest order

$$\Delta v_{\mathrm{n}}(0) = -v_{\mathrm{n},\infty} \qquad \frac{\dot{W}}{T} = \frac{\kappa}{T\delta} \Delta T(0). \tag{28-24}$$

In the case where $\nabla \cdot \boldsymbol{v}_{\mathrm{n}}$ is restricted at the boundary one has

$$\Delta T(0) = v_{\mathrm{n},\infty} A_{\infty}, \tag{28-25}$$

so that the temperature jump is second order, as opposed to the other solution where it is first order in the heat flow.

The solution (28-25) is the temperature discontinuity motivated by the discussions in § 6. In the limit where the dissipation vanishes the thickness of the discontinuity vanishes.

There is reason to suspect that the solution (28-25) is the only tenable solution since for a given heat flow it involves a much smaller entropy

Notes p. 176

production. For the one dimensional geometry the entropy production is to lowest order

$$\frac{\Sigma}{T} = \frac{\kappa}{T^2}\left(\frac{\partial T}{\partial x}\right)^2 + \frac{\Lambda}{T}\left(\frac{\partial v_n}{\partial x}\right)^2 . \tag{28-26}$$

One now verifies that the entropy production for the solution where ΔT is second order (28-25) is a factor of $v_{n,\infty}/u_2$ less than the case where ΔT is first order. A closed system goes to a state, the equilibrium state, where Σ vanishes. Similarly it is generally expected, though not proven, that for given external fluxes, which prevent an open system from going to equilibrium, the fluid will be driven to a state of minimum entropy production. Thus we expect that when higher order terms are included the solution (28-24) will be found to be unstable. This still remains to be demonstrated explicitly.

Finally we comment on the situation where the T which appears in the two fluid equations is not the effective temperature, T_{eff} (i.e., $T(0) \neq T_B$) but differs from it by a term proportional to $\nabla \cdot \boldsymbol{v}_n$. Then we set

$$T_{\text{eff}} = T + \alpha \nabla \cdot \boldsymbol{v}_n, \tag{28-27}$$

and

$$T_{\text{eff}}(0) = T_B . \tag{28-28}$$

In the case where $\partial v_n/\partial x$ is first order one finds that no solution is possible unless $\alpha = 0$. For the situation where ΔT is second order a solution exists for any α, provided $\rho s \alpha + \Lambda \neq 0$ for which case Σ is singular. These solutions correspond to an exponential decay of the effective temperature from T_B to $T_B - \boldsymbol{v}_{n,\infty} \cdot \boldsymbol{A}_\infty$ so that the behavior of T_{eff} is independent of α.

In addition to the temperature discontinuity discussed here, there is also a Kapitza resistance at a boundary where heat enters He II. This larger effect, which exists also in many other systems will complicate efforts to observe the thermal boundary shock wave discussed in this section; the latter being unique to He II.

29 Thermal Superconductivity

When liquid helium is cooled by the method of evaporation under reduced pressure it ceases to boil in the usual manner (i.e., by bubble

Notes p. 176

formation) as T_λ is crossed. This is related to the unusual ability of He II to transmit heat by a process of internal convection which involves no net mass flow. In § 7 we saw already that in He II thermal disturbances can propagate as waves (second sound) instead of by diffusion. In the previous section we showed that in a one dimensional geometry such as is physically achieved for heat flow between two concentric spheres there is a temperature drop at the boundary which is *quadratic* in the heat flow. Below, heat flow in He II in a two dimensional geometry (capillary) will be investigated following London [8]. It will be seen that when dissipation is taken into account there is, in this case, a ∇T *linear* in the heat flux. But it is so small that it is almost impossible to maintain an appreciable temperature gradient in He II. This of course prevents the bubble formation associated with boiling.

We ignore the (higher order) thermal discontinuities which take place at the boundaries where heat enters or leaves the fluid, and for concreteness examine heat flow in a parallel slit geometry. The slits lie in the x, y plane at $z = \pm\frac{1}{2}d$. Let all velocities be functions of z and be in the x direction. For this geometry $\nabla \cdot \boldsymbol{v}_\mathrm{n} = 0$, $(\boldsymbol{v}_\mathrm{n} \cdot \nabla)\boldsymbol{v}_\mathrm{n} = 0$, $(\boldsymbol{v}_\mathrm{s} \cdot \nabla)\boldsymbol{v}_\mathrm{s} = 0$. Ignoring the small changes in ρ_s leads to $\nabla \cdot \rho_\mathrm{s}(\boldsymbol{v}_\mathrm{n} - \boldsymbol{v}_\mathrm{s}) = 0$.

From (21-2) and (4-8) one finds in the stationary state

$$\nabla p = \rho s \nabla T + \rho_\mathrm{n} \nabla \tfrac{1}{2}(v_\mathrm{n} - v_\mathrm{s})^2. \tag{29-1}$$

From (21-4) and (21-13) one obtains

$$\nabla p = \eta \nabla^2 \boldsymbol{v}_\mathrm{n}. \tag{29-2}$$

As $\boldsymbol{v}_\mathrm{n}$ is in the x direction the z component of (29-2) yields $\partial p/\partial z = 0$, which combined with the z component of (29-1) implies

$$\frac{\partial T}{\partial z} = -\frac{\rho_\mathrm{n}}{2s\rho}\frac{\partial (v_\mathrm{n} - v_\mathrm{s})^2}{\partial z}. \tag{29-3}$$

Approximating $\rho_\mathrm{n}/\rho s$ as constant we then find

$$T = T_1(x) - \frac{\rho_\mathrm{n}}{2\rho s}(v_\mathrm{n} - v_\mathrm{s})^2, \tag{29-4}$$

where $T_1(x)$ is undetermined. Equating the x component of (29-2) with that of (29-1) yields

$$\eta \nabla^2 v_{\mathrm{n},x} = \rho s \frac{\partial T}{\partial x}. \tag{29-5}$$

Notes p. 176

The left hand side of (29-5) is a function only of z whereas the right hand side is a function only of x, since from (29-4), $\partial T/\partial x = \partial T_1/\partial x$. Thus for (29-5) to have a solution both sides must separately be constant implying

$$\boldsymbol{v}_{\mathrm{n}} = \frac{3\bar{v}_{\mathrm{n}}}{2}\left(1 - \frac{4z^2}{d^2}\right)\hat{\boldsymbol{e}}_x, \tag{29-6}$$

$$T_1 = T_0 - \frac{\eta}{\rho s}\frac{12\bar{v}_{\mathrm{n}}}{d^2}x, \tag{29-7}$$

where T_0 is a constant, $\bar{v}_{\mathrm{n}}$ is the average of $\boldsymbol{v}_{\mathrm{n}}$ and we have ignored the T dependence of $\eta/\rho s$. Combining (29-7) with (29-4) implies

$$T = T_0 - \frac{\eta}{\rho s}\frac{12\bar{v}_{\mathrm{n}}}{d^2}x - \frac{\rho_{\mathrm{n}}}{2\rho s}(v_{\mathrm{n}} - v_{\mathrm{s}})^2. \tag{29-8}$$

By dint of the internal convection the heat flux in the He II in lowest order is [see (21-1)]

$$\boldsymbol{f} = \rho s T \boldsymbol{v}_{\mathrm{n}} - \kappa \nabla T. \tag{29-9}$$

Let us first examine the heat flow in the x direction. From (29-9) and (29-8) we find that the average heat flow $\bar{f}_x$ in the x direction is

$$\bar{f}_x = -\left(\tfrac{1}{12}d^2 K + \kappa\right)\frac{\partial T}{\partial x}, \tag{29-10}$$

where $K \equiv (\rho s)^2 T/\eta$. The coefficient of $\partial T/\partial x$ in (29-10) is called the effective thermal conductivity which we see is geometry dependent and involves the viscosity. In a classical liquid the term involving K would be absent, but for He II this term dominates. In fact for $d = 10^{-2}$ cm, $\frac{1}{12}d^2K \approx 10^{11}$ erg/cm sec °K which is 10^7 times greater than the upper bound on κ determined by second sound absorption (25-19), or equivalently, is also 10^7 times greater than the value of κ just above T_λ. Because heat transport by internal convection is so much larger than by conduction the ordinary thermal conductivity κ of He II has not yet been measured. This superthermalconductivity of He II was first (accidentally) observed by Keesom [24] in 1935 while making specific heat measurements.

As d, f_x, $\partial T/\partial x$ are experimentally measurable and K is known (29-10) can be checked. This has been done by Brewer and Edwards [9] who found that it is valid up to a critical value of the heat flux above which the relation between $\partial T/\partial x$ and f_x was cubic. This is again a

Notes p. 176

question relating to the critical velocities which we discuss in § 42. We remark that Brewer and Edwards performed their experiments in a capillary rather than a slit and instead of (29-10) the appropriate formula then is

$$\bar{f}_x = -\left(\tfrac{1}{32}d^2K + \kappa\right)\frac{\partial T}{\partial x}. \tag{29-11}$$

Finally let us look at heat flow in the z direction. As $\boldsymbol{v}_\mathrm{n}$ is in the x direction we find from (29-9) that the heat flux in the z direction is

$$f_z = -\kappa\frac{\partial T}{\partial z}.$$

As $\partial T/\partial z$ is known from (29-8) then in principle a measurement of f_z could determine κ. However, since typical velocities are on the order of 1 cm/sec and since $s \approx 10^6$ erg/g °K the effect is very small.

The superfluid velocity v_s will be independent of z since $\nabla \times \boldsymbol{v}_\mathrm{s} = 0$. Thus its value can be determined by the condition of no net mass flow or $\rho_\mathrm{n}\bar{v}_\mathrm{n} + \rho_\mathrm{s}v_\mathrm{s} = 0$. Although on the average there is no net mass flow, there is locally a mass flow, i.e., $\rho_\mathrm{n}\boldsymbol{v}_\mathrm{n} + \rho_\mathrm{s}\boldsymbol{v}_\mathrm{s}$, that will not vanish for all z. On the other hand $\rho_\mathrm{n}v_\mathrm{n} + \rho_\mathrm{s}v_\mathrm{s}$ must vanish for all z at the boundary. The difference in mass flows at the boundary and in the bulk can probably be understood in terms of entrance corrections which have been ignored here, and have not yet been investigated for He II.

30 The Superfluid Venturi Tube

For a classical fluid the Bernoulli law (1-17) for incompressible flow implies that in regions where the fluid is moving quickly the pressure is diminished. Thus in the experimental arrangement as indicated in Fig. 26a the level is lowest in the central standpipe where by dint of the continuity law the liquid must flow fastest. The levels in the right and left standpipes are not quite equal due to the small viscous corrections to the Euler equations.

Since in He II the superfluid has zero viscosity one might expect that the Venturi tube would be an especially efficient means of measuring the velocity field. However, Meservey [10] has shown that since $\nabla \times \boldsymbol{v}_\mathrm{s} = 0$ for He II, all three levels must be equal (for stationary flow) as in Fig. 26b.

Notes p. 176

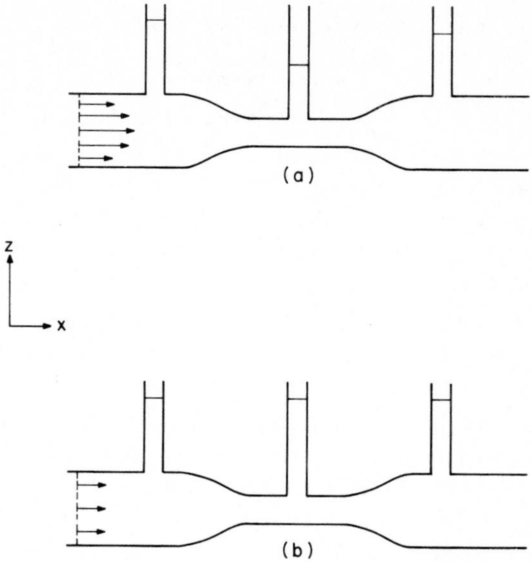

Fig. 26. The fluid level in Venturi tubes attached to a converging stream of (a) a classical fluid, (b) He II. The velocity profiles are indicated by the arrows. For the He II only the velocity profile of the superfluid is shown.

To understand this result one must first examine in detail the situation as regards the classical fluid. Due to its viscosity the classical fluid will be at rest at the boundaries. If the standpipe is small enough not to interfere with the flow then the fluid in it will be at rest as indicated in Fig. 27a. In this way the pressure at the top is simply equal to that at the bottom plus the gravitational head. The pressure at the bottom will in turn equal that of the central streamline since from (12-10),

Fig. 27. Streamlines in the vicinity of the Venturi tube. For the classical fluid, (a) the fluid in the standpipe is at rest. For He II, (b) the streamlines of $\boldsymbol{v}_s$ enter the standpipe since $\nabla \times \boldsymbol{v}_s = 0$.

Notes p. 176

$\partial p/\partial z = 0$. Along this streamline, which also coincides with the x axis, we find from (12-10) that

$$\rho v_x \frac{\partial v_x}{\partial x} = -\frac{\partial p}{\partial x} + \eta \nabla^2 v_x, \tag{30-1}$$

which says that p varies according to Bernoulli's law, except for a small viscous correction. In this way (30-1) leads to a pressure difference between the bases of the standpipes which must then be compensated for by the level differences.

If one could have applied Bernoulli's law directly to the tops of the standpipes one would find that the levels must be equal, since $\boldsymbol{v} = 0$ and the pressures are the same at these locations. Of course such a procedure is forbidden since no matter how small the viscosity, the fluid is at rest in the standpipes and there is no streamline connecting them.

As $\nabla \times \boldsymbol{v}_s = 0$ for He II the fluid cannot be at rest at the boundary and furthermore the fluid in the standpipes cannot be at rest since this would imply the presence of a vortex sheet at the opening. Meservey has shown that the streamlines now enter the standpipe and extend to the top as shown in Fig. 27b.

Now one can apply the superfluid Bernoulli law, $\mu + \frac{1}{2}v_s^2 + gz =$ constant, to the tops of the standpipes (z is measured from the central streamline). Thus

$$\Delta\mu + \Delta\tfrac{1}{2}v_s^2 + g\Delta z = 0, \tag{30-2}$$

or

$$-s\Delta T + \frac{1}{\rho}\Delta p + \frac{\rho_s}{\rho}\Delta\tfrac{1}{2}v_s^2 + \frac{\rho_n}{\rho}\Delta(\boldsymbol{v}_n \cdot \boldsymbol{v}_s - \tfrac{1}{2}v_n^2) + g\Delta z = 0, \tag{30-3}$$

where $\Delta\mu$ indicates the difference in chemical potential at the tops of the two standpipes. The pressures at the tops of the standpipes must equal the vapor pressure, and since variations in the gas pressure are negligible due to its small density, we have $\Delta p = 0$. Meservey has shown that v_s drops off exponentially with height in the standpipe. In fact for a standpipe taller than it is wide we can to excellent accuracy take $\Delta v_s = 0$, or

$$s\Delta T = g\Delta z, \tag{30-4}$$

where we have also noted that $v_n = 0$ at the top of each standpipe. So for flow of He II the standpipes do not yield a measure of the velocity.

Notes p. 176

Under conditions of isothermal flow we finally obtain $\Delta z = 0$. Although standpipes do not reflect the Bernoulli pressure drop it should however be registered on pressure sensitive diaphragms located say at the entrance to the standpipes.

By forcing He II through an arrangement such as in Fig. 26b Van Alphen [11] has actually observed $\Delta z = 0$, for superfluid velocities that are not too large. In his experiments the flow path was packed with jewelers rouge so as to provide a narrow channel and higher critical velocity. This always has the side effect of clamping the normal fluid at rest ($v_n = 0$). But our considerations here suggest that even if the normal fluid were free to move the superfluid Bernoulli law still requires no level difference, provided of course that the critical velocities are not exceeded.

Other experiments which observe a state of flow where $\nabla \times \boldsymbol{v}_s = 0$ plays a crucial role were performed by Craig and Pellam [12]. In a classical liquid the Kutta–Joukowski theorem requires that a circulation be formed about a wing (W in Fig. 28) as it flows by, and this is true no matter how small the viscosity. Thus classical flow past the wing will lead to a Magnus lift which in lowest order is independent of the viscosity.

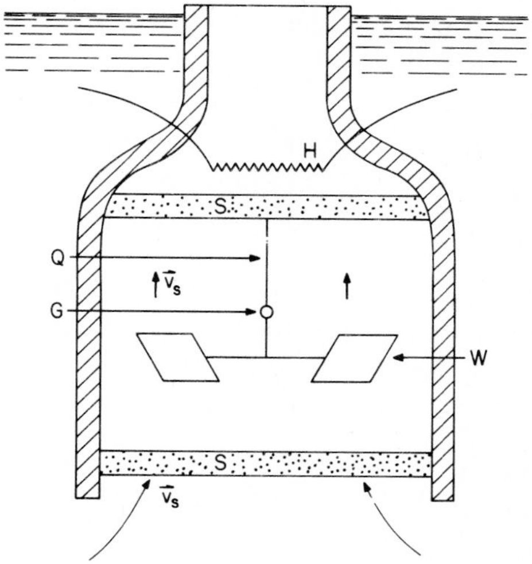

Fig. 28. The superfluid wind-tunnel of Craig and Pellam. The superleaks S keep the normal fluid at rest, while the heater H sucks superfluid through as indicated by the $\boldsymbol{v}_s$ streamlines.

Notes p. 176

Craig and Pellam reasoned that since for the supercomponent $\nabla \times \boldsymbol{v}_s = 0$ it cannot form a circulation about the wing and hence there should be no Magnus effect. As with the experiment of Hess and Fairbank (§ 19) this result would demonstrate that $\nabla \times \boldsymbol{v}_s = 0$ is more stringent than the requirement of vanishingly small viscosity.

It is crucial in this experiment that the normal fluid be kept at rest since it behaves like a classical fluid and we wish to observe the effects of the superflow. This was accomplished by means of the superfluid wind-tunnel sketched in Fig. 28. At each end of the tunnel were superleaks S or regions packed with very fine powder. The normal fluid cannot flow through this powder due to its viscosity; thus when the heater H is turned on superfluid is sucked towards it as in § 6, and the normal fluid which flows away cannot get through the superleak into the wind-tunnel. By this technique $\boldsymbol{v}_s$ is along the path indicated and $\boldsymbol{v}_n = 0$ in the wind-tunnel. The torque or Magnus lift on the wings would twist the quartz fiber Q, and be seen from light reflected by the mirror G.

Their sensitivity was much better than that required to observe the torque in a classical liquid of vanishingly small viscosity. To the accuracy of their experiment they found that below a critical velocity there was no lift consistent with the requirement $\nabla \times \boldsymbol{v}_s = 0$. In a disconnected geometry one could have $\nabla \times \boldsymbol{v}_s = 0$ everywhere and still have circulation and lift. But the geometry in Fig. 28 is connected and therefore $\nabla \times \boldsymbol{v}_s = 0$ everywhere implies no circulation.

The observation here of no circulation is similar to the zero circulation states of Whitmore and Zimmermann discussed in § 10. However, in flow around a wire there is no requirement that a circulation forms, even in a classical fluid. So the results of Craig and Pellam show that not only can flows with $\nabla \times \boldsymbol{v}_s = 0$ be observed, but that below a critical velocity it is required. In parallel with the Whitmore and Zimmermann work one expects that above the critical velocity quantized vortices form around the wing and lead to a lift, but unlike the classical fluid we do not know the mechanism which leads to the creation of circulation in He II.

Notes p. 176

31 The Free Energy and Motion of Quantized Vortices in Two Dimensions, Neglecting Dissipation

In this section we derive the general formula for the free energy of an arbitrary array of quantized vortex lines in a cylindrical rotating bucket. It will be seen that in terms of this free energy the motion of the vortices assumes Hamilton's form.

We follow the method used in § 18 to evaluate the free energy of an off center vortex. In the presence of N vortices one must introduce N branch cuts as in Fig. 29. Then instead of (18-35) the free energy becomes

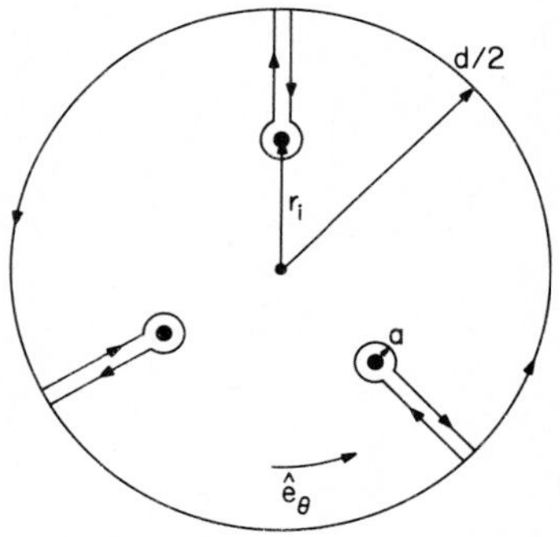

Fig. 29. Contour of integration for evaluating the free energy when many vortices are present.

$$F = \rho_s \ell \sum_{i=1}^{N} \int_{r_i+a}^{\frac{1}{2}d} (\phi_+ - \phi_-)(\tfrac{1}{2}\boldsymbol{v}_s - \boldsymbol{\omega} \times \boldsymbol{r}) \cdot \hat{\boldsymbol{e}}_\theta \, \mathrm{d}r + \tfrac{1}{2} N \rho_s \pi \gamma^2 \ell, \tag{31-1}$$

where d is the diameter and as before

$$\phi_+ - \phi_- = 2\pi\gamma. \tag{31-2}$$

The contribution to $\boldsymbol{v}_s$ in (31-1) comes from all the vortices and their images. Assuming that all the vortices have the same sense we find

$$F = \pi\gamma^2 \rho_s \ell \left\{ \sum_{i=1}^{N} \log \left[\frac{\frac{1}{4}d^2 - r_i^2}{(d/2\sqrt{\mathrm{e}})a} \right] + \sum_{i<j=2}^{N} \log \left(\frac{\frac{1}{4}d^2 - 2r_i r_j \cos\theta_{ij} + 4r_i^2 r_j^2/d^2}{r_i^2 - 2r_i r_j \cos\theta_{ij} + r_j^2} \right) - \sum_{i=1}^{N} \frac{\omega}{\gamma} (\tfrac{1}{4}d^2 - r_i^2) \right\}, \tag{31-3}$$

Notes p. 176

where $\theta_{ij} \equiv \theta_i - \theta_j$ and we remark that $\frac{1}{2}\sum_{i \neq j} = \sum_{i<j}$. Except for the $\sqrt{e}$ (31-3) is the same as first derived by Hess [13].

We define $\mathscr{H}$ and $\boldsymbol{L}$ by

$$F = \mathscr{H} - \boldsymbol{\omega} \cdot \boldsymbol{L}, \tag{31-4}$$

then it can be seen that $\mathscr{H}$ is a Hamiltonian for the motion of the vortex lines in that

$$\dot{x}_i = \frac{\partial}{\partial y_i}(\mathscr{H}/2\pi\gamma\rho_s\ell), \qquad \dot{y}_i = -\frac{\partial}{\partial x_i}(\mathscr{H}/2\pi\gamma\rho_s\ell), \tag{31-5}$$

or in cylindrical coordinates

$$\dot{\theta}_i = -\frac{\partial}{\partial(r_i^2)}(\mathscr{H}/\pi\gamma\rho_s\ell), \qquad (\dot{r_i^2}) = \frac{\partial}{\partial\theta_i}(\mathscr{H}/\pi\gamma\rho_s\ell). \tag{31-6}$$

Equations (31-5,6) are verified by simply showing that the derivatives lead to the velocity at the vortex core i due to all the other vortices and images. By the Kelvin theorem this must be the velocity $\dot{\boldsymbol{r}}_i$ of the given vortex. That such a Hamiltonian formulation for the motion of vortices is possible in any two dimensional geometry was shown by Lin [14]. Of course to derive these results we have assumed $\nabla \cdot \boldsymbol{v}_s = 0$.

From (31-3) and (31-6) one sees that if $\partial F/\partial r_i = 0$ such as is required in equilibrium then all the vortices are rotating with the local velocity of the normal fluid.

The minimization of (31-3) leads to the stable equilibrium array of quantized vortices. Stauffer and Fetter [15] have investigated this problem for high ω and found that the vortex lattice has no particular symmetry. In general the vortices arrange themselves in concentric circles, but do not in general form a triangular or hexagonal, etc., lattice.

When all the vortices are at the wall so that $r_i \approx \frac{1}{2}d - a$, then the free energy as given by (31-3) becomes the free energy of no vortex as should be the case.

From (31-5) we see that x_i, y_i giving the location of a vortex can be looked upon as canonical momenta. This suggests a quantization of the vortex motion through the usual prescription for the commutation relations (e.g., $[x_i, y_i] = i\hbar/2\pi\gamma\rho_s\ell$ for two dimensional motions). This procedure which is at most valid for the incompressible approximation has been followed by Fetter [16]. He finds that the Hamiltonian formulation can be extended to vortex motions, such as waves propagating

Notes p. 176

along the vortex, which involve small displacements from the two dimensional symmetry.

A question that has received much attention is that of calculating the normal modes of oscillation when an array of vortex lines receives a small disturbance from the equilibrium state in such a way that the two dimensionality is maintained. Let the equilibrium quantities be denoted by subscript zero; then

$$x_i = x_{i,0} + \delta x_i, \tag{31-7}$$

$$y_i = y_{i,0} + \delta y_i, \tag{31-8}$$

where δ denotes the deviation from the equilibrium configuration. Expanding the Hamiltonian we find

$$\mathscr{H} = \mathscr{H}_0 + \left(\frac{\partial \mathscr{H}}{\partial x_\alpha}\right)_0 \delta x_\alpha + \left(\frac{\partial \mathscr{H}}{\partial y_\alpha}\right)_0 \delta y_\alpha + \left(\frac{\partial^2 \mathscr{H}}{\partial x_\alpha \, \partial x_\beta}\right)_0 \frac{\delta x_\alpha \, \delta x_\beta}{2}$$
$$+ \left(\frac{\partial^2 \mathscr{H}}{\partial y_\alpha \, \partial y_\beta}\right)_0 \frac{\delta y_\alpha \, \delta y_\beta}{2} + \left(\frac{\partial^2 \mathscr{H}}{\partial x_\alpha \, \partial y_\beta}\right)_0 \delta x_\alpha \, \delta y_\beta, \tag{31-9}$$

so that the equations of motion become in linear approximation

$$2\pi\gamma\rho_s \ell \; \delta\dot{x}_i = \left(\frac{\partial^2 \mathscr{H}}{\partial y_\alpha \, \partial y_i}\right)_0 \delta y_\alpha + \left(\frac{\partial^2 \mathscr{H}}{\partial x_\alpha \, \partial y_i}\right)_0 \delta x_\alpha, \tag{31-10}$$

$$-2\pi\gamma\rho_s \ell \; \delta\dot{y}_i = \left(\frac{\partial^2 \mathscr{H}}{\partial y_\alpha \, \partial x_i}\right)_0 \delta y_\alpha + \left(\frac{\partial^2 \mathscr{H}}{\partial x_\alpha \, \partial x_i}\right)_0 \delta x_\alpha, \tag{31-11}$$

where we have used

$$2\pi\gamma\rho_s \ell \; \dot{x}_{i,0} = (\partial \mathscr{H}/\partial y_i)_0, \tag{31-12}$$

$$2\pi\gamma\rho_s \ell \; \dot{y}_{i,0} = -(\partial \mathscr{H}/\partial x_i)_0, \tag{31-13}$$

so that $\delta\dot{\mathbf{r}}_i$ is the velocity of the vortex relative to the rotating coordinate system. As a vortex is displaced from its equilibrium location, the velocity which it induces at the other vortices changes and thus by the Kelvin theorem they are set into motion. Equations (31-10,11) describe the resulting motion. In principle for a given ω, d, one must minimize (31-3) to find the equilibrium configuration and thus the equilibrium Hamiltonian. Using this function one looks for a solution to (31-10,11) in the form $\delta r_i \sim e^{i\omega t}$ by the requirement that the determinant of the coefficients of the homogeneous equations vanishes. This solution for the normal

Notes p. 176

modes ω_i can be carried out exactly at best for a couple of vortex lines. Otherwise approximations must be used.

The case of greatest interest has been quick rotation $\omega \gg \omega_{cr}$ so that many vortices are present, with a uniform density per unit area $n_0 = 2\omega m/h$ (20-1). All papers on this subject have considered an infinite array of vortices. In this way they use translational invariance to greatly simplify the mathematics. In the work of Fetter et al. [17] the rotation of the equilibrium lattice was incorrectly neglected, so that they didn't even start out with equations equivalent to (31-10,11). This mistake was pointed out by Stauffer [18], who showed that when rotation is included their results agree with Tkachenko [19], which were later derived again by Fetter [16].

One can doubt that the results obtained for an infinite lattice have any relation to reality. The velocities of the vortex lines are long-range and thus the location of the boundary becomes crucial. Also for this approximation the axis of rotation which is clearly a preferred location does not enter the results. Finally the angular momentum of *each* vortex in an infinite lattice is strongly divergent. A satisfactory approach to this problem would be to solve for the normal modes in a bucket of large but finite radius R and then let R go to infinity. This more complicated procedure has not been carried out.

Reatto [20] has commented that the calculations based upon (31-3,5,6) have a shortcoming in that each vortex instantaneously feels the disturbance or motion of the other vortices. He *assumed* that, when one removes the incompressibility assumption, ($\nabla \cdot \boldsymbol{v}_s = 0$) the vortex signals will propagate at the speed of sound and thus he solved the normal mode problem for an infinite lattice, but with retarded signals. It is perhaps questionable that vorticity signals propagate at the speed of sound, since any superposition of sound waves identically satisfies $\nabla \times \boldsymbol{v}_s = 0$. Yet when a vortex moves the curl is changing at the core where $\rho_s = 0$.

32 *The Drag on Quantized Vortices*

As we have seen in § 18 the superfluid vortices must be moving with the normal fluid in equilibrium. Thus in order for the two fluid theory to be self-consistent it must include a drag which the normal fluid exerts on vortices so as to force them to the equilibrium state. In the previous section we ignored the effects of friction on the motion of quantized

Notes p. 176

vortices. Here we will see that the bulk viscosity ζ_3, which contributes to the absorption of second sound propagating with respect to quiescent He II, determines the normal fluid drag on the quantized vortices.

Even in equilibrium the velocity field of a vortex is complicated. Thus off equilibrium we must make some simplifying assumptions. As in § 18 we will consider vortex motions which maintain T, $\mu + \frac{1}{2}v_s^2 - \boldsymbol{v}_n \cdot \boldsymbol{v}_s$, constant and $\boldsymbol{v}_n = \boldsymbol{\omega} \times \boldsymbol{r}$. For this case we show directly from the two fluid equations

$$\frac{\mathrm{d}F}{\mathrm{d}t} = -\int \Sigma \,\mathrm{d}V = -\int \zeta_3[\nabla \cdot \rho_s(\boldsymbol{v}_s - \boldsymbol{v}_n)]^2 \,\mathrm{d}V. \tag{32-1}$$

This equation is the basic description of the drag on quantized vortices.

To derive (32-1) first use the thermodynamics (4-5,6) to show

$$\rho_s(\boldsymbol{v}_s - \boldsymbol{v}_n) \cdot \frac{\partial \boldsymbol{v}_s}{\partial t} = \frac{\partial U}{\partial t} - (\mu + \tfrac{1}{2}v_s^2 - \boldsymbol{v}_n \cdot \boldsymbol{v}_s)\frac{\partial \rho}{\partial t} - T\frac{\partial \rho s}{\partial t} - \boldsymbol{v}_n \cdot \frac{\partial \boldsymbol{J}}{\partial t}. \tag{32-2}$$

Integrating over the volume of fluid, the terms in $\partial U/\partial t$ and $\partial \rho/\partial t$ can be converted to surface integrals since these are conserved and $\mu + \frac{1}{2}v_s^2 - \boldsymbol{v}_n \cdot \boldsymbol{v}_s$ is constant. Similarly the term in $\partial \boldsymbol{J}/\partial t$ can be converted to a surface integral since $\boldsymbol{v}_n = \boldsymbol{\omega} \times \boldsymbol{r}$ and the stress tensor is symmetric. Along with the other surface contributions we neglect it. From the entropy law (21-1) we then find

$$\int \rho_s(\boldsymbol{v}_s - \boldsymbol{v}_n) \cdot \frac{\partial \boldsymbol{v}_s}{\partial t} \mathrm{d}V = -\int \Sigma \,\mathrm{d}V, \tag{32-3}$$

which in view of the definition of the free energy (18-14) and the value of Σ (21-10) yields Eq. (32-1). Note that according to (32-1) the vortex must always move so as to decrease the free energy. Also the dissipation will vanish only when $\nabla \cdot \rho_s(\boldsymbol{v}_s - \boldsymbol{v}_n) = 0$, or the vortex moves with the local normal fluid velocity.

We first evaluate (32-1) for parallel vortex lines in the approximation where $\nabla \cdot \boldsymbol{v}_s = 0$ such as was taken for the reversible behavior. This implies that the superfluid density distribution is frozen to the vortex line. Then (32-1) becomes

$$\frac{\mathrm{d}F}{\mathrm{d}t} = -\zeta_3 \int [(\boldsymbol{v}_s - \boldsymbol{v}_n) \cdot \nabla \rho_s]^2 \,\mathrm{d}V. \tag{32-4}$$

If one used (18-25) for ρ_s then (32-4) becomes a square of a delta function which is too singular. This is only a formal difficulty and can be resolved

Notes p. 176

by choosing a smoother more physical distribution for ρ_s. We will assume that $\nabla\rho_s$ has a constant magnitude $\rho_{s,0}/a$ in a cylindrical region of radius a and is directed radially outward from the core. Since the velocity due to the core is perpendicular to $\nabla\rho_s$ (32-4) becomes

$$\frac{\mathrm{d}F}{\mathrm{d}t} = -\zeta_3 \frac{\rho_{s,0}^2}{a^2} \int [(\boldsymbol{v}_{s,e} - \boldsymbol{v}_n)_i \cdot \hat{\boldsymbol{e}}_{r_i}]^2 \,\mathrm{d}V, \tag{32-5}$$

where $\hat{\boldsymbol{e}}_{r_i}$ points radially outward from the core of the ith vortex, and $\boldsymbol{v}_{s,e}$ is the superfluid velocity at the core due to all other (external) vortices and images, the integral extends over the cylinder of radius a, and one must sum over all the vortex cores (all i). The normal fluid and external velocities do not vary appreciably over the core, provided of course that it is more than a healing length from the boundary, thus (32-5) becomes

$$\frac{\mathrm{d}F}{\mathrm{d}t} = -\tfrac{1}{2}\zeta_3 \rho_s^2 \ell \pi \sum_{i=1}^{N} (\boldsymbol{v}_{s,e} - \boldsymbol{v}_n)_i^2,$$

where the velocities are evaluated at each of the N vortices present and we have dropped the zero subscript from ρ_s.

A more careful consideration of the problem reveals that this result is too small by a factor of four. The mistake was in assuming a strictly circular core in calculating $(\boldsymbol{v}_s - \boldsymbol{v}_n)\cdot\nabla\rho_s$. As discussed in § 18 [see (18-25)] the core is a line of constant $\frac{1}{2}v_s^2 - \boldsymbol{v}_n \cdot \boldsymbol{v}_s$. Thus there is also an angular component to $\nabla\rho_s$ which although tiny compared with $\rho_{s,0}/a$ yields a significant contribution to $(\boldsymbol{v}_s - \boldsymbol{v}_n)\cdot\nabla\rho_s$ since it is multiplied by the large velocity of the vortex core. In a similar situation as discussed following Eq. (18-44) this term yields an equal contribution to $(\boldsymbol{v}_s - \boldsymbol{v}_n)\cdot\nabla\rho_s$. To demonstrate this fact it is useful to note that if Θ_i is the angle as measured around the ith vortex that the relation between angular and radial derivatives is

$$\frac{\partial\rho_s}{\partial\Theta_i} = \frac{\partial\rho_s}{\partial|\boldsymbol{r}-\boldsymbol{r}_i|} \frac{\partial(\frac{1}{2}v_s^2 - \boldsymbol{v}_n\cdot\boldsymbol{v}_s)/\partial\Theta_i}{\partial(\frac{1}{2}v_s^2 - \boldsymbol{v}_n\cdot\boldsymbol{v}_s)/\partial|\boldsymbol{r}-\boldsymbol{r}_i|},$$

where the fact that ρ_s is a function of $\frac{1}{2}v_s^2 - \boldsymbol{v}_n\cdot\boldsymbol{v}_s$ has been used. Thus a better expression for $\mathrm{d}F/\mathrm{d}t$ is

$$\frac{\mathrm{d}F}{\mathrm{d}t} = -2\zeta_3 \rho_s^2 \ell \pi \sum_{i=1}^{N} (\boldsymbol{v}_{s,e} - \boldsymbol{v}_n)_i^2. \tag{32-6}$$

Notes p. 176

One might wonder if in view of (31-3) and (31-5) $\mathrm{d}F/\mathrm{d}t \equiv 0$. Although off equilibrium each vortex moves with the local velocity of the superfluid at the core, this velocity due to the dissipation is no longer simply the superposition of the velocities generated by the other vortices and images and thus (31-5,6) do not apply off equilibrium. Equation (32-6) in fact is a statement of how the dissipation modifies the vortex motion and $\boldsymbol{v}_s$. As F is a function of the location of the vortices:

$$\frac{\mathrm{d}F}{\mathrm{d}t} = \frac{\partial F}{\partial (r_i^2)} \frac{\mathrm{d}(r_i^2)}{\mathrm{d}t} + \frac{\partial F}{\partial \theta_i} \frac{\mathrm{d}\theta_i}{\mathrm{d}t}. \tag{32-7}$$

Setting:

$$r_i^2 = r_{i,0}^2 + \delta(r_i^2), \qquad \theta_i = \theta_{i,0} + \delta\theta_i, \tag{32-8}$$

where the subscript zero and the δ denote the reversible and irreversible contributions, implies that

$$\frac{\mathrm{d}F}{\mathrm{d}t} = \frac{\partial F}{\partial (r_i^2)} \frac{\mathrm{d}\,\delta(r_i^2)}{\mathrm{d}t} + \frac{\partial F}{\partial \theta_i} \frac{\mathrm{d}\,\delta\theta_i}{\mathrm{d}t}, \tag{32-9}$$

where we have used (31-3), (31-6). As the time derivatives are already first order small in the dissipation we can to this order of accuracy evaluate $\partial F/\partial r_i^2$ and $\partial F/\partial \theta_i$ for the reversible case. That is we can use (31-3), or equivalently (18-20) along with $\nabla \cdot \boldsymbol{v}_s = 0$. Similarly in (32-4) one can evaluate $\boldsymbol{v}_{s,e}$ by simply superimposing the contributions of the images and other vortices. In this way we finally obtain

$$\sum_{i=1}^{N} 2\pi\rho_s \ell \boldsymbol{\gamma} \cdot \left[(\boldsymbol{v}_n - \boldsymbol{v}_{s,e})_i \times \frac{\mathrm{d}\,\delta \boldsymbol{r}_i}{\mathrm{d}t} \right] = \zeta_3 \rho_s^2 2\pi\ell \sum_{i=1}^{N} (\boldsymbol{v}_{s,e} - \boldsymbol{v}_n)_i^2, \tag{32-10}$$

where we have used (31-3,5) and assigned γ a direction by the right hand rule. When $\boldsymbol{v}_{s,e}$ is calculated by superimposing the contributions of the images and other vortices Eq. (32-10) describes the first order dissipative contribution to vortex motion. The complete description of vortex motion is obtained by adding the $\mathrm{d}\boldsymbol{r}_i/\mathrm{d}t$ obtained from (32-10), to the non-dissipative contribution to $\mathrm{d}\boldsymbol{r}_i/\mathrm{d}t$ that can be calculated by the methods of § 31.

It is important to note that in describing the motion of more than one vortex the summations can be removed from both sides of (32-10) yielding for each vortex

$$2\pi\rho_s \ell \boldsymbol{\gamma} \cdot \left[(\boldsymbol{v}_n - \boldsymbol{v}_{s,e})_i \times \frac{\mathrm{d}\,\delta \boldsymbol{r}_i}{\mathrm{d}t} \right] = \zeta_3 \rho_s^2 2\pi\ell (\boldsymbol{v}_{s,e} - \boldsymbol{v}_n)_i^2, \tag{32-11}$$

Notes p. 176

which says that the dissipation at the core of the ith vortex equals the decrease in its contribution to the free energy. To justify this *local* description of vortex motion we show that the *changes* in free energy can be localized to the core region.

In the same manner that led to (32-1) it can be shown that except for a surface term

$$\frac{\partial}{\partial t}\int\left[\int \rho_s(\boldsymbol{v}_s - \boldsymbol{v}_n)\cdot \mathrm{d}\boldsymbol{v}_s\right]\mathrm{d}V = -\int \zeta_3[\nabla\cdot\rho_s(\boldsymbol{v}_s - \boldsymbol{v}_n)]^2\mathrm{d}V,$$

where the volume of integration is arbitrary. If we choose *any* volume which includes the ith vortex then the right hand side becomes equal to the right hand side of (32-11) and the left hand side becomes

$$-\int \frac{\partial\phi}{\partial t}\nabla\cdot\rho_s(\boldsymbol{v}_s - \boldsymbol{v}_n)\,\mathrm{d}V,$$

where another surface term has been dropped. With $\nabla\cdot\boldsymbol{v}_s = 0$ this term has a contribution only from the core region which by the usual methods employed here and in § 18 equals the left hand side of (32-11) thus justifying (32-11) as valid for each vortex.

Note that the right hand side of (32-10) and hence the drag is proportional to the length ℓ of the vortex. Also the equilibrium case $\boldsymbol{v}_{s,e} - \boldsymbol{v}_n = 0$ is an exact solution of (32-10). Some authors [21] have claimed that in the presence of vortex lines additional terms must be added to the two fluid equations to describe their motion. We have seen here that just as with classical hydrodynamics the motion of a vortex follows from the basic equations that describe the development of the velocity with time.

We now solve (32-10) in the special case of a single vortex line in a cylindrical bucket of He II rotating at angular velocity $\boldsymbol{\omega}$, so that

$$\boldsymbol{\gamma}\cdot\left[(\boldsymbol{v}_n - \boldsymbol{v}_{s,e})_1 \times \frac{\mathrm{d}\boldsymbol{r}_1}{\mathrm{d}t}\right] = \zeta_3\rho_s(v_n - v_{s,e})_1^2,$$

or

$$\frac{\mathrm{d}r_1}{\mathrm{d}t} = -\frac{\rho_s\zeta_3}{\gamma}(\boldsymbol{v}_n - \boldsymbol{v}_s)_1\cdot\hat{\boldsymbol{e}}_\theta = -\frac{\rho_s\zeta_3}{\gamma}\left(\omega - \frac{\gamma}{\frac{1}{4}d^2 - r_1^2}\right)r_1, \qquad (32\text{-}12)$$

which is the time irreversible equation describing the dissipative motion of an off-center vortex. For an off-center vortex moving reversibly only

Notes p. 176

under the influence of its image, $dr_1/dt = 0$, but in the presence of dissipation the modifications of $\boldsymbol{v}_s$ lead to (32-12).

First consider the motion of a vortex near $r_1 = 0$, then (32-12) becomes

$$\frac{dr_1}{dt} = -\frac{\rho_s \zeta_3}{\gamma}\left(\omega - \frac{4\gamma}{d^2}\right) r_1, \tag{32-13}$$

which describes an exponential time behavior. If

$$\omega > \gamma/\tfrac{1}{4}d^2, \tag{32-14}$$

then the vortex will move to the center, $r_1 = 0$ and stay there. Thus we see that if (32-14) is obeyed the vortex at the center is dynamically stable against small perturbations. On the other hand if

$$\omega < \gamma/\tfrac{1}{4}d^2$$

the vortex will move to the wall and is thus unstable at the center. These results are the hydrodynamic demonstration of the behavior of an off-center vortex that was elucidated in § 18. Since we now have a dynamic description we not only can describe the equilibrium state but also the time constant that governs the relaxation to this state. From (32-13) we find that it is

$$\frac{1}{\alpha} = \frac{\gamma}{\rho_s \zeta_3(\omega - 4\gamma/d^2)}. \tag{32-15}$$

For $\omega \approx \omega_{cr}$ and $d \approx 0.2$ cm (25-16) implies that $1/\alpha = 1.0$ sec at $T = 1.5$ °K, which is quite long. The greater ω the greater the restoring force and hence the shorter the decay time. When ω satisfies (32-14) and the vortex is located at the maximum of the free energy one finds from (32-12) that a small displacement will push it either to the wall or the center but the exact time behavior is a bit more complicated.

As the radial location of the vortex changes, so does the angular momentum of the fluid. Yet if $\boldsymbol{v}_n$ is exactly solid body rotation there is no way in which the boundaries can exert the necessary torque. The qualitative resolution of this difficulty is that when the vortex moves $\boldsymbol{v}_n \neq \boldsymbol{\omega} \times \boldsymbol{r}$ but experiences a reaction torque that is transmitted to the boundary through its viscosity.

The same dissipative effects which push the quantized vortex lines to their locally stable locations also exert a drag on vortex rings moving with respect to the normal fluid. We now calculate this effect assuming first that the vortex ring moves in an infinite otherwise quiescent He II

Notes p. 176

with $\boldsymbol{v}_n = 0$, T and $\mu + \frac{1}{2}v_s^2 - \boldsymbol{v}_n \cdot \boldsymbol{v}_s$ both constant. In the same manner that leads to (32-1) one finds

$$\frac{\mathrm{d}}{\mathrm{d}t}\int \left[\int \rho_s \boldsymbol{v}_s \cdot \mathrm{d}\boldsymbol{v}_s \right] \mathrm{d}V = - \int \zeta_3 (\nabla \cdot \rho_s \boldsymbol{v}_s)^2 \mathrm{d}V. \tag{32-16}$$

Introducing again the fact that ρ_s drops to zero at a core radius from the ring as in (18-25) the left hand side becomes

$$\frac{\mathrm{d}}{\mathrm{d}t}\left[\int \tfrac{1}{2}\rho_s v_s^2 \,\mathrm{d}V + \rho_{s,0}\gamma^2\pi^2 R^2 \right],$$

so that the kinetic energy of a superfluid vortex ring is not simply $\frac{1}{2}\int \rho_s v_s^2 \,\mathrm{d}V$ but is modified by a core energy. We do not wish to emphasize this point since the effects are small and are related to the assumptions on the behavior of ρ_s near the core. Note that this extra term would slightly change the vortex kinetic energy for the hollow core model as given by (10-8), to

$$\text{K.E.}_{\text{R}} = 2\pi^2 \rho_{s,0}\gamma^2 R \left(\log \frac{8R}{a} - \frac{3}{2} \right). \tag{32-17}$$

Evaluating the right hand side of (32-16) as before, by taking $\nabla \cdot \boldsymbol{v}_s = 0$, we find for the dissipative contribution to the vortex motion

$$\frac{\mathrm{dK.E.}_{\text{R}}}{\mathrm{d}t} = -4\zeta_3 \int (\boldsymbol{v}_{s,e} \cdot \nabla\rho_s)^2 \mathrm{d}V = -\zeta_3 \rho_{s,0}^2 2\pi R v_{\text{R}}^2, \tag{32-18}$$

where R is the radius of the vortex ring and we used the fact that each element of the ring moves with the ring velocity $\boldsymbol{v}_{\text{R}} = \boldsymbol{v}_{s,e}$:

$$v_{\text{R}} = \frac{\gamma}{2R}\left(\log \frac{8R}{a} - \frac{1}{2} \right), \tag{32-19}$$

which is directed perpendicular to the plane of the vortex ring. From (32-17,18) the dissipative correction to vortex motion is:

$$\frac{\mathrm{d}R}{\mathrm{d}t} = -\frac{\rho_{s,0}\zeta_3}{4\pi R}\left(\log \frac{8R}{a} - \frac{1}{2} \right). \tag{32-20}$$

When dissipation is neglected $\mathrm{d}R/\mathrm{d}t = 0$, but when taken into account the vortex shrinks ($\mathrm{d}R/\mathrm{d}t < 0$) and thus loses energy. Note that the quantum of vorticity γ, does not appear in (32-20), and that $\mathrm{d}R/\mathrm{d}t$ is not proportional to R. Equation (32-20) cannot be integrated exactly but to

Notes p. 176

an excellent approximation one can ignore the variations in log R, and obtain

$$R^2(t) = R^2(0) - \frac{\rho_s \zeta_3}{2\pi}\left(\log \frac{8R(0)}{a} - \frac{1}{2}\right) t, \qquad (32\text{-}21)$$

where we have dropped the subscript zero from ρ_s and $R(t)$ is the radius of the ring at time t. The characteristic time required for a vortex ring to shrink to $R(0)/\sqrt{2}$ is

$$\frac{\pi R^2(0)}{\rho_s \zeta_3[\log 8R(0)/a - \frac{1}{2}]}, \qquad (32\text{-}22)$$

which for $R(0) \approx 10^{-4}$ cm is roughly 10^{-4} sec at 1.5 °K, or such a vortex will disappear before it has travelled 10^{-3} cm, which is very quick. Imperfect knowledge of ζ_3 and the idealized behavior near the core could easily lead to a modification of this result by a factor of 30. The change of R^2 with time is independent of time and since the impulse I_R of a ring is proportional to R^2 the vortex ring loses momentum at a steady rate:

$$\frac{\mathrm{d}\,|I_R|}{\mathrm{d}t} = -\pi \rho_s^2 \zeta_3 \gamma \left(\log \frac{8R}{a} - \frac{1}{2}\right), \qquad (32\text{-}23)$$

we have used (10-14) for I_R.

As the vortex ring shrinks it accelerates increasing $v_R - v_n$. This goes on until $R \approx 2a$ at which point it disappears like a vortex cancelling its image at a boundary. If the core radius is determined by the stability condition (18-56) then it will be moving just at the speed of sound when it collapses.

In the case where a vortex ring moves in a fluid where v_n is constant but non-zero and $\boldsymbol{v}_s$ has contributions external to the vortex ring one directly obtains instead of (32-18) by the same methods used to justify (32-11):

$$\frac{\mathrm{d}}{\mathrm{d}t}\mathrm{K.E.}_R + (\boldsymbol{v}'_{s,e} - \boldsymbol{v}_n)\cdot \frac{\mathrm{d}\boldsymbol{I}_R}{\mathrm{d}t} = -\zeta_3 \rho_s^2 2\pi R(\boldsymbol{v}_R + \boldsymbol{v}'_{s,e} - \boldsymbol{v}_n)^2, \qquad (32\text{-}24)$$

where $\mathrm{K.E.}_R$, $\boldsymbol{I}_R$ and $\boldsymbol{v}_R$ are still the energy, impulse, velocity of a vortex ring in an infinite quiescent fluid, and we have set $\boldsymbol{v}_{s,e} = \boldsymbol{v}_R + \boldsymbol{v}'_{s,e}$ so that $\boldsymbol{v}'_{s,e}$ is the superfluid velocity at the core of the ring due to causes external to the ring; it is assumed that $\boldsymbol{v}'_{s,e}$ changes slowly over the region

Notes p. 176

occupied by the vortex ring. The velocity of the ring is then $\boldsymbol{v}_\mathrm{R} + \boldsymbol{v}'_\mathrm{s,e}$ and according to (32-24) the dissipation only vanishes when the ring moves with the normal fluid velocity. Due to the modification of K.E.$_\mathrm{R}$ (32-17) to include the core energy as required by the two fluid theory:

$$\mathrm{d}(\mathrm{K.E.}_\mathrm{R}) = \boldsymbol{v}_\mathrm{R} \cdot \mathrm{d}\boldsymbol{I}_\mathrm{R}, \tag{32-25}$$

and Eq. (32-24) can then be simplified to:

$$(\boldsymbol{v}_\mathrm{R} + \boldsymbol{v}'_\mathrm{s,e} - \boldsymbol{v}_\mathrm{n}) \cdot \frac{\mathrm{d}\boldsymbol{I}_\mathrm{R}}{\mathrm{d}t} = -2\pi R \zeta_3 \rho_\mathrm{s}^2 (\boldsymbol{v}_\mathrm{R} + \boldsymbol{v}'_\mathrm{s,e} - \boldsymbol{v}_\mathrm{n})^2. \tag{32-26}$$

If v_n is large enough then (32-26) can in some geometries lead to an increase in the radius of the vortex ring.

A vortex ring can never be in stable dynamic equilibrium in He II under conditions that lead to (32-2). When the radius of the ring is such that $\boldsymbol{v}_\mathrm{R} + \boldsymbol{v}'_\mathrm{s,e} = \boldsymbol{v}_\mathrm{n}$ the term on the right hand side of (32-26) vanishes. But if a small disturbance increases the radius the vortex slows down and according to (32-26), $\mathrm{d}\boldsymbol{I}_\mathrm{R}/\mathrm{d}t$ changes so as to increase the radius and slow it down still more. The same considerations lead to the conclusion that if a vortex ring shrinks the dissipation acts to shrink it still more. A vortex ring will either keep expanding until it cancels with the boundary or continually collapse until self-annihilation.

An expression for $R(t)$ can be obtained for a one dimensional geometry ($\boldsymbol{v}_\mathrm{R}$ parallel to $\boldsymbol{v}'_\mathrm{s,e} - \boldsymbol{v}_\mathrm{n}$) by a direct integration of (32-26) to get

$$\log\left[\frac{1 + (v'_\mathrm{s,e} - v_\mathrm{n})/v_\mathrm{R}(t)}{1 + (v'_\mathrm{s,e} - v_\mathrm{n})/v_\mathrm{R}(0)}\right] - (v'_\mathrm{s,e} - v_\mathrm{n})\left[\frac{1}{v_\mathrm{R}(t)} - \frac{1}{v_\mathrm{R}(0)}\right]$$

$$= \frac{\rho_\mathrm{s}\zeta_3 (v'_\mathrm{s,e} - v_\mathrm{n})^2 t}{\pi\gamma^2 (\log 8R/a - \frac{1}{2})}. \tag{32-27}$$

Two limiting cases can be easily investigated:

$$\left|\frac{v'_\mathrm{s,e} - v_\mathrm{n}}{v_\mathrm{R}}\right| \ll 1, \tag{32-28}$$

$$\left|\frac{v'_\mathrm{s,e} - v_\mathrm{n}}{v_\mathrm{R}}\right| \gg 1. \tag{32-29}$$

The first case is that discussed before (32-21) as may be demonstrated by expanding the logarithm in a Taylor series. The second case applies

Notes p. 176

when the ring is either very large or the superfluid flowing rapidly. Then (32-27) becomes

$$R(t) - R(0) = -\frac{\rho_s \zeta_3}{2\pi\gamma}(v'_{s,e} - v_n)t, \tag{32-30}$$

where we have assumed that the ring moves in the plus x direction. Opposite polarization can be easily incorporated by letting γ go to $-\gamma$. From (32-30) one finds that when the ring velocity and $(v'_{s,e} - v_n)$ have the same sense, the ring always shrinks and disappears quickly. When oppositely directed the ring keeps expanding.

As there is as yet no technique capable of observing the locations of the quantized vortex lines there is no way to check the formulas such as (32-10). However, the quantized vortex rings are more easily observed, since as Rayfield and Reif [22] have demonstrated, a single ring can be associated with a negative ion, and the properties of the ring can be observed through the motion of the ion. As vortex lines terminate on boundaries their motion is complicated by their interaction with it. Vortex rings close into themselves and are correspondingly easier to study.

Meyer and Reif [23] observed that as the electric field is increased for a given temperature the mobility (or terminal velocity in response to this accelerating force) of the negative ions suffers a great drop at high enough field. This is now understood as being due to the creation of a quantized vortex ring by the ion. For a given energy the velocity of a quantized vortex ring plus ion is far less than that of an ion alone, the decrease in velocity being about a factor of 100.

As the drag force on a particle moving through a fluid is proportional to its velocity it is clear that the energy loss of the ion itself in traversing a region of given length is greatly diminished when it forms a vortex ring. But the total energy loss must include that of the vortex ring. At 1.5 °K the ring loses its energy over a distance of 10^{-4} cm, (32-22) and consistent with this Rayfield and Reif found that the loss of energy at high temperatures was very large. At 1.5 °K it is too large to measure with their apparatus which is much longer than 10^{-4} cm. At very low temperatures $T \lesssim 0.6$ °K, however, they found that the rings could flow without much energy loss. A typical value was a 5% to 10% loss of energy per cm. There is no way to compare these values with (32-22) since no reliable data on second sound absorption exist at these tem-

Notes p. 176

peratures. However, Eq. (32-18) predicts that at given temperature the loss of energy in time should be proportional to $1/R$ and this was accurately confirmed over a range of radii 1.6×10^{-5} cm $< R < 10^{-4}$ cm. This last result was already explained by Rayfield and Reif who proposed that the motion of the vortex ring would obey an equation of the form (32-18).

Notes

[1] E. L. Andronikashvili, Zh. Eksp. Teor. Fiz. **16**(1946)780; **18**(1948)424; J. Phys. USSR **10**(1946)201.

[2] A. C. Hollis-Hallett, Proc. Roy. Soc. **A210**(1951)404.

[3] K. Dransfeld, J. A. Newell and J. Wilks, Proc. Roy. Soc. **A243**(1958)500. C. E. Chase and M. A. Herlin, Phys. Rev. **97**(1955)1447. C. E. Chase, Phys. Fluids **1**(1958)193.

[4] W. B. Hanson and J. R. Pellam, Phys. Rev. **95**(1954)321.

[5] I. M. Khalatnikov, *An Introduction to the Theory of Superfluidity* (Benjamin, New York, 1965) Chap. 9.

[6] A Clark, Jr., Ph. D. Thesis, Massachusetts Institute of Technology (1963).

[7] R. Kronig and A. Thellung, Physica **16**(1950)678. This solution is also discussed by K. R. Atkins, *Liquid Helium* (Cambridge Univ. Press, Cambridge, 1959) p. 202.

[8] F. London, *Superfluids* (Wiley, New York, 1954) Vol. 2, p. 155.

[9] D. F. Brewer and D. O. Edwards, Phil. Mag. **6**(1961)775.

[10] R. Meservey, Phys. Fluids **8**(1965)1209.

[11] W. M. van Alphen, R. de Bruyn Ouboter, K. W. Taconis and E. van Spronsen, Physica **39**(1968)109. Also W. M. van Alphen, Ph. D. Thesis, Leiden (1969).

[12] P. P. Craig and J. R. Pellam, Phys. Rev. **108**(1957)1109.

[13] G. B. Hess, Phys. Rev. **161**(1967)189.

[14] C. C. Lin, *On the Motion of Vortices in Two Dimensions* (Oxford Univ. Press, London, 1943).

[15] D. Stauffer and A. L. Fetter, Phys. Rev. **168**(1968)156.

[16] A. L. Fetter, Phys. Rev. **162**(1967)143.

[17] A. L. Fetter, P. C. Hohenberg and P. Pincus, Phys. Rev. **147**(1966)140.

[18] D. Stauffer, Phys. Letters **24A**(1967)72.

[19] V. K. Tkachenko, Zh. Eksp. Teor. Fiz. **50**(1966)1573 [Sov. Phys. JETP **23**(1966)1049].

[20] L. Reatto, Phys. Rev. **167**(1968)191.

[21] W. F. Vinen, in: *Progress in Low Temperature Physics*, ed. C. J. Gorter (North-Holland, Amsterdam, 1961) Vol. III, Chap. 1. L. Campbell, J. Low Temp. Phys. **3**(1970)175. The criticism here is directed at those works which insist on introducing extra parameters to describe the motion of the *individual* vortex lines. In some papers (e.g., Ref. [5] Chap. 16, and, H. E. Hall and W. F. Vinen, Proc. Roy. Soc. (London) **A238**(1956)204,215) extra parameters have been introduced to describe a macro-macroscopic theory in which many vortex lines are present in each volume element and for which $\boldsymbol{v}_s$ is now taken to be an *average* of the vortex velocity fields

so that $\nabla \times \boldsymbol{v}_s \neq 0$. The additional dissipative coefficients which enter these theories must also be related to ζ_3 if the averaging is properly carried out.

[22] G. W. Rayfield and F. Reif, Phys. Rev. Letters **11**(1963)305; Phys. Rev. **136**(1964) A1194.
[23] F. Reif and L. Meyer, Phys. Rev. **119**(1960)1164; Phys. Rev. Letters **5**(1960)1.
[24] W. H. Keesom and A. P. Keesom, Physica **2**(1935)557.

CHAPTER IV

Incorporation of Thermal Fluctuations in the Two Fluid Theory

33 *Introduction: Time Reversible First Principles versus the Time Irreversible Macroscopic Description*

The first principle of physics from which the two fluid theory is expected to follow is the Schrödinger equation. This equation is time reversible, but as we have seen the two fluid theory shows dissipation and hence is time irreversible. For instance according to the two fluid theory a sphere moving through He II will be dragged on by the normal fluid and eventually be brought to rest where it remains. A paradox then arises as to how the time irreversible two fluid theory can be consistent with the microscopic laws of physics.

Above is an example of the classical problem of reconciling the generally irreversible macroscopic theories of physics with the time reversible first principles. The resolution lies in the fact that the usual macroscopic laws such as hydrodynamics are contracted and in some sense averaged descriptions; thus they involve an error. The macroscopic laws comprise just a few variables (contraction) compared with the Avagadro number of degrees of freedom that enter the exact microscopic description. As a result a single macroscopic configuration corresponds to very many possible microscopic configurations. If one now imagines each of these possible microscopic configurations to evolve in time then it is clear that at a later time they will *not* all correspond to the same macroscopic state. Thus the correct macroscopic description cannot be strictly causal in conflict with say the hydrodynamics presented here. The macroscopic descriptions become causal, and thus also dissipative only when averaged, but in general we see that there must be (thermal) fluctuations about this average. The averaging process which we have in mind consists of averaging the results of many 'experiments' with the same initial macroscopic configuration. This is generally referred to as the ensemble average.

Notes p. 203

To correct the hydrodynamics for fluctuations one must add to the total two fluid stress tensor a thermal fluctuating stress tensor $\check{\tau}_{ij}$ whose average, but not square average vanishes. Due to $\check{\tau}_{ij}$ the moving sphere comes to rest only on the average, but in general there is a non-zero probability of various mean square displacements. This particular thermal fluctuation is called the Brownian motion, and it reflects the fact that the first principles from which the complete macroscopic theories must follow, are time reversible.

The purpose of this chapter is to complete the two fluid hydrodynamics by including the thermal fluctuations following very closely the procedure outlined by Fox and Uhlenbeck [1]. When modified to include the fluctuations the macroscopic theory becomes stochastic rather than causal. Also the fluctuations will be seen to be related to the dissipation through the fluctuation dissipation relations, showing indeed that a dissipative theory is not complete until fluctuations are included.

We will especially be interested in applications to the quantized vortices and light scattering.

34 *Stationary Gaussian Markovian Processes and the General Fluctuation Dissipation Relation*

The most general case for which it has been shown that the fluctuations can be related to the dissipation is a stationary, Gaussian, Markovian (S.G.M.) process. To define an S.G.M. process one introduces the probability distribution functions:

$w_1(a^1, t^1)\,\mathrm{d}a^1 \equiv$ probability at time t^1 that the value of $a(t)$ is between a^1 and $a^1 + \mathrm{d}a^1$,

$w_2(a^1, t^1; a^2, t^2)\,\mathrm{d}a^1\,\mathrm{d}a^2 \equiv$ probability that at time t^1 the value of $a(t)$ is between a^1 and $a^1 + \mathrm{d}a^1$ and that at time t^2 the value of $a(t)$ is between a^2 and $a^2 + \mathrm{d}a^2$,

(34-1)

where $a(t)$ denotes a time dependent random process. In this manner one can also define the higher distributions w_3, w_4, etc..

The condition that the process $a(t)$ is a *stationary* process is equivalent to the requirement that all distribution functions for $a(t)$ are invariant under time translations. Thus w_1 would be independent of time and w_2

Notes p. 203

would depend only on $t^2 - t^1$ if $a(t)$ is stationary. A stationary process is also Gaussian if all the distribution functions have Gaussian form. For w_1 and w_2 this means

$$w_1(a^1) \sim \exp\left[-\tfrac{1}{2}a^1 E a^1\right],$$

$$w_2(a^1; a^2, t) \sim \exp\left[-\tfrac{1}{2}a^1 A(t) a^1 - a^1 B(t) a^2 - \tfrac{1}{2}a^2 C(t) a^2\right]. \quad (34\text{-}2)$$

If the process $a(t)$ represents a vector of n random processes, then E, A, B, C are matrices and a, a^1, a^2 are vectors.

A process is Markovian if knowledge of $a(t)$ at time t_1 does not influence the distribution of values of $a(t)$ at time $t_3 > t_1$ when there is also information giving the value of $a(t)$ at the intermediate time t_2. Such a process is completely characterized by w_2.

It has been shown [1] that the most general S.G.M. process takes the form of a coupled linear regression equation for the average $\langle a_i \rangle$ of the random variables $\acute{a}_i$:

$$\frac{\mathrm{d}\langle a_i \rangle}{\mathrm{d}t} + G_{ij}\langle a_j \rangle = 0, \quad (34\text{-}3)$$

where G_{ij} is independent of all the a_k and the subscript runs over the n random processes denoted by a. Although S.G.M. implies (34-3) the converse is not true. If, however, the equation of motion for the a_i is

$$\frac{\mathrm{d}a_i}{\mathrm{d}t} + G_{ij} a_j = \check{F}_i(t), \quad (34\text{-}4)$$

where $\check{F}_i(t)$ is a purely random, stationary Gaussian 'force' then (34-4) is an S.G.M. process. For $\check{F}_i(t)$ these restrictions are equivalent to the statements

$$\langle \check{F}_i(t) \rangle = 0, \quad (34\text{-}5)$$

$$\langle \check{F}_i(t) \check{F}_j(t') \rangle = 2Q_{ij}\,\delta(t - t'). \quad (34\text{-}6)$$

The fluctuation dissipation theorems which have been derived [1] for this case relate Q_{ij}, which is the strength of the fluctuating forces, to the entropy matrix E_{ij}

$$2Q_{ij} = G_{ik} E^{-1}_{kj} + E^{-1}_{ik} G^{+}_{kj}, \quad (34\text{-}7)$$

where the superscript (-1) denotes inverse and the superscript $(+)$ denotes transpose; E_{ij} is determined by the first distribution function:

$$w_1(a_i) = w \exp\left[-\tfrac{1}{2}a_i E_{ij} a_j\right], \quad (34\text{-}8)$$

Notes p. 203

which is a generalization of (34-2); with w, a normalization coefficient. As $w_1(a_i)$ is a measure of the probability of finding the system in state a_i it is clear that $a_i E_{ij} a_j$ is proportional to the entropy change from the equilibrium state where $a_i = 0$.

The general procedure for investigating the effects of thermal fluctuations is to first deal only with those systems (or approximations) where the equations of motion take the form (34-3). Then one interprets the variables in these dissipative equations as being averaged say over an ensemble of experiments. To describe the non-averaged behavior it is then *assumed* that the thermal bath can be accounted for by purely random stationary Gaussian forces which act on the system. Then the fluctuation dissipation relations (34-7) can be used to relate the strength Q_{ij} of the fluctuating forces to the dissipation.

In this chapter we will apply this procedure to the hydrodynamics of He II following the approach used in Ref. [1] for a classical fluid.

35 The Brownian Motion of a Quantized Vortex Line: A Simple Example of the Fluctuation Dissipation Theorem

As an illustration of the fluctuation dissipation theorems let us consider the equation of motion of a line vortex Eq. (32-12). This equation is not of the form (34-3) and hence cannot represent a stationary Gaussian Markovian process unless for example the vortex is near the center of the bucket so that $r_1^2 \ll \frac{1}{4}d^2$. Making this assumption we are led to (32-13) which is of the form of an S.G.M. process (34-3). When supplemented by a fluctuating force it becomes

$$\frac{\mathrm{d}r_1}{\mathrm{d}t} = -\alpha r_1 + \check{F}(t), \tag{35-1}$$

where

$$\alpha = \frac{\rho_s \zeta_3}{\gamma}\left(\omega - \frac{4\gamma}{d^2}\right). \tag{35-2}$$

Equation (35-1) is isomorphic to the Langevin equation and leads to the Brownian motion of a quantized vortex line. As we use polar coordinates, $r_1 > 0$ and thus one might be concerned that to be consistent with this $\check{F}(t)$ cannot be random when $r_1 = 0$. This mathematical difficulty can

Notes p. 203

be overcome as follows. In the approximation, $r_1^2 \ll \frac{1}{4}d^2$ the vortex rotates at constant angular velocity

$$\dot{\theta}_1 = 4\gamma/d^2 \tag{35-3}$$

due to its image. Construct a line through the center of the circle and the initial condition $\boldsymbol{r}_1(0)$. Letting this line rotate at the angular velocity given by (35-3), implies that the vortex is constrained to move on this line. Arbitrarily assign the half of the line in the first or fourth quadrant at $t = 0$, values of positive r_1, and the other half negative values of r_1 so that $-\frac{1}{2}d < r_1 < \frac{1}{2}d$. With this new interpretation (32-13) still applies and now in (35-1) $\check{F}(t)$ is unrestricted when $r_1 = 0$.

The solution of (35-1) is

$$\langle r_1(t) \rangle = r_1(0)\,\mathrm{e}^{-\alpha t}, \tag{35-4}$$

$$\langle [r_1(t)]^2 \rangle = [r_1(0)]^2\mathrm{e}^{-2\alpha t} + (Q/\alpha)(1 - \mathrm{e}^{-2\alpha t}), \tag{35-5}$$

where we have taken

$$\langle \check{F}(t)\check{F}(t') \rangle = 2Q\,\delta(t - t'), \qquad \langle \check{F}(t) \rangle = 0. \tag{35-6}$$

The average of $r_1(t)$ over an ensemble of identical systems with the same initial conditions shows dissipation, but the average of r_1^2 shows a fluctuation through the term proportional to Q, the strength of the fluctuating force. In fact for large t

$$\langle r_1 \rangle = 0, \tag{35-7}$$

$$\langle r_1^2 \rangle = Q/\alpha, \tag{35-8}$$

so that the mean square displacement from the origin is not zero. We cannot say more about $\langle r_1^2 \rangle$ unless Q can be related to measured quantities. This can be done through the fluctuation dissipation relations which we demonstrate as follows.

When a vortex moves off center it leads to a decrease in the generalized entropy (16-7) or equivalently an increase in free energy (18-37), which is given by

$$\Delta F = \pi\gamma^2\rho_s\ell\left(\frac{\omega}{\gamma} - \frac{4}{d^2}\right)r_1^2. \tag{35-9}$$

In this way the thermal (statistical) probability for *large t* that the vortex is at r_1 is

Notes p. 203

$$w_1(r_1) = w \exp\left[- \frac{\pi\gamma^2\rho_s \ell r_1^2}{k_B T} \left(\frac{\omega}{\gamma} - \frac{4}{d^2} \right) \right], \tag{35-10}$$

where k_B is Boltzmann's constant. From the probability distribution $w_1(r_1)$ arrived at by these statistical mechanics arguments one finds for large t

$$\langle r_1 \rangle = 0, \qquad \langle r_1^2 \rangle = \frac{k_B T}{2\pi\gamma^2\rho_s \ell} \left(\frac{\omega}{\gamma} - \frac{4}{d^2} \right)^{-1}. \tag{35-11}$$

Comparison of (35-11) with (35-8) leads to the fluctuation dissipation relation

$$Q = \frac{k_B T \alpha}{2\pi\gamma^2\rho_s \ell} \left(\frac{\omega}{\gamma} - \frac{4}{d^2} \right)^{-1}. \tag{35-12}$$

In terms of the notation used in § 34 we have for this simplified case taken $a_1 \equiv r_1$; $G_{11} \equiv \alpha$, and

$$E_{11} = \frac{2\pi\gamma^2\rho_s \ell}{k_B T} \left(\frac{\omega}{\gamma} - \frac{4}{d^2} \right),$$

so that the general theorem (34-7) is the relation (35-12) which we have just explicitly demonstrated for this special case. Equation (35-1) supplemented by (35-6) and (35-12) provide the complete description of the Brownian motion of the quantized vortex line in a cylindrical vessel for the approximation considered here.

We have been treating the superfluid as a classical system except for the single requirement that the circulation be quantized. It is in this spirit that a thermal Brownian motion of the quantized vortex has been discussed. It is clear that from the microscopic point of view the superfluid must be looked upon as a single coherent macroscopically occupied quantum state. Thus it seems like a big assumption to say that this macroscopic quantum state thermally fluctuates. One can say that some aspects of the superfluid state such as ρ_s, or the degree of occupation of the quantum state, are thermally determined and it is these properties which are affected by the thermal fluctuations. Indeed we saw that the dissipation and fluctuations depend upon $\nabla\rho_s$, such as in (32-4). Nevertheless we have here the unusual situation where the thermal fluctuations lead to changes in the parameters that describe a quantum state (the vortex moves!), and the situation begs for a microscopic understanding.

For He II the tables are turned in that the range of the thermal

Notes p. 203

fluctuations (the mean free path of the excitations) is much less than the range of the observable quantum state, which for a bucket of diameter d, is d! There remains also the question as to whether quantum fluctuations will play a role in the behavior of the superfluid. We return to this question in § 48.

From (35-11) we see that the length of the Brownian motion for a bucket of length $\ell = 1$ cm, diameter $d = 0.2$ cm rotating at the first critical angular velocity ω_{cr} is about 200 Å. At 1.5 °K, $1/\alpha \approx 3.0$ sec, which is therefore the time over which this thermal motion takes place.

The Brownian motion of the quantized vortex rings, say when $\boldsymbol{v}_n = \boldsymbol{v}_s = 0$ cannot be obtained by adding a fluctuating force to the right hand side of (32-23) since this equation is not of the form required of an S.G.M. process (34-3). In fact one easily verifies that supplementing (32-23) with a fluctuating force which obeys (34-6) leads to an equation where $\langle I_R^2 \rangle$ shows no approach to equilibrium [2].

To obtain the Brownian motion of the quantized vortex rings it is best to derive the general thermally fluctuating two fluid equations (§ 36) and then investigate (§ 37) the fluctuation analog of Eq. (32-1) describing the drag on quantized vortices.

While the description obtained by this procedure is more basic than others, the difference with them is academic. The requirements of dimensional analysis assure that answers obtained by use of the different fluctuation equations will always be within the same order of magnitude. Furthermore simplifying assumptions must always be made in order to arrive at concise results and so greater accuracy would be meaningless.

Iordanskii [3], Langer and Fisher [4], and especially Donnelly and Roberts [5] have emphasized the importance of the role of thermal fluctuations in understanding the 'critical' velocities. In Chapter VI we will investigate this point of view.

36 The General Two Fluid Hydrodynamics Modified to Include Thermal Fluctuations

In this section we will see that the two fluid equations including dissipation can be put in the form (34-3) of an S.G.M. process in some approximation. Next we will assume that the effects of the thermal fluctuations are such so as to modify it to the form (34-4). From the off-equilibrium entropy we will then arrive at the fluctuation-dissipation relations.

Notes p. 203

By this procedure one arrives at the general fluctuating two fluid hydrodynamics, which form the basis for the macroscopic description of the effects of thermal fluctuations in He II.

In order to write the two fluid equations in the form of a general S.G.M. process (34-3) we linearize them about rotational equilibrium. We remark that the equilibrium variables, denoted by subscript zero, are not necessarily constant. For the continuity equation (21-3) we find:

$$\frac{\partial\,\delta\rho}{\partial t} + \nabla\cdot\delta\boldsymbol{J} = 0, \tag{36-1}$$

where δ denotes the deviation from equilibrium. In terms of the variables $\boldsymbol{v}_{\mathrm{n}}$, $\boldsymbol{v}_{\mathrm{s}}$:

$$\delta\boldsymbol{J} = \rho_{\mathrm{n},0}\,\delta\boldsymbol{v}_{\mathrm{n}} + \boldsymbol{v}_{\mathrm{n},0}\,\delta\rho_{\mathrm{n}} + \rho_{\mathrm{s},0}\,\delta\boldsymbol{v}_{\mathrm{s}} + \boldsymbol{v}_{\mathrm{s},0}\,\delta\rho_{\mathrm{s}}.$$

For the superfluid equation in linear approximation (21-2,12) yields

$$\frac{\partial\,\delta\boldsymbol{v}_{\mathrm{s}}}{\partial t} + \nabla(\delta\mu + \boldsymbol{v}_{\mathrm{s},0}\cdot\delta\boldsymbol{v}_{\mathrm{s}} + \zeta_3\nabla\cdot\delta\rho_{\mathrm{s}}\boldsymbol{w} - \zeta_4\nabla\cdot\delta\boldsymbol{v}_{\mathrm{n}}) = 0, \tag{36-2}$$

where $\boldsymbol{w} \equiv \boldsymbol{v}_{\mathrm{n}} - \boldsymbol{v}_{\mathrm{s}}$, and for our applications it is sufficient to use the Khalatnikov fluxes. The momentum and energy equations (21-4,5) become

$$\frac{\partial\,\delta J_i}{\partial t} + \frac{\partial}{\partial r_\beta}[\delta P_{i\beta} + \tau_{i\beta}] = 0, \tag{36-3}$$

$$\frac{\partial\,\delta U}{\partial t} + \frac{\partial}{\partial r_\beta}\left[\delta Q_\beta + v_{\mathrm{n},0,\alpha}\tau_{\alpha\beta} - \rho_{\mathrm{s},0}w_{0,\beta}(\zeta_3\nabla\cdot\delta\rho_{\mathrm{s}}\boldsymbol{w} - \zeta_4\nabla\cdot\delta\boldsymbol{v}_{\mathrm{n}}) - \kappa\frac{\partial\,\delta T}{\partial r_\beta}\right] = 0, \tag{36-4}$$

where

$$\tau_{ij} = -\eta\left(\frac{\partial\,\delta v_{\mathrm{n},i}}{\partial r_j} + \frac{\partial\,\delta v_{\mathrm{n},j}}{\partial r_i} - \tfrac{2}{3}\delta_{ij}\nabla\cdot\delta\boldsymbol{v}_{\mathrm{n}}\right) - \delta_{ij}(-\zeta_1\nabla\cdot\delta\rho_{\mathrm{s}}\boldsymbol{w} + \zeta_2\nabla\cdot\delta\boldsymbol{v}_{\mathrm{n}}). \tag{36-5}$$

By use of the equations of state the above become eight linear equations for eight unknowns. They assume the form (34-3) if in addition to the discrete index one introduces the continuous index $\boldsymbol{r}$ which runs over the volume of the fluid. In this way (34-3) becomes

$$\frac{\partial\langle a_i(\boldsymbol{r})\rangle}{\partial t} + \int G_{ij}(\boldsymbol{r},\boldsymbol{r}')\langle a_j(\boldsymbol{r}')\rangle\,\mathrm{d}^3r' = 0, \tag{36-6}$$

Notes p. 203

where we let i run from one to eight, so that

$$a_1(\boldsymbol{r}) \equiv \delta\rho(\boldsymbol{r}), \quad a_{2,3,4}(\boldsymbol{r}) \equiv \delta \boldsymbol{v}_s(\boldsymbol{r}), \quad a_{5,6,7}(\boldsymbol{r}) \equiv \delta \boldsymbol{J}(\boldsymbol{r}), \quad a_8(\boldsymbol{r}) \equiv \delta U(\boldsymbol{r}). \tag{36-7}$$

Then by use of the equations of state (36-1,2,3,4) can be put in the form (36-6) and the derivation of the fluctuating corrections to the dissipative theory is straightforward. To avoid the formidable algebra we will use the following procedure. First note that whereas the convenient variables for describing the time derivatives are given by (36-7) the convenient variables for describing the dissipation are

$$\begin{aligned} b_1 &\equiv \delta[(\mu + \tfrac{1}{2}v_s^2 - \boldsymbol{v}_n \cdot \boldsymbol{v}_s)/T], \quad b_{2,3,4} \equiv -\delta(\rho_s \boldsymbol{w}/T), \\ b_{5,6,7} &\equiv \delta(\boldsymbol{v}_n/T), \quad b_8 \equiv -\delta(1/T), \end{aligned} \tag{36-8}$$

which are the conjugate variables to (36-7). Introducing the first and second laws of thermodynamics for He II, (4-5,6):

$$\mathrm{d}\rho s = \frac{1}{T}\left[\mathrm{d}U - (\mu + \tfrac{1}{2}v_s^2 - \boldsymbol{v}_n \cdot \boldsymbol{v}_s)\mathrm{d}\rho - \boldsymbol{v}_n \cdot \mathrm{d}\boldsymbol{J} + \rho_s \boldsymbol{w} \cdot \mathrm{d}\boldsymbol{v}_s\right] \tag{36-9}$$

one can verify that the transformation matrix T_{ij} from a_i to b_i is symmetric; where

$$b_i = T_{i\alpha} a_\alpha. \tag{36-10}$$

To see this one uses the Maxwell relations implied by flipping around all the derivatives on the right side of (36-9). By use of the b_i, (36-6) can be written:

$$\frac{\partial \langle a_i(\boldsymbol{r})\rangle}{\partial t} + \int G'_{ij}(\boldsymbol{r}, \boldsymbol{r}') < b_j(\boldsymbol{r}')> \mathrm{d}^3 r' = 0, \tag{36-11}$$

where

$$G'_{i\alpha} T_{\alpha j} = G_{ij}. \tag{36-12}$$

The matrix G'_{ij} can be written as the sum of an anti-symmetric and a symmetric matrix. The anti-symmetric matrix derives from all the terms which do *not* involve dissipation, whereas the symmetric matrix $S'_{ij}(\boldsymbol{r}, \boldsymbol{r}') = S'_{ji}(\boldsymbol{r}', \boldsymbol{r})$ includes the dissipation and is the part which we will need.

From the equations of motion one obtains

Notes p. 203

$$S'_{ij} = \begin{pmatrix} 0 & 0 & 0 & 0 \\ 0 & S'_{\alpha\beta}(\boldsymbol{r}, \boldsymbol{r}') & S'_{\alpha q}(\boldsymbol{r}, \boldsymbol{r}') & S'_{\alpha 8}(\boldsymbol{r}, \boldsymbol{r}') \\ 0 & S'_{p\beta}(\boldsymbol{r}, \boldsymbol{r}') & S'_{pq}(\boldsymbol{r}, \boldsymbol{r}') & S'_{p8}(\boldsymbol{r}, \boldsymbol{r}') \\ 0 & S'_{8\beta}(\boldsymbol{r}, \boldsymbol{r}') & S'_{8q}(\boldsymbol{r}, \boldsymbol{r}') & S'_{88}(\boldsymbol{r}, \boldsymbol{r}') \end{pmatrix} \tag{36-13}$$

where we temporarily let α, β run over 2,3,4, and p, q equal 5,6,7 and

$$S'_{\alpha\beta} = \zeta_3 T_0 \frac{\partial^2 \delta(\boldsymbol{r} - \boldsymbol{r}')}{\partial r_\alpha \, \partial r'_\beta}, \tag{36-14}$$

$$S'_{\alpha q} = \zeta_4 T_0 \frac{\partial^2 \delta(\boldsymbol{r} - \boldsymbol{r}')}{\partial r_\alpha \, \partial r'_q}, \tag{36-15}$$

$$S'_{\alpha 8} = -\zeta_3 T_0 \frac{\partial^2 [\rho_{\mathrm{s},0}(\boldsymbol{r})\, w_{0,\mu}(\boldsymbol{r})\, \delta(\boldsymbol{r} - \boldsymbol{r}')]}{\partial r_\alpha \, \partial r'_\mu} + \zeta_4 T_0 \frac{\partial^2 [v_{\mathrm{n},0,\mu}(\boldsymbol{r})\, \delta(\boldsymbol{r} - \boldsymbol{r}')]}{\partial r_\alpha \, \partial r'_\mu}, \tag{36-16}$$

$$S'_{pq} = \eta T_0 \frac{\partial^2 \delta(\boldsymbol{r} - \boldsymbol{r}')}{\partial r_\mu \, \partial r'_\nu} (\delta_{p\mu}\delta_{\nu q} + \delta_{pq}\delta_{\mu\nu}) + (\zeta_2 - \tfrac{2}{3}\eta) T_0 \frac{\partial^2 \delta(\boldsymbol{r} - \boldsymbol{r}')}{\partial r_p \, \partial r'_q}, \tag{36-17}$$

$$S'_{p8} = -\zeta_1 T_0 \frac{\partial^2 [\rho_{\mathrm{s},0}(\boldsymbol{r})\, w_{0,\mu}(\boldsymbol{r})\, \delta(\boldsymbol{r} - \boldsymbol{r}')]}{\partial r_p \, \partial r'_\mu} + (\zeta_2 - \tfrac{2}{3}\eta) T_0 \frac{\partial^2 [v_{\mathrm{n},0,\mu}(\boldsymbol{r})\, \delta(\boldsymbol{r} - \boldsymbol{r}')]}{\partial r_p \, \partial r'_\mu}$$
$$+ \eta T_0 \left\{ \frac{\partial^2 [v_{\mathrm{n},0,\mu}(\boldsymbol{r})\, \delta(\boldsymbol{r} - \boldsymbol{r}')]}{\partial r'_p \, \partial r_\mu} + \frac{\partial^2 [v_{\mathrm{n},0,p}(\boldsymbol{r})\, \delta(\boldsymbol{r} - \boldsymbol{r}')]}{\partial r_\mu \, \partial r'_\mu} \right\}, \tag{36-18}$$

$$2S'_{88} = v_{\mathrm{n},0,p}(\boldsymbol{r})\, S'_{p8}(\boldsymbol{r}, \boldsymbol{r}') - \rho_{\mathrm{s},0}(\boldsymbol{r})\, w_{0,\alpha}(\boldsymbol{r})\, S'_{\alpha 8}(\boldsymbol{r}, \boldsymbol{r}') + v_{\mathrm{n},0,p}(\boldsymbol{r}')\, S'_{p8}(\boldsymbol{r}', \boldsymbol{r})$$
$$- \rho_{\mathrm{s},0}(\boldsymbol{r}')\, w_{0,\alpha}(\boldsymbol{r}')\, S'_{\alpha 8}(\boldsymbol{r}', \boldsymbol{r}) + 2\kappa T_0^2 \frac{\partial\, \delta(\boldsymbol{r} - \boldsymbol{r}')}{\partial r_\mu \, \partial r'_\mu}, \tag{36-19}$$

and

$$(r_2, r_3, r_4) = (r_5, r_6, r_7) = (x, y, z).$$

The other components of S'_{ij} follow from its symmetry and we note that S'_{ij} cannot be symmetric unless $\zeta_1 = \zeta_4$, (21-16).

Next we need an expression for the off-equilibrium entropy. This can best be obtained by working back from the entropy production of the fluid which is given by

$$\frac{\mathrm{d}}{\mathrm{d}t} \int \rho s \, \mathrm{d}V = \iint b_i(\boldsymbol{r})\, S'_{ij}(\boldsymbol{r}, \boldsymbol{r}')\, b_j(\boldsymbol{r}')\, \mathrm{d}^3 r \, \mathrm{d}^3 r', \tag{36-20}$$

Notes p. 203

which is verified by demonstrating that it yields (21-1,10). To obtain (21-1,10) from (36-20) one must neglect a surface integral which represents a flow of entropy across the boundary of the fluid. In view of (34-8) the off-equilibrium entropy can be written in the general form

$$\int \rho s \, \mathrm{d}V = \int \rho_0 s_0 \, \mathrm{d}V - \tfrac{1}{2} k_{\mathrm{B}} \iint a_i(\boldsymbol{r}) \, E_{ij}(\boldsymbol{r}, \boldsymbol{r}') \, a_j(\boldsymbol{r}') \, \mathrm{d}^3 r \, \mathrm{d}^3 r', \quad (36\text{-}21)$$

where our objective is to determine $E_{ij}(\boldsymbol{r}, \boldsymbol{r}')$. From the time derivative of (36-21) we find

$$\frac{\mathrm{d}}{\mathrm{d}t} \int \rho s \, \mathrm{d}V = k_{\mathrm{B}} \iiint a_i(\boldsymbol{r}) \, E_{ij}(\boldsymbol{r}, \boldsymbol{r}'') G'_{jk}(\boldsymbol{r}'', \boldsymbol{r}') \, b_k(\boldsymbol{r}') \, \mathrm{d}^3 r \, \mathrm{d}^3 r' \, \mathrm{d}^3 r'', \quad (36\text{-}22)$$

where we have used (36-11). As b_i is related to a_i by a symmetric transformation only the symmetric part of $G'_{ij}(\boldsymbol{r},\boldsymbol{r}')$ will appear in (36-22) so

$$\frac{\mathrm{d}}{\mathrm{d}t} \int \rho s \, \mathrm{d}V = k_{\mathrm{B}} \iiint a_i(\boldsymbol{r}) \, E_{ij}(\boldsymbol{r}, \boldsymbol{r}'') \, S'_{jk}(\boldsymbol{r}'', \boldsymbol{r}') \, b_k(\boldsymbol{r}') \, \mathrm{d}^3 r \, \mathrm{d}^3 r' \, \mathrm{d}^3 r''. \quad (36\text{-}23)$$

Comparison with (36-20) and use of (36-10) yields

$$E_{ij}(\boldsymbol{r}, \boldsymbol{r}') = \frac{T_{ij}}{k_{\mathrm{B}}} \, \delta(\boldsymbol{r} - \boldsymbol{r}'). \quad (36\text{-}24)$$

Thus it is seen that the Landau two fluid equations when linearized about equilibrium can be put in the form of an S.G.M. process for the averaged variables. Now we interpret the variables in the dissipative two fluid equations (36-1,2,3,4) as being averaged say over an ensemble of processes with the same initial conditions. To remove the averages one must take account of the thermal fluctuations by means of random fluctuating forces $\check{F}_i(\boldsymbol{r}, t)$ that are added to the right side of these equations. The strengths of these forces depend upon the off-equilibrium entropy through the fluctuation dissipation theorem (34-7):

$$\langle \check{F}_i(\boldsymbol{r},t) \check{F}_j(\boldsymbol{r}',t') \rangle = 2\delta(t-t') \int [G_{ik}(\boldsymbol{r},\boldsymbol{r}'') E^{-1}_{kj}(\boldsymbol{r}'',\boldsymbol{r}') + E^{-1}_{ik}(\boldsymbol{r},\boldsymbol{r}'') G^{+}_{kj}(\boldsymbol{r}'',\boldsymbol{r}')] \mathrm{d}^3 r''. \quad (36\text{-}25)$$

By use of (36-24) and (36-12) and the symmetry of T_{ij} we find

$$\langle \check{F}_i(\boldsymbol{r}, t) \, \check{F}_j(\boldsymbol{r}', t') \rangle = 2 k_{\mathrm{B}} \, S'_{ij}(\boldsymbol{r}, \boldsymbol{r}') \, \delta(t - t'). \quad (36\text{-}26)$$

As $S'_{11} = 0$ there is no fluctuating force in the continuity equation (36-1). One easily verifies that the form of S'_{ij} is such that the fluctuating forces conserve energy and momentum. Furthermore they conserve the

Notes p. 203

circulation of the superfluid velocity $\boldsymbol{v}_s$. Introducing the fluctuating, stress tensor $\check{\tau}_{ij}(\boldsymbol{r}, t)$ energy flux density $\check{Q}'_i(\boldsymbol{r}, t)$, and off-equilibrium chemical potential $\check{H}(\boldsymbol{r}, t)$, the two fluid equations become

$$\frac{\partial \boldsymbol{v}_s}{\partial t} + \nabla(\mu + \tfrac{1}{2}v_s^2 + H + \check{H}) = 0, \tag{36-27}$$

$$\frac{\partial J_i}{\partial t} + \frac{\partial}{\partial r_\alpha}(p\delta_{i\alpha} + \rho_n v_{n,i} v_{n,\alpha} + \rho_s v_{s,i} v_{s,\alpha} + \tau_{i\alpha} + \check{\tau}_{i\alpha}) = 0, \tag{36-28}$$

$$\frac{\partial U}{\partial t} + \nabla\cdot(\boldsymbol{Q} + \boldsymbol{Q}' + \check{\boldsymbol{Q}}') = 0, \tag{36-29}$$

where $\boldsymbol{Q}'$ is given by (21-19) and

$$\boldsymbol{Q} = (\mu + \tfrac{1}{2}v_s^2 - \boldsymbol{v}_n\cdot\boldsymbol{v}_s)\boldsymbol{J} + \rho s T\boldsymbol{v}_n + [\rho_n\boldsymbol{v}_n\cdot(\boldsymbol{v}_n - \boldsymbol{v}_s)]\boldsymbol{v}_n.$$

It is to be expected that whatever the approximation the fluctuating forces will take the form given by (36-27,28,29) so that energy, momentum and $\boldsymbol{v}_s$ circulation are conserved. But in order to make use of the fluctuation dissipation relations for $\check{H}$, $\check{\tau}_{ij}$, $\check{\boldsymbol{Q}}'$ which follow from (36-26) it is understood that the above equations can only be rigorously applied with accuracy linear in the deviation from equilibrium. It is more convenient for us to work with the fluctuating heat flow

$$\check{q}_i(\boldsymbol{r}, t) \equiv \check{Q}'_i(\boldsymbol{r}, t) - \check{\tau}_{i\alpha}(\boldsymbol{r}, t)v_{n,\alpha} + \rho_s w_i \check{H}(\boldsymbol{r}, t). \tag{36-30}$$

From the two fluid equations modified to include fluctuations, Eq. (36-30), and the expression (36-9) for the entropy, one obtains the fluctuating entropy law:

$$T\left\{\frac{\partial \rho s}{\partial t} + \nabla\cdot\left[\rho s\boldsymbol{v}_n + \frac{(\boldsymbol{q} + \check{\boldsymbol{q}})}{T}\right]\right\}$$

$$= -\frac{(\boldsymbol{q} + \check{\boldsymbol{q}})}{T}\cdot\nabla T - (\tau_{\alpha\beta} + \check{\tau}_{\alpha\beta})\frac{\partial v_{n,\alpha}}{\partial r_\beta} + (H + \check{H})\nabla\cdot\rho_s\boldsymbol{w}. \tag{36-31}$$

The fluctuation dissipation relations follow from (36-26):

$$\langle \check{H}(\boldsymbol{r}, t)\,\check{H}(\boldsymbol{r}', t')\rangle = 2k_B T_0\zeta_3\,\delta(\boldsymbol{r} - \boldsymbol{r}')\,\delta(t - t'), \tag{36-32}$$

$$\langle \check{\tau}_{p\mu}(\boldsymbol{r}, t)\,\check{\tau}_{q\nu}(\boldsymbol{r}', t')\rangle = 2k_B T_0\,\delta(\boldsymbol{r} - \boldsymbol{r}')\,\delta(t - t')$$

$$\times\,[\eta(\delta_{p\mu}\delta_{\nu q} + \delta_{pq}\delta_{\mu\nu}) + (\zeta_2 - \tfrac{2}{3}\eta)\delta_{\mu p}\delta_{\nu q}], \tag{36-33}$$

$$\langle \check{H}(\boldsymbol{r}, t)\,\check{\tau}_{p\mu}(\boldsymbol{r}', t')\rangle = 2k_B T_0\zeta_4\,\delta(\boldsymbol{r} - \boldsymbol{r}')\,\delta(t - t')\,\delta_{\mu p}, \tag{36-34}$$

Notes p. 203

$$\langle \check{q}_i(\boldsymbol{r}, t)\, \check{q}_j(\boldsymbol{r}', t')\rangle = 2k_B T_0^2 \kappa\, \delta_{ij}\, \delta(\boldsymbol{r} - \boldsymbol{r}')\, \delta(t - t'). \tag{36-35}$$

All other correlations vanish and we remark that in the approximation where the conservation laws are first order in the deviation from equilibrium the entropy law is second order.

The eight equations (36-27,28,29,31) supplemented by the fluctuation dissipation relations (36-32,33,34,35) yield the fundamental description of He II when thermal fluctuations are taken into account.

The two fluid equations including dissipation followed from the basic assumptions that eight variables are a complete set and that the circulation of $\boldsymbol{v}_s$ is conserved. In order to derive the modifications to include thermal fluctuations we have had to additionally assume that these fluctuations lead to S.G.M. processes for the eight basic variables.

37 *The Brownian Motion of Quantized Vortex Rings and Lines*

Substitution of expressions for the time derivatives of energy, momentum, entropy and density (36-1,28,29,31) into the time derivative of the first and second laws of thermodynamics (36-9) yields

$$\frac{\mathrm{d}F}{\mathrm{d}t} \equiv \int \rho_s(\boldsymbol{v}_s - \boldsymbol{v}_n) \cdot \frac{\partial \boldsymbol{v}_s}{\partial t}\, \mathrm{d}V = \int [\check{H} - \zeta_3 \nabla \cdot \rho_s(\boldsymbol{v}_s - \boldsymbol{v}_n)] \nabla \cdot \rho_s(\boldsymbol{v}_s - \boldsymbol{v}_n)\, \mathrm{d}V, \tag{37-1}$$

where we have again taken T, $\mu + \frac{1}{2}v_s^2 - \boldsymbol{v}_n \cdot \boldsymbol{v}_s$ as constant and $\boldsymbol{v}_n = \boldsymbol{\omega} \times \boldsymbol{r}$. To derive (37-1) a surface integral was neglected.

Equation (37-1) yields the basic description of the drag and Brownian motion of the quantized vortex rings and lines when supplemented with the fluctuation dissipation relation (36-32) for $\check{H}$:

$$\langle \check{H}(\boldsymbol{r}, t)\, \check{H}(\boldsymbol{r}', t')\rangle = 2k_B T \zeta_3\, \delta(\boldsymbol{r} - \boldsymbol{r}')\, \delta(t - t'). \tag{37-2}$$

When fluctuations are neglected (37-1) reduces to the equation previously derived for the drag on quantized vortices.

As a check of the internal consistency of the procedure developed here we derive from the fluctuating hydrodynamics (37-1,2) the Brownian motion of a quantized vortex line in a rotating bucket. Due to the fluctuations Eq. (32-11) becomes:

Notes p. 203

$$\gamma \cdot (\boldsymbol{v}_n - \boldsymbol{v}_{s,e})_1 \times \frac{d\boldsymbol{r}_1}{dt} = \zeta_3 \rho_{s,0}(v_n - v_{s,e})_1^2 - \frac{1}{2\pi\rho_{s,0}\ell}\int \check{H}(\boldsymbol{r}, t)\nabla \cdot \rho_s(\boldsymbol{v}_s - \boldsymbol{v}_n)dV. \tag{37-3}$$

The integral involving $\check{H}(\boldsymbol{r}, t)$ can be viewed as a fluctuating force. But its value will not be zero since $(\boldsymbol{v}_n - \boldsymbol{v}_s)$ will depend upon $\check{H}(\boldsymbol{r}, t)$ through equation (37-3). This difficulty can be overcome by dividing by $\gamma(v_{s,e} - v_n)_1$ to obtain

$$\frac{d\boldsymbol{r}_1}{\partial t} = -\frac{\rho_{s,0}\zeta_3}{\gamma}\left(\omega - \frac{\gamma}{\frac{1}{4}d^2 - r_1^2}\right)r_1 - \frac{1}{2\pi\gamma\rho_{s,0}\ell(v_{s,e} - v_n)_1} \times \int \check{H}(\boldsymbol{r}, t)\,\nabla \cdot \rho_s(\boldsymbol{v}_s - \boldsymbol{v}_n)\,dV, \tag{37-4}$$

where r_1 must be interpreted as taking on both positive and negative values, as in the discussion following (35-2), but now the diameter which the vortex moves on must rotate at angular velocity

$$\dot{\theta}_1 = \gamma/(\tfrac{1}{4}d^2 - r_1^2). \tag{37-5}$$

If the fluctuating force $\check{F}(t)$ is defined by

$$\check{F}(t) = -\frac{1}{2\pi\gamma\rho_{s,0}\ell\,(v_{s,e} - v_n)_1}\int \check{H}(\boldsymbol{r}, t)\,\nabla \cdot \rho_s(\boldsymbol{v}_s - \boldsymbol{v}_n)\,dV, \tag{37-6}$$

then from $\langle \check{H}(\boldsymbol{r}, t)\rangle = 0$ we will show

$$\langle \check{F}(t)\rangle = 0. \tag{37-7}$$

As in the derivation of the drag on quantized vortices we take $\nabla \cdot \boldsymbol{v}_s = 0$ so that

$$\nabla \cdot \rho_s(\boldsymbol{v}_s - \boldsymbol{v}_n) = (\boldsymbol{v}_s - \boldsymbol{v}_n)\cdot \nabla\rho_s = 2(\boldsymbol{v}_{s,e} - \boldsymbol{v}_n)_1 \cdot \frac{\partial \rho_s}{\partial|\boldsymbol{r} - \boldsymbol{r}_1|}\hat{\boldsymbol{e}}_{r_1}, \tag{37-8}$$

where $\partial\rho_s/\partial|\boldsymbol{r} - \boldsymbol{r}_1|$ is approximately $\rho_{s,0}/a$ in magnitude, $\hat{\boldsymbol{e}}_{r_1}$ points radially outward from the line, (37-8) is non-zero only in the core region. Eq. (37-6) then becomes

$$\check{F}(t) = -\frac{1}{\pi\gamma\ell a}\int_0^{\ell}\int_0^{a}\int_0^{2\pi} \check{H}([\boldsymbol{r}_1 + \boldsymbol{r}], z, t)\cos\Theta_1\, r dr\, d\Theta_1\, dz, \tag{37-9}$$

where Θ_1 is the angle as measured about the vortex line. The ensemble average of (37-9) can be interchanged with the (definite) limits of integra-

Notes p. 203

tion, implying the desired result (37-7) provided of course that $\langle \check{H}(\boldsymbol{r},t)\rangle = 0$.

The square correlation of $F(t)$ follows from (37-9) and (37-2) and is given by:

$$\langle \check{F}(t)\, \check{F}(t')\rangle = \frac{k_{\mathrm{B}}T\zeta_3}{\pi\gamma^2\ell}\,\delta(t-t'), \qquad (37\text{-}10)$$

which is for $r_1 \ll \frac{1}{2}d$ identical with (35-6) supplemented by (35-12). By working with the general two fluid hydrodynamics including thermal fluctuations we have derived an equation valid for all r_1 and not just $r_1 \ll \frac{1}{2}d$. This equation (37-4) is not of the form (34-3) and is thus not an S.G.M. process. The entropy equation (36-31) from which (37-1) was derived is also not an S.G.M. process. In fact the approach of the average value of the entropy to equilibrium need not be monotonic as mentioned in Ref. [1]. These equations, however, follow from S.G.M. processes and are thus still valid.

The Brownian motion of quantized vortex rings also follows from (37-1). First consider a vortex ring in otherwise quiescent He II. From (37-1) the fluctuating generalization of (32-23) is

$$\boldsymbol{v}_{\mathrm{R}}\cdot\frac{\mathrm{d}\boldsymbol{I}_{\mathrm{R}}}{\mathrm{d}t} = -2\pi\zeta_3\rho_{\mathrm{s,0}}^2 R v_{\mathrm{R}}^2 + \int \check{H}(\boldsymbol{r},t)\,\nabla\cdot\rho_{\mathrm{s}}\boldsymbol{v}_{\mathrm{s}}\,\mathrm{d}V. \qquad (37\text{-}11)$$

Introduce the fluctuating force

$$\check{F}_{\mathrm{R}}(t) = \frac{1}{v_{\mathrm{R}}R}\int \check{H}(\boldsymbol{r},t)\,\nabla\cdot\rho_{\mathrm{s}}\boldsymbol{v}_{\mathrm{s}}\,\mathrm{d}V, \qquad (37\text{-}12)$$

which acts on the entire ring. By the usual approximations:

$$\check{F}_{\mathrm{R}}(t) = \frac{2\rho_{\mathrm{s,0}}}{a}\int_0^{2\pi}\int_0^{2\pi}\int_0^{a} \check{H}([\boldsymbol{r}_1+\boldsymbol{r}+R\hat{\boldsymbol{e}}_{\Theta}],t)\cos\Theta_1\, r\mathrm{d}r\,\mathrm{d}\theta\,\mathrm{d}\Theta_1, \qquad (37\text{-}13)$$

where $\boldsymbol{r}_1$ is the location of the center of the ring, see Fig. 30; $\hat{\boldsymbol{e}}_{\Theta}$ is a unit vector from the center in the direction of a core element at angle θ, Θ_1 is the angle about the center line of the core. As before $\langle \check{H}(r,t)\rangle = 0$ now implies $\langle \check{F}_{\mathrm{R}}(t)\rangle = 0$, and (37-2) yields

$$\langle \check{F}_{\mathrm{R}}(t)\,\check{F}_{\mathrm{R}}(t')\rangle = 8\pi^2\rho_{\mathrm{s,0}}^2 k_{\mathrm{B}}T\zeta_3\,\delta(t-t')\left\langle\frac{1}{R}\right\rangle, \qquad (37\text{-}14)$$

Notes p. 203

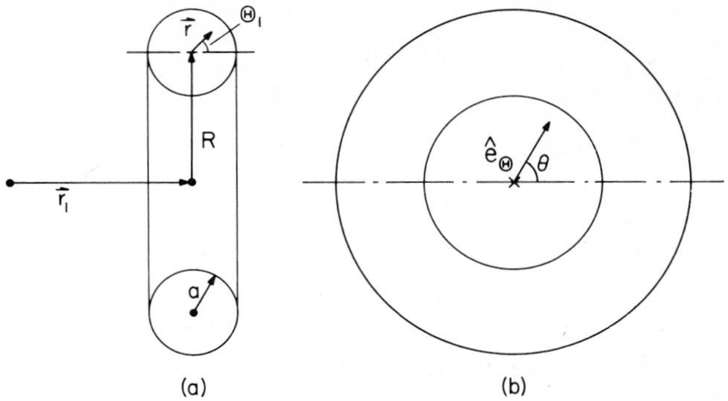

Fig. 30. Section (a) and front view (b) of vortex ring, indicating integration variables.

so that the strength of the fluctuating force is a function of $\langle R^{-1} \rangle$ and hence time. To obtain (37-14) from (37-13) first note that the ensemble average of the fluctuating force for given R is from (37-13,2):

$$\langle \check{F}_{\mathrm{R}}(t)\, \check{F}_{\mathrm{R}}(t') \rangle_{\mathrm{R}} = 8\pi^2 \rho_{\mathrm{s,0}}^2 k_{\mathrm{B}} T \zeta_3\, \delta(t - t') \frac{1}{R}. \tag{37-15}$$

If for given initial condition one calculates the ensemble average of the fluctuating force only for those rings which have radius R at time t the result (37-15) is obtained. The general ensemble square average of $\check{F}_{\mathrm{R}}(t)$ will depend on the relative number of rings having radius R at time t and is thus given by (37-14).

For the more general case where a vortex ring moves relative to non-zero external super and normal fluid velocities we obtain the fluctuating generalization of (32-26)

$$\frac{1}{R} \frac{\mathrm{d}I_{\mathrm{R}}}{\mathrm{d}t} = -2\pi \zeta_3 \rho_{\mathrm{s,0}}^2 (v_{\mathrm{R}} + v_{\mathrm{s,e}}' - v_{\mathrm{n}}) + \check{F}_{\mathrm{R}}(t), \tag{37-16}$$

where

$$\check{F}_{\mathrm{R}}(t) = \frac{1}{R(v_{\mathrm{R}} + v_{\mathrm{s,e}}' - v_{\mathrm{n}})} \int \check{H}(\boldsymbol{r}, t)\, \nabla \cdot \rho_{\mathrm{s}} (\boldsymbol{v}_{\mathrm{s}} - \boldsymbol{v}_{\mathrm{n}})\, \mathrm{d}V, \tag{37-17}$$

Notes p. 203

so that

$$\langle \check{F}_{\mathrm{R}}(t) \rangle = 0,$$

$$\langle \check{F}_{\mathrm{R}}(t)\, \check{F}_{\mathrm{R}}(t') \rangle = 8\pi^2 \rho_{\mathrm{s},0}^2 k_{\mathrm{B}} T \zeta_3\, \delta(t - t') \left\langle \frac{1}{R} \right\rangle.$$

In (37-15) as in (37-12), I_{R}, v_{R} are positive for motion in the plus x direction and negative otherwise; R is always positive, we assume that $v'_{\mathrm{s,e}} - v_{\mathrm{n}}$ is oriented along the x axis. It should be recalled that $v'_{\mathrm{s,e}}$ is the superfluid velocity at the core of the vortex ring due to all sources other than the ring.

38 Light Scattering From Superfluid Helium

The aim of any phenomenological theory is to incorporate as many phenomena as possible into a single, self-consistent closed description. For this reason we have especially emphasized that the same Landau two fluid equations which describe the motion of and drag on vortex lines also describe the propagation and absorption of sound with respect to He II at rest. In the same manner the Landau two fluid theory when modified to include thermal fluctuations describes both the Brownian motion of the quantized vortices and the scattering of light from He II.

A monochromatic oscillating electric field

$$\boldsymbol{E}_0 \exp(i\boldsymbol{k} \cdot \boldsymbol{r} - i\omega_0 t),$$

incident on a medium, as in Fig. 31, produces an oscillating polarization

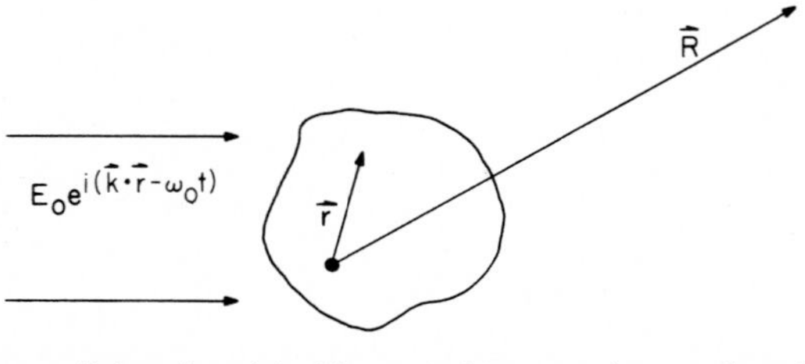

Fig. 31. Radiation parallel to $\boldsymbol{k}$ and incident on the scattering medium leads to scattered radiation propagating in direction $\boldsymbol{k}'$ parallel to $\boldsymbol{R}$.

Notes p. 203

at each point equal to the polarizability, $\alpha_p(\boldsymbol{r}, t)$ times the driving electric field. In turn this oscillating polarization radiates an electric field. From the electromagnetic theory, the field scattered by this process to point $\boldsymbol{R}$ at time t is [6]

$$E_{\text{scatt}}(\boldsymbol{R}, \boldsymbol{K}, t) = E_0 \left(\frac{\omega_0}{c}\right)^2 \frac{\exp(i\boldsymbol{k}' \cdot \boldsymbol{R} - i\omega_0 t)}{R} \times \sin\phi \int_V \alpha_p(\boldsymbol{r}, t) \exp(-i\boldsymbol{K} \cdot \boldsymbol{r}) \, d^3 r, \quad (38\text{-}1)$$

where the integral extends over the volume occupied by the fluid, $\boldsymbol{k}'$ points in the direction of the scattered wave;

$$\boldsymbol{K} \equiv \boldsymbol{k}' - \boldsymbol{k}, \quad (38\text{-}2)$$

and to excellent accuracy

$$|\boldsymbol{k}| = |\boldsymbol{k}'|. \quad (38\text{-}3)$$

To derive (38-1) we have assumed $R \gg r$ where the origin of coordinates is located somewhere in the scattering medium; ϕ is the angle between the polarization vector of the incident wave and the propagation vector of the scattered wave, c is the speed of light.

If the fluid is not being driven by external forces such as a sound transducer then according to the hydrodynamics without fluctuations, (§ 21), all variables are constant. Hence α_p is also independent of $\boldsymbol{r}, t$ and according to (38-1) scattering can take place only in the forward direction, $\boldsymbol{k}' = \boldsymbol{k}$. However, due to the thermal fluctuations a fluid undisturbed from outside will nevertheless be filled with thermally excited variations in ρ, s, $\boldsymbol{v}_n$, $\boldsymbol{v}_s$ which lead to variations in α_p, and thus a possibility of light scattering in other than the forward direction. If we set α_p equal to its 'equilibrium' (i.e., constant) value $\alpha_{p,0}$ plus the deviation from equilibrium then:

$$\alpha_p(\boldsymbol{r}, t) = \alpha_{p,0} + \delta\alpha_p(\boldsymbol{r}, t), \quad (38\text{-}4)$$

and the scattered field for $\boldsymbol{K} \neq 0$ is

$$E_{\text{scatt}}(\boldsymbol{R}, \boldsymbol{K}, t) = E_0 \left(\frac{\omega_0}{c}\right)^2 \frac{\exp(i\boldsymbol{k}' \cdot \boldsymbol{R} - i\omega_0 t)}{R} (2\pi)^{3/2} \delta\alpha_p(\boldsymbol{K}, t), \quad (38\text{-}5)$$

Notes p. 203

where

$$\delta\alpha_p(\boldsymbol{K}, t) = \frac{1}{(2\pi)^{3/2}} \int \exp(-i\boldsymbol{K}\cdot\boldsymbol{r})\delta\alpha_p(\boldsymbol{r}, t)\,\mathrm{d}^3 r. \tag{38-6}$$

Light scattering into the direction $\boldsymbol{k}'$ comes from modulations in α_p with wave vector $\boldsymbol{K} = \boldsymbol{k}' - \boldsymbol{k}$, which is Bragg's law.

The average power scattered into solid angle $\mathrm{d}\Omega$ about $\boldsymbol{R}$ is for the time interval 2Υ

$$\mathrm{d}P(\boldsymbol{K}, \boldsymbol{R}) = \frac{c}{4\pi}\frac{1}{2\Upsilon}\int_{-\Upsilon}^{\Upsilon} E_{\mathrm{scatt}}(\boldsymbol{R}, \boldsymbol{K}, t)\, E^*_{\mathrm{scatt}}(\boldsymbol{R}, \boldsymbol{K}, t)\,\mathrm{d}t\, R^2\,\mathrm{d}\Omega. \tag{38-7}$$

Associating the time average with an ensemble average over the unknown initial microscopic conditions and using the identity

$$\int_{-\infty}^{\infty} \mathrm{d}\tau \int_{-\infty}^{\infty} \mathrm{e}^{i\omega\tau}\,\mathrm{d}\omega = 2\pi, \tag{38-8}$$

implies that

$$\mathrm{d}P(\boldsymbol{K}, \boldsymbol{R}) = \int \mathrm{d}P(\boldsymbol{K}, \Delta\omega)\,\mathrm{d}\omega, \tag{38-9}$$

where

$$\mathrm{d}P(\boldsymbol{K}, \Delta\omega) = \frac{c}{4\pi}\frac{(2\pi)^3 E_0^2\omega_0^4 \sin^2\phi}{2\Upsilon c^4}\langle \delta\alpha_p(\boldsymbol{K}, \Delta\omega)\,\delta\alpha_p^*(\boldsymbol{K}, \Delta\omega)\rangle\,\mathrm{d}\Omega, \tag{38-10}$$

and

$$\delta\alpha_p(\boldsymbol{K}, \Delta\omega) = \frac{1}{(2\pi)^2}\int_{-\infty}^{\infty} \mathrm{d}t \int \exp(-i\boldsymbol{K}\cdot\boldsymbol{r} + i\Delta\omega t)\,\delta\alpha_p(\boldsymbol{r}, t)\,\mathrm{d}^3 r, \tag{38-11}$$

$$\Delta\omega \equiv \omega - \omega_0. \tag{38-12}$$

From (38-9,10) we see that $\mathrm{d}P(\boldsymbol{K}, \Delta\omega)\,\mathrm{d}\omega$ is the scattered power between frequencies ω and $\omega + \mathrm{d}\omega$; this result (38-10,11) applies only in the limit of large Υ.

The above conclusions follow from the electromagnetic theory. Expressions for the square correlation of $\delta\alpha_p$ follows from the two fluid equations including fluctuations which we next solve. First note that α_p like all macroscopic scalar parameters is a function of ρ, T, $(\boldsymbol{v}_n - \boldsymbol{v}_s)^2$.

Notes p. 203

As we will solve the fluctuating two fluid equations in linear approximation we can neglect the dependence on $(\boldsymbol{v}_n - \boldsymbol{v}_s)^2$. For all investigated fluids the dependence on T is so small compared with that on ρ that it is also neglected. For He II this should also be the case. Although experiments [7] are consistent with this fact the measurements of α_p are not yet accurate enough to demonstrate that light scattering from temperature fluctuations should a priori be negligible compared to light scattering from density fluctuations. We shall make this usual assumption in order to simplify the calculation, but return to this question at the end of the section.

Taking α_p as a function only of ρ (38-10) becomes

$$\mathrm{d}P(\boldsymbol{K}, \Delta\omega) = \frac{c}{4\pi}\frac{(2\pi)^3 E_0^2 \omega_0^2 \sin^2\phi}{2\Upsilon c^4}\left[\left(\frac{\partial \alpha_p}{\partial \rho}\right)_T\right]^2 \langle\, \delta\rho(\boldsymbol{K}, \Delta\omega)\,\delta\rho^*(\boldsymbol{K}, \Delta\omega)\rangle\, \mathrm{d}\Omega. \tag{38-13}$$

To calculate the square correlation of $\delta\rho$ we linearize the fluctuating two fluid equations (36-1,27,28,31) about the state $\boldsymbol{v}_n = \boldsymbol{v}_s = 0$:

$$\frac{\partial\, \delta\rho}{\partial t} + \nabla \cdot \delta \boldsymbol{J} = 0, \tag{38-14}$$

$$\rho \frac{\partial\, \delta s}{\partial t} + \rho_s s \nabla \cdot \delta \boldsymbol{w} - \frac{\kappa}{T} \nabla^2 \delta T = -\nabla \cdot \frac{\breve{\boldsymbol{q}}}{T}, \tag{38-15}$$

$$\begin{aligned} &\frac{\partial\, \delta \boldsymbol{J}}{\partial t} + \nabla \delta p - \frac{\eta}{\rho} \nabla^2 \delta \boldsymbol{J} - \frac{1}{\rho}(\tfrac{1}{3}\eta + \zeta_2)\nabla(\nabla \cdot \delta \boldsymbol{J}) \\ &\qquad - \frac{\rho_s \eta}{\rho}\nabla^2 \delta \boldsymbol{w} + \frac{\rho_s}{\rho}(\rho\zeta_1 - \tfrac{1}{3}\eta - \zeta_2)\nabla(\nabla \cdot \delta \boldsymbol{w}) = -\frac{\partial \breve{\tau}_{ij}}{\partial r_j}, \end{aligned} \tag{38-16}$$

$$\begin{aligned} &\rho_n \frac{\partial\, \delta \boldsymbol{w}}{\partial t} + \rho s \nabla \delta T - \frac{\eta}{\rho} \nabla^2 \delta \boldsymbol{J} - \frac{1}{\rho}(\tfrac{1}{3}\eta + \zeta_2 - \rho\zeta_4)\nabla(\nabla \cdot \delta \boldsymbol{J}) \\ &\qquad - \frac{\rho_s \eta}{\rho}\nabla^2 \delta \boldsymbol{w} - \frac{\rho_s}{\rho}[\tfrac{1}{3}\eta + \zeta_2 - \rho(\zeta_1 + \zeta_4) + \rho^2\zeta_3]\nabla(\nabla \cdot \delta \boldsymbol{w}) \\ &\qquad = -\frac{\partial \breve{\tau}_{ij}}{\partial r_j} + \rho \nabla \breve{H}. \end{aligned} \tag{38-17}$$

Equation (38-17) was obtained by subtracting (36-27) multiplied by ρ from (36-28).

Notes p. 203

Due to the thermal fluctuations the linearized equations have become *in*homogeneous. These linear equations no longer imply a dispersion law; instead there is now a solution for $\delta\rho$ as a function of $\check{\boldsymbol{q}}$, $\check{\tau}_{ij}$ and $\check{H}$. From this solution and the fluctuation dissipation relations one obtains the square correlation of $\delta\rho$. Fourier analyze all the variables in these equations as follows

$$\delta\rho(\boldsymbol{r}, t) = \frac{1}{(2\pi)^2} \int \mathrm{d}\boldsymbol{K} \int \exp(i\boldsymbol{K}\cdot\boldsymbol{r} - i\Delta\omega t)\, \delta\rho(\boldsymbol{K}, \omega)\, \mathrm{d}\omega, \quad (38\text{-}18)$$

and similarly for the others. Then we find for the Fourier amplitudes $\delta\rho(\boldsymbol{K}, \omega)$, $\delta T(\boldsymbol{K}, \omega)$, etc.,

$$-i\Delta\omega\, \delta\rho + i\boldsymbol{K}\cdot\delta\boldsymbol{J} = 0, \quad (38\text{-}19)$$

$$-i\rho\Delta\omega\, \delta s + i\rho_s s\boldsymbol{K}\cdot\delta\boldsymbol{w} + \frac{\kappa K^2}{T}\delta T = -i\boldsymbol{K}\cdot\frac{\check{\boldsymbol{q}}}{T}, \quad (38\text{-}20)$$

$$-i\Delta\omega\, \delta\boldsymbol{J} + i\boldsymbol{K}\delta p + \frac{\eta K^2}{\rho}\delta\boldsymbol{J} + \frac{1}{\rho}(\tfrac{1}{3}\eta + \zeta_2)\boldsymbol{K}(\boldsymbol{K}\cdot\delta\boldsymbol{J}) + \frac{\rho_s\eta}{\rho}K^2\delta\boldsymbol{w}$$

$$+ \frac{\rho_s}{\rho}(\tfrac{1}{3}\eta + \zeta_2 - \rho\zeta_1)\boldsymbol{K}(\boldsymbol{K}\cdot\delta\boldsymbol{w}) = -iK_j\check{\tau}_{ij}, \quad (38\text{-}21)$$

$$-i\rho_n\Delta\omega\, \delta\boldsymbol{w} + i\rho s\boldsymbol{K}\delta T + \frac{\eta}{\rho}K^2\delta\boldsymbol{J} + \frac{1}{\rho}(\tfrac{1}{3}\eta + \zeta_2 - \rho\zeta_4)\boldsymbol{K}(\boldsymbol{K}\cdot\delta\boldsymbol{J})$$

$$+ \frac{\rho_s\eta}{\rho}K^2\delta\boldsymbol{w} + \frac{\rho_s}{\rho}[\tfrac{1}{3}\eta + \zeta_2 - \rho(\zeta_1 + \zeta_4) + \rho^2\zeta_3]\boldsymbol{K}(\boldsymbol{K}\cdot\delta\boldsymbol{w})$$

$$= -iK_j\check{\tau}_{ij} + i\rho\boldsymbol{K}\check{H}. \quad (38\text{-}22)$$

From the above equations it follows that the only contributions to $\delta\rho$ come from fluctuations in $\delta\boldsymbol{J}$, $\delta\boldsymbol{w}$ which are parallel to $\boldsymbol{K}$. Hence we take $\boldsymbol{K}\times\delta\boldsymbol{J} = \boldsymbol{K}\times\delta\boldsymbol{w} = 0$ and find

$$D\,\delta\rho = \tfrac{1}{3}\check{\tau}_{\alpha\alpha}\left[\rho_s s K^4\left(\frac{\partial p}{\partial T}\right)_\rho - \rho\rho_s s^2 K^4 + (\Delta\omega)^2\rho_n\rho K^2\left(\frac{\partial s}{\partial T}\right)_\rho\right]$$

$$-\rho\rho_s s K^4\left(\frac{\partial p}{\partial T}\right)_\rho \check{H} + (\Delta\omega)\rho_n K^3\left(\frac{\partial p}{\partial T}\right)_\rho \frac{\check{q}}{T}, \quad (38\text{-}23)$$

where D is the determinant of the coefficients of $\delta\rho$, δT, $\delta\boldsymbol{J}$, $\delta\boldsymbol{w}$, and terms of the order of a fluctuating force multiplying a dissipative coeffi-

Notes p. 203

cient have been neglected. By Fourier analyzing the fluctuation dissipation relations (36-32,33,34,35) for the space–time correlations, we obtain the fluctuation dissipation relations for the frequency wave vector correlations:

$$\langle \check{H}(\boldsymbol{K},\omega)\,\check{H}^*(\boldsymbol{K},\omega)\rangle = \frac{2k_{\mathrm{B}}T}{(2\pi)^4}\zeta_3 V(2\Upsilon), \tag{38-24}$$

$$\langle \tfrac{1}{3}\check{\tau}_{\alpha\alpha}(\boldsymbol{K},\omega)\,\tfrac{1}{3}\check{\tau}^*_{\beta\beta}(\boldsymbol{K},\omega)\rangle = \frac{2k_{\mathrm{B}}T}{(2\pi)^4}(\tfrac{4}{3}\eta + \zeta_2)V(2\Upsilon), \tag{38-25}$$

$$\langle \check{H}(\boldsymbol{K},\omega)\,\tfrac{1}{3}\check{\tau}^*_{\alpha\alpha}(\boldsymbol{K},\omega)\rangle = \frac{2k_{\mathrm{B}}T}{(2\pi)^4}\zeta_4 V(2\Upsilon), \tag{38-26}$$

$$\langle \check{q}_i(\boldsymbol{K},\omega)\,\check{q}^*_j(\boldsymbol{K},\omega)\rangle = \frac{2k_{\mathrm{B}}T}{(2\pi)^4}\kappa T\delta_{ij}V(2\Upsilon), \tag{38-27}$$

where V is the volume of the fluid and 2Υ is the time over which the scattered power is averaged. From (38-23) we then find

$$\begin{aligned}
&\langle \delta\rho(\boldsymbol{K},\omega)\,\delta\rho^*(\boldsymbol{K},\omega)\rangle \\
&\quad= \frac{2k_{\mathrm{B}}TV(2\Upsilon)}{(2\pi)^4\,|D|^2}\Bigg\{(\Delta\omega)^2\rho_{\mathrm{n}}^2K^6\left(\frac{\partial p}{\partial T}\right)_\rho^2\frac{\kappa}{T} + \rho^2\rho_{\mathrm{s}}^2s^2K^8\left(\frac{\partial p}{\partial T}\right)_\rho^2\zeta_3 \\
&\quad -2\zeta_4\rho\rho_{\mathrm{s}}sK^4\left(\frac{\partial p}{\partial T}\right)_\rho\left[\rho_{\mathrm{s}}sK^4\left(\frac{\partial p}{\partial T}\right)_\rho - \rho\rho_{\mathrm{s}}s^2K^4 + (\Delta\omega)^2\rho_{\mathrm{n}}\rho K^2\left(\frac{\partial s}{\partial T}\right)_\rho\right] \\
&\quad + (\tfrac{4}{3}\eta + \zeta_2)\left[\rho_{\mathrm{s}}\rho sK^4\left(\frac{\partial p}{\partial T}\right)_\rho - \rho\rho_{\mathrm{s}}s^2K^4 + (\Delta\omega)^2\rho_{\mathrm{n}}\rho K^2\left(\frac{\partial s}{\partial T}\right)_\rho\right]^2\Bigg\}.
\end{aligned} \tag{38-28}$$

Equation (38-28) combined with (38-13) provides the complete solution to the light scattering problem. To simplify this result note that the roots $\Delta\omega(K)$ of D determine the speed and attenuations of sound, in fact

$$\begin{aligned}
|D^2| = \left[\rho_{\mathrm{n}}\rho\left(\frac{\partial s}{\partial T}\right)_\rho\right]^2 &[(\Delta\omega - Ku_1)^2 + u_1^2\alpha_1^2][(\Delta\omega + Ku_1)^2 + u_1^2\alpha_1^2] \\
&\times [(\Delta\omega - Ku_2)^2 + u_2^2\alpha_2^2][(\Delta\omega + Ku_2)^2 + u_2^2\alpha_2^2],
\end{aligned} \tag{38-29}$$

where u_1, u_2, α_1, α_2 are the speed and attenuation of the two sound modes. This factorization of D suggests a partial fraction decomposition

Notes p. 203

of (38-28). In this way one can separate the contributions of first and second sound modes to the density–density correlations and find

$$\langle \delta\rho(\boldsymbol{K},\omega)\,\delta\rho^*(\boldsymbol{K},\omega)\rangle$$

$$= \frac{2k_B T}{(2\pi)^4} V(2\Upsilon)\left\{\frac{(\frac{4}{3}\eta+\zeta_2)K^4}{[(\Delta\omega-Ku_1)^2+u_1^2\alpha_1^2][(\Delta\omega+Ku_1)^2+u_1^2\alpha_1^2]}+K^4\frac{C_p-C_V}{C_p}\right.$$

$$\left.\times\frac{-\dfrac{2\kappa}{C_p}u_1^2u_2^4+\dfrac{\rho_s\Lambda}{\rho_n}u_1^2u_2^2(u_1^2-3u_2^2)+\dfrac{(\Delta\omega)^2}{K^2}\left[\dfrac{\kappa}{C_p}u_1^2(u_1^2+u_2^2)+\dfrac{2\rho_s\Lambda}{\rho_n}u_1^2u_2^2\right]}{(u_1^2-u_2^2)^3[(\Delta\omega-Ku_2)^2+u_2^2\alpha_2^2][(\Delta\omega+Ku_2)^2+u_2^2\alpha_2^2]}\right\}, \tag{38-30}$$

where $\Lambda \equiv \frac{4}{3}\eta + \zeta_2 - \rho(\zeta_1+\zeta_4) + \rho^2\zeta_3$ and in the contributions of first and second sound we have in each case kept terms of lowest order in the small quantity $(\partial\rho/\partial T)_p$. To this end the following identities are useful:

$$\left(\frac{\partial p}{\partial T}\right)_\rho \equiv -\left(\frac{\partial \rho}{\partial T}\right)_p\left(\frac{\partial \rho}{\partial p}\right)_T^{-1} \equiv -\rho^2\left(\frac{\partial s}{\partial \rho}\right)_T. \tag{38-31}$$

In this approximation u_1, u_2 are given by (7-18,19) and α_1, α_2 are given by (25-10,11). Since in light scattering one works with given K instead of given ω it is better to write for α_1, α_2:

$$\alpha_1 = \frac{K^2}{2\rho u_1}(\tfrac{4}{3}\eta+\zeta_2), \tag{38-32}$$

$$\alpha_2 = \frac{K^2}{2\rho u_2}\frac{\rho_s}{\rho_n}\left(\Lambda+\frac{\rho_n}{\rho_s}\frac{\kappa}{C_p}\right). \tag{38-33}$$

For temperatures above 1.0 °K, $u_2^2 \ll u_1^2$ and (38-30) then simplifies to [8]

$$\langle \delta\rho(\boldsymbol{K},\omega)\,\delta\rho^*(\boldsymbol{K},\omega)\rangle$$

$$= \frac{2k_B T}{(2\pi)^4} V(2\Upsilon)K^4\left\{\frac{\frac{4}{3}\eta+\zeta_2}{[(\Delta\omega-Ku_1)^2+\alpha_1^2u_1^2][(\Delta\omega+Ku_1)^2+\alpha_1^2u_1^2]}\right.$$

$$\left.+\frac{C_p-C_V}{C_p}\frac{(\rho_s/\rho_n)\Lambda u_2^2+(\Delta\omega/K)^2\kappa/C_p}{u_1^2[(\Delta\omega-Ku_2)^2+\alpha_2^2u_2^2][(\Delta\omega+Ku_2)^2+\alpha_2^2u_2^2]}\right\}. \tag{38-34}$$

Notes p. 203

From (38-13,30) one sees that the spectrum of light scattered from He II consists of four peaks or so to speak two Brillouin doublets [9]. Each peak has a Lorentzian form as is schematically represented in Fig. 32.

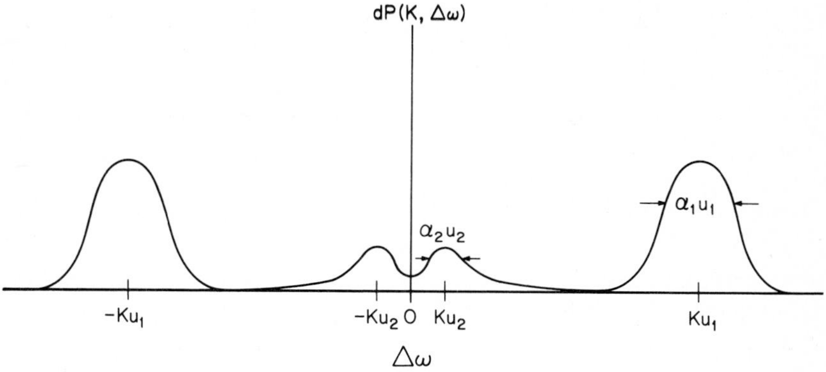

Fig. 32. Schematic representation of the light scattered by He II. The denominators of (38-34) have minima at $\Delta\omega = \pm Ku_1$ and $\Delta\omega = \pm Ku_2$. Therefore the scattered light will exhibit maxima at these frequency shifts. The half widths are determined by the absorption coefficients of sound.

One of the doublets is due to density fluctuations which propagate with the speed of first sound and hence lead to a Doppler shift Ku_1 in the frequency of the incident light. The other doublet results from scattering off density fluctuations which propagate with second sound velocity and hence is Doppler shifted Ku_2 in frequency. As second sound involves small density variations (§ 7) the integrated intensity of light scattered by second sound is much less than scattered by first sound. When $u_2 \ll u_1$ this ratio is $(C_p - C_V)/C_p$.

Light scattering from classical liquids consists of three peaks [10]: a Brillouin doublet resulting from scattering off sound and a central unshifted peak due to scattering off density fluctuations associated with thermal conduction. As thermal disturbances are not conducted but convected in He II the unshifted peak of the classical fluid is split into the second sound Brillouin doublet. For the classical fluid the relative intensity of the central peak to the sound peaks is also $(C_p - C_V)/C_p$. The width of the peaks is determined by the absorption of sound and is given by $\alpha_1 u_1$ and $\alpha_2 u_2$.

Thermal fluctuations present in the fluid lead everywhere to spon-

Notes p. 203

taneous density fluctuations which then propagate and decay with the speed and absorption of sound. Light incident on this 'lattice' of thermal fluctuations is scattered off these sound wave fronts. Only those wave fronts which reflect the incident wave vector $\boldsymbol{k}$ into the scattered vector $\boldsymbol{k}'$ [Eq. (38-1,2)] lead to constructive interference with intensities given by (38-13,30).

By use of the Laser, light sufficiently monochromatic can be obtained. Scattering from first sound was observed by Vinen et al. [11] but since the intensity of light scattered by second sound is much smaller its effects are much more difficult to observe. Scattering from second sound was first observed by Woolf and Petrac [12], but they used an arrangement where second sound was mechanically imposed rather than thermally fluctuated.

Very near the superfluid transition temperature and especially under pressure $(C_p - C_V)/C_p$ can be made to assume larger values (say on the order of 0.3). Greytak et al. [8] and Vinen et al. [13] have observed thermally induced scattering from both first and second sound in this region.

In deriving these results we have ignored the temperature dependence of α_p and thus the scattering from temperature fluctuations. In scattering from first sound this results in an error of order

$$\left(\frac{\partial \alpha_\mathrm{p}}{\partial T}\right)_\rho \left(\frac{\partial \alpha_\mathrm{p}}{\partial \rho}\right)_T^{-1} \left(\frac{\mathrm{d}T}{\mathrm{d}\rho}\right)_1 \approx \left(\frac{\partial \alpha_\mathrm{p}}{\partial T}\right)_\rho \left(\frac{\partial \alpha_\mathrm{p}}{\partial \rho}\right)_T^{-1} \frac{C_p - C_V}{C_p} \left(\frac{\partial \rho}{\partial T}\right)_p^{-1}, \tag{38-35}$$

where $(\mathrm{d}T/\mathrm{d}\rho)_1$ is the change in T for given variation in ρ when first sound propagates as is given by (7-24,25). Measurements [7] of the temperature dependence of α_p are accurate enough to show that this quantity is small for all T. The error in neglecting scattering from temperature fluctuations related to second sound is similarly of order

$$\left(\frac{\partial \alpha_\mathrm{p}}{\partial T}\right)_\rho \left[\left(\frac{\partial \alpha_\mathrm{p}}{\partial \rho}\right)_T \left(\frac{\partial \rho}{\partial T}\right)_p\right]^{-1}. \tag{38-36}$$

Although $(\partial \alpha_\mathrm{p}/\partial T)_\rho$ is small so is $(\partial \rho/\partial T)_p$. Still it is expected, though not yet experimentally demonstrated that $(\partial \alpha_\mathrm{p}/\partial T)_\rho$ is sufficiently small so that this term may be neglected at almost all temperatures. The qualification 'almost all' is required since near 1.17 °K $(\partial \rho/\partial T)_p$ passes through zero. At this temperature the extremely small contributions to the second sound peak will be determined by scattering from temperature fluctuations.

Notes p. 203

In § 27 we saw that in the presence of a counterflow ($\boldsymbol{v}_n - \boldsymbol{v}_s \neq 0$) transverse shear waves were coupled to temperature variations. Thus thermal fluctuations about a counterflow will, through the expansion coefficient $(\partial\rho/\partial T)_p$ lead to a *fifth central peak* in the light scattering spectrum of He II. Its intensity will be down by a factor of roughly $(\boldsymbol{v}_n - \boldsymbol{v}_s)^2/u^2$ from the second sound peak.

Notes

[1] R. Fox and G. E. Uhlenbeck, Phys. Fluids **13**(1970)1893,2881. R. Fox, Thesis, Rockefeller University (1969).

[2] Although, R. J. Donnelly and P. H. Roberts, Phil. Trans. Roy. Soc. (London) **271**(1971)41; M. Chester and R. Ziff, J. Low Temp. Phys. **5**(1971)285, have proposed describing the Brownian motion of quantized vortex rings by adding a fluctuating force to Eq. (32-23) the above comments are *not* in conflict with their approach since their fluctuating force is not of the form (34-6). In particular the strength Q of their fluctuating force depends upon I_R (and hence also upon time). This raises another question; namely how can an ensemble average depend on an (unaveraged) random variable.

[3] S. V. Iordanskii, Zh. Eksp. Teor. Fiz. **48**(1965)708 [Sov. Phys. JETP **21**(1965)467].

[4] J. S. Langer and M. E. Fisher, Phys. Rev. Letters **19**(1967)560.

[5] Reference [2], and R. J. Donnelly and P. H. Roberts, Proc. Roy. Soc. **A312**(1969)519; Phys. Rev. Letters **24**(1970)367.

[6] L. I. Komarov and I. Z. Fisher, Zh. Eksp. Teor. Fiz. **43**(1962)1927 [Sov. Phys. JETP **16**(1963)1358]. For a simple discussion see G. Benedek and T. Greytak, Proc. IEEE **53**(1965)1623.

[7] H. Edwards, Can. J. Phys. **36**(1958)884; C. E. Chase, E. Maxwell and W. E. Millett, Physica **27**(1961)1129.

[8] This result was presented by G. Winterling, F. S. Holmes and T. J. Greytak, Phys. Rev. Letters **30**(1973)427.

[9] This was first remarked by V. L. Ginzburg, Zh. Eksp. Teor. Fiz. **13**(1943)243.

[10] R. D. Mountain, Rev. Mod. Phys. **38**(1966)205.

[11] E. R. Pike, J. M. Vaughan and W. F. Vinen, Phys. Letters **30A**(1969)373.

[12] D. Petrac and M. Woolf, Phys. Rev. Letters **28**(1972)283.

[13] W. F. Vinen, Paper presented at Thirteenth International Conference on Low Temperature Physics, Boulder, Colorado (1972).

CHAPTER V

Hydrodynamics of Clamped Superfluid Helium

39 *The Hydrodynamics of He II Clamped in a Superleak in the Non-dissipative Approximation*

One of the most striking properties of He II is its ability to flow through narrow constrictions without any resistance. In such situations the superfluid is flowing freely while the normal fluid is held at rest due to its viscous interaction with the walls. As the behavior of the normal fluid is suppressed, the super nature of He II is emphasized by these geometries. In this chapter we investigate the hydrodynamics of He II when the normal fluid is clamped ($\boldsymbol{v}_n = 0$) in such an arrangement.

By tightly packing a region with fine powder such as jeweler's rouge or Al_2O_3 channels of diameter 200 Å or less can be obtained. In such a 'superleak' any flow of normal fluid would involve great dissipation and hence on the level where dissipation is neglected one must take the normal fluid velocity equal to the velocity of the superleak. We will always work in the preferred Galilean reference frame in which the superleak is at rest so that $\boldsymbol{v}_n = 0$.

With this restriction the He II is described by five and not eight independent variables. However, if we described its flow in this situation by simply setting $\boldsymbol{v}_n = 0$ in the ideal two fluid equations we would end up with eight equations for five variables. This difficulty can be resolved by noting that since we must in general exert an outside force to keep the superleak at rest (as there are interactions between super and normal fluids which accelerate the normal fluid, see § 9) the momentum $\rho_s \boldsymbol{v}_s$ of the clamped fluid is not conserved. Thus when He II is clamped in a superleak the momentum conservation equation must not be used, leaving us with the required five equations.

Taking $\boldsymbol{v}_n = 0$ in the continuity (4-1), entropy (4-2), and superfluid (4-3) equations we find

Notes p. 234

$$\frac{\partial \rho}{\partial t} + \nabla \cdot \rho_s \boldsymbol{v}_s = 0, \tag{39-1}$$

$$\frac{\partial \rho s}{\partial t} = 0, \tag{39-2}$$

$$\frac{\mathrm{D}_s \boldsymbol{v}_s}{\mathrm{D}t} = -\nabla \mu, \tag{39-3}$$

The energy relation follows from putting $\boldsymbol{v}_n = 0$ in (4-5,6):

$$\mathrm{d}U = (\mu + \tfrac{1}{2}v_s^2)\,\mathrm{d}\rho + T\,\mathrm{d}\rho s + \rho_s \boldsymbol{v}_s \cdot \mathrm{d}\boldsymbol{v}_s. \tag{39-4}$$

Equations (39-1,2,3) are five equations for the five basic variables ρ, s, $\boldsymbol{v}_s$ provided that equations of state for ρ_s, μ are furnished.

To find the momentum balance equations for the momentum of the fluid we note that from (39-1,3) follows

$$\frac{\partial \rho_s v_{s,j}}{\partial t} + \frac{\partial}{\partial r_\alpha}(p\delta_{j\alpha} + \rho_s v_{s,\alpha} v_{s,j}) = \frac{\partial p}{\partial r_j} - \rho_s \frac{\partial \mu}{\partial r_j} - v_{s,j}\frac{\partial \rho_n}{\partial t}. \tag{39-5}$$

Defining the pressure p for clamped He II by setting $\boldsymbol{v}_n = 0$ in the pressure of unclamped He II yields

$$p = \rho(\mu + \tfrac{1}{2}v_s^2) + \rho s T - U \tag{39-6}$$

or using (39-4) this becomes

$$\mathrm{d}p = \rho s\,\mathrm{d}T + \rho\,\mathrm{d}\mu + \rho_n\,\mathrm{d}\tfrac{1}{2}v_s^2. \tag{39-7}$$

The momentum of the fluid is not conserved but is supplied to the fluid at the rate given by the right hand side of (39-5). This is understandable because if the normal fluid were free to move its equation of motion would be (9-1)

$$\rho_n \frac{\mathrm{D}_n \boldsymbol{v}_n}{\mathrm{D}t} = -\nabla p + \rho_s \nabla \mu - (\boldsymbol{v}_n - \boldsymbol{v}_s)\left(\frac{\partial \rho_n}{\partial t} + \nabla \cdot \rho_n \boldsymbol{v}_n\right), \tag{39-8}$$

so if $\boldsymbol{v}_n$ stays zero the superleak must oppose the right hand side of (39-8) which for $\boldsymbol{v}_n = 0$ is just the outside momentum flux in (39-5).

Although momentum is not conserved, energy is conserved, because the applied force is a force which keeps the system at rest and hence can do no work. From (39-1,2,3,4) the energy conservation equation is found to be

Notes p. 234

$$\frac{\partial U}{\partial t} + \nabla \cdot [\rho_s \boldsymbol{v}_s(\mu + \tfrac{1}{2}v_s^2)] = 0. \tag{39-9}$$

From (39-3) it still follows that the circulation $\oint \boldsymbol{v}_s \cdot d\boldsymbol{\ell}$ is conserved.

A simple application of the ideal equations of clamped He II is realized when one investigates the linearized equations for possible sound modes as in §§ 1 and 7. One finds that there is a sound mode (fourth sound) unique to He II in a superleak with phase velocity u_4 given by

$$u_4^2 = \rho_s \left(\frac{\partial \mu}{\partial \rho}\right)_{\rho s}. \tag{39-10}$$

By straightforward thermodynamic manipulations (39-10) becomes

$$u_4^2 = \frac{\rho_s}{\rho} u_1^2 \left[1 + \frac{2sT}{\rho C_p}\left(\frac{\partial \rho}{\partial T}\right)_p\right] + \frac{\rho_n}{\rho} u_2^2, \tag{39-11}$$

which to an error of at most 2% becomes $u_4^2 = (\rho_s \rho) u_1^2$, where u_1, u_2 are given by (7-18,19). To obtain (39-11) the following identities are useful:

$$\left(\frac{\partial T}{\partial \rho}\right)_{s\rho} \equiv \left(\frac{\partial T}{\partial \rho}\right)_s - \frac{s}{\rho}\left(\frac{\partial T}{\partial s}\right)_\rho, \tag{39-12}$$

$$\left(\frac{\partial T}{\partial \rho}\right)_s \equiv -\frac{1}{\rho^2}\left(\frac{\partial \rho}{\partial T}\right)_p \left(\frac{\partial s}{\partial T}\right)_p^{-1} \left(\frac{\partial p}{\partial \rho}\right)_s. \tag{39-13}$$

The speed of fourth sound vanishes at the transition temperature and equals the speed of first sound at low temperature as seen in Fig. 33. Fourth sound is essentially a pressure wave and has been observed by Shapiro and Rudnick [1].

As the He II can flow through the narrow channels without friction, a circulation once started will continue indefinitely. These persistent currents can be formed for instance by cooling through T_λ a rotating superleak filled with liquid helium. On bringing the container to rest the superfluid will then hold onto its circulation. Although persistent currents can be observed in bulk geometries [2] they are most readily observed in superleaks [3], partly because the normal fluid is suppressed. But most important persistent currents are metastable states which can arise only if there are 'forces' which prevent the quantized vortex lines from moving to their equilibrium location, which in the above case is the boundary of the container. We say that the vortex lines must be pinned.

Notes p. 234

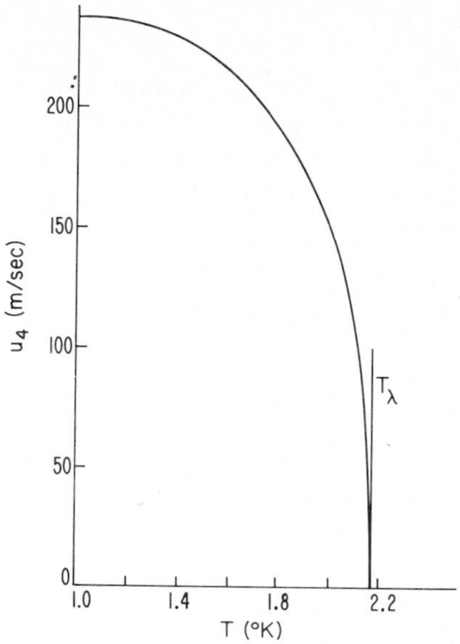

Fig. 33. The speed of fourth sound as a function of temperature at the vapor pressure.

In bulk geometries they might pin to surface roughnesses at the top and bottom of the vessel, but still have a lot of freedom of motion through bending. In a superleak the pinning effects are clearly greatly enhanced.

To date the most accurate means of observing the persistent currents is through their effect on the fourth sound velocity [4]. As with classical fluids a steady background velocity leads to a Doppler shift, through which the speed of the persistent current can be measured.

The Doppler shift can be calculated from (39-1,2,3) by linearizing about the equilibrium state where $v_s = v_{s,0} \neq 0$. For a travelling wave $[\sim \exp(ik_0x - i\omega t)]$ these equations become

$$-\omega\frac{\partial\rho}{\partial T}T' - \omega\frac{\partial\rho}{\partial p}p' - \omega\frac{\partial\rho}{\partial\frac{1}{2}w^2}v_sv_s' + k_0\rho_sv_s' + v_sk_0\frac{\partial\rho_s}{\partial p}p' + v_sk_0\frac{\partial\rho_s}{\partial T}T' = 0, \quad (39\text{-}14)$$

$$-\omega\frac{\partial\rho s}{\partial p}p' - \omega\frac{\partial\rho s}{\partial T}T' - \omega\frac{\partial\rho s}{\partial\frac{1}{2}w^2}v_sv_s' = 0, \quad (39\text{-}15)$$

Notes p. 234

$$-\omega v_s' + \frac{\rho_s}{\rho} k_0 v_s v_s' - s k_0 T' + \frac{1}{\rho} k_0 p' = 0, \tag{39-16}$$

where $w \equiv v_n - v_s$ and the subscript zero has been dropped from equilibrium quantities and we have kept terms at most linear in v_s.

The Doppler shift of fourth sound follows from equating the determinant of (39-14,15,16) to zero and is

$$u_4 = \frac{\rho_s}{\rho} v_s + \left[s \frac{\partial(\rho_n/\rho)}{\partial T} \left(\frac{\partial s}{\partial T} \right)^{-1} - \rho \frac{\partial(\rho_n/\rho)}{\partial p} \left(\frac{\partial \rho}{\partial p} \right)^{-1} \right] v_s \pm u_{4,0}, \tag{39-17}$$

where small terms of order $(\partial\rho/\partial T)_p$ have been neglected, and $u_{4,0}$ is the speed of fourth sound in He II at rest [Eq. (39-11)]. The pressure dependence of ρ_n/ρ and thus also of ρ_s can be determined from performing Andronikashvili's experiment or second sound under pressure [5]. In this way a measurement of the Doppler shift of fourth sound can be used to determine the velocity of the superfluid in the superleak. Below 1.4 °K the term in brackets is negligible and the Doppler shift is simply

$$u_4 = (\rho_s/\rho) v_s \pm u_{4,0}.$$

In a typical experiment a torus packed with fine powder and filled with He II is brought from rest into rotation at angular velocity ω_n. By fourth sound measurements performed relative to the rotating system the average superfluid angular velocity ω_s can be measured.

The results are shown schematically in Fig. 34. Up to a 'critical' angular velocity denoted by ω_{c1}, ω_s versus ω_n is linear with slope less than unity; the 45° line represents the behavior of a classical fluid. Below ω_{c1} the response of the He II is reversible in that a counter-rotation or slowing down of the superleak returns the superfluid to rest along the same curve. Above ω_{c1} there is a change in shape of the curve and the response of the superfluid is no longer reversible. If counter-rotated from above ω_{c1} (say B) the response is to follow B–C which is initially parallel to A–O. If brought all the way to rest the initial state $\omega_n = \omega_s = 0$ will not in general be recovered. Finally if the rotation is continued past B it is found that ω_s eventually follows a 45° line corresponding to a maximum value of $\omega_n - \omega_s$.

This behavior can at best be qualitatively interpreted. Below A one expects that there are no vortices in the fluid as the behavior is reversible. The superfluid rotation in this circulation free state comes from the

Notes p. 234

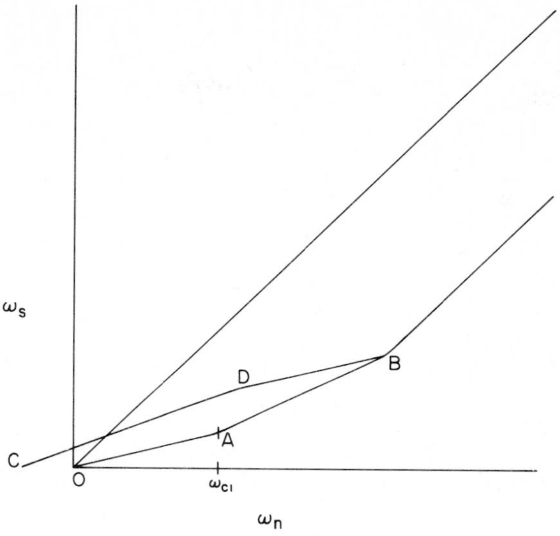

Fig. 34. The average superfluid angular velocity ω_s of He II contained in a superleak rotating at angular velocity ω_n. The 45° line through the origin O indicates the response of a classical fluid.

motion of the superleak through the superfluid as was first observed and emphasized by Mehl and Zimmermann [3]. This effect also exists in principle in a classical Euler fluid and can be calculated from the vector identity

$$\int \boldsymbol{v}\,\mathrm{d}V \equiv -\int \boldsymbol{r}(\nabla\cdot\boldsymbol{v})\,\mathrm{d}V + \int \boldsymbol{r}(\boldsymbol{v}\cdot\mathrm{d}\boldsymbol{S}), \tag{39-18}$$

where $\mathrm{d}\boldsymbol{S}$ is an element of surface bounding the volume of integration. Replacing $\boldsymbol{v}$ with $\boldsymbol{v}_s$ and ignoring compressibility effects so that $\nabla\cdot\boldsymbol{v}_s = 0$ one finds that the momentum of the superfluid in a given volume is

$$\int \rho_s\boldsymbol{v}_s\,\mathrm{d}V = \int \rho_s\boldsymbol{r}(\boldsymbol{v}_s\cdot\mathrm{d}\boldsymbol{S}), \tag{39-19}$$

where the surface integral bounds the volume. Now consider a sphere of diameter d moving with velocity $\boldsymbol{U}$ through the superfluid in a container at rest as in Fig. 35. From the boundary conditions of no mass and no heat flow through the surfaces one finds $\boldsymbol{v}_s\cdot\mathrm{d}\boldsymbol{S} = 0$ at all surfaces except that of the sphere where

$$\boldsymbol{v}_s\cdot\mathrm{d}\boldsymbol{S} = \boldsymbol{U}\cdot\mathrm{d}\boldsymbol{S}. \tag{39-20}$$

Notes p. 234

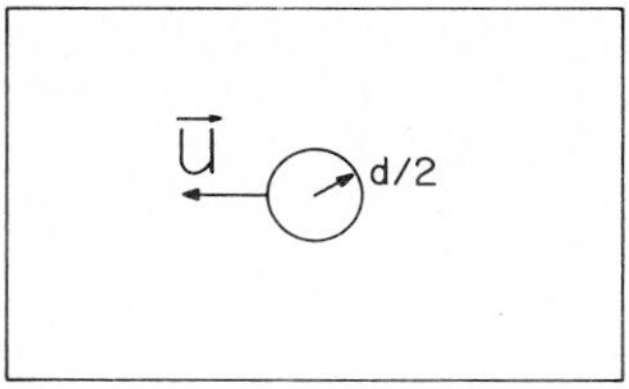

Fig. 35. A sphere of diameter d moves with velocity $\boldsymbol{U}$ through fluid in a closed stationary container.

A simple integration now yields that the momentum of the fluid is:

$$\tfrac{1}{2}(\tfrac{1}{6}\rho_s \pi d^3)\boldsymbol{U}, \tag{39-21}$$

which is half the momentum the fluid would have if it occupied the volume of the sphere and moved with velocity $\boldsymbol{U}$. An identical calculation reveals that for a cylinder one must replace the coefficient of one half with unity.

In a toroidal geometry this inertial momentum effect becomes an angular momentum about the axis. For moving bodies whose size is small compared with the container the inertial angular momentum is equal to their distance from the axis multiplied by the inertial momentum. It is important to note that for an arbitrary number and distribution of spheres and cylinders (39-18) implies that the momenta or angular momenta are additive.

This inertial motion of the superfluid depends only on the velocity of the superleak and is thus reversible as is the behavior in O–A. From the total weight of the fine powder and from the average size of a particle one can determine the number of particles. The exact shape of the packing particles is not known especially since they are packed under pressure. However, the slope of O–A always lies between what one would calculate using the limiting cases of spheres and cylinders.

The vortex free state of the fluid in O–A can also be called a persistent current since it corresponds to a metastable relative velocity of the super and normal fluids which will persist when isolated. We call this state metastable because on cooling through T_λ He II rotating at any ω the 45° line is always achieved.

The irreversibility that sets in at ω_{c1} can be interpreted as being due to the entrance of quantized vortex lines which become pinned to the superleak. In counter-rotating B → C the superfluid loses at first only

Notes p. 234

the circulation free angular momentum. As counter-rotation is continued one eventually reaches another critical angular velocity D at which vortices are either destroyed or enter with opposite sign.

The best understood aspect of this experiment is the circulation free Landau state for which $\nabla \times \boldsymbol{v}_s = 0$ everywhere. The critical velocities such as ω_{c1} and the maximum value of $\omega_n - \omega_s$, which also characterize the experiment, and the fact that no metastability is observed on cooling under rotation are not so well understood and will be returned to in Chapter VI where we discuss the general problem of the critical velocities.

40 *The Hydrodynamics of He II in a Superleak Including Dissipative Effects*

The dissipative theory of clamped He II does not follow from setting $\boldsymbol{v}_n = 0$ in the dissipative two fluid equations § 21. The two fluid theory including dissipation has been obtained in an expansion where the normal fluid is in first instance free to move and in next approximation experiences little friction. That is why at this level we included dissipative fluxes that were linear in the gradients of $\boldsymbol{v}_n$. For clamped He II expansion must be quite different because here the normal fluid is in first instance completely immobilized and in next approximation perhaps free to jiggle only a little bit.

We derive the dissipative equations of clamped He II by a direct generalization of the ideal equations of clamped He II. In the presence of dissipation there can be a normal fluid current $\boldsymbol{J}_n$ so that the continuity equation becomes

$$\frac{\partial \rho}{\partial t} + \nabla \cdot (\rho_s \boldsymbol{v}_s + \boldsymbol{J}_n) = 0. \tag{40-1}$$

There might also be a heat flux $\boldsymbol{q}$ and an entropy production Σ/T so that (39-2) becomes

$$\frac{\partial \rho s}{\partial t} + \nabla \cdot \frac{\boldsymbol{q}}{T} = \frac{\Sigma}{T}. \tag{40-2}$$

In the presence of dissipation we still insist on conservation of circulation of $\boldsymbol{v}_s$ and therefore (39-3) becomes

$$\frac{\mathrm{D}_s \boldsymbol{v}_s}{\mathrm{D}t} = -\nabla\mu - \nabla H. \tag{40-3}$$

Notes p. 234

The restriction that (40-1,2,3) imply a law of energy conservation yields

$$\Sigma = -\boldsymbol{J}_{\mathrm{n}} \cdot \nabla(\mu + \tfrac{1}{2}v_{\mathrm{s}}^2) - \frac{\boldsymbol{q}}{T} \cdot \nabla T - H\nabla \cdot \rho_{\mathrm{s}}\boldsymbol{v}_{\mathrm{s}}, \tag{40-4}$$

and

$$\frac{\partial U}{\partial t} = -\nabla \cdot [(\rho_{\mathrm{s}}\boldsymbol{v}_{\mathrm{s}} + \boldsymbol{J}_{\mathrm{n}})(\mu + \tfrac{1}{2}v_{\mathrm{s}}^2) + \boldsymbol{q} + \rho_{\mathrm{s}}\boldsymbol{v}_{\mathrm{s}}H]. \tag{40-5}$$

From the requirement that the entropy production be positive definite and the approximations that we restrict the dissipative fluxes to first order in the deviation from equilibrium and permit only scalar dissipative coefficients we find

$$\boldsymbol{J}_{\mathrm{n}} = -\sigma\nabla(\mu + \tfrac{1}{2}v_{\mathrm{s}}^2) + \sigma\alpha\nabla T, \tag{40-6}$$

$$\boldsymbol{q} = -\kappa\nabla T + T\sigma\beta\nabla(\mu + \tfrac{1}{2}v_{\mathrm{s}}^2), \tag{40-7}$$

$$H = -\zeta\nabla \cdot \rho_{\mathrm{s}}\boldsymbol{v}_{\mathrm{s}}, \tag{40-8}$$

where σ, κ, ζ must be positive and

$$(\alpha + \beta)^2 < 4\kappa/T\sigma.$$

The Onsager symmetry principle requires that $\alpha = \beta$ so that in all there are four independent transport coefficients. From (40-6,7) we see that the motion of the normal fluid is similar to diffusion in classical fluid mixtures.

41 Hydrodynamics of the Superfluid Helium Film

In the early days of superfluid research it was found that when two vessels were arranged as in Fig. 36, some mysterious process led to a quick equalization of the levels [6]. At first it was thought that this was

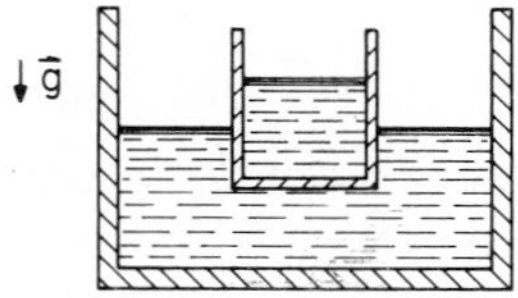

Fig. 36. When two vessels of He II are arranged as shown a flow of film over the walls leads to a quick equalization of the levels.

Notes p. 234

due to a rapid evaporation condensation effect. Rollin [6] suggested that this effect was due to an adsorbed film of He II which forms a bridge between the vessels. Later Daunt and Mendelssohn [7] showed that the equalization took place through a flow of this film. This flow can actually be observed through optical techniques [8].

A solid body in contact with the vapor of any substance has an adsorbed film form on it due to the short ranged Van der Waals force of attraction that exists between the molecules of the substrate (e.g., beaker) and the substance. In the geometry pictured in Fig. 37, this film

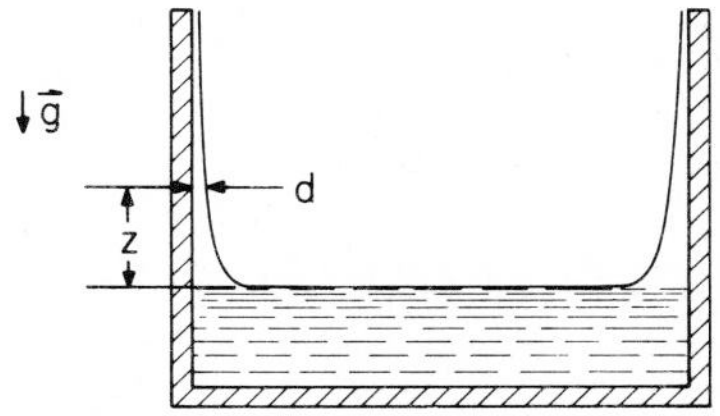

Fig. 37. The He II film which forms on the walls of a container in contact with He^4 vapor. The thickness of the film d depends upon the height above the bath z. For heights greater than a millimeter $d \lesssim 200$ Å.

will be about 200 Å thick. For a He II film part will be super and part normal. The normal fluid owing to its viscosity will like a classical fluid be unable to flow in such a narrow constriction. The super component, however, will flow to the lower chemical potential (i.e., lower level) as follows from its equation of motion

$$\frac{\mathrm{D_s}\boldsymbol{v}_\mathrm{s}}{\mathrm{D}t} = -\nabla\mu - \nabla\Omega, \tag{41-1}$$

where Ω is the potential of external forces. The film is a self-starting superfluid syphon.

The equations of motion of the He II film are not quite the same as He II in a superleak, § 39, since now the normal fluid is free to flow perpendicular to the substrate: $v_{\mathrm{n}\perp} \neq 0$. For motion in this direction the momentum is conserved. Thus we are led to six equations for the six variables ρ, s, $\boldsymbol{v}_\mathrm{s}$, $v_{\mathrm{n}\perp}$. Neglecting the external forces they are

$$\frac{\partial\rho}{\partial t} + \nabla\cdot\rho_\mathrm{s}\boldsymbol{v}_\mathrm{s} + \nabla_\perp\,\rho_\mathrm{n}v_{\mathrm{n}\perp} = 0, \tag{41-2}$$

Notes p. 234

$$\frac{\partial \rho s}{\partial t} + \nabla_{\perp} \rho s v_{n\perp} = 0, \tag{41-3}$$

$$\frac{D_s \boldsymbol{v}_s}{Dt} = -\nabla \mu, \tag{41-4}$$

$$\frac{\partial}{\partial t}(\rho_s v_s + \rho_n v_n)_{\perp} + \nabla_{\perp} p + \nabla_{\perp}(\rho_n v_{n\perp} v_{n\perp}) + \frac{\partial}{\partial r_{\alpha}}(\rho_s v_{s,\alpha} v_{s\perp}) = 0, \tag{41-5}$$

where

$$d\mu = -s\,dT + \frac{1}{\rho}\,dp - \frac{\rho_n}{2\rho}\,d(v_s^2 + v_{n\perp}^2 - 2v_{s\perp}v_{n\perp}). \tag{41-6}$$

The first and second law for this case is

$$dU = (\mu + \tfrac{1}{2}v_s^2 - v_{n\perp}v_{s\perp})\,d\rho + T\,d\rho s + v_{n\perp}\,dJ_{\perp} + \rho_s \boldsymbol{v}_s \cdot d\boldsymbol{v}_s - \rho_s v_{n\perp}\,dv_{s\perp}. \tag{41-7}$$

The energy conservation equation is obtained by setting all the components of $\boldsymbol{v}_n$, other than $v_{n\perp}$, equal to zero in (4-7). To include external forces one must replace μ by $\mu + \Omega$ in (41-4,7) but not in (41-6). Also $-\rho\nabla_{\perp}\Omega$ must be added to the right hand side of (41-5). The potential Ω will have in general contributions from gravity, Ω_g and the Van der Waals attraction, Ω_v:

$$\Omega = \Omega_v + \Omega_g. \tag{41-8}$$

The form of Ω_v is discussed below.

Due to the Van der Waals force of attraction per unit mass, $-\nabla\Omega_v$, a wave analogous to long gravity waves in a classical fluid can propagate in the He II film. To derive the speed of this so called third sound wave we look for a solution to the linearized equations with wavelength long compared with the film thickness d:

$$1/k_0 \gg d, \tag{41-9}$$

so that oscillations perpendicular to the substrate are negligible in comparison with the longitudinal motion. Integrating the continuity equation (41-2) over a volume element of length dz as indicated in Fig. 38, yields the equation of motion:

$$\rho\frac{\partial\,\delta\xi}{\partial t} + \bar{\rho}_s d\frac{\partial v_s}{\partial z} = 0, \tag{41-10}$$

Notes p. 234

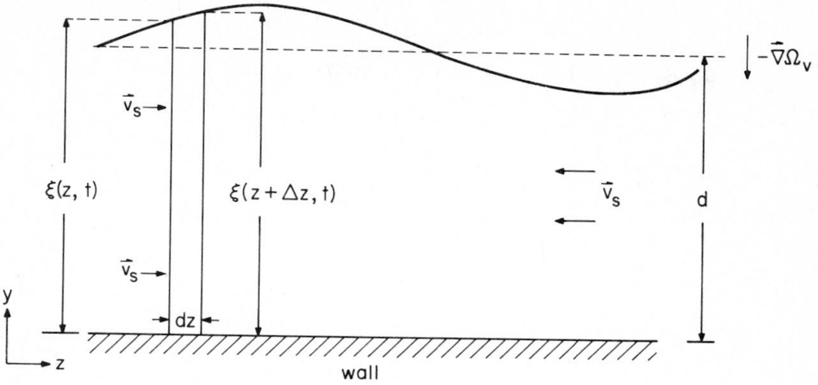

Fig. 38. The variation of quantities of interest in a third sound wave at time t.

where $\bar{\rho}_s$ denotes the average over the equilibrium film thickness d and $\delta\xi$ is the deviation in thickness ξ from the equilibrium value due to the third sound disturbance

$$\xi(z, t) = d + \delta\xi(z, t). \tag{41-11}$$

In Eq. (41-10) v_s should also be averaged in some sense. The advantage of dealing with long waves is that the variations of $\boldsymbol{v}_s$ with y are higher order and thus neglected. In deriving (41-10) variations in mass due to the z variations in ρ have been neglected. This is a good approximation since the speed of third sound is much less than the speed of ordinary sound. The first term in (41-10) represents the change in mass due to change in thickness of the film. Thus ρ is to be evaluated near the surface and not averaged over the thickness of film. From the component of (41-4,5) perpendicular to the substrate one finds by including the external potential (note that for motion perpendicular to the substrate the gravitational force is always negligible compared with the Van der Waals force)

$$\frac{\partial p}{\partial y} = -\rho \frac{\partial \Omega_v(y)}{\partial y}, \tag{41-12}$$

$$\frac{\partial T}{\partial y} = 0, \tag{41-13}$$

so that temperature depends only on z. Integrating the entropy equation over the slab of side dz yields

Notes p. 234

$$s\frac{\partial\,\delta\xi}{\partial t} + d\frac{\partial\bar{s}}{\partial T}\frac{\partial\,\delta T}{\partial t} = 0, \tag{41-14}$$

where

$$T = T_0 + \delta T(z, t), \tag{41-15}$$

and $(\partial\,\delta p/\partial t)\partial\bar{s}/\partial p$ has as usual been ignored. In view of (41-13) one might expect that one could replace

$$\bar{s} \equiv \frac{1}{d}\int_0^d s\,\mathrm{d}y, \tag{41-16}$$

with s the value of the entropy at the free surface. This cannot be justified since the variations of pressure in the *equilibrium* state are huge.

According to the stress tensor (41-5) the pressure at the gas–film interface must be continuous. The gas density is of course very low. Therefore the fluid pressure is a constant p_g at the free surface, or from (41-12)

$$p = \int_y^\xi \rho\frac{\partial\Omega_v(y')}{\partial y'}\mathrm{d}y' + p_g. \tag{41-17}$$

Variations in p in the third sound wave will come from variations in ξ and thus are independent of y. In fact to first order

$$\delta p = \rho\frac{\partial\Omega_v}{\partial d}\,\delta\xi, \tag{41-18}$$

where ρ is the density near the surface as in (41-10).

Averaging the component of (41-4) parallel to the substrate we obtain

$$\frac{\partial v_s}{\partial t} - \bar{s}\frac{\partial\,\delta T}{\partial z} + \frac{\partial\Omega_v(d)}{\partial d}\frac{\partial\,\delta\xi}{\partial z} = 0, \tag{41-19}$$

where incompressibility has again been assumed.

Equations (41-10,14,19) are three linear equations for the variables v_s, δT, $\delta\xi$ that characterize the third sound wave. We look for a travelling wave solution of the form:

$$\delta T = T'\exp(ik_0 z - i\omega t), \tag{41-20}$$

$$\delta\xi = \xi'\exp(ik_0 z - i\omega t), \tag{41-21}$$

$$v_s = v_s'\exp(ik_0 z - i\omega t). \tag{41-22}$$

Notes p. 234

Substitution in the above equations yields the dispersion law for the speed of third sound:

$$\frac{\omega^2}{k_0^2} = \frac{\bar{\rho}_s \bar{s} s}{\rho}\left(\frac{\partial \bar{s}}{\partial T}\right)_p^{-1} + \frac{\bar{\rho}_s d}{\rho}\frac{\partial \Omega_v(d)}{\partial d}. \tag{41-23}$$

The temperature variation in the third sound wave comes from the flow of the superfluid which carries no entropy. Where the film is thick and the superfluid mounds up the entropy is diluted and temperature decreases. In the troughs the reverse is the case. The first term on the right hand side of (41-23) is the contribution to the third sound speed from the associated temperature variations. However, this term is spurious in that it disappears from a more careful treatment of the problem.

As there are variations in temperature of the film one can expect a contribution to the change in thickness from evaporation condensation exchange with the vapor. In equilibrium the net evaporation is zero. Off equilibrium one thus expects to first order that the evaporation will be proportional to the element of surface multiplied by the deviation of temperature from equilibrium, δT. Denoting the proportionality coefficient by K, (41-10) becomes

$$\rho \frac{\partial\, \delta\xi}{\partial t} + \bar{\rho}_s d \frac{\partial v_s}{\partial z} = -K\,\delta T, \tag{41-24}$$

where we note that an evaporation results in a net decrease of film mass. Evaporation from the film extracts a latent heat per gram L, in addition to the entropy carried away by the particles. Thus (41-14) is modified to

$$s\frac{\partial\, \delta\xi}{\partial t} + d\frac{\partial \bar{s}}{\partial T}\frac{\partial\, \delta T}{\partial t} = -\frac{K(L+sT)}{\rho T}\delta T. \tag{41-25}$$

A plane wave solution to (41-19,24,25) now yields the dispersion law

$$\frac{\omega^2}{k_0^2} = \frac{\bar{\rho}_s d}{\rho}\frac{\partial \Omega_v(d)}{\partial d} + \frac{\bar{\rho}_s s T}{\rho}\left(\bar{s} + \frac{iK}{\rho\omega}\frac{\partial \Omega_v(d)}{\partial d}\right)\left(T\frac{\partial \bar{s}}{\partial T} + \frac{iKL}{\rho\omega d}\right)^{-1}. \tag{41-26}$$

The coefficient K which is defined by (41-24) must be determined by experiment. There is some evidence [9] that in order of magnitude it is given by

$$K \approx \left(\frac{\mathscr{M}}{2\pi R T}\right)^{1/2}\left(\frac{\mathrm{d}p}{\mathrm{d}T}\right)_{\mathrm{co}}, \tag{41-27}$$

Notes p. 234

where $\mathcal{M}$ is the molecular weight, R the gas constant and the subscript 'co' indicates that the derivative is taken along the coexistence curve. A simple kinetic theory argument given at the end of this section also yields (41-27).

For He^4 $K = 0.13$ and 5.5 g/cm^2 sec °K at 1 °K and 2 °K respectively. Thus the terms involving K in (41-27) dominate the fraction (for $\omega < 10^4$ sec^{-1}) and we find

$$u_3^2 = \frac{\bar{\rho}_s d}{\rho} \frac{\partial \Omega_v(d)}{\partial d}\left(1 + \frac{sT}{L}\right). \tag{41-28}$$

The quantity sT/L is small at all T being a maximum at T_λ where it is $\frac{1}{7}$; at 1 °K it is 0.01. We see that evaporation condensation can be an important aspect of third sound.

It is useful to compare third sound with classical long gravity waves that propagate with velocity

$$u_g^2 = gd. \tag{41-29}$$

This result follows from the Euler equations, § 1, by the same analysis presented here in deriving (41-23). We note that by replacing Ω_v with Ω_g in (41-23) we do *not* obtain (41-29). First there is a difference in the factor of ρ_s/ρ which is obviously due to the fact that although the external field acts on the whole fluid, only the superfluid component can flow and participate in the wave. The extra term of the form $\rho_n u_2^2/\rho$ arises from the fact that reversible fluid motion leads to dynamical temperature gradients in He II. As we remarked in § 2 the behavior of He II can become like that of a classical fluid only when the temperature variations vanish. When evaporation condensation effects are included the temperature variations which led to the entropy term in (41-23) become smoothed out. In this 'isothermal' limit the speed of third sound (41-28) becomes quite analogous to the formula for the speed of long gravity waves.

Third sound was first observed by Pickar and Atkins [8] using an optical technique. The most accurate measurements are made through the use of thin aluminium films evaporated onto the substrate. By imposing an external magnetic field and biasing currents these strips can be operated near their superconducting transition. Thus a small change in temperature leads to a huge change in resistance. In this way third sound is detected through its associated temperature variations.

Notes p. 234

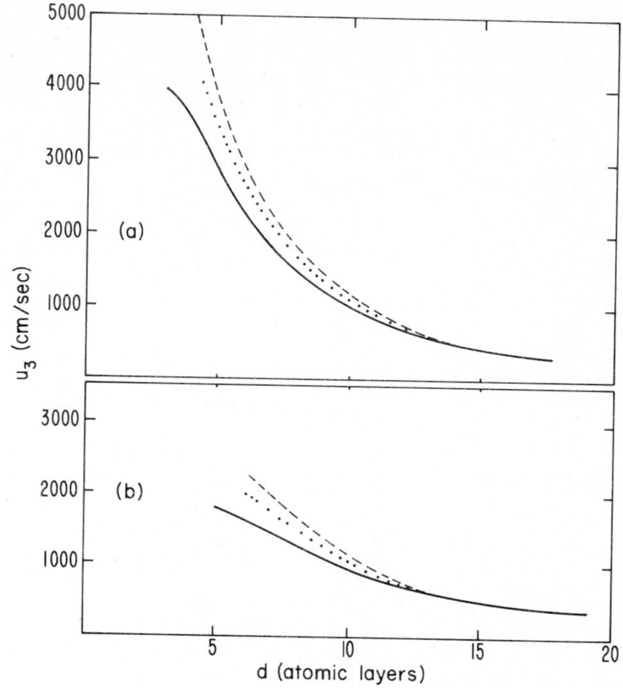

Fig. 39. The speed of third sound (solid lines) versus film thickness at (a) 1.315 °K and (b) 1.778 °K. The dashed lines represent Eq. (41-44) evaluated for ρ_s/ρ at the vapor pressure and the dotted lines are Eq. (41-28) including pressure variations of ρ_s/ρ and a solid layer. Note that an atomic layer is 3.6 Å.

In Fig. 39 is shown the speed of third sound (solid line) as a function of film thickness at 1.3 °K and 1.8 °K [10]. Experimentally it is the pressure p'_g in the vapor far above the film which is measured. If p_v is the vapor pressure of bulk He II the film thickness d is determined by

$$\Omega_v(d) = -\frac{RT}{\mathscr{M}} \log \frac{p_v}{p'_g}. \tag{41-30}$$

To derive (41-30) we must assume that the vapor is an ideal gas with density much less than that of He^4. From the ideal gas equation of state:

$$p_g = \rho_g \frac{RT}{\mathscr{M}}, \tag{41-31}$$

Notes p. 234

one finds for the variation of the chemical potential at constant temperature

$$\mu_g(p, T) = \mu_g(p_v, T) + \frac{RT}{\mathscr{M}} \log \frac{p'_g}{p_v} + \frac{RT}{\mathscr{M}} \log \frac{p}{p'_g}. \tag{41-32}$$

We now interpret p as the pressure in the ideal gas just outside the film. Since for a classical gas the hydrostatic equilibrium, such as follows from the Euler equations (§ 1), implies

$$\mu_g + \Omega = \text{constant}, \tag{41-33}$$

we find

$$\frac{RT}{\mathscr{M}} \log \frac{p}{p'_g} = -\Omega_v(d). \tag{41-34}$$

Then (41-32) becomes

$$\mu_g(p, T) - \mu_g(p_v, T) + \Omega_v(d) = \frac{RT}{\mathscr{M}} \log \frac{p'_g}{p_v}. \tag{41-35}$$

Even in the presence of an external field the equilibrium condition (6-12) is valid. Thus:

$$\mu(p, T) = \mu_g(p, T), \qquad \mu(p_v, T) = \mu_g(p_v, T), \tag{41-36}$$

and we obtain for the thickness of a He^4 film:

$$\mu(p, T) - \mu(p_v, T) + \Omega_v(d) = \frac{RT}{\mathscr{M}} \log \frac{p'_g}{p_v}. \tag{41-37}$$

Since the density of the gas is far less than that of He^4 the term $\mu(p, T) - \mu(p_v, T)$ is negligible compared with the right hand side of (41-37). Dropping it leads to the desired result (41-30).

In the course of the above derivation we assumed that the gas is a continuum into which the Van der Waals force extends. It turns out that to the contrary the range of these forces is much less than the mean free path ($\sim 10^{-5}$ cm) of the He^4 vapor. We thus present now a modified discussion in which Ω_v is ignored as far as the gas is concerned.

Instead of (41-33) one now has that μ_g is constant so that $p = p'_g$ or (41-32) is replaced by

$$\mu_g(p, T) = \mu_g(p_v, T) + \frac{RT}{\mathscr{M}} \log \frac{p'_g}{p_v}.$$

Notes p. 234

By including the Van der Waals force in the liquid, but not the gas (41-36) becomes

$$\mu(p, T) + \Omega_v(d) = \mu_g(p, T), \qquad \mu(p_v, T) = \mu_g(p_v, T),$$

so that the above relation yields again (41-37) from which (41-30) follows as before.

The Van der Waals potential relative to infinity at a distance y from the substrate has the form

$$\Omega_v(y) = -\frac{\alpha}{y^3}\left(1 + \frac{y}{d'}\right)^{-1}, \tag{41-38}$$

where α, d' are material parameters. Experimental evidence for (41-38) comes from measurements of extremely high frequency first sound resonances in He II films [11]. For $y \ll d'$ (41-38) becomes

$$\Omega_v(y) = -\frac{\alpha}{y^3}. \tag{41-39}$$

For $y \gg d'$ there is a transition to a $1/y^4$ dependence as was first predicted by Casimir and Polder [12] who took retardation effects into account. Experiments [11] show that for calcium fluoride, CaF_2,

$$d' \approx 165\,\text{Å} \approx 46 \text{ atomic layers}, \qquad \mathscr{M}\alpha/R = 23.0\,^\circ\text{K (atomic layers)}^3, \tag{41-40}$$

where we note that an atomic layer equals 3.6 Å. One also has

$$\alpha = 2.2 \times 10^{-14} \text{ erg cm}^3/\text{g}. \tag{41-41}$$

By performing third sound on both CaF_2 and glass one can determine α, d' for glass as

$$\mathscr{M}\alpha/R = 27.0\,^\circ\text{K (atomic layers)}^3, \qquad d' \gtrsim 150\,\text{Å}. \tag{41-42}$$

Additional verifications of (41-38) and determinations of α have been obtained by optical techniques [13].

As p'_g approaches the bulk vapor pressure, d increases to infinity indicating that at the saturated vapor pressure there is no longer a film, but instead bulk liquid whose depth is of course determined by the quantity of fluid in the container. As p'_g decreases d decreases.

In Fig. 39 is also plotted on the dashed lines:

$$\left(\frac{\rho_s d}{\rho}\frac{\partial \Omega_v(d)}{\partial d}\right)^{1/2}, \tag{41-43}$$

Notes p. 234

where ρ_s/ρ is determined from say second sound at the vapor pressure. At the thicknesses of interest $d < d'$ one has to accuracy better than 3% that (41-43) becomes

$$\left[-\frac{3\rho_s}{\rho}\,\Omega_v(d)\right]^{1/2}. \tag{41-44}$$

From the two fluid theory the existence of a disagreement is not surprising since $\bar{\rho}_s/\rho$ is not equal to ρ_s/ρ evaluated at the vapor pressure. In the film the Van der Waals force leads to huge pressure variations. In fact from the hydrostatic equation (41-12) one finds that the pressure reaches the solidification pressure of 25 atm at a distance of between one and two atomic layers from the substrate. Thus it is customary to assume that the film is separated from the substrate by a solid layer. This assumption reduces $\bar{\rho}_s/\rho$ but not nearly enough to obtain agreement between experiment and (41-28). Even in the film the pressure variations lead to ρ_s variations and one might wonder if including these effects will further improve the agreement. At 1.8 °K this is the case but at 1.3 °K experiments [5] show that ρ_s *increases* under pressure. In any event the dotted lines in Fig. 39 represent

$$\left[-\frac{3\bar{\rho}_s}{\rho}\,\Omega_v(d)\right]^{1/2},$$

where pressure dependence and the solid layer have been taken into account in calculating $\bar{\rho}_s$.

We conclude that the third sound velocities are in conflict with the two fluid hydrodynamics. Qualitatively this discrepancy is understood by saying that the superfluid density ρ_s obeys the boundary condition that it vanish at the substrate and probably also at the free surface (which we will assume). The distance over which it drops to zero, or equivalently the non-superfluid liquid region is called the healing length a. The total non-superfluid region of the film is then

$$D = d_s + 2a, \tag{41-45}$$

where d_s is the thickness of the solid layer. The behavior of ρ_s is sketched in Fig. 40, and with this picture

$$\frac{\bar{\rho}_s}{\rho} = \left(\frac{\rho_s}{\rho}\right)_b \frac{d - d_s - 2a}{d}, \tag{41-46}$$

Notes p. 234

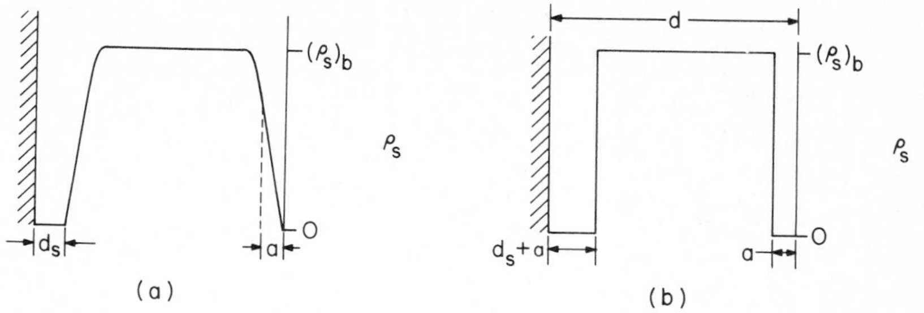

Fig. 40. The behavior of ρ_s in He II films as suggested by third sound experiments (a). In (b) a more simplified view is presented. The subscript 'b' stands for the bulk value.

where the subscript 'b' stands for evaluation at the bulk value, which is the thick film limit at the saturated vapor pressure. Measurements of third sound velocity now yield D and if $d_s = 3.6\,\text{Å}$ these measurements determine a. Experimentally it is found that a is independent of d and its temperature dependence (Fig. 41), can be represented by the relation

$$a = \frac{T}{T_\lambda \rho_s/\rho} \text{ atomic layers,} \tag{41-47}$$

valid between 1.0 °K and T_λ.

As $\rho_s \to 0$ at the boundaries, the total density ρ drops to ρ_n and thus also varies significantly. It is with this conclusion in mind that we emphasized that in Eq. (41-10) ρ is to be evaluated near but not at the free surface. As the surface area of the film remains unchanged for a long wave the change in mass of a slab of film is determined by the bulk value of ρ. The same considerations apply to (41-18). However, if the density variations are to be properly included one might wonder if instead of (41-19) we should have derived by averaging (41-4):

$$\frac{\partial v_s}{\partial t} - \bar{s}\frac{\partial\, \delta T}{\partial z} + \frac{\rho}{\bar{\rho}}\frac{\partial \Omega_v(d)}{\partial d}\frac{\partial\, \delta\xi}{\partial z} = 0,$$

where $\bar{\rho}$ is ρ averaged over the entire thickness of the film. Even if the pressure induced variations are neglected ρ will have a contribution from the boundary condition on ρ_s. Such a term would drastically affect the interpretation of third sound results. That this term should not appear in a complete analysis of the problem can be seen by working with the superfluid equation (3-27) which is modified to include the possibility of $\rho_s \to 0$. Averaging it across the film thickness yields

Notes p. 234

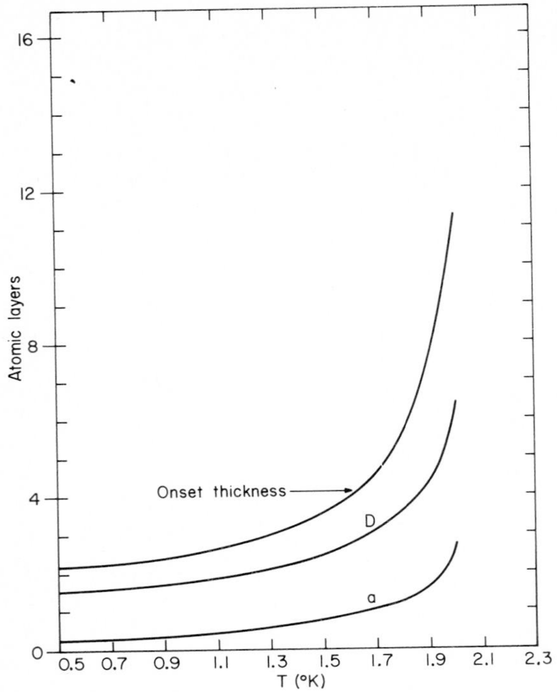

Fig. 41. The temperature dependence of the healing length a and non-superfluid length $D = d_s + 2a$ as determined by third sound measurements. Also shown is the onset thickness below which the attenuation has become so large that detection of third sound is experimentally impractical.

$$\bar{\rho}_s \frac{\partial v_s}{\partial t} - \overline{\rho_s S} \frac{\partial \delta T}{\partial z} + \overline{\left(\frac{\rho_s}{\rho}\right) \rho \frac{\partial \Omega_v}{\partial d} \frac{\partial \delta \xi}{\partial z}} = 0. \qquad (41\text{-}48)$$

With the present model for ρ_s as given by (41-46) and Fig. 40, Eq. (41-48) becomes the same as (41-19) if the *pressure* induced variations in ρ are neglected. According to (3-27) the superfluid equation (41-4) applies only where $\rho_s \neq 0$ or in the bulk, away from the boundaries. Thus an average of (41-4) will be an average only over the region where ρ_s, ρ are at the bulk values as implied by (41-48).

The imposition of a boundary condition on ρ_s is inconsistent with the two fluid theory since in this theory ρ_s is determined by the local values of p, T, $(\boldsymbol{v}_n - \boldsymbol{v}_s)^2$. This shortcoming along with others is discussed in

Notes p. 234

Chapter VII. For the time being we note that in the picture where the superfluid is a macroscopically occupied quantum state, § 10, a boundary condition on the wave function becomes a boundary condition on ρ_s.

Evidence for a boundary depletion of ρ_s comes also from experiments on persistent currents in He II films [14]. In § 39 we mentioned that persistent currents could be observed by gyroscopic techniques. These methods naturally also yield a quantitative measure of the angular momentum of a persistent current. It is found that as the thickness of the film participating in a *given* persistent current decreases so also does its angular momentum. These results can be extrapolated to a thickness of film at which the mass partaking in the persistent current and thus also its angular momentum vanish. This thickness is not zero but is interpreted as the non-superfluid part D of the film. Values of D and a found by this method are in fairly good agreement with those found from third sound.

Crucial to the interpretation and performance of these experiments is that as the thickness of a film undergoing a persistent current changes only the mass partaking in the current changes and not the superfluid velocity field $\boldsymbol{v}_s$. That this is in fact true is not obvious because the vapour that condenses into the film to, say, increase its thickness is stationary whereas the current has a velocity and we might wonder whether or not momentum is transferred between them. First, as we have seen in § 6, the He II and its vapour are in equilibrium with respect to momentum transfer when the normal fluid velocity equals the vapour velocity which is the case here. Second, the superfluid will behave so as to conserve circulation (4-9) such as was demonstrated in a somewhat similar experiment by Mehl and Zimmermann (§ 9).

Thus the vapour condenses into the film, as the pressure increases, without net angular momentum transfer. Part of the increase in mass goes into the normal component and part into the supercomponent. The increase in angular momentum of the supercomponent is then balanced by the change in angular momentum of normal fluid plus walls (superleak) to which it is clamped. The torque needed to bring the normal fluid plus walls back to rest equals the net increase in angular momentum of He II for this process.

Evidence for one solid layer also comes from these persistent current experiments by Reppy et al. [15]. In these investigations neon was introduced into the superleak prior to the He^4. When up to one layer was deposited none of the properties of the He II in a film of some given

Notes p. 234

total thickness were changed. For instance the thickness of the thinnest film in which superfluidity could be observed was unchanged. When more than a layer of neon was admitted the properties of a given film changed.

The thinnest film in which third sound has been observed was of *total* thickness 2.1 atomic layers [16]. The speed of third sound was about 7.0×10^3 cm/sec and the healing length was 0.25 atomic layers. These experiments were carried out at 0.5 °K.

A natural attitude is to expect that a continuum macroscopic theory such as the two fluid hydrodynamics would break down in geometries measured in Ångstroms rather than centimeters. While this has happened to some degree one can actually be surprised since all the experiments, even in the thinnest film, make use of well defined temperature variations which is clearly a macroscopic concept. If the superfluid is a coherent macroscopic quantum state then one would expect to be able to describe it with a macroscopic (quantum) continuum theory and trust the results down to an atomic dimension, i.e., 1.0 Å. What third sound emphasizes is that the two fluid hydrodynamics do not provide this quantum continuum theory. Perhaps the two fluid hydrodynamics is the WKB limit of the 'correct' He II quantum hydrodynamics, and thus not accurate near nodes ($\rho_s = 0$) of the wavefunction. As we have seen, third sound measurements suggest that ρ_s has a node at least at the substrate and this seriously affects the third sound velocity.

The description of the third sound results relied on a combination of two inconsistent ideas: the two fluid hydrodynamics and a boundary condition on ρ_s. The insufficiency of this approach is emphasized by measurements of the absorption of third sound which are in drastic disagreement with the two fluid theory including dissipation. Before discussing these experiments we derive the dissipative two fluid hydrodynamics of the He II film.

The most general modifications of (41-2,3,4,5) consistent with mass, momentum (perpendicular component) and circulation conservation and positive definite entropy production are

$$\frac{\partial \rho}{\partial t} + \nabla \cdot (\rho_s \boldsymbol{v}_s + \boldsymbol{J}_n) + \nabla_\perp \rho_n v_{n\perp} = 0, \tag{41-49}$$

$$\frac{\partial \rho s}{\partial t} + \nabla_\perp \rho s v_{n\perp} + \nabla \cdot \frac{\boldsymbol{q}}{T} = \frac{\Sigma}{T}, \tag{41-50}$$

Notes p. 234

$$\frac{D_s \boldsymbol{v}_s}{Dt} = -\nabla(\mu + H), \tag{41-51}$$

$$\frac{\partial}{\partial t}(\rho_s v_s + \rho_n v_n)_\perp + \nabla_\perp p + \nabla_\perp(\rho_n v_{n\perp} v_{n\perp}) + \frac{\partial}{\partial r_\alpha}(\rho_s v_{s,\alpha} v_{s\perp} + \tau_{\alpha\perp}) = 0. \tag{41-52}$$

The requirement that these equations imply energy conservation leads to

$$\Sigma = -\boldsymbol{J}_n \cdot \nabla(\mu + \tfrac{1}{2}v_s^2 - v_{n\perp} v_{s\perp}) - \frac{\boldsymbol{q}}{T} \cdot \nabla T - \tau_{\alpha\perp} \frac{\partial v_{n\perp}}{\partial r_\alpha}$$
$$- H(\nabla \cdot \rho_s \boldsymbol{v}_s - \nabla_\perp(\rho_s v_{n\perp})]. \tag{41-53}$$

To first order the expressions which satisfy the requirements of Galilean covariance for motion perpendicular to the substrate are

$$q_\perp = -\kappa \nabla_\perp T, \qquad J_{n\perp} = 0, \tag{41-54}$$

$$J_{n\parallel} = -\sigma \nabla_\parallel(\mu + \tfrac{1}{2}v_s^2 - v_{n\perp} v_{s\perp}) + \sigma\alpha \nabla_\parallel T, \tag{41-55}$$

$$q_\parallel = -\kappa \nabla_\parallel T + \sigma\beta T \nabla_\parallel(\mu + \tfrac{1}{2}v_s^2 - v_{n\perp} v_{s\perp}), \tag{41-56}$$

$$H = -\zeta_3(\nabla \cdot \rho_s \boldsymbol{v}_s - \nabla_\perp \rho_s v_{n\perp}) - \zeta_4 \nabla_\perp v_{n\perp}, \tag{41-57}$$

$$\tau_{\alpha\perp} = -\eta\left(\frac{\partial v_{n\perp}}{\partial r_\alpha} - \delta_{\alpha\perp}\frac{\partial v_{n\perp}}{\partial r_\perp}\right) - \zeta_2 \delta_{\alpha\perp}\frac{\partial v_{n\perp}}{\partial r_\perp} - \zeta_1 \delta_{\alpha\perp}(\nabla \cdot \rho_s \boldsymbol{v}_s - \nabla_\perp \rho_s v_{n\perp}). \tag{41-58}$$

The non-symmetry of the stress tensor reflects the fact that the angular momentum is not conserved. The external forces can be included by replacing μ with $\mu + \Omega$ in all the above relations.

According to a detailed calculation of third sound absorption, as first presented by Bergmann [17] the dissipative processes within the film account for a negligible contribution. In largest part the absorption is determined by evaporation condensation exchange with the gas and thermal diffusion to gas and substrate.

These considerations are developed below. But when all these effects are combined one obtains an absorption which is far less than experimentally observed [18] (see Fig. 42) except near one thickness. We return to this and other shortcomings of the two fluid theory at its present stage of development in Chapter VII. The anomalous absorption may be related to the boundary condition on ρ_s.

Notes p. 234

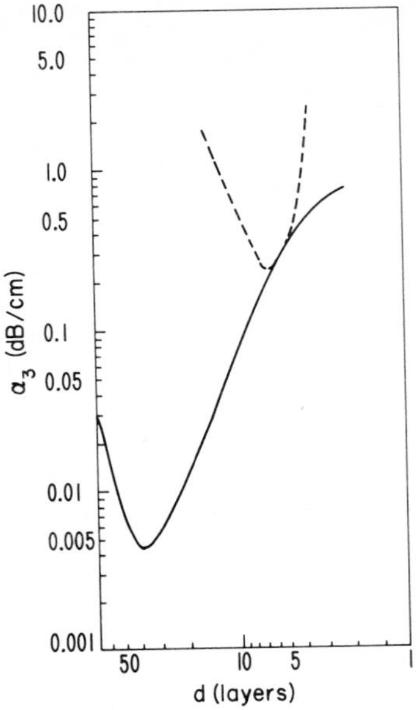

Fig. 42. The experimentally measured and calculated absorption of third sound versus film thickness at 1.3 °K for a frequency of 200 c.p.s. Note that 1 cm^{-1} ≡ 8.69 dB/cm.

First let us compare the contribution of dissipative processes within the fluid to the evaporation effects. The thermal conductivity κ will lead to a dissipation which is down by a factor

$$\frac{d\kappa\nabla^2\,\delta T}{K(L+sT)\,\delta T} \approx \frac{dk_0^2\kappa}{K(L+sT)} \approx \frac{d\omega^2\kappa}{u_3^2K(L+sT)} < 10^{-8}$$

from the evaporation dissipation. This suggests that dissipative effects within the film are according to the two fluid hydrodynamics of no importance as far as third sound absorption is concerned.

In the equilibrium between He II and its vapor the temperatures are equal and so are the generalized chemical potentials (6-12,13). Off equilibrium there can be heat and mass exchange between the two phases and to lowest order in the deviation from equilibrium we assume that the exchange fluxes are linear in the differences. Neglecting quadratic velocity terms we are led to the generalizations of (41-24,25):

$$\rho\frac{\partial\,\delta\xi}{\partial t} + \bar{\rho}_s d\frac{\partial v_s}{\partial z} = -K(\delta T - \delta T_g) - K_\mu[\delta(\mu+\Omega_v) - \delta\mu_g], \qquad (41\text{-}59)$$

Notes p. 234

$$\rho s \frac{\partial\,\delta\xi}{\partial t} + \rho d \frac{\partial \bar{s}}{\partial T} \frac{\partial\,\delta T}{\partial t}$$

$$= -\frac{B_1}{T}(\delta T - \delta T_{\mathrm{w}}) - K_T(\delta T - \delta T_{\mathrm{g}}) - K'[\delta(\mu + \Omega_{\mathrm{v}}) - \delta\mu_{\mathrm{g}}], \quad (41\text{-}60)$$

where δT_{g}, $\delta\mu_{\mathrm{g}}$ and $\delta(\mu + \Omega_{\mathrm{v}})$ must be evaluated at the gas–film interface. By the Onsager symmetry requirement

$$K' = K. \quad (41\text{-}61)$$

In addition to the exchange flux with the gas we have also included a thermal exchange with the substrate characterized by the term B_1; δT_{w} is the swing in temperature at the wall bounding the film. As there can be no mass flow between the wall and film there are no terms involving $\delta\mu_{\mathrm{w}}$.

The requirement that the entropy production be positive definite off equilibrium implies that

$$K_\mu > 0, \qquad K_T > 0, \qquad B_1 > 0,$$
$$(K + K')^2 \leqslant 4K_\mu K_T. \quad (41\text{-}62)$$

We should note that the simplified description of evaporation condensation effects as embodied in (41-24,25) is in conflict with the Onsager reciprocity relation and the second law of thermodynamics for irreversible processes (41-62).

The coefficient B_1 which relates the thermal discontinuity at a solid boundary to the entropy flow across it, is commonly referred to as the Kapitza resistance coefficient. We see that the gas–liquid interface has mass and entropy fluxes across it which have a similar form. If one wishes to have a phenomenological theory in which the dissipative effects drive the off-equilibrium system to equilibrium then terms of this form are mandatory at the interface between two phases.

The entropy flow between solid and liquid must also be determined by the temperature gradient in the wall, thus at $y = 0$:

$$\kappa_{\mathrm{w}} \frac{\partial\,\delta T_{\mathrm{w}}}{\partial y} = B_1(\delta T - \delta T_{\mathrm{w}}), \quad (41\text{-}63)$$

where κ_{w} is the thermal conductivity of the wall (substrate). The entropy flow between film and gas will be due to evaporation as well as diffusion. By integrating the Navier–Stokes equation (12-2) one finds that the

Notes p. 234

entropy flow to the gas equals the entropy per gram of gas multiplied by the mass flow plus the thermal diffusion or, at $y = d$:

$$K_T(\delta T - \delta T_g) + K'[\delta(\mu + \Omega_v) - \delta\mu_g]$$

$$= s_g K(\delta T - \delta T_g) + s_g K_\mu[\delta(\mu + \Omega_v) - \delta\mu_g] - \frac{\kappa_g}{T}\frac{\partial\, \delta T_g}{\partial y}, \quad (41\text{-}64)$$

where κ_g is the thermal conductivity of the gas. This equation determines the thermal conduction between film and gas in terms of the temperature and chemical potential jumps and is a generalization of (41-63).

To complete the phenomenological theory one needs the equations of motion for δT_w, δT_g which are

$$\rho_w C_w \frac{\partial\, \delta T_w}{\partial t} = \kappa_w \nabla^2 \delta T_w, \quad (41\text{-}65)$$

$$\rho_g C_g \frac{\partial\, \delta T_g}{\partial t} = \kappa_g \nabla^2 \delta T_g, \quad (41\text{-}66)$$

where C_w, C_g are the specific heats of wall and vapor.

The equation for v_s (41-19) is unchanged and we furthermore set

$$\delta\mu_g = -s_g\, \delta T_g, \quad (41\text{-}67)$$

since the Van der Waals force doesn't affect the gas. The solution to these equations is straightforward but involved.

First from (41-65) we find by looking for a plane wave:

$$\delta T_w = T'_w \exp(-i\omega t + ikz + q_w y), \quad (41\text{-}68)$$

$$q_w^2 = k^2 - i\rho_w C_w \omega/\kappa_w, \quad (41\text{-}69)$$

where the root with real part of q_w positive must be selected. Next (41-63) yields

$$T'_w = \frac{B_1}{B_1 + \kappa_w q_w} T', \quad (41\text{-}70)$$

which enables one to eliminate T'_w in favor of T' in (41-60). Similarly in the gas

$$\delta T_g = T'_g \exp[-i\omega t + ikz - q_g(y - d)], \quad (41\text{-}71)$$

$$q_g^2 = k^2 - i\rho_g C_g \omega/\kappa_g, \quad (41\text{-}72)$$

Notes p. 234

and again the real part of q_g must be positive. Use of (41-64) yields

$$T_g'(\kappa_g q_g/T + K_T - 2s_g K + s_g^2 K_\mu)$$
$$= T'(K_T - s_g K - sK + ss_g K_\mu) + (K - s_g K_\mu)\frac{\partial \Omega_v}{\partial d}\xi', \quad (41\text{-}73)$$

which can be used to eliminate T_g' from (41-59,60). Substituting (41-73,70) into (41-59,60) and use of (41-19) yields the detailed dispersion law for third sound propagation and absorption

$$\frac{\omega^2}{k^2} = \frac{i\omega\bar{\rho}_s d\bar{s}(b_4 + i\omega\rho s) + i\omega\bar{\rho}_s d(\partial\Omega_v/\partial d)(b_3 + i\omega\rho d\,\partial\bar{s}/\partial T)}{(b_2 + i\omega\rho)(b_3 + i\omega\rho d\,\partial\bar{s}/\partial T) - b_1(i\omega\rho s + b_4)}, \quad (41\text{-}74)$$

where we have set:

$$b_1 = -K(1 - a_1) + sK_\mu - s_g a_1 K_\mu, \quad (41\text{-}75)$$

$$b_2 = Ka_2 - K_\mu \frac{\partial \Omega_v}{\partial d} - K_\mu s_g a_2, \quad (41\text{-}76)$$

$$b_3 = -B/T - K_T(1 - a_1) + sK - s_g a_1 K, \quad (41\text{-}77)$$

$$b_4 = K_T a_2 - K\frac{\partial \Omega_v}{\partial d} - Ks_g a_2, \quad (41\text{-}78)$$

where a_1 and a_2 have been introduced by the definition

$$T_g' \equiv a_1 T' + a_2 \xi', \quad (41\text{-}79)$$

and comparison with (41-73); the quantity B is defined as

$$B = \frac{\kappa_w q_w}{1 + \kappa_w q_w/B_1}. \quad (41\text{-}80)$$

This completes the phenomenological description of the third sound propagation and attenuation. One might think that, in view of the new coefficients K_μ, K_T which have not been previously determined, no worthwhile comparison can be made with the theory. However, since K_μ, K, K', K_T refer to exchange fluxes with an ideal gas one can use very simple kinetic theory arguments to get an excellent grip on these quantities. From the Maxwell–Boltzmann distribution

$$(\rho_g/m)(m/2\pi k_B T)^{3/2} \exp(-mv^2/2k_B T) d^3v \quad (41\text{-}81)$$

Notes p. 234

for the number of molecules per unit volume with velocity between v and $v + dv$ one can easily calculate the number per second to strike a unit area as

$$\frac{\rho_g}{m}\sqrt{\frac{k_B T}{2\pi m}}, \tag{41-82}$$

where k_B is Boltzmann's constant:

$$\frac{k_B}{m} = \frac{R}{\mathscr{M}} = 2.08 \times 10^7 \text{ erg/g °K for He}^4,$$

and ρ_g the mass density of the gas. The best variables to work with are μ, T since these are the fundamental quantities that characterize the equilibrium between gas and liquid. For an ideal gas

$$\rho_g = \rho_0 \exp\left\{\frac{m}{k_B}\left[\frac{\mu}{T} - \left(\frac{\mu}{T}\right)_0 + \frac{3k_B}{2m}\log\frac{T}{T_0}\right]\right\}, \tag{41-83}$$

where the zero refers to some reference state. The number to strike unit area per second is thus as a function of μ, T:

$$\frac{\rho_0}{m}\sqrt{\frac{k_B T}{2\pi m}}\exp\left\{\frac{m}{k_B}\left[\frac{\mu}{T} - \left(\frac{\mu}{T}\right)_0 + \frac{3k_B}{2m}\log\frac{T}{T_0}\right]\right\}. \tag{41-84}$$

The liquid is a far more complicated system than the gas, however, in equilibrium the number of atoms to leave the liquid must equal the number of gas atoms to enter it. If we assume that each gas atom to strike the liquid sticks, then by the detailed balance argument, (41-84) describes the number of atoms to escape the liquid per second in equilibrium.

To first approximation (41-84) will describe the number of atoms to leave the liquid off equilibrium if μ, T are the chemical potential and temperature of the liquid, which are different from those of the gas. In this way one is led to an expression for the increase in film mass when the gas and liquid are off equilibrium. Keeping terms to first order in $(T - T_g)$ and $(\mu - \mu_g)$ we arrive at the right hand side of (41-59) but now

$$K = \frac{\rho_g}{T}\sqrt{\frac{k_B T}{2\pi m}}\left(\frac{m}{k_B}s_g - \frac{1}{2}\right), \tag{41-85}$$

$$K_\mu = \rho_g\sqrt{\frac{m}{2\pi k_B T}}, \tag{41-86}$$

Notes p. 234

where we have used the identity for the ideal gas:

$$\frac{\mu_g}{T_g} + s_g = \frac{5}{2}\frac{k_B}{m}. \tag{41-87}$$

The expression (41-85) is, except for the small correction term of $\frac{1}{2}$ the same as introduced in (41-24,27). From the velocity distribution (41-81) the energy to strike the liquid is

$$\rho_g \sqrt{\frac{2}{\pi}} \left(\frac{k_B T}{m}\right)^{3/2}. \tag{41-88}$$

The first and second law of thermodynamics

$$dE_g = T\,dS_g + \mu\,dM_g$$

relates the entropy flux of the gas to the liquid in terms of the energy and mass fluxes (41-82,88). By the above arguments we again find a net entropy exchange off equilibrium and are led to

$$K_T = \sqrt{\frac{k_B T}{2\pi m}}\frac{\rho_g}{T}\left(\frac{9}{4}\frac{k_B}{m} - s_g + \frac{m}{k_B}s_g^2\right), \qquad K' = K, \tag{41-89}$$

so that the Onsager symmetry is demonstrated. Note also that the conditions (41-62) are satisfied. Now all quantities are well determined and it is a matter of arithmetic to solve (41-74) for the real and imaginary parts of k for given ω, hence determining the speed and absorption of third sound. Some values of the quantities which appear in the dispersion law are (at about 1.5 °K):

$$\kappa_w = 3.5 \times 10^3 \text{ erg/cm °K sec}$$

$$\kappa_g = 300.0 \text{ erg/cm °K sec}$$

$$B_1 = 5.0 \times 10^5 \text{ erg/cm}^2 \text{ sec °K}$$

$$\rho_w C_w = 500.0 \text{ erg/cm}^3 \text{ °K}$$

$$\rho_g C_g = 10^4 \text{ erg/cm}^3 \text{ °K}$$

$$s_g = 10^8 \text{ erg/g °K}$$

$$\rho_g = 2.2 \times 10^{-4} \text{ g/cm}^3$$

$$K = 1.6 \text{ g/cm}^2 \text{ sec °K}$$

$$s = 2.0 \times 10^6 \text{ erg/g °K}$$

Notes p. 234

$$T(\partial s/\partial T) = 1.1 \times 10^7 \text{ erg/g °K}$$

$$\rho_s/\rho = 0.88.$$

In simplifying the dispersion law the following identity is useful

$$b_2 b_3 - b_1 b_4 = -b_2 \frac{B}{T} + (K_\mu K_T - K^2) \frac{\partial \Omega_v}{\partial d} \frac{\kappa_g q_g/T}{\kappa_g q_g/T + K_T - 2s_g K + s_g^2 K_\mu}.$$

Notes

[1] K. A. Shapiro and I. Rudnick, Phys. Rev. **137**(1965)A1383. The existence of this new sound mode was first implied by J. R. Pellam and R. B. Scott, Phys. Rev. **73**(1948)608.

[2] J. D. Reppy and D. Depatie, Phys. Rev. Letters **12**(1964)187.

[3] J. D. Reppy, Phys. Rev. Letters **14**(1965)733; J. R. Clow and J. D. Reppy, Phys. Rev. Letters **16**(1966)887; G. Kukich, R. P. Henkel and J. D. Reppy, Phys. Rev. Letters **21**(1968)197. J. B. Mehl and W. Zimmermann, Jr., Phys. Rev. Letters **14**(1965)815; Phys. Rev. **167**(1968)214. W. M. van Alphen, K. W. Taconis and E. van Spronsen, Physica **39**(1968)109.

[4] I. Rudnick, H. Kojima, W. Veith and R. S. Kagiwada, Phys. Rev. Letters **23**(1969) 1220; H. Kojima, W. Veith, S. J. Putterman, E. Guyon and I. Rudnick, Phys. Rev. Letters **27**(1971)714.

[5] R. D. Maurer and M. A. Herlin, Phys. Rev. **81**(1951)444. R. H. Romer and R. J. Duffy, Phys. Rev. **186**(1969)255. The pressure dependence of the specific heat and entropy is provided by O. V. Lounasmaa, Cryogenics **1**(1961)212; C. J. N. van den Meijdenberg, K. W. Taconis and R. de Bruyn Ouboter, Physica **27**(1961)197. The density under pressure is provided by W. H. Keesom, *Helium* (Elsevier, Amsterdam, 1942) p. 240, and the expansion coefficient under pressure is provided by C. Boghosian and H. Meyer, Phys. Rev. **152**(1966)200; **163**(1967)206E; D. L. Elwell and H. Meyer, Phys. Rev. **164**(1967)245.

[6] H. Kamerlingh Onnes, Trans. Faraday Soc. **18**(1922)No. 53. B. V. Rollin and F. Simon, Physica **6**(1939)269.

[7] J. G. Daunt and K. Mendelssohn, Nature **141**(1938)911; **142**(1938)475; Proc. Roy. Soc. **A170**(1939)423,439.

[8] K. A. Pickar and K. R. Atkins, Phys. Rev. **178**(1969)389.

[9] K. R. Atkins, B. Rosenbaum and H. Seki, Phys. Rev. **113**(1959)751. T. Wang, D. D. Elleman, E. E. Olli and M. M. Saffren, Phys. Rev. Letters **30**(1973)485.

[10] I. Rudnick, R. S. Kagiwada, J. C. Fraser and E. Guyon, Phys. Rev. Letters **20**(1968) 430. R. S. Kagiwada, J. C. Fraser, I. Rudnick and D. Bergmann, Phys. Rev. Letters **22**(1969)338. K. R. Atkins and I. Rudnick, in: *Progress in Low Temperature Physics*, ed. C. J. Gorter (North-Holland, Amsterdam, 1970) Vol. VI, p. 37.

[11] E. S. Sabisky and C. H. Anderson, Phys. Rev. **A7**(1973)790.

[12] H. B. G. Casimir and D. Polder, Phys. Rev. **73**(1948)360.

[13] L. G. Grimes and L. C. Jackson, Phil. Mag. **4**(1959)1346.
[14] R. P. Henkel, E. N. Smith and J. Reppy, Phys. Rev. Letters **23**(1969)1276.
[15] H. W. Chan, A. W. Yanof, F. D. M. Pobell and J. D. Reppy, Paper presented at Thirteenth International Conference on Low Temperature Physics, Boulder, Colorado (1972).
[16] J. Scholtz, E. O. McLean and I. Rudnick, Phys. Rev. Letters **32**(1974)147.
[17] D. Bergmann, Phys. Rev. **A3**(1971)2058.
[18] T. Wang and I. Rudnick, J. Low Temp. Phys. **9**(1972)425.

CHAPTER VI

The Problem of the Critical Velocities

42 *Introduction: Critical Velocities in Classical Fluids and He II*

In most experiments it is found that there are either bounds on the applicability of the two fluid equations or regimes where perhaps a 'simple' solution of the two fluid equations no longer works. This is represented by the existence of a critical velocity above which the easy solutions to the two fluid hydrodynamics apparently fail.

For instance in the experiment of Kapitza, § 2, it was found that for a large heating rate and thus a large superfluid velocity in the superleak $\nabla\mu \neq 0$. In the experiments which observed the fundamental property of frictionless flow it was always found that for fast flow rates a pressure head was required. Andronikashvili, § 24, observed that for large amplitudes of oscillation the change in period of the disc no longer yielded ρ_n/ρ but that somehow part of the superfluid was also entrained. Van Alphen found that the levels of the standpipes, § 30, remained equal only when the flow rate was sufficiently small. In the heat flow experiments London's relation (29-10) provided an accurate description of the effective conductivity only up to a critical heat flow or convection velocity. Above this velocity the temperature gradient becomes cubic rather than linear in the heat current.

Such limitations or critical velocities exist also in the theory of classical fluids. One knows for instance that for the flow between parallel plates the smooth Poiseuille solution of the Navier–Stokes equations becomes unstable above a critical velocity and that a regime of turbulent flow develops. Since incompressible classical flow can be characterized by a dimensionless number (the so-called Reynolds number):

$$R = \frac{d\rho v}{\eta}, \qquad (42\text{-}1)$$

where d and v are a length and velocity characteristic of the experimental arrangement, it is better to speak of a critical Reynolds number instead of a critical velocity. For Poiseuille flow one finds empirically that the critical value of R is of order 10^3.

Since for He II ρ/η is of order 10^4 sec/cm^2 one expects that for flows through a capillary of diameter $d = 0.1$ cm the laminar regime will break down for a velocity $v_n \approx 1$ cm/sec. Indeed Staas et al. [1] found that in their heat flow experiments the London description broke down when the heating rate was so large that v_n led to a Reynolds number for which the corresponding classical flow becomes turbulent.

What is most interesting is that in many experiments critical velocities without a classical interpretation are observed. As an example Chase [1] and Brewer and Edwards [2] have found that at some temperatures the London heat flow relation (29-10) breaks down at values of $\boldsymbol{v}_n$ quite a bit smaller than would be required for classical turbulence. One is naturally tempted to attribute this behavior to the superfluid velocity $\boldsymbol{v}_s$. However, it is quite possible that this behavior is also due to the normal fluid.

This assertion is based on the fact that the normal fluid of He II does not always behave classically. An example of this property and the resulting complications as far as stability is concerned, is the Couette flow which takes place between two concentric rotating cylinders. We look for a steady state solution with $\boldsymbol{v}_s = 0$ and $\boldsymbol{v}_n$ circulating about the axis of symmetry. Then from (21-4,13) one finds

$$v_n = ar + \frac{b}{r}, \tag{42-2}$$

where a and b must be chosen so that at each cylinder v_n equals the velocity of the boundary:

$$v_n(\tfrac{1}{2}d_1) = \tfrac{1}{2}\omega_1 d_1, \tag{42-3}$$

$$v_n(\tfrac{1}{2}d) = \tfrac{1}{2}\omega d, \tag{42-4}$$

where $\omega_1, \frac{1}{2}d_1$ and $\omega, \frac{1}{2}d$ are the angular velocity and radius of the inner and outer cylinders. Therefore,

$$a = (\omega d^2 - \omega_1 d_1^2)/(d^2 - d_1^2), \tag{42-5}$$

$$4b = (\omega - \omega_1)\, d_1^2 d^2/(d_1^2 - d^2), \tag{42-6}$$

Notes p. 265

From (21-4,13) and (21-2) one further obtains

$$\nabla\mu = 0, \tag{42-7}$$

$$\frac{\partial p}{\partial r} = \rho_n \frac{v_n^2}{r}. \tag{42-8}$$

The basic thermodynamic identity (4-8) yields

$$\frac{\partial T}{\partial r} = \frac{\rho_n}{s\rho}\left(\frac{v_n^2}{r} - \frac{\partial}{\partial r}\frac{v_n^2}{2}\right) = \frac{\rho_n}{s\rho}\left(\frac{2ab}{r} - \frac{2b^2}{r^3}\right). \tag{42-9}$$

Unlike a classical fluid the Couette flow in He II leads to a temperature gradient. This thermal variation must be considered in any attempt to understand the dynamical stability. For instance there must now be a heat flow in the radial direction. We know that He II prefers to transport heat by convection rather than conduction. Thus the above solution might develop an instability with respect to internal convection. Couette flow is the best understood classical stability problem. Yet no one has attempted an investigation of the corresponding flow in He II based on the two fluid theory. These possible dynamical thermal instabilities might play a role in the heat flow experiments since as we have seen in Eq. (29-3) they involve temperature gradients across the width of the capillary which are quite analogous to (42-9).

The association of thermal disturbances with normal fluid motion is no surprise since in § 5 we saw that the normal fluid vortices were actually thermal vortices. In fact one might expect that if the thermal instabilities alluded to above actually do exist then the turbulent state would be characterized by thermal vortices.

Incidentally, Gorter and Mellink [3] have tried to understand the cubic temperature gradient in the supercritical heat flow regime by adding a mutual friction term $\rho_s\rho_n A(\boldsymbol{v}_n - \boldsymbol{v}_s)^3$ to the right hand side of (21-2). To be consistent with energy conservation one must also include an additional term $\rho_n\rho_s A(\boldsymbol{v}_n - \boldsymbol{v}_s)^4$ in the entropy production (21-10). The entropy production will be positive if the new dissipative coefficient $A > 0$. This term therefore leads to equilibrium states for which $\boldsymbol{v}_n = \boldsymbol{v}_s$ and thus must not be taken as a serious description of the superflow. As we have seen in § 18, $\boldsymbol{v}_n = \boldsymbol{v}_s$ is completely contrary to the nature of rotating He II.

Even in experimental arrangements where the normal fluid is at rest and the flow is isothermal so that the above mentioned difficulties

Notes p. 265

probably do not occur one finds that there are critical velocities which must then be associated with the superfluid motion. In the arrangements where the He II flows in a linear geometry such as takes place between parallel slits or in a capillary it is found that the experimental results are well described by the empirical relation [4]

$$v_{s,c} d^{1/4} = 1.0 \text{ c.g.s.,} \tag{42-10}$$

where $v_{s,c}$ is the superfluid critical velocity in cm/sec and d the width of the capillary in cm. This temperature independent critical velocity has been verified for thicknesses

$$8 \times 10^{-7} \text{ cm} < d < 1 \text{ cm}. \tag{42-11}$$

For thinner geometries $v_{s,c}$ drops to zero and is temperature dependent [5]. For all d one observes a temperature dependence near the lambda temperature where $v_{s,c}$ also drops to zero.

Experimentally the most efficient means of preventing the normal fluid from interfering with the flow is by introducing superleaks at the ends of the capillary as indicated in Fig. 43. This method was first

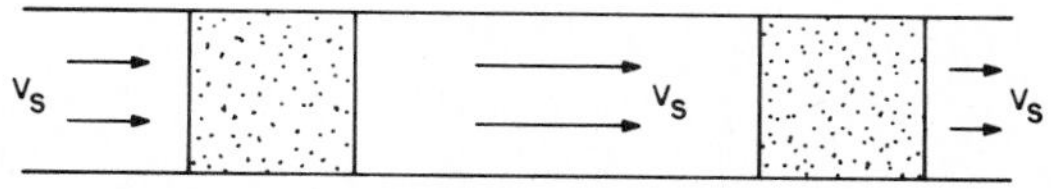

Fig. 43. The superfluid wind-tunnel used by Van Alphen to investigate critical velocities when $v_n = 0$.

introduced by Pellam (see § 30) and is referred to as a superfluid wind-tunnel. The narrow paths in the fine powder act like solid walls to the normal fluid and prevent it from entering the flow region. Van Alphen [4] has carried out extensive measurements with this arrangement. He reasoned that if the superfluid became turbulent it would dissipate heat and looked for this effect by enclosing the capillary in a calorimeter. It was found that up to a critical velocity which obeyed (42-10) there was no heat dumped into the calorimeter. These experiments were conducted for 10^{-3} cm $< d <$ 1 cm [6]. Keller and Hammel [7] have further 'verified' (42-10) down to $d = 3 \times 10^{-5}$ cm by observing forced isothermal flow between two parallel slits. At the entrance and exit to the narrow slits were standpipes whose level difference indicated the pressure head necessary to drive the flow. Up to a critical velocity consistent with (42-10) no level difference was required. This experiment

Notes p. 265

also demonstrated the temperature dependence of the critical velocity showing that it dropped suddenly to zero above about 2.0 °K. Below this temperature $v_{s,c}$ was constant.

Critical velocities in still thinner geometries have been observed by measurements on the flow properties of the He II film. Consider the arrangement in Fig. 44 where the vapor of He^4 is contained in a closed

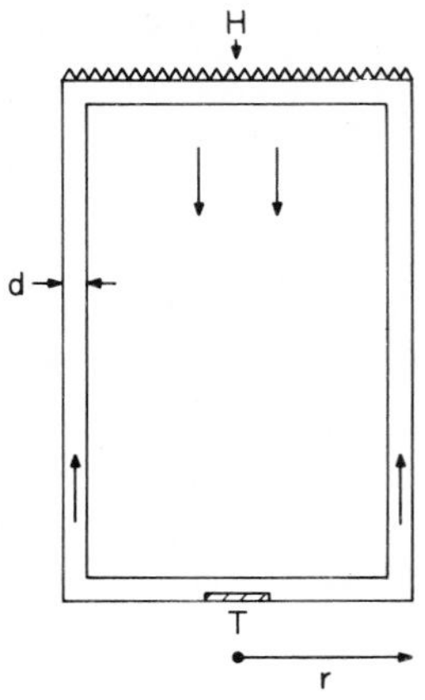

Fig. 44. The apparatus used to investigate critical flow velocities in the He II film.

vessel at a pressure less than the vapor pressure. Due to the Van der Waals force a film will form on all the walls.

When heat is supplied by the heater H film will first evaporate. If $T > T_\lambda$ the film will be unable to flow in to replace the evaporated molecules. Thus as heat is continually supplied it will be transmitted through the gas via ordinary conduction. There will result a temperature gradient which can be measured by reference to thermometer T. However, if $T < T_\lambda$, the film, because of superfluidity, will be able to flow in and replace the evaporated molecules as the heat is supplied. In this case the evaporated atoms will *convect* through the vapor region, condense on the walls and flow back to the heater as indicated by the arrows. In this heat flow by convection there should be a much smaller temperature difference between T and the film at the heater.

Experimentally it is verified that as the temperature is lowered below T_λ, the temperature difference for a given heating rate suddenly disappears. This only happens for small enough heating rates. When the heating rate becomes too large the return flow in the film apparently

Notes p. 265

exceeds a critical velocity, above which a temperature difference develops.

The heat $\dot{W}$ to leave the heater per second goes into the latent heat of vaporization L plus the heat supplied to the incoming superfluid:

$$\dot{W} = (L + Ts)\dot{M}, \tag{42-12}$$

where $\dot{M}$ is the mass per second to evaporate. This result also follows directly from the equations of mass and entropy continuity of film and gas. As the normal fluid is at rest the mass per second to flow into the heater is

$$\dot{M} = 2\pi r \bar{\rho}_s v_s d, \tag{42-13}$$

where d is the total thickness of the film, the container has radius r and again $\bar{\rho}_s$ is the average superfluid density in the film. From the measured pressure one determines d by (41-30). Third sound yields $\bar{\rho}_s$. Hence from measurements of $\dot{W}$ one determines v_s [5]; the critical velocities for various thicknesses are shown in Fig. 45 for $T = 1.5$ and 1.75 °K.

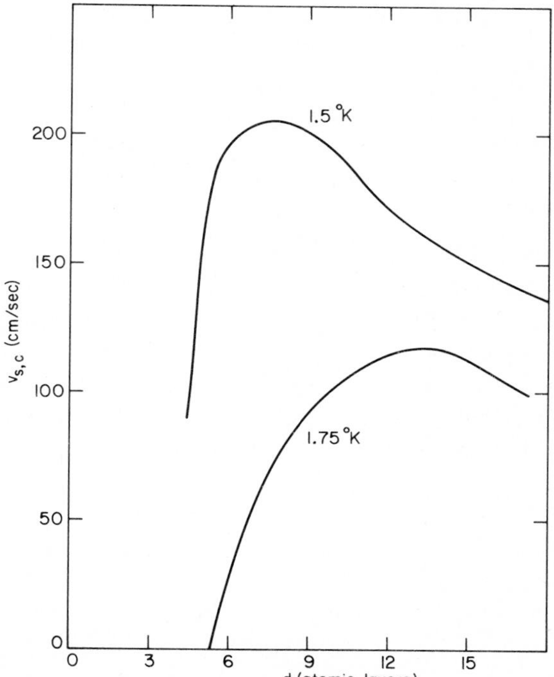

Fig. 45. The critical superfluid velocity as a function of film thickness for $T = 1.5$ °K and 1.75 °K.

Notes p. 265

That the superfluid has reached a critical velocity has been directly verified by means of Doppler shifted third sound [8]. If one linearizes the equations of motion of the He II film around an equilibrium state in which $v_n = 0$ but $v_s \neq 0$ then the speed of third sound is found to be

$$u_3 = u_{3,0} + \frac{v_s}{2}\left[\frac{\rho_s}{\rho} + \frac{\bar{\rho}_s}{\rho} + d\frac{\partial\Omega_v(d)}{\partial d}\left(\frac{\partial\bar{\rho}_s}{\partial p} - \frac{1}{\rho}\frac{\partial\bar{\rho}}{\partial\frac{1}{2}w^2} - \frac{T}{\rho L}\frac{\partial\overline{\rho s}}{\partial\frac{1}{2}w^2}\right)\right], \tag{42-14}$$

where $u_{3,0}$ is given by (41-28) and quantities without bars are to be evaluated in the bulk. As the heat flow $\dot{W}$ is increased so does the Doppler shift. But as the region of critical heat flow is reached the Doppler shift will not increase further. The values of $v_{s,c}$ determined from (42-14) by this technique agree well with those obtained from (42-12,13).

As the film gets thinner the critical velocity approaches zero. Below this 'onset' point superfluidity cannot be observed. Similarly in third sound, § 41, there exists a critical thickness consistent with those obtained by the above measurements [23] below which superfluidity cannot be observed. In third sound this onset is shown to occur at a non-zero value of ρ_s. In thin films it may thus be more accurate to think in terms of a critical thickness rather than a critical velocity.

There is no explanation for the critical velocities that occur in linear geometries. Neither the *value* or the *mechanism* can be understood, though it is generally accepted that, except perhaps in films $v_{s,c}$ is due to the formation of quantized vortices which lead to quantum turbulence and dissipation in the flow.

It is possible to understand how the formation and flow of vortices can lead to a pressure drop. As an example consider the flow of He II between two reference points at different values of $\mu + \frac{1}{2}v_s^2$. Ignoring compressibility effects we will show following Anderson [9] that there exist two solutions to the superfluid equation

$$\frac{\partial \boldsymbol{v}_s}{\partial t} = -\nabla(\mu + \tfrac{1}{2}v_s^2). \tag{42-15}$$

One is a simple linear acceleration of fluid between these points so that $\partial \boldsymbol{v}_s/\partial t$ balances the difference in $\mu + \frac{1}{2}v_s^2$. The other is a more complicated flow in which vortex lines pass between the two points. To see how this second solution works consider Fig. 46, in which a polar coordinate system has been attached to a vortex and lines of constant angle have been drawn. The vortex is indicated by a dot at the intersection of the

Notes p. 265

horizontal and vertical axis. For a vortex line the angle θ with respect to a reference axis has physical meaning since it is within a factor of $\hbar/m$ of the velocity potential. That is:

$$\boldsymbol{v}_s = \nabla\phi, \tag{42-16}$$

and for a singly quantized line

$$\phi = (\hbar/m)\theta. \tag{42-17}$$

In Fig. 46a is drawn the angle (or velocity potential in units of $\hbar/m$) for a single quantized vortex line in an infinite medium. In Figs. 46b,c,d the change in phase difference between points 1 and 2 is shown as a vortex moves from $-\infty$ to $+\infty$. When the vortex line is at $-\infty$ the two points have phases arbitrarily close to zero ($\varepsilon \ll 1$). When the vortex is situated

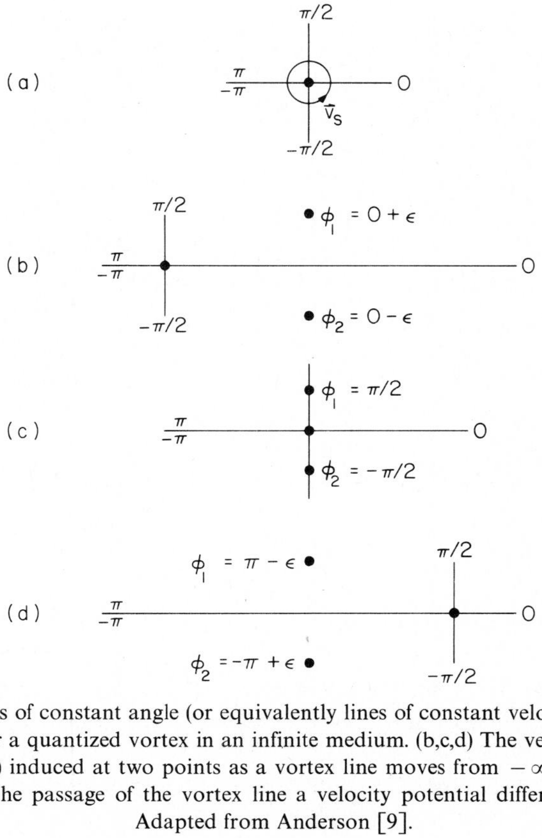

Fig. 46. (a) Lines of constant angle (or equivalently lines of constant velocity potential in units of $\hbar/m$) for a quantized vortex in an infinite medium. (b,c,d) The velocity potentials (in units of $\hbar/m$) induced at two points as a vortex line moves from $-\infty$ (b) to $+\infty$ (d). As a result of the passage of the vortex line a velocity potential difference h/m exists. Adapted from Anderson [9].

Notes p. 265

between the points the phase difference is π and finally in the limit that the vortex goes to $+\infty$ the phase difference becomes 2π or equivalently the change in the difference of the velocity potentials of the two points as the vortex line goes from $-\infty$ to $+\infty$ is $2\pi\hbar/m$. If vortices move between the points at a rate v then the change in the velocity potential in time is

$$\frac{\partial \phi}{\partial t} = v\frac{h}{m}. \tag{42-18}$$

Thus (42-15) can be satisfied when there is a difference in chemical potentials, $\mu + \frac{1}{2}v_s^2$ between two points if vortices move between them at a rate

$$v = \frac{m}{h}\left[\mu_2 + \tfrac{1}{2}v_{s,2}^2 - (\mu_1 + v_{s,1}^2)\right]. \tag{42-19}$$

This is the quantum turbulent solution. For isothermal flow a chemical potential gradient becomes a pressure gradient.

Although vortex flow can explain the critical effects, it has not been demonstrated experimentally that they actually appear above $v_{s,c}$ in linear geometries. Furthermore no one can show, in general, how vortex lines will enter the fluid in any geometry. Classically, vortex lines enter a fluid from the boundary layer which forms due to viscosity, and has a high vorticity. In principle their origin can be understood from the Navier–Stokes equation. In He II the superfluid has no viscosity and thus no boundary layer. It is thus difficult to see how vortices form and it is not known whether their origin is consistent or inconsistent with the two fluid theory.

The best understood critical velocity is that which results when a cylindrical bucket of He II is rotated too quickly. In § 18 we saw that for

$$\omega > \omega_{cr} = \frac{4\hbar}{md^2}\log\frac{d\sqrt{e}}{2a}$$

the thermodynamic equilibrium state should correspond to a vortex on the axis of rotation whereas for $\omega < \omega_{cr}$ the stable state is $v_s = 0$. Here one can understand and observe the value of ω_{cr} but again there is no explanation for how the vortices enter as the bucket is brought into rotation.

In § 10 we presented the argument of Onsager and Feynman which determined a critical velocity from the minimum velocity at which the

Notes p. 265

energy and momentum of $\boldsymbol{v}_s$ = constant flow can be converted to quantized vortex rings. Just as in the above cases this discussion is at best suggestive since it also doesn't explain why or how the vortices form. We should also note that their expression for the critical velocity:

$$v_{s,c} = \frac{4\hbar}{md}\left(\log\frac{4d}{a} - 2\right) \tag{42-20}$$

yields values which are two orders of magnitude too *small* in 1 cm capillaries.

The derivation of (42-20) has been criticized by Fineman and Chase [10] who assert that a vortex ring with a radius nearly equal to that of the capillary has vanishingly small energy and therefore concluded that based on the above argument (§ 10) $v_{s,c} = 0$. Huggins has shown [11] that the impulse of a vortex ring in a capillary is not uniquely defined and can also be taken to be zero at the boundary so that $\text{K.E.}_{\cdot\text{R}}/I_\text{R}$ is still finite as the radius R of the ring goes to $\frac{1}{2}d$. Finally, Raja Gopal and Van Vijfeijken et al. [12] claim to have shown that the energy near the wall is finite.

The different results for the energy of a vortex ring near the walls can be accounted for by different core models [e.g., see discussion following (32-16)]. However, this debate about the properties of a ring near the wall is irrelevant to the derivation of a relation like (42-20). In order for the vortex ring production at the wall of the capillary to dissipate the flow and lead to a pressure gradient the ring must contract across the entire width of the capillary and shrink to zero radius. This is the only fashion in which ring production leads to a $\partial\phi/\partial t$ as discussed in connection with Fig. 46.

We have seen in § 32 that friction forces within the fluid affect the radius of quantized vortex rings. Imagine that many rings form near the wall of the capillary. If the frictional forces are such that they drive the rings back into the wall the flow will *not* be dissipated. A firmer understanding of the derivation of (42-20) requires an investigation of the motion of the vortex rings in capillaries.

First note that the relation between kinetic energy $\text{K.E.}_{\cdot\text{R}}$, velocity $\boldsymbol{v}_\text{R}$, and impulse $\boldsymbol{I}_\text{R}$ of a vortex ring:

$$\text{d}\,\text{K.E.}_{\cdot\text{R}} = \boldsymbol{v}_\text{R}\cdot\text{d}\boldsymbol{I}_\text{R} \tag{42-21}$$

is still valid for a ring in a capillary as can be derived directly by methods similar to those employed in § 18. Changes in impulse still follow from

Notes p. 265

(10-14). Its derivation in Appendix V is independent of geometry. But total impulse is not now well defined. As Huggins [11] points out it depends on how the ring is formed. We will consider the case where rings are formed with radius equal to that of the capillary so that their core is nearly coincident with the wall. Then due to its image this formation results in an arbitrarily small change in the overall velocity field and thus requires zero impulse.

For a given externally imposed flow, v_s' (the subscript 'e' of $v_{s,e}'$ can now be dropped), one finds from (32-26) that the changes in the impulse of a vortex ring in this flow obey

$$\frac{dI_R}{dt} = -2\pi R\zeta_3\rho_s^2(v_R + v_s'), \tag{42-22}$$

where we have taken $v_n = 0$, and v_R is now the velocity of the ring in the capillary of diameter d. Consider first a ring of radius $R \approx \frac{1}{2}d$, polarized opposite to the flow. By this it is meant that if the ring was in an infinite fluid its velocity would be opposite to v_s'. For $R \approx \frac{1}{2}d$ in a capillary an oppositely polarized ring has velocity in the same sense as v_s'. This follows from the fact that as the radius of a ring increases its energy decreases when it is arbitrarily close to the wall. Placing $d\,\text{K.E.}_R < 0$ into (42-21) and using (10-14) for dI_R yields $v_R > 0$ (note that v_s' is in the positive x direction).

Now for $R \approx \frac{1}{2}d$, $(v_R + v_s') > 0$ and according to (42-22) the friction forces act to decrease the momentum or increase the radius (note polarization). Rings formed arbitrarily close to the wall are pushed back into the wall by the friction and do not dissipate the flow. The kinetic energy of a ring in the capillary has a maximum [12] at $R \equiv R_m \approx 0.9(\frac{1}{2}d)$. According to (42-21) for $R > R_m$: $v_R > 0$, for $R = R_m$: $v_R = 0$, and for $R < R_m$: $v_R < 0$. Thus any ring with $R > R_m$ will, because of the friction, be driven to the wall. A ring must clear the energy maximum in order to dissipate the flow. Precisely it must achieve a radius corresponding to $v_R + v_s' = 0$, regardless of polarization.

In the creation of a vortex ring (from the boundary) that leads to dissipation the energy (somehow) received from the flow must be at least the energy maximum. It is the energy at the maximum and not at the wall that determines $v_{s,c}$. The energy at the maximum is within 20% of the energy of the same size ring in an infinite medium [12]. In this way if one assumes that impulse, energy of the creation of vortex rings is supplied by the change of momentum, energy of the flow, one is led to

Notes p. 265

equations closely paralleling (10-11,12). Keeping the detailed correction to K.E._{R}, etc., would not change the result (42-20) by more than a factor of 2.

One might wonder if it is possible to write (42-10) in terms of quantities in the two fluid theory. If this were not possible it would then indicate a definite shortcoming of the hydrodynamic theory as far as critical velocities are concerned. This question is best investigated by writing the two fluid hydrodynamic equations in dimensionless form. We will do this for the two fluid equations linearized around a steady flow and variations in ρ_{n}, ρ, s will be neglected. For this approximation the continuity law is

$$\rho_{\text{n}} \nabla \cdot \delta \boldsymbol{v}_{\text{n}} + \rho_{\text{s}} \nabla \cdot \delta \boldsymbol{v}_{\text{s}} = 0,$$

where δ denotes the deviation from the steady flow and other quantities are evaluated for the unperturbed flow. The entropy law is

$$\rho s \nabla \cdot \delta \boldsymbol{v}_{\text{n}} - \frac{\kappa}{T} \nabla^2 \delta T = 0.$$

The superfluid equation becomes

$$\frac{\partial\, \delta \boldsymbol{v}_{\text{s}}}{\partial t} + (\boldsymbol{v}_{\text{s}} \cdot \nabla) \delta \boldsymbol{v}_{\text{s}} + (\delta \boldsymbol{v}_{\text{s}} \cdot \nabla) \boldsymbol{v}_{\text{s}} - s \nabla \delta T + \frac{1}{\rho} \nabla \delta p$$
$$- \frac{\rho_{\text{n}}}{\rho} \nabla (\boldsymbol{w} \cdot \delta \boldsymbol{w}) + (\rho \zeta_3 - \zeta_4) \nabla (\nabla \cdot \delta \boldsymbol{v}_{\text{n}}) = 0.$$

The normal fluid motion is described by

$$\rho_{\text{n}} \frac{\partial\, \delta \boldsymbol{v}_{\text{n}}}{\partial t} + \rho_{\text{n}} (\boldsymbol{v}_{\text{n}} \cdot \nabla) \delta \boldsymbol{v}_{\text{n}} + \rho_{\text{n}} (\delta \boldsymbol{v}_{\text{n}} \cdot \nabla) \boldsymbol{v}_{\text{n}}$$
$$= -\rho_{\text{s}} s \nabla \delta T - \frac{\rho_{\text{n}}}{\rho} \nabla \delta p - \frac{\rho_{\text{s}} \rho_{\text{n}}}{\rho} \nabla (\boldsymbol{w} \cdot \delta \boldsymbol{w}) - \rho_{\text{n}} \boldsymbol{w} (\nabla \cdot \delta \boldsymbol{v}_{\text{n}})$$
$$- \rho_{\text{n}} \delta \boldsymbol{w} (\nabla \cdot \boldsymbol{v}_{\text{n}}) + \eta \nabla^2 \delta \boldsymbol{v}_{\text{n}} + [\rho_{\text{s}} (\rho \zeta_3 - \zeta_4) + \zeta_2 - \rho \zeta_1 + \tfrac{1}{3} \eta] \nabla (\nabla \cdot \delta \boldsymbol{v}_{\text{n}}),$$

where

$$\boldsymbol{w} \equiv \boldsymbol{v}_{\text{n}} - \boldsymbol{v}_{\text{s}}.$$

In order to put these equations into dimensionless form introduce a temperature T_0 and streaming velocities U_{n}, U_{s} characteristic of the flow. Also let the distance over which quantities change be d. Then the operator

$$\underset{\sim}{\nabla} \equiv \mathrm{d} \nabla$$

Notes p. 265

is a dimensionless gradient and

$$\underset{\sim}{t} \equiv tU_n/d$$

is a dimensionless time. In this way the continuity law becomes in dimensionless form:

$$\underset{\sim}{\nabla} \cdot \delta \underset{\sim}{v}_n + \frac{\rho_s U_s}{\rho_n U_n} \underset{\sim}{\nabla} \cdot \delta \underset{\sim}{v}_s = 0,$$

where we have introduced the dimensionless velocities

$$\delta \underset{\sim}{v}_n = \delta \boldsymbol{v}_n / U_n, \qquad \delta \underset{\sim}{v}_s = \delta \boldsymbol{v}_s / U_s.$$

The entropy law now becomes

$$\underset{\sim}{\nabla} \cdot \delta \underset{\sim}{v}_n - \frac{\kappa}{U_n \rho s d} \underset{\sim}{\nabla}^2 \delta \underset{\sim}{T} = 0,$$

where

$$\delta \underset{\sim}{T} = \delta T / T_0 .$$

The superfluid equation is

$$\frac{\partial\, \delta \underset{\sim}{v}_s}{\partial \underset{\sim}{t}} + \frac{U_s}{U_n} (\underset{\sim}{v}_s \cdot \underset{\sim}{\nabla}) \delta \underset{\sim}{v}_s + \frac{U_s}{U_n} (\delta \underset{\sim}{v}_s \cdot \underset{\sim}{\nabla}) \underset{\sim}{v}_s - \frac{sT}{U_n U_s} \underset{\sim}{\nabla} \delta \underset{\sim}{T}$$

$$+ \underset{\sim}{\nabla} \delta \underset{\sim}{p} - \frac{\rho_n}{\rho} \frac{(U_n - U_s)^2}{U_n U_s} \underset{\sim}{\nabla} (\underset{\sim}{w} \cdot \delta \underset{\sim}{w}) + \frac{\rho \zeta_3 - \zeta_4}{d U_s} \underset{\sim}{\nabla} (\underset{\sim}{\nabla} \cdot \delta \underset{\sim}{v}_n) = 0,$$

where

$$\delta \underset{\sim}{p} = \delta p / \rho U_n U_s,$$

and the normal fluid law is

$$\frac{\partial\, \delta \underset{\sim}{v}_n}{\partial \underset{\sim}{t}} + (\underset{\sim}{v}_n \cdot \underset{\sim}{\nabla}) \delta \underset{\sim}{v}_n + (\delta \underset{\sim}{v}_n \cdot \underset{\sim}{\nabla}) \underset{\sim}{v}_n$$

$$= - \frac{\rho_s s T}{\rho_n U_n^2} \underset{\sim}{\nabla} \delta \underset{\sim}{T} - \frac{U_s}{U_n} \underset{\sim}{\nabla} \delta \underset{\sim}{p} - \frac{\rho_s}{\rho} \frac{(U_n - U_s)^2}{U_n^2} \underset{\sim}{\nabla} (\underset{\sim}{w} \cdot \delta \underset{\sim}{w})$$

$$+ \frac{U_n - U_s}{U_n} \underset{\sim}{w} (\underset{\sim}{\nabla} \cdot \delta \underset{\sim}{v}_n) + \frac{U_n - U_s}{U_n} \delta \underset{\sim}{w} (\underset{\sim}{\nabla} \cdot \underset{\sim}{v}_n) + \frac{\eta}{d \rho_n U_n} \underset{\sim}{\nabla}^2 \delta \underset{\sim}{v}_n$$

$$+ \frac{\rho_s (\rho \zeta_3 - \zeta_4) + \zeta_2 - \rho \zeta_1 + \frac{1}{3}\eta}{d \rho_n U_n} \underset{\sim}{\nabla} (\underset{\sim}{\nabla} \cdot \delta \underset{\sim}{v}_n).$$

Notes p. 265

If these equations possess any instabilities or so-called critical velocities they must be characterized by some value of the dimensionless quantities that appear in them. These quantities are

$$\frac{\rho_{\rm n}}{\rho}, \quad \frac{U_{\rm s}}{U_{\rm n}}, \quad \frac{\kappa}{U_{\rm n}\rho s d}, \quad \frac{sT}{U_{\rm s}^2}, \quad \frac{\rho\zeta_3 - \zeta_4}{dU_{\rm s}}, \quad \frac{\zeta_2 - \rho\zeta_1}{\rho_{\rm n}U_{\rm n}d}, \quad \frac{\eta}{d\rho_{\rm n}U_{\rm n}}.$$

Thus if an instability appears, it will do so when some function of these dimensionless quantities equals a pure number characteristic of the shape (but not size) of the geometry in question. Now if Eq. (42-10) can be represented this way then it may be possible to explain the critical velocities starting from the Landau two fluid hydrodynamics. Indeed (42-10) is equivalent to

$$\frac{\rho}{\rho_{\rm n}} \frac{d\rho_{\rm n}U_{\rm n}}{\eta} \frac{U_{\rm s}}{U_{\rm n}} \left(\frac{U_{\rm s}^2}{sT}\right)^{3/2} \approx 10^{-5},$$

so that perhaps a hydrodynamic interpretation is possible. We should remark that for a classical fluid in the approximation considered, only one dimensionless quantity, the Reynolds number,

$$\frac{\rho d U}{\eta}$$

characterizes the flow, so that the stability problem for He II is much richer.

The question of the critical velocities is clearly the question of how vortices enter the superfluid. Various possibilities are motivated and listed below. In the following sections they are discussed in detail as best as possible.

Consider the simplest case of a cylindrical bucket of rotating He II. In § 18 we showed that the free energy F of a quantized vortex off center at distance r_1 from the axis has the form shown in Fig. 47 when $\omega > \omega_{\rm cr}$. Now imagine that a bucket of He II is rotating at $\omega > \omega_{\rm cr}$ and has no vortex, which means $v_{\rm s} = 0$ or equivalent that a vortex is at the wall where it cancels its image. The stable equilibrium state, however, is one with a vortex at the axis, $r_1 = 0$. In order for a vortex to get to this location from the wall it must overcome a free energy barrier:

$$\Delta F = \pi\gamma^2\rho_{\rm s,0}\ell \left(\log\frac{\gamma\sqrt{\rm e}}{\omega a d/2} - 1\right), \tag{42-23}$$

Notes p. 265

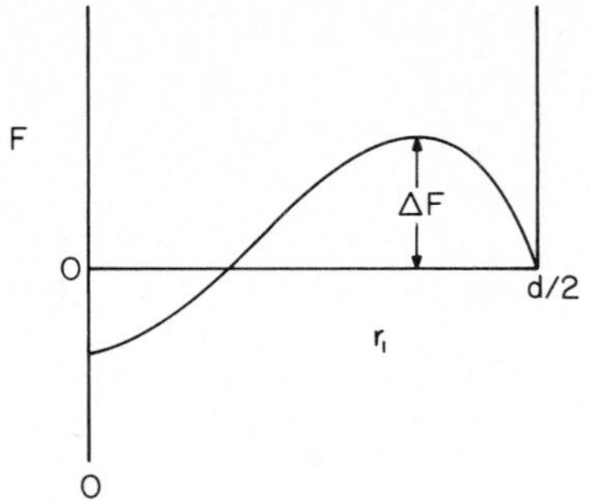

Fig. 47. The free energy of a quantized vortex line located a distance r_1 from the axis of a cylindrical vessel rotating at $\omega > \omega_{cr}$.

where $\gamma = \hbar/m$, ℓ is the height of the bucket and $\rho_{s,0}$ is the superfluid density far from the vortex core.

Since the hydrodynamics always drives the vortex to the minimum in free energy, Eq. (32-1), it cannot possibly drive it over the barrier. However, any event can take place by *thermal fluctuations*: if one waits long enough. Thus one might wonder if the two fluid equations modified to include thermal fluctuations (Chapter IV) can give a correct description of the penetration of the barrier by the vortex line. The possibility of thermally fluctuated vortex lines is discussed in § 44.

The larger the free energy barrier the longer one must wait for a thermal fluctuation to create a vortex line. As ω increases ΔF *decreases*, until at

$$\omega = \omega_c = \frac{2\hbar}{mad\sqrt{e}} \tag{42-24}$$

the barrier and fluctuation time vanish. For $\omega > \omega_c$ the $v_s = 0$ solution becomes *unstable* against small disturbances. Now the two fluid hydrodynamics will drive a vortex from the wall to the axis. Formula (42-24) must be regarded as only an approximation of the value of ω for which ΔF disappears. The expression (18-37) for the free energy was derived ignoring effects of order $a/(\frac{1}{2}d - r_1)$ whereas such terms can affect the derived value of ω_c. The role of *hydrodynamic stability* in causing the entrance of the vortex lines is discussed in § 43.

The observed times for the approach to equilibrium and the observed critical velocities cannot be explained by hydrodynamic stability and thermal fluctuations, except perhaps near T_λ. In many experiments it

Notes p. 265

appears that mechanical vibrations play a role in the origin of the vortex lines. For instance the metastability that always accompanies rotation experiments is lessened when mechanical vibrations are enhanced [13]. As the superfluid has no viscosity mechanical vibrations will have to couple to it in a basically quantum mechanical fashion, which is perhaps analogous to the role of a time varying field leading to a *stimulated transition.* This is a means whereby quantized vortices can enter an ideal Bose gas. The ideal Bose gas is discussed in Chapter VIII and some comments on mechanical vibrations and further remaining critical velocity puzzles are made in § 45.

43 Quantized Vortex Hydrodynamic Instabilities

In the last section we showed that there exists a critical angular velocity ω_c above which the hydrodynamics pushes a vortex into the fluid from the boundary. This happens at an average value of $\overline{|v_n - v_s|}$ given by

$$v_{s,c} \equiv \overline{|v_s - v_n|}_c = \hbar/2ma\sqrt{e} \tag{43-1}$$

Using the experimentally determined value of a (41-47) we find

$$v_{s,c} = \frac{\rho_s}{\rho} \frac{\hbar T_\lambda}{2mT\sqrt{e}\,(3.6 \times 10^{-8}\ \text{cm})} = \frac{\rho_s}{\rho} \frac{T_\lambda}{T} (540\ \text{cm/sec}). \tag{43-2}$$

Although we have motivated this result from the entrance of the first vortex line, it applies to the entrance of additional vortices whenever $\overline{|v_n - v_s|}$ exceeds the critical value given by (43-1). This can be proven by considering the free energy of many vortices as given by (31-3). A similar analysis of the energy barrier presented to a vortex in a capillary also leads to a critical velocity close to (43-1). In all these cases a vortex can move from the wall into the fluid and at the same time continually reduce the free energy. Thus for $v_s > v_{s,c}$ as given by (43-1,2) there is a hydrodynamic instability with respect to the entrance of vortices from the boundary.

In the same way that thermal fluctuations lead to spontaneous first and second sound signals, they also provide for the fluctuation of quantized vortices. Now one can ask what must be the externally imposed superflow so that these omnipresent thermal vortices become unstable and expand. From (42-22) it follows that if they are polarized

Notes p. 265

parallel to the external flow they must always contract and are thus not unstable. But those which are polarized opposite to the external flow v_s' will expand if

$$|v_s'| \geqslant |v_{R_{th}}|, \tag{43-3}$$

where R_{th} is the radius of the thermal vortex and we are ignoring the effects of the boundaries. This turns out to be an excellent approximation as the radii of thermal vortices will be seen to be quite small. This leads to a critical velocity:

$$v_{s,c} = \frac{\gamma}{2R_{th}}\left(\log\frac{8R_{th}}{a} - \frac{1}{2}\right). \tag{43-4}$$

To determine R_{th} one must equate $k_B T$ with the change in energy caused by the appearance of a vortex ring, or

$$k_B T = \int \tfrac{1}{2}\rho_s v_s^2 \, dV - \int \tfrac{1}{2}\rho_s (v_s')^2 \, dV. \tag{43-5}$$

The energy required to fluctuate a vortex ring is modified by the external flow and from (43-5) we find that it is

$$\text{K.E.}_R + \boldsymbol{v}_s' \cdot \boldsymbol{I}_R, \tag{43-6}$$

where as usual K.E._R, $\boldsymbol{I}_R$ are the kinetic energy and impulse of a quantized vortex for no external flow ($v_s' = 0$). For the infinite geometry considered here:

$$I_R = 2\pi^2 \rho_s \gamma R^2, \tag{43-7}$$

$$\text{K.E.}_R = 2\pi\rho_s\gamma^2 R\left(\log\frac{8R}{a} - \frac{3}{2}\right). \tag{43-8}$$

Combining the above we find for the thermal radius of rings polarized opposite to the flow

$$k_B T = 2\pi\rho_s\gamma^2 R_{th}\left(\log\frac{8R_{th}}{a} - \frac{3}{2}\right) - |v_s'|\, 2\pi^2\rho_s\gamma R_{th}^2. \tag{43-9}$$

The critical velocity occurs for $v_s' = -v_{R_{th}}$ or from (43-4,9)

$$k_B T = 2\pi\rho_s\gamma^2 R_{th}\left(\log\frac{8R_{th}}{a} - \frac{3}{2} - \frac{\pi}{2}\right). \tag{43-10}$$

Equation (43-10) determines the thermal radius of rings polarized opposite to the flow when the flow is just fast enough to cause them to

Notes p. 265

become unstable. The corresponding critical velocity is determined by (43-4). The solution to (43-10) is

$$R_{\text{th}} \approx 6a, \tag{43-11}$$

which determines a critical velocity:

$$v_{\text{s,c}} \approx \frac{\hbar}{4ma}. \tag{43-12}$$

The critical velocities (43-1,12) have been motivated from different points of view. In one case we calculated the velocity at which the free-energy barrier presented to the entrance of vortices from the boundary disappears. In the other case the critical velocity is due to the vanishing of the free-energy barrier posed to vortex lines that will always be present due to the thermal fluctuations. The similar values are as far as the macroscopic theory is concerned an accident. For the coherence length a as given by (41-47) it turns out that the radius of a thermal vortex is close to a, and this accounts for the similarities of the two results.

According to (43-2) the critical velocity goes to zero as temperature approaches T_λ. In the persistent currents of Rudnick et al. (§ 39) it was found that when the superfluid was cooled under rotation, the stable state with the superfluid threaded by vortex lines so that it approximated solid body rotation as best as possible was always achieved. Yet when He II ($T < T_\lambda$) was brought from rest into rotation the system achieved a metastable state where no vortices entered until a rather high angular velocity was reached. The difference in behavior can now be attributed to the vanishing of the free-energy barrier as T_λ is crossed.

Fig. 48 shows the maximum stable relative velocity ($v_{\text{n}} - v_{\text{s}}$) observed in the persistent current experiments as a function of temperature for He II contained in a superleak where the spacing between particles was a few hundred Ångstrom. Above 1.9 °K it can be described empirically by [14]

$$v_{\text{s,c}} \approx \frac{\rho_{\text{s}}}{\rho}(100 \text{ cm/sec}), \tag{43-13}$$

which is off by a factor of five from the results which follow from a simple application of the two fluid hydrodynamics. Below 1.9 °K there is a transformation to a different mechanism which is not understood. Furthermore deviations from a critical velocity proportional to ρ_{s}/ρ take place at higher temperatures for wider channels.

Notes p. 265

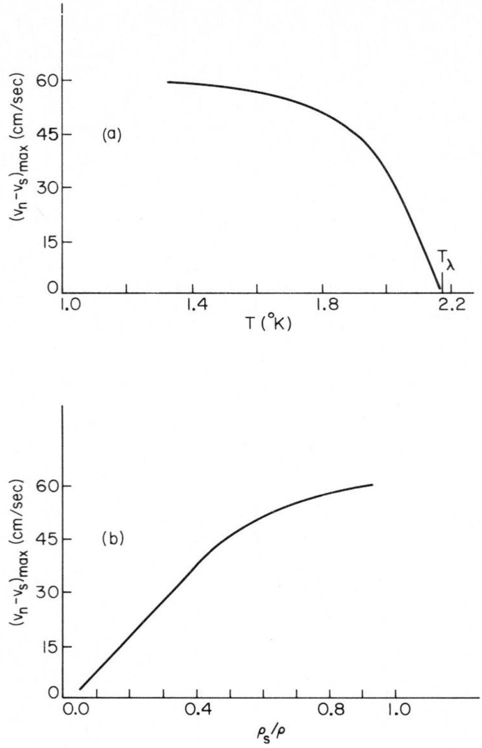

Fig. 48. Maximum stable relative velocity $(v_n - v_s)$ in persistent current experiments: (a) as a function of T, (b) as a function of ρ_s/ρ.

A careful consideration of all factors which influence the free energy, of vortices near a boundary, and of small vortices, might lead to an improved understanding of the experiments near T_λ. Also the critical velocity which is experimentally observed is an averaged quantity. Since the rotation of the superfluid satisfies $\nabla \times \boldsymbol{v}_s = 0$ there might be throughout the fluid strong deviations from the average so that the experimentally observed $v_{s,c}$ actually corresponds to a local $v_{s,c}$ closer to those derived in this section.

In view of these corrections it appears possible to understand the critical velocity effects near T_λ according to the two fluid hydrodynamics.

Notes p. 265

44 The Thermal Fluctuation of Quantized Vortices

Even when $|\boldsymbol{v}_s - \boldsymbol{v}_n|$ is less than $v_{s,c}$ as determined by the vanishing of the free energy barrier vortices can enter through thermal fluctuations. The closer $|\boldsymbol{v}_s - \boldsymbol{v}_n|$ is to $v_{s,c}$ the smaller the barrier and the greater the probability of fluctuating a vortex across it. Thus the critical velocity $v_{s,c}$ (43-2,4) calculated from the two fluid hydrodynamics including dissipation will not be sharp, but according to the thermal fluctuations (Chapter IV) it will be smoothed out. Thermal fluctuations will allow the persistent current to decay below $v_{s,c}$. The role of thermal fluctuations as regards critical velocities has been emphasized by Iordanskii [15], Langer, Fisher and Reppy [16], and Donnelly and Roberts [17]. The approach in this and the previous section most closely parallels that of Ref. [16]. It must be emphasized that all of the results presented here can be derived from the two fluid equations including thermal fluctuations as derived in Chapter IV.

To gain insight into the role of thermal fluctuations let us consider the simplified case of a bucket of He II rotating at

$$\omega' \equiv \frac{4\hbar}{md^2} < \omega < \omega_{cr},$$

so that the free energy is given by Fig. 49. Consider a vortex at the axis.

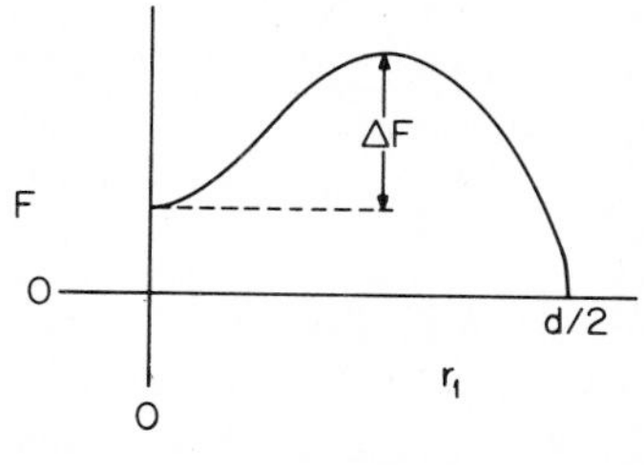

Fig. 49. The free energy of a quantized vortex in a bucket rotating at angular velocity ω such that: $\omega' < \omega < \omega_{cr}$.

It will be stable against small disturbances but the globally stable state consists of no vortex. Let us calculate the time for thermal fluctuations to induce this transition.

If the transition occurs by the vortex fluctuating over the barrier then Eqs. (37-4,10) provide the complete description of the process. To avoid

Notes p. 265

the difficult mathematics we obtain an approximate answer. From (37-4) one finds that

$$\alpha^{-1} = \left[\frac{\rho_s \zeta_3}{\gamma}\left(\omega - \frac{4\gamma}{d^2}\right)\right]^{-1} \tag{44-1}$$

is approximately the thermalization time, or the position of the vortex at a time $t + \alpha^{-1}$ will be unrelated to it position at time t. Thus we can imagine that the vortex is making α^{-1} attempts per second to get over the free energy barrier holding it near the axis. Equation (34-8) from which the fluctuation equations follow implies that the probability of an attempt taking the vortex over the barrier is

$$\exp(-\Delta F/k_B T), \tag{44-2}$$

where ΔF is the free energy at the maximum minus that at the origin. Therefore the time required for the vortex to thermally jump over the barrier is

$$\alpha^{-1} \exp(\Delta F/k_B T). \tag{44-3}$$

From (31-3):

$$\Delta F = \pi\gamma^2 \rho_s \ell \left(\log \frac{\omega'}{\omega} - 1 + \frac{\omega}{\omega'}\right). \tag{44-4}$$

For $\omega = \frac{1}{2}(\omega' + \omega_{cr})$ and $d = 0.2$ cm, $\ell = 1$ cm the thermal metastability time is on the order of exp (10^8) sec which is huge. However, there are other ways in which the transition to the stable state can occur. For instance a vortex doublet (two lines of opposite polarization) might form off center and then be driven to a state where one line goes to the center cancelling the line already there and the other goes to the wall cancelling with its image. In this case the free energy barrier will be about the same, but the attempt frequency will be greatly increased. Although the thermalization time for a *given* vortex doublet will be about the same, there will be vortex doublets throughout the fluid which are fluctuating, in an attempt to break apart. However, even if one assumes Avogadro's number of doublets the thermal metastability time is still huge. Perhaps a more clever choice of an intermediate fluctuation process will yield a metastability time more on the order of those observed in the laboratory. Then again it might turn out that this process cannot be described by the thermal fluctuation mechanism.

Notes p. 265

Consider the temperature region near T_λ for which Eq. (43-12) provides the qualitative description of the critical velocity. If a flow of He II is started with velocity greater than $v_{s,c}$ it will dissipate quickly until $v_{s,c}$ is achieved. Once reached the flow will continue to diminish by dint of the thermal fluctuations. In principle this decay can be described by the two fluid equations modified to include thermal fluctuations.

The scattering of light by thermal fluctuations takes place off of the thermally generated sound waves. Thus to describe it, the thermally fluctuating state of the fluid was (Fourier) analyzed in terms of plane waves § 38. The persistent current decay takes place by 'scattering' of the $\boldsymbol{v}_s$ field off of the thermally driven vortex inhomogeneities. In this case the parallel procedure would be to 'vortex analyze' the thermally fluctuating state of the fluid expressing it as a collection of vortices and then use Eq. (37-1) to describe the thermal motion of the vortices and resulting interaction with the imposed flow. It is not clear how to mathematically carry out this rigorous procedure. However, we can easily arrive at results based on the two fluid theory plus fluctuations by use of some approximations as below.

Consider a torus of diameter d and perimeter $\ell \gg d$, then if thermal fluctuations lead to the formation of a ring in the fluid and its subsequent expansion and annihilation at the boundary the phase change (see Fig. 46) will lead to a change in the superfluid velocity $\boldsymbol{v}'_s$. If these rings are polarized opposite to $\boldsymbol{v}'_s$ and are formed at a rate ν then the decay is given by

$$\frac{\mathrm{d}v'_s}{\mathrm{d}t} = -\frac{h\nu}{m\ell}. \tag{44-5}$$

For a given $v'_s < v_{s,c}$ the free energy will have a maximum at some finite ring radius. This then is the barrier which the ring must fluctuate over in order to dissipate the flow. When fluctuations drive it over this barrier, the hydrodynamics then push it to the wall as described by (42-22). This picture for the decay of persistent currents is similar to that for the condensation of a supersaturated vapor. A vapor condenses (in the absence of impurities) by forming little droplets which then expand until all the vapor has condensed. However, due to the existence of a finite nonvanishing surface tension the droplet will contract and evaporate away unless it has a certain minimum size. So the thermal fluctuations lead to the creation of droplets of varying sizes which are

Notes p. 265

all unstable. Those which are too small disappear and those which are large enough expand taking the system to the stable state. The droplets are analogous to the vortex rings and the surface tension analogous to the finite non-vanishing circulation h/m of the vortex rings.

The probability that a given ring will fluctuate over the barrier is from (34-2)

$$\exp(-\Delta F/k_B T), \tag{44-6}$$

where ΔF is the increase in $\int \frac{1}{2}\rho_s v_s^2 \mathrm{d}V$ required to reach the barrier. The number per second to escape, ν, is given by the probability per attempt (44-6) multiplied by the number of attempts per second $V\nu_0$, which we calculate later in terms of the two fluid theory. As $V = \frac{1}{4}\pi\ell\, d^2$ Eq. (44-5) becomes

$$\frac{\mathrm{d}v_s'}{\mathrm{d}t} = -\frac{h\pi d^2}{4m}\nu_0 \exp(-\Delta F/k_B T). \tag{44-7}$$

The decay of the persistent current is non-negligible only for v_s' close to $v_{s,c}$. Thus we expand ΔF as

$$\Delta F(v_s') = \Delta F(v_{s,c}) + \left(\frac{\partial \Delta F}{\partial v_s'}\right)_c (v_s' - v_{s,c}), \tag{44-8}$$

where the subscript 'c' means evaluated at $v_s' = v_{s,c}$. As $v_{s,c}$ is defined by $\Delta F(v_{s,c}) = 0$ we have

$$\Delta F(v_s') = \left(\frac{\partial \Delta F}{\partial v_s'}\right)_c (v_s' - v_{s,c}), \tag{44-9}$$

where as usual v_s' is the flow in the absence of vortex rings. The solution to (44-7,9) is

$$v_s'(t) = v_{s,c} + k_B T\left(\frac{\partial \Delta F}{\partial v_s'}\right)_c^{-1} \times \log\left\{\exp\left[\left(\frac{\partial \Delta F}{\partial v_s'}\right)_c \frac{v_s'(0) - v_{s,c}}{k_B T}\right] - \left(\frac{\partial \Delta F}{\partial v_s'}\right)_c \frac{\pi h d^2 \nu_0 t}{4mk_B T}\right\}, \tag{44-10}$$

where the integration constant has been chosen so that the flow velocity at time zero is $v_s'(0)$. For large t (44-10) becomes

$$v_s' = v_{s,c} + k_B T\left(\frac{\partial \Delta F}{\partial v_s'}\right)_c^{-1} \log\left[-\left(\frac{\partial \Delta F}{\partial v_s'}\right)_c \frac{\pi h d^2 \nu_0 t}{4mk_B T}\right], \tag{44-11}$$

Notes p. 265

which is independent of the initial condition and exhibits the logarithmic decay characteristic of persistent currents. Experimentally it is found, that in the region near T_λ where the critical velocity is proportional to ρ_s/ρ [as given by (43-13)], the fractional decay per decade is [16,18]

$$\frac{\log 10}{v_{s,c}} \frac{d(v_{s,c} - v_s')}{d(\log t)} = \Delta\left(\frac{v_{s,c} - v_s'}{v_{s,c}}\right) = 0.12. \tag{44-12}$$

Close enough to T_λ, the decay and critical velocities are described by (44-12) and (43-13) for any channel diameter. Thus these are referred to as intrinsic properties of the fluid. Depending on the channel diameter the deviations from (44-12), (43-13) take place at different temperatures, the wider the channel the higher the temperature. Also in the temperature range where decay depends on channel diameter persistent currents corresponding to the same average flow velocity v_s' are observed to decay at vastly different rates [19]. These varying decay rates are related to the different procedures by which the persistent currents are established. For example the decay rate can depend on the state of the He II as T_λ was crossed in preparing the given sample.

Although (44-11) has the same form as (44-12) it remains to be seen what exactly is meant by large t and how the numbers compare.

The contribution to the free energy of flow at velocity v_s', due to a quantized vortex is from (43-6)

$$\mathrm{F} = \mathrm{K.E.}_{\cdot\mathrm{R}} + \boldsymbol{v}_s' \cdot \boldsymbol{I}_\mathrm{R}, \tag{44-13}$$

where $\mathrm{K.E.}_{\cdot\mathrm{R}}$, $\boldsymbol{I}_\mathrm{R}$ are the energy, impulse of a quantized vortex for no external flow ($v_s' = 0$).

When $v_s' = v_{s,c}$ (43-12) the required change in free energy ΔF of a vortex of thermal energy $k_\mathrm{B}T$, in order to escape over the barrier is $\Delta F = 0$, as was shown in § 43. For $v_s' < v_{s,c}$, $\Delta F > 0$ and we wish to calculate $(\partial\,\Delta F/\partial v_s')_c$ since according to the derived decay formula (44-11) the decay per decade is

$$-\frac{k_\mathrm{B}T \log 10}{v_{s,c}}\left(\frac{\partial \Delta F}{\partial v_s'}\right)_c^{-1}. \tag{44-14}$$

The change in the free energy barrier ΔF with respect to changes in v_s' will have two contributions. One from the direct dependence of F on v_s' and the other from the change in radius of the ring of maximum F as v_s' changes. The radius of this ring is given by

$$v_s' = |v_{\mathrm{R_m}}| \tag{44-15}$$

Notes p. 265

and the corresponding free energy barrier is

$$\Delta F = F_{\mathrm{m}} - k_{\mathrm{B}}T = \mathrm{K.E.}_{\mathrm{R_m}} - v_{\mathrm{s}}'|I_{\mathrm{R_m}}| - k_{\mathrm{B}}T, \tag{44-16}$$

where the subscript 'm' means evaluated at the maximum and we recall that the rings under consideration have polarization opposite to that of v_{s}'. From (44-16)

$$\frac{\partial \Delta F}{\partial v_{\mathrm{s}}'} = \left(\frac{\partial \mathrm{K.E.}_{\mathrm{R}}}{\partial R} - v_{\mathrm{s}}' \frac{\partial |I_{\mathrm{R}}|}{\partial R}\right)_{\mathrm{m}} \frac{\mathrm{d}R_{\mathrm{m}}}{\mathrm{d}v_{\mathrm{s}}'} - I_{\mathrm{R_m}}. \tag{44-17}$$

However, since $\mathrm{d}\,\mathrm{K.E.}_{\mathrm{R}} = \boldsymbol{v}_{\mathrm{R}} \cdot \mathrm{d}\boldsymbol{I}_{\mathrm{R}}$

$$\frac{\partial \Delta F}{\partial v_{\mathrm{s}}'} = -\,|I_{\mathrm{R_m}}|, \tag{44-18}$$

where (44-15) has been used. When to lowest order all quantities are evaluated at the critical velocity this implies

$$\left(\frac{\partial \Delta F}{\partial v_{\mathrm{s}}'}\right)_{\mathrm{c}} = -|I_{\mathrm{R_{th}}}|_{\mathrm{c}} = -72\pi^2 \rho_{\mathrm{s}} \gamma a^2, \tag{44-19}$$

where the radius of the thermally generated rings at critical flow is given by (43-11).

Substituting (44-19) into (44-14) yields for the theoretical fractional decay per decade of a persistent current

$$\frac{k_{\mathrm{B}}T \log 10}{18\pi^2 \gamma^2 \rho_{\mathrm{s}} a}. \tag{44-20}$$

Use of (41-47) converts this to

$$\frac{k_{\mathrm{B}}T_{\lambda} \log 10}{18\pi^2 \gamma^2 \rho (3.6 \times 10^{-8}\ \mathrm{cm})} \approx 0.04,$$

which is a factor of 3 less than experiment (44-12).

The decay is simple logarithmic as given by (44-11) only for t large enough. To see how large this must be, the attempt frequency per unit volume ν_0 must be evaluated. This will be given by the product of the number of thermally generated vortex rings and the frequency for a given ring. As an approximation we shall assume that there are as many vortex rings as can fit into the fluid. Since a thermal ring has radius $6a$:

$$\nu_0 \approx \alpha/(12a)^3, \tag{44-21}$$

Notes p. 265

where α^{-1} is the thermalization time of a given ring, and follows from the equation of motion of a ring (42-22). We will get an approximation to v_0 by using the thermalization time of a vortex ring of the thermal radius R_{th} appropriate to v_s' as given by (43-9). To lowest order:

$$(v_{R_{th}} + v_s') = (v_{R_{th}} + v_s')_c + \left[\frac{\partial(v_{R_{th}} + v_s')}{\partial v_s'}\right]_c (v_s' - v_{s,c}). \quad (44\text{-}22)$$

But since $(v_{R_{th}} + v_s')_c = 0$:

$$(v_{R_{th}} + v_s') = \left[\frac{\partial(v_{R_{th}} + v_s')}{\partial v_s'}\right]_c (v_s' - v_{s,c}). \quad (44\text{-}23)$$

By differentiating (43-9) first with respect to R_{th} and then with respect to v_s' yields

$$(|v_{R_{th}}| - v_s')\left(\frac{d|I_R|}{dR}\right)_{th} - |I_{R_{th}}|\frac{dv_s'}{dR_{th}} = 0, \quad (44\text{-}24)$$

$$(|v_{R_{th}}| - v_s')\left(\frac{d^2|I_R|}{dR^2}\right)_{th}\frac{dR_{th}}{dv_s'} + \left(\frac{d|I_R|}{dR}\right)_{th}\frac{d(|v_{R_{th}}| - v_s')}{dv_s'} - \left(\frac{d|I_R|}{dR}\right)_{th} = 0. \quad (44\text{-}25)$$

Eliminating dR_{th}/dv_s' from (44-25) by use of (44-24) yields

$$\frac{\partial(v_{R_{th}} + v_s')}{\partial v_s'} = \left[I_R \frac{d^2 I_R}{dR^2}\left(\frac{dI_R}{dR}\right)^{-2}\right]_{th} - 1. \quad (44\text{-}26)$$

In view of the fact that $I_R \sim R^2$ the right hand side of (44-26) is simply $-\frac{1}{2}$.

Thus the motion of a ring of the thermal radius is from (42-22)

$$\frac{dR}{dt} = -\frac{\rho_s \zeta_3}{4\pi\gamma}\frac{(v_{s,c} - v_s')}{2}. \quad (44\text{-}27)$$

This implies a characteristic frequency (inverse of the thermalization time)

$$\alpha = \frac{\rho_s \zeta_3 (v_{s,c} - v_s')}{8\pi\gamma R_{th}}. \quad (44\text{-}28)$$

Combining (44-28,21) the term involving t in the logarithm of (44-10) becomes

$$\frac{4\rho_s \gamma^3}{10^3 k_B T a}\left(\frac{d^2}{a^2}\right)\frac{\rho_s \zeta_3}{\gamma}\frac{v_{s,c} - v_s'}{v_{s,c}}t. \quad (44\text{-}29)$$

Notes p. 265

For a given fraction $(v_{s,c} - v'_s)/v_{s,c} \approx 0.1$ this term is of order $(10^6 \text{ sec}^{-1})t$ at $T_\lambda - T = 10^{-2}$ °K and increases sharply for lower T. The other (time independent) term in the logarithm is of order

$$\exp\left(\frac{18\pi^2\gamma^2\rho_s a}{k_B T}\frac{v_{s,c} - v'_s}{v_{s,c}}\right). \tag{44-30}$$

This term is temperature independent and of order e^6. Thus for times greater than 10^{-3} sec (44-29) is greater than (44-30). This situation is always realized experimentally.

The rough agreement obtained between theory and experiment by the simplified approach presented here certainly suggests that thermal fluctuations play a role in some critical velocity phenomena in He II. However, there are some experimental observations which definitely are not explainable by invoking thermal fluctuations. For instance as discussed in § 39 when He II contained in a superleak is brought into rotation $v_n - v_s$ increases and no vortices enter until a 'critical' angular velocity $\omega_{c,1}$ is attained. At ω_{c1} vortices enter and $v_n - v_s$ still continues to increase as the superleak is rotated faster. We conclude that $\omega_{c,1}$ cannot possibly be explained by thermal fluctuations across a barrier. For if that were the case it would be impossible to understand how $v_n - v_s$ continued to increase. The mechanism whereby vortices enter at ω_{c1} is probably characteristic of the critical velocities observed in most experiments sufficiently far from the lambda transition.

45 The Role of Mechanical Vibrations

In the experiments of Reppy and Lane [13] in which the angular momentum of He II contained in a rotating vessel was measured it was found sometimes, that at rotational speeds where the equilibrium state would consist of many vortices, none were present, $v_s = 0$. This rarely observed metastable state could be easily destroyed by tapping the bucket. Such an observation is a rough demonstration of the possible effect of mechanical vibrations as far as inducing the entrance of vortex lines.

For a classical fluid the coupling of vibrations to the fluid motion can take place through its viscous interaction with the wall. The superfluid has no viscosity and therefore its coupling must be quite different. We will motivate here a discussion where the induced transitions take

Notes p. 265

place in a fashion similar to those induced in say a hydrogen atom by a time varying external electromagnetic field.

Let us consider He II in a rotating cylindrical container and regard the states with zero, one, two, etc., quantized vortex lines in their stable locations as orthogonal eigenstates. Denote the amplitude for the occupation of these states as C_0, C_1, etc., and from now on focus attention on the two lowest states. For perfect cylindrical symmetry the states with no vortex line and a vortex on the axis are orthogonal. If there is, however, a bump on the wall so that the cylindrical symmetry is destroyed, these states will be coupled, with a potential denoted by K. Then in parallel with the quantum theory the time development of C_0, C_1 is given by

$$i\hbar \frac{\partial C_0}{\partial t} = \mathscr{F}_0 C_0 + K C_1, \tag{45-1}$$

$$i\hbar \frac{\partial C_1}{\partial t} = \mathscr{F}_1 C_1 + K C_0, \tag{45-2}$$

where K is to be regarded as a perturbation, and $\mathscr{F}_0, \mathscr{F}_1$ are the free energies *per superfluid particle* in the respective states. If K is time dependent, such as will happen if the bump is vibrating then (45-1,2) describe transitions between these two states. Such transitions can only be expected to have appreciable probability for frequency components of K close to $(\mathscr{F}_1 - \mathscr{F}_0)/\hbar = (\omega_{cr} - \omega)$. Denoting the component of K at this frequency by K' one is led to a characteristic transition time of

$$\hbar/|K'| \tag{45-3}$$

for first order perturbation theory. As an estimate we evaluate $|K'|$ by assuming that it is given by the average change in energy of the given superfluid state due to the motion of the bump through the fluid. For instance the state with no vortex is no longer characterized by $v_s = 0$. Due to the motion of the bump the fluid near it will be pushed along as discussed in § 39. This fluid will acquire angular momentum and energy. Let the total volume of bumps on the boundary be δV and their amplitude of vibration at frequency $\omega_{cr} - \omega$ be δx. Then the change in energy per particle of the $v_s = 0$ state due to the vibration of the bump at frequency $\omega_{cr} - \omega$ is about

$$m[(\omega_{cr} - \omega)\, \delta x]^2\, \delta V/V \tag{45-4}$$

Notes p. 265

and the characteristic time of transitions stimulated by the vibrating bump is

$$\frac{\hbar V}{m\,\delta V[(\omega_{\rm cr}-\omega)\,\delta x]^2}. \tag{45-5}$$

If we consider a 1 mm bucket which is 'mismounted' 10μm off axis and is vibrating at a velocity 10^{-4} cm/sec one is led for $\omega = \frac{1}{2}\omega_{\rm cr}$ to a quantum transition time of 10^4 sec which must be regarded as a conservative estimate, the vibrations at such low frequencies might turn out to be larger.

The above argument is very rough and only intended to be suggestive of the kind of quantum mechanisms which might play a role in the *macroscopic* quantum transitions that take place in He II when vortices enter. A bump on the wall leads to an overlap (coupling) between two quantum states, and its vibrations stimulate transitions in much the same manner as an external electromagnetic field stimulates transitions in an atom.

A number of assumptions were made which require further investigation. For instance it is doubtful that one can use superposition [as implied by (45-1,2)] in describing the macroscopic quantum states since these states are seriously affected by mutual superfluid interactions. Also the relationship of this procedure to the basic two fluid hydrodynamics including quantization is not at all clear.

There is another manner by which vortices can enter the He II through mechanical vibrations and which does follow from the two fluid theory. As discussed in § 31 vortex lines distributed in the fluid posses definite normal modes of oscillation. If there is a bump on the boundary it can exchange angular momentum and energy with the vortices. Especially if the bump oscillates at the frequency of the normal modes a resonance can be set up which can continuously pump in energy and lead to a vortex transition.

Mechanical vibrations might play a dominant role in many critical velocity experiments, yet they have not been carefully studied either, theoretically or experimentally.

Although the critical velocities were one of the first difficulties to be encountered in He II research they are perhaps the least understood aspect today. It is generally assumed that the critical velocities are related to the appearance of quantized vortex lines in the superfluid. But if this is the case how can one account for the drastically different

Notes p. 265

critical velocities for rotation and linear flow. The Bijl–Onsager–Feynman expression (42-20) for the critical velocity would be the analogue of the rotational critical velocity ω_{cr} in linear geometries [24]. However, this expression deviates seriously from the law (42-10) observed in linear geometries.

Another puzzle as far as rotation vs. linear flow is concerned is the inability to observe persistent currents in He II film adsorbed to the outside of a 1 cm diameter cylinder [20]. This experiment would have been able to detect relative flows between film and cylinder equal to one per cent of the linear critical velocity (~ 100 cm/sec) by means of Doppler-shifted third sound. The negative results were obtained by two methods: (a) by bringing to rest a cylinder cooled through T_λ while rotating and, (b) by bringing into rotation a cylinder which was cooled at rest. In each case no relative flow was detected. These observations have been recently confirmed [21] by experiments where in addition to rotation the film could be induced to flow parallel to the axis of rotation by means of an appropriately located heater. Now the total velocity of the film was due to rotation plus a linear flow towards the heater. The critical heating rate, and thus maximum velocity of linear flow towards the heater was completely unaffected by rotation thus indicating that whereas the film would flow linearly with respect to the cylinder it would not flow rotationally with respect to it. Had there been a relative rotational flow the critical heating rate would have been lessened.

There are of course differences between the linear flow and rotation. A measurable persistent current would correspond to a coherent quantum state with $n > 10^4$ which perhaps is very unstable. This is further suggested by the experiments of Reppy et al. [22] in which persistent currents are observed in films which coat a superleak. In this case it appears that the total persistent current is built up out of many small circulations ($n < 5$) around the individual powder grains [25].

Notes

[1] F. A. Staas, K. W. Taconis and W. M. van Alphen, Physica **27**(1961)893. See also C. E. Chase, Phys. Rev. **127**(1962)361; **131**(1963)1898.

[2] D. F. Brewer and D. O. Edwards, Phil. Mag. **6**(1961)775; Proc. Roy. Soc. **A251** (1959)247.

[3] C. J. Gorter and J. H. Mellink, Physica **15**(1949)285.

[4] W. M. Van Alphen, J. F. Olijhoek, R. de Bruyn Ouboter and K. W. Taconis, Physica

32(1966)1901. R. de Bruyn Ouboter, K. W. Taconis and W. M. Van Alphen, in: *Progress in Low Temperature Physics*, ed. C. J. Gorter (North-Holland, Amsterdam, 1967) Vol. 5.

[5] K. Fokkens, K. W. Taconis and R. de Bruyn Ouboter, Physica **32**(1966)2129; Reference [8], and D. F. Brewer and K. Mendelssohn, Proc. Roy. Soc. **A260**(1961)1.

[6] In similar isothermal flow experiments, Kidder and Fairbank, Phys. Rev. **127**(1962) 987 observe critical velocities significantly smaller than predicted by (42-10). These measurements were made with standpipes connected to the flow region of interest. Since the He II streamlines extend into the standpipes (§ 30), it is quite possible that they measured the critical velocity of the standpipes.

[7] W. E. Keller and E. F. Hammel, Physics **2**(1966)221.

[8] K. Telschow, Ph. D. Thesis (1973).

[9] P. W. Anderson, in: *Quantum Fluids*, ed. D. F. Brewer (North-Holland, Amsterdam, 1969) p. 146; Rev. Mod. Phys. **38**(1966)298.

[10] J. C. Fineman and C. E. Chase, Phys. Rev. **129**(1963)1.

[11] E. R. Huggins, Phys. Rev. Letters **17**(1966)1284.

[12] E. S. Raja Gopal, Ann. Physics **25**(1963)196. A. G. van Vijfeijken, A. Walraven and F. A. Staas, Physica **44**(1969)415.

[13] J. D. Reppy and C. T. Lane, Phys. Rev. **140**(1965)A106.

[14] J. R. Clow and J. D. Reppy, Phys. Rev. Letters **16**(1966)887; **19**(1967)289. H. Kojima, Ph. D. Thesis, UCLA (1972).

[15] S. V. Iordanskii, Zh. Eksp. Teor. Fiz. **48**(1965)708 [Sov. Phys. JETP **21**(1965)467].

[16] J. S. Langer and M. E. Fisher, Phys. Rev. Letters **19**(1967)560. J. S. Langer and J. D. Reppy, in: *Progress in Low Temperature Physics*, ed. C. J. Gorter (North-Holland, Amsterdam, 1970) Vol. 6.

[17] R. J. Donnelly and P. H. Roberts, Phil. Trans. Roy. Soc. (London) **271**(1971)41.

[18] G. Kukich, R. P. Henkel and J. D. Reppy, Phys. Rev. Letters **21**(1968)197.

[19] H. Kojima, see Ref. [14].

[20] T. Wang, Paper presented at Thirteenth International Conference on Low Temperature Physics, Boulder, Colorado (1972).

[21] F. Wagner, J. Low Temp. Phys. **13**(1973)185.

[22] R. P. Henkel, E. N. Smith and J. Reppy, Phys. Rev. Letters **23**(1969)1276.

[23] E. S. Sabisky and C. H. Anderson, Phys. Rev. Letters **30**(1973)1122.

[24] The value of ω_{cr} was derived from the thermohydrodynamics. The Bijl–Onsager–Feynman $v_{s,c}$ was motivated by an energy, momentum balance argument whose relationship with the thermohydrodynamic theory is unclear. In fact shrinking a vortex ring across a capillary can always result in a net decrease of free energy. In this sense the analogue of ω_{cr} in linear flow is $v_{s,c} = 0$! We have seen that the free energy barrier is what really counts. The Bijl $v_{s,c}$ and ω_{cr} are then analogous in that the size of the *barrier* presented at each is the same.

[25] H. Verbeek, H. Mars, H. van Beelen, R. de Bruyn Ouboter and K. W. Taconis (Physica, 1974) report observing a persistent current in a film which coats the inside of a capillary of radius 0.01 cm (closed into itself) and of length 10^4 cm! The interpretation of this experiment might perhaps be complicated by the presence of a superleak along the flow path. On the other hand the reported negative results of others might be due to vorticity at the top and bottom of the cylinder, or to difficulties with the critical velocity determined by the cylinder's *height*.

CHAPTER VII

Possible Shortcomings of the Landau Two Fluid Theory of He II

46 *Introduction: The Landau Two Fluid Theory and the Macroscopic Quantum Effects*

In Chapter VI we saw that there are some critical velocities in He II above which a simple description of the flow according to the two fluid hydrodynamics breaks down. It is not clear whether these critical velocities indicate a shortcoming of the hydrodynamic theory or whether we are not clever enough to find the more complicated solution to the two fluid hydrodynamics appropriate to the given situation. Classically one knows that vortices are related to the critical velocities (as is the case with He II) and there for instance it has not been shown how to describe theoretically the critical velocity (i.e., critical Reynolds number) for flow in a capillary; although it is generally accepted that these effects can be described by the Navier–Stokes equations.

In some simple situations where the two fluid equations can be solved it is found that there is disagreement with experiment. An example is third sound, a wave which propagates on the surface of a He II film (§ 41). The speed of third sound (41-28)

$$u_3^2 = \frac{\bar{\rho}_s d}{\rho} \frac{\partial \Omega_v(d)}{\partial d} \tag{46-1}$$

as calculated from the two fluid theory using the equation of state for ρ_s say as measured by second sound (under pressure) is in disagreement with experiments. This disagreement vanishes in the thick film limit and becomes important only for the thinner films. One might therefore wonder if this indicates a general breakdown of a macroscopic or hydrodynamical approach. For instance in classical fluids the Navier–Stokes equations break down in describing variations over distances comparable with the interatomic spacing or mean free path. In such a

Notes p. 285

situation a description starting from the microscopic first principles is necessitated. Since for third sound one can get agreement between (46-1) and experiment by saying that ρ_s vanishes in regions of the size of an atomic spacing near the boundaries then perhaps the discrepancy between (46-1) and experiment is indicative of the breakdown of *any* hydrodynamic approach.

We will however, take the point of view that as far as the superfluid motion is concerned a disagreement between theory and experiment traceable to behavior in regions of atomic dimension does *not* indicate the need for a microscopic approach to the problem. Instead it indicates the need for a better macroscopic theory. As the superfluid is a single macroscopically occupied quantum state we will always have in mind that it should be possible to describe it with a continuum theory, which may not be the Landau two fluid theory, down to dimensions the size of a He^4 atom (1 Å). Regarding the normal fluid motion we of course expect a breakdown under the same conditions that apply in the classical hydrodynamics. Thus we work with the opinion that the overall range of applicability of the He II hydrodynamics should be *greater* than that of the classical or Navier–Stokes hydrodynamics!

The question of the failure of the two fluid hydrodynamics in thin geometries aside, we will see (§§ 47,48) that even in thick or bulk geometries there are some possible disagreements between the Landau two fluid theory and experiment. In this chapter we will take the opinion that any such shortcomings should be accounted for by the need to more fully incorporate coherent macroscopic quantum effects in the hydrodynamic description. As was emphasized in § 10 the Landau two fluid theory plus quantization is analogous to the old quantum theory where one selected a discrete set of states from the classical dynamics by quantizing the adiabatic invariants of the motion. Just as the old quantum theory has its shortcoming one expects the same of the two fluid theory plus the Onsager–Feynman quantization.

Before discussing the macroscopic quantum effects in somewhat more detail let us review the Landau two fluid theory. The basic underlying assumption was that an additional velocity field $\boldsymbol{v}_s$ was required in order to completely specify the state of the fluid. Whereas five variables characterize a classical fluid, eight are needed for superfluid helium. From this assumption and a Kelvin circulation theorem for $\boldsymbol{v}_s$ follow the two fluid thermodynamics (4-5,6,8) and hydrodynamics (4-1,2,3,4). When dissipative processes are allowed for, no further assumptions are

Notes p. 285

required to obtain the irreversible generalizations (21-1,2,3,4) supplemented by (21-10,11,12,13) or more exactly, the fluxes given in Appendix VI. To arrive at these results use was made of first principles such as mass, momentum, energy conservation, Galilean covariance and the first and second laws of thermodynamics. The modification of these equations to include fluctuations followed from the additional assumption that the basic variables represented stationary, Gaussian, Markovian processes as discussed in Chapter IV. Numerous successful applications of these equations have been discussed on the linear and non-linear levels and especially relating to the new role of temperature (e.g., second sound, superthermalconductivity).

It is generally accepted that the reason for the appearance of an extra macroscopic variable lies in the role of quantum theory on a macroscopic level in He II, $\boldsymbol{v}_s$ being the velocity of the particles in the coherent superfluid quantum state. But if the two fluid hydrodynamics is a quantum theory it doesn't show it since Planck's constant does not appear therein, or more exactly, based on this hydrodynamics there is no experiment which can be performed which will determine Planck's constant. As mentioned in § 10 this situation changed when these equations were supplemented by the quantization rule

$$\oint \boldsymbol{v}_s \cdot \mathrm{d}\boldsymbol{\ell} = nh/m, \tag{46-2}$$

which is consistent with them and which has been experimentally verified.

The two fluid hydrodynamics plus (46-2) constitute the most complete theory of He II available.

Let us now consider the superfluid more from the point of view of a macroscopically occupied quantum state Ψ. For argument sake interpret Ψ as in the basic quantum theory, but normalize Ψ so that $\Psi^*\Psi$ is equal to the superfluid density ρ_s instead of the probability density:

$$\Psi^*\Psi = \rho_s. \tag{46-3}$$

As Ψ is complex the most general form consistent with (46-3) is

$$\Psi = \sqrt{\rho_s}\, \mathrm{e}^{i\varphi}. \tag{46-4}$$

That the superfluid should be described with such a macroscopic wave function was first emphasized by Onsager [1] and Penrose [2], but no one knows the macroscopic wave equation that Ψ should obey. Never-

Notes p. 285

theless, insight can be gained by investigating the single particle Schrödinger equation:

$$i\hbar\frac{\partial \Psi}{\partial t} = -\frac{\hbar^2}{2m}\nabla^2\Psi + m\Omega\Psi, \tag{46-5}$$

where $m\Omega$ is an external potential. Substituting (46-4) into (46-5) yields for the real and imaginary parts:

$$\frac{\partial \rho_s}{\partial t} + \nabla\cdot\left(\rho_s\frac{\hbar}{m}\nabla\varphi\right) = 0, \tag{46-6}$$

$$\frac{D_s\boldsymbol{v}_s}{Dt} = -\nabla\left(\Omega - \frac{\hbar^2}{2m^2}\frac{\nabla^2\sqrt{\rho_s}}{\sqrt{\rho_s}}\right), \tag{46-7}$$

where we have introduced

$$\boldsymbol{v}_s = \frac{\hbar}{m}\nabla\varphi. \tag{46-8}$$

This expression for $\boldsymbol{v}_s$ is suggested by the continuity equation (46-6) where $\hbar\nabla\varphi/m$ is seen to be the velocity of the superfluid particles. This transcription of the Schrödinger equation to hydrodynamic form was first presented by Madelung [3].

Equations (46-6,7) are certainly not the two fluid theory but they contain quite elegantly the macroscopic quantum ideas. For instance (46-8) is the basic equation

$$\nabla \times \boldsymbol{v}_s = 0, \tag{46-9}$$

which Landau always supplemented his theory with and which is consistent with it. Experiments which verify this condition were discussed in § 30.

From the fact that the wave function Ψ must be single valued upon going around a hole in the fluid leads to

$$\varphi = n\theta + f(\boldsymbol{r}),$$

where $f(\boldsymbol{r})$ is single valued so that

$$\oint \boldsymbol{v}_s \cdot d\ell = nh/m, \tag{46-10}$$

where we have used (46-8). From the quantum approach the condition (46-10) is obtained quite easily. This is the relation that introduces Planck's constant into the macroscopic *dynamics*.

Notes p. 285

The conditions (46-9,10) which are motivated by the ordinary quantum theory are consistent with the two fluid theory. In the quantum theory one generally imposes a boundary condition on Ψ, for instance

$$\Psi \to 0 \text{ at a boundary.} \tag{46-11}$$

For present purposes this suggests

$$\rho_s \to 0 \text{ at a boundary,} \tag{46-12}$$

which in fact we invoked in § 41 to obtain an understanding of the observed third sound velocities. This condition (46-12) is *inconsistent* with the two fluid theory. As mentioned ρ_s according to this theory must be considered to be a function of p, T, $(\boldsymbol{v}_n - \boldsymbol{v}_s)^2$. With T constant and $v_n = v_s = 0$ as in a film one has $\rho_s = \rho_s(p)$. At temperatures away from T_λ there is no pressure for which $\rho_s(p) = 0$ thus demonstrating the inconsistency of (46-12) and the two fluid theory. Our discussion so far is summarized by the first three lines of Table 1. A basic question in He II research is to find the single theory which unifies the macroscopic quantum ideas such as (46-10,12) with the Landau two fluid hydrodynamics.

TABLE 1

Macroscopic quantum effect	Microscopic analogue	Consistency of the macroscopic quantum effect with the Landau two fluid theory
$\nabla \times \boldsymbol{v}_s = 0$		consistent
$\oint \boldsymbol{v}_s \cdot d\boldsymbol{\ell} = nh/m$	$\oint p\, dq = nh$	consistent
$\rho_s \to 0$ at a boundary	$\Psi \to 0$ at a boundary	inconsistent
$\Delta v_{s,i} \Delta r_i \approx \hbar/2m$	$\Delta p \Delta q \approx \hbar/2$	inconsistent

It appears that the Landau two fluid hydrodynamics may be the WKB or 'classical' limit of the complete quantum hydrodynamics of He II. In the WKB approximation the term in $\nabla^2 \sqrt{\rho_s}$ is dropped from (46-7). Not only does this make (46-7) look more like (4-3) but since this term has been dropped one can no longer impose a boundary condition on ρ_s [i.e., (46-11)] which is just the case in the two fluid hydrodynamics.

Notes p. 285

Also in the WKB approximation while one loses (46-11) one retains the quantization of the adiabatic invariants. Thus perhaps the modification of the two fluid theory to include quantum boundary effects (46-12) will involve terms containing higher order derivatives in ρ_s.

One can try perhaps to work backwards and ask what is the macroscopic wave equation for Ψ interpreted as in (46-4,8) so that the real and imaginary parts yield the He II continuity and superfluid equations:

$$\frac{\partial \rho}{\partial t} + \nabla \cdot (\rho_s \boldsymbol{v}_s + \rho_n \boldsymbol{v}_n) = 0, \tag{46-13}$$

$$\frac{\mathrm{D}_s \boldsymbol{v}_s}{\mathrm{D}t} = -\nabla(\mu + \Omega). \tag{46-14}$$

The wave equation which contains (46-13,14) is

$$i\hbar \frac{\partial \Psi}{\partial t} = -\frac{\hbar^2}{2m} \nabla^2 \Psi + \left(m\mu + m\Omega + \frac{\hbar^2}{2m} \frac{\nabla^2 \sqrt{\rho_s}}{\sqrt{\rho_s}} \right) \Psi - \frac{i\hbar}{2\rho_s} \left(\frac{\partial \rho_n}{\partial t} + \nabla \cdot \rho_n \boldsymbol{v}_n \right) \Psi. \tag{46-15}$$

This equation is not Hermitian because for He II the superfluid density is not conserved as there can be super–normal transitions. It should be compared with the WKB form of (46-5) or

$$i\hbar \frac{\partial \Psi}{\partial t} = -\frac{\hbar^2}{2m} \nabla^2 \Psi + \left(m\Omega + \frac{\hbar^2}{2m} \frac{\nabla^2 \sqrt{\rho_s}}{\sqrt{\rho_s}} \right) \Psi. \tag{46-16}$$

To go from the WKB equation (46-16) to the full Schrödinger equation amounts to dropping the term in $\nabla^2 \sqrt{\rho_s}$. One is thus tempted to adopt the same procedure with (46-15) but it is unclear how to un-WKB the Landau equations and remain consistent with the conservation principles for the two fluid system.

In the following sections we discuss some additional experiments whose validity would demonstrate shortcomings of the Landau two fluid theory.

Notes p. 285

47 *The Thickness of a Moving He II Film*

According to the two fluid thermodynamics, a moving film of He II in stable equilibrium should be thinner than the corresponding stationary film. We demonstrate this following the argument of Kantorovich [4].

Inclusion of an external field (of potential Ω) does not affect the validity of the equilibrium relations (6-12,13,14,15) between the free surface of He II and its adjoining vapor. From the hydrostatic equilibrium of the superfluid or (46-14) one finds

$$\nabla(\mu + \tfrac{1}{2}v_s^2) + \nabla\Omega = 0. \tag{47-1}$$

Use of the relation between μ and pressure (4-8)

$$d\mu = -s\,dT + \frac{1}{\rho}dp - \frac{\rho_n}{2\rho}d(\boldsymbol{v}_n - \boldsymbol{v}_s)^2 \tag{47-2}$$

yields from (47-1)

$$\frac{1}{\rho}\nabla p + \frac{\rho_s}{\rho}\nabla\tfrac{1}{2}v_s^2 + \nabla\Omega = 0, \tag{47-3}$$

where we have taken temperature constant and $v_n = 0$. Integrating (47-3) between two points 1 and 2 so that $v_s = 0$, $\Omega = 0$ at 1 yields, ignoring compressibility effects

$$\frac{1}{\rho}(p_2 - p_1) + \frac{\rho_s v_s^2}{2\rho} + \Omega_2 = 0, \tag{47-4}$$

where the subscript 2 has been dropped from v_s. Now let the points 1 and 2 be at the free surface of the film as in Fig. 50. Then from the equi-

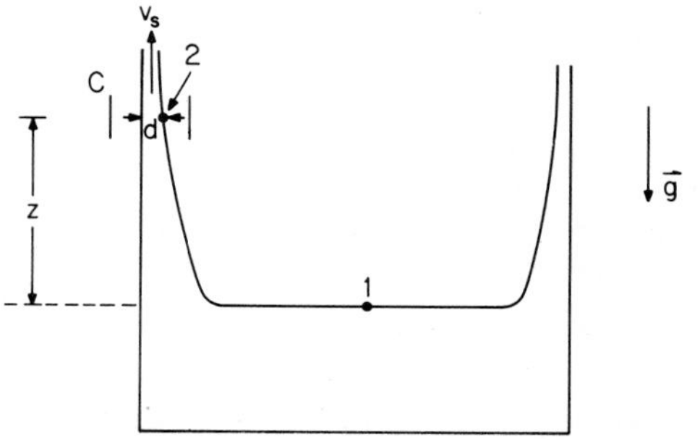

Fig. 50. The arrangement used by Keller to investigate the thickness of a moving He II film.

Notes p. 285

librium relation (6-15) the pressure in the He II at the surface equals that in the vapor. Due to the negligible vapor density, its variations in pressure caused by the external fields are negligible compared with those in the He II. Therefore

$$p_2 = p_1, \tag{47-5}$$

so that

$$\frac{\rho_s v_s^2}{2\rho} + \Omega_2 = 0. \tag{47-6}$$

This solution satisfies *all* the requirements imposed by thermodynamics on the equilibrium state of a moving film.

The external potential derives from two causes in general, gravity, and the Van der Waals force:

$$\Omega = \Omega_g + \Omega_v, \tag{47-7}$$

or

$$\Omega = gz + \Omega_v(d),$$

where $\Omega_v(d)$ is determined by various experiments as discussed in § 41; it can be expressed approximately by (41-38).

For a stationary film the thickness d as a function of height above the bath is determined by

$$gz = -\Omega_v(d). \tag{47-8}$$

In fact this relation is sometimes used as a means of measuring the Van der Waals force [5]. From (47-6) we see that the thickness of a film is affected by its motion, in that it should become thinner. To first order in the change in thickness δd of the film one obtains

$$\delta d = -\frac{\rho_s v_s^2}{2\rho}\left[\frac{\partial \Omega_v(d)}{\partial d}\right]^{-1}, \tag{47-9}$$

for velocities of the order of 40 cm/sec the change should be 20 layers or roughly 25 percent change in thickness.

This experiment was performed by Keller [6] who measured the film thickness through the changes it would cause in the capacitance of the plates C in Fig. 50. To the accuracy of his experiment ($\sim$1 layer) he detected no change in thickness of a moving film. Furthermore he verified

Notes p. 285

by the use of standpipes (see § 30) that the critical velocity was not exceeded. Otherwise our considerations would be seriously complicated by the phase slip $\partial\phi/\partial t$ [see (4-12)] which was here ignored. The presence of vorticity, as occurs above the critical velocity, would prevent any meaningful comparison of his results with the Landau two fluid thermohydrodynamics.

As the films are in the vicinity of 80 layers thick and since this is a zeroth order result it poses a definite contradiction with the Landau two fluid theory. However, there are experiments which claim to observe the Bernoulli film thinning. Especially notable are the measurements of Verbeek et al. who see a thinning within 30% of that predicted by (47-9) in a film brought into a state of persistent flow [14]. For a persistent current $\partial\phi/\partial t$ is negligible and the flow is undoubtedly steady. On the other hand there are experiments by Telschow who measures the film thickness via the Doppler shift of third sound propagating with and against an imposed superflow. He can unambiguously define the critical velocity (§ 42) and also knows that his flows are subcritical, and finds the thickness unchanged [15].

This controversial experimental situation can perhaps best be resolved by measurements of the free surface of *bulk* He II when $\boldsymbol{v}_n \neq \boldsymbol{v}_s$. For instance can one see the dimple where a quantized vortex meets the free surface? Will superfluid accelerated through a converging channel with $v_n = 0$ show a drop in the free surface to a lower gravitational potential? Also what will be the shape of the free surface of rotating He II when $v_s = 0$, $\boldsymbol{v}_n = \boldsymbol{\omega} \times \boldsymbol{r}$? Such states have been obtained in metastable situations for rather high ω by Reppy and Lane [8]. In this case (47-1,2) yield

$$\frac{1}{\rho}\nabla p - \frac{\rho_n}{\rho}\nabla\tfrac{1}{2}v_n^2 + \nabla gz = 0. \qquad (47\text{-}10)$$

Taking pressure constant along the free surface (47-10) yields for the height z of a point on the surface a distance r from the axis of rotation (Fig. 51):

$$z = \frac{\rho_n}{\rho}\frac{\omega^2 r^2}{2g}, \qquad (47\text{-}11)$$

which is parabolic but shrunken in the factor of ρ_n/ρ from what is found in a classical fluid. To determine whether the meniscus shrinks as a result of $\boldsymbol{v}_n \neq \boldsymbol{v}_s$ one must be prepared to measure its shape as well as the angular momentum of the He II. Otherwise an observation of a

Notes p. 285

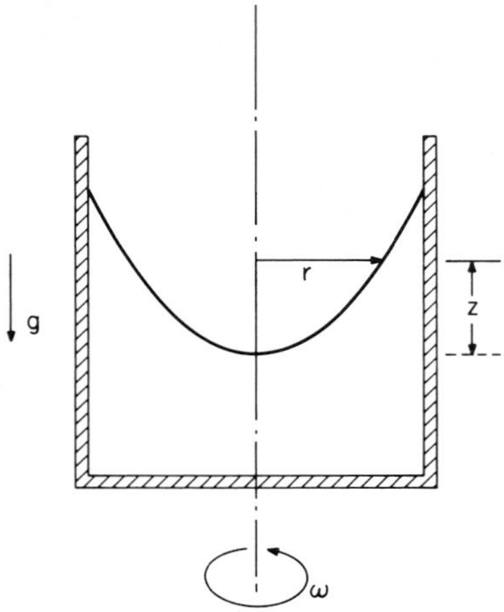

Fig. 51. The parabolic meniscus of a rotating fluid.

classical meniscus could be due either to the absence of the Bernoulli effect or to rotation induced by vortex lines [9]. An observation of a classical meniscus when $v_s = 0$ would be an historic irony since the earliest experiments which led to the rotation paradox measured the free surface [13].

Various ideas have been advanced to explain the tentative possibility that the Bernoulli law does not in some situations affect the shape of the free surface. It has been noted that the pressure in the vapor near a Bernoulli thinned film is greater than the saturated vapor pressure (of stationary He II) and that this might cause gas to condense affecting the observed thickness [16]. We have seen, however, that the Bernoulli thinned film satisfies all the requirements of thermodynamic equilibrium and is thus a stable solution. The vapor pressure like the other thermodynamic variables can depend on $(\boldsymbol{v}_n - \boldsymbol{v}_s)^2$ [10]. It has also been suggested that a small velocity dependent surface tension can affect the meniscus [17] but this theory leads to a third sound Doppler shift in clear disagreement with experiment. Finally based upon our analysis of third sound (§ 41) and the macroscopic wave function approach it seems reasonable to expect a boundary condition on ρ_s at the free surface [e.g. (46-12)] where all quantities had to be evaluated in order to obtain (47-6) from (47-4). The quantum stresses involved in bringing ρ_s to zero are not included in the Landau two fluid theory and might also affect the meniscus [7].

Notes p. 285

48 *A Macroscopic Quantum Uncertainty Principle for Superfluid Helium*

In many experiments it becomes impossible to observe the super properties of He II when the geometry is too constrained. For instance, below an onset thickness in films it is impossible to observe persistent currents, third sound (§ 41) or thermally induced superflow (§ 42). A close analysis reveals that the onset point is actually somewhat a matter of taste as in third sound experiments where the absorption increases dramatically as onset is approached. The point at which the third sound no longer propagates is in part a reflection of how strongly it can be driven and how sensitive are the receivers. Thus, the physical quantity of interest as far as third sound is concerned is the attenuation.

In § 41 we remarked that the measured attenuation of third sound is in complete conflict with that which follows from the two fluid hydrodynamics. Here we will interpret these experiments in terms of a macroscopic quantum uncertainty principle to be applied to the superfluid motions.

As continually emphasized, the two fluid theory is analogous to the old quantum theory where the Bohr–Sommerfeld quantization

$$\oint p \, \mathrm{d}q = nh \tag{48-1}$$

was employed to pick out of the classical or deterministic description the allowed states of the system. For He II the Onsager quantization

$$\oint \boldsymbol{v}_\mathrm{s} \cdot \mathrm{d}\boldsymbol{\ell} = nh/m \tag{48-2}$$

is used to pick out the allowed states of the deterministic two fluid hydrodynamics. Just as the old quantum theory had to be replaced by a theory which took into account the wave particle duality, one expects to have to modify the He II hydrodynamics to include a macroscopic wave particle duality. The incorporation of wave particle duality in the ordinary quantum theory is most simply reflected by the uncertainty principle:

$$\Delta p \, \Delta q \gtrsim \tfrac{1}{2}\hbar. \tag{48-3}$$

Comparison of (48-1) with (48-2) suggests for He II the macroscopic uncertainty relation [11]

$$\Delta v_{\mathrm{s},i} \, \Delta r_i \approx \hbar/2m \tag{48-4}$$

as is shown in the last line of Table 1.

Notes p. 285

The role of the uncertainty principle in understanding the unusual properties of He II was always emphasized by London, who showed that it was the zero point motion of the *individual* He^4 atoms which prevented it from solidifying as the temperature was lowered at the vapor pressure. The fact that a system is fluid or solid is certainly macroscopic, but (48-4) is still a stronger uncertainty relation since it says that the uncertainty or zero point motion of the superfluid atoms is *coherent* or in phase. In a dilute gas one expects that the degrees of freedom will be quantized according to (48-1) and exhibit dispersion according to (48-3). However, for this gas the particles will be randomly distributed over the quantum states so that the overall hydrodynamics is the same as Newtonian hydrodynamics. For a superfluid this is true of the normal fraction, but the superfraction will coherently sit in the same quantum state and exhibit a macroscopic quantization and macroscopic uncertainty motion.

To apply (48-4) to the helium film we first note that if d is the total thickness of the film, then the uncertainty in location of a superfluid particle is

$$\Delta y = (d - D)/\sqrt{12}, \tag{48-5}$$

where we assume that all locations are equally likely and D is the non-superfluid part of the film. In this way the uncertainty in superfluid velocity perpendicular to the substrate is

$$\Delta v_{s,y} \approx \frac{\hbar}{2m\Delta y} = \frac{\hbar\sqrt{12}}{2m(d - D)}. \tag{48-6}$$

When the uncertainty in velocity becomes comparable with or greater than the third sound velocity u_3 one expects the uncertainty motion to wash out the third sound wave. In this way we arrive at the onset criterion for d:

$$\Delta v_{s,y} \geqslant u_3, \tag{48-7}$$

or

$$u_3(d - D) \geqslant \frac{\hbar\sqrt{12}}{2m}. \tag{48-8}$$

For $T = 1.315\ ^\circ$K where $D = 2$ layers the onset thickness predicted by (48-8) is 4 layers and the observed onset is 3 layers.

In Fig. 52 is graphed $u_3(d - D)$ versus film thickness d. Not only is (48-8) satisfied when the film is too thin, but also when it is too thick!

Notes p. 285

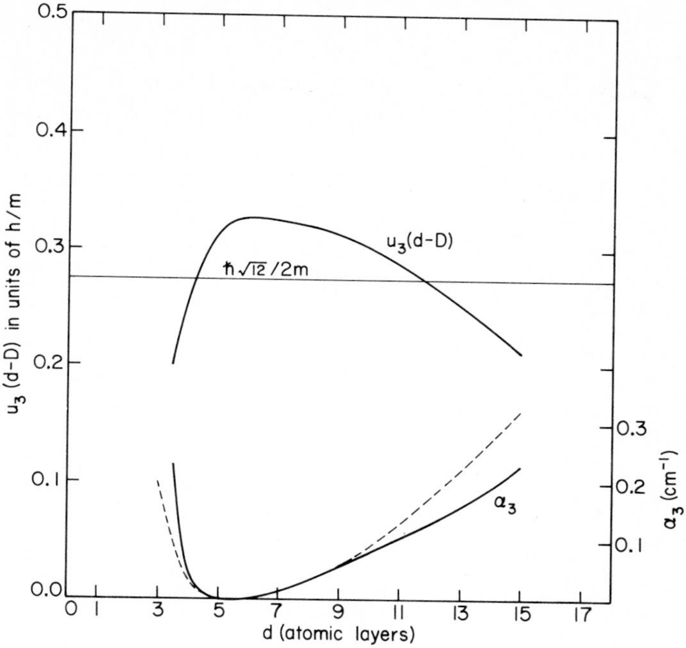

Fig. 52. The observed speed of third sound, multiplied by the experimentally determined $(d - D)$ versus film thickness d. Also shown is the measured attenuation in excess of that determined from the two fluid hydrodynamics. The dashed line is the calculated absorption as determined from the macroscopic uncertainty relation for He II. Experiments were performed at 200 c.p.s.

The absorption α_3 of the third sound is also plotted (after subtracting out the generally small hydrodynamic contribution) and shows a large increase for the thick as well as the thin films.

Of course these arguments are dimensional analysis. Now we present a calculation of the absorption working from the macroscopic uncertainty relation (48-4) and the two fluid hydrodynamics. At best such a calculation is to be considered suggestive since the uncertainty relation is inconsistent with the two fluid hydrodynamics.

The uncertainty relation (48-4) leads to a zero point motion of the free surface which means that film thickness will be wiggling around the average d. Third sound velocity depends on the local film thickness so that the third sound wave impressed on this zero point motion equilibrium state will have large gradients in velocity. In fact the wiggle in the

Notes p. 285

surface causes the formation of shock waves which lead to a quantum mechanical attenuation of the third sound.

To calculate this effect, first estimate the wiggle in film thickness d' by equating the zero point kinetic energy to the change in potential energy:

$$\frac{\partial \Omega_v(d)}{\partial d} d' = \frac{\bar{\rho}_s}{\rho} \frac{(\Delta v_s)^2}{2} \approx \frac{\bar{\rho}_s}{\rho} \frac{3\hbar^2}{m^2(d - D)^2}. \tag{48-9}$$

As stated, the third sound which is introduced is not propagated with respect to a flat quiescent film, but with respect to one with possibly large variations in thickness. Hence, in calculating the absorption, one should take into account the deformation of the wave due to non-linear effects.

As discussed in § 8 for the special case of second sound, various points on the profile move at different velocities when non-linear effects are included. The speed of third sound at a point in the fluid where the amplitude is ξ' is

$$u_3 = u_{3,0} + \frac{\partial u_3}{\partial p} p' + \frac{\partial u_3}{\partial T} T' + \frac{\partial u_3}{\partial d} \xi' + \frac{\partial u_3}{\partial v_s} v_s' \equiv u_{3,0} + \frac{\mathrm{d}u_3}{\mathrm{d}\xi} \xi', \tag{48-10}$$

where $u_{3,0}$ is the stationary (zeroth order) speed of third sound, and we have used the fact that in a sound wave all quantities are related.

Due to non-linearities, the crests of the wave travel at different velocities than the troughs. When they overtake each other, shock waves will form whose dissipation we now calculate for the stable saw tooth form, shown in Fig. 53. The circles indicate points of zero amplitude and

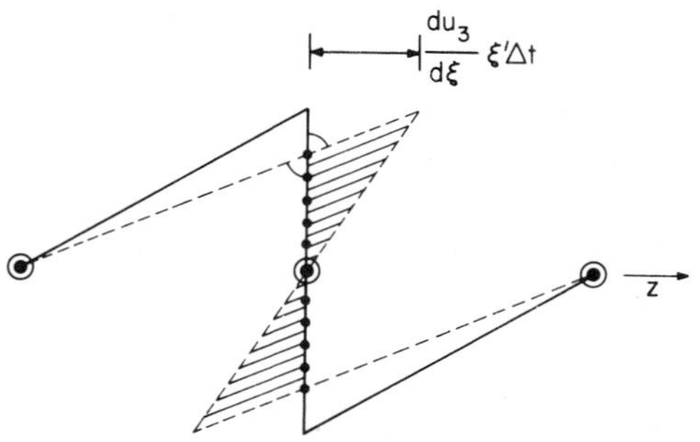

Fig. 53. A representation of the wave front of a saw-tooth shock wave. As points of different amplitude move at different velocities the amplitude of the shock diminishes in time.

Notes p. 285

the solid line indicates the wave profile as seen by an observer travelling with velocity $u_{3,0}$ at time t. At time $t + \Delta t$, Eq. (48-10) implies that the wave form will be given by the dashed lines. This situation is unphysical since it implies that the independent variables have become multiple valued. What actually happens is that the wave has spilled over so that the shaded rarefactions and compressions have cancelled leaving the dotted line as the true wave front at time $t + \Delta t$. Thus the wave has diminished in amplitude. By considering similar triangles with the common indicated angle:

$$\frac{\partial \xi'}{\partial t} = -\frac{k}{\pi}(\xi')^2 \left|\frac{du_3}{d\xi}\right|, \tag{48-11}$$

where the absolute value is taken so as to insure that a shock wave dissipates regardless of whether the shock forms at the leading or trailing edge. Equation (48-11) yields the time derivative for an observer moving with the wave. In the laboratory frame we have

$$\frac{\partial \xi'}{\partial z} = -\frac{\omega(\xi')^2}{\pi u_3^2}\left|\frac{du_3}{d\xi}\right|. \tag{48-12}$$

The impressed third sound wave of amplitude y' sits on top of the omnipresent zero point oscillations of amplitude d' so the total amplitude of the travelling wave is then

$$\xi' = d' + y'. \tag{48-13}$$

However, it is only the impressed wave which dissipates as the zero point motion certainly is not converted into entropy. Thus in substituting (48-13) into (48-12) one must correct for the absorption of the zero point motion by subtracting

$$\frac{\partial d'}{\partial z} = -\frac{\omega(d')^2}{\pi u_3^2}\left|\frac{du_3}{d\xi}\right|, \tag{48-14}$$

to obtain

$$\frac{\partial y'}{\partial z} = -\frac{\omega[(y')^2 + 2y'd']}{\pi u_3^2}\left|\frac{du_3}{d\xi}\right|. \tag{48-15}$$

In general $y' \ll d'$ so we find an *exponential* decay given by an absorption coefficient

Notes p. 285

$$\alpha_3 = \frac{2\omega d'}{\pi u_3^2}\left|\frac{\mathrm{d}u_3}{\mathrm{d}\xi}\right|. \tag{48-16}$$

Experimentally the observed attenuation is weakly dependent on frequency and may be either linear in ω or perhaps proportional to $\sqrt{\omega}$. Substituting from (48-9) for d' yields

$$\alpha_3 = \frac{6\omega}{\pi u_3^2}\left(\frac{\rho_s}{\rho}\right)^2 \frac{\hbar^2}{m^2 u_3^2 d}\left|\frac{\mathrm{d}u_3}{\mathrm{d}\xi}\right|. \tag{48-17}$$

To complete the expression for α_3 we calculate $\mathrm{d}u_3/d\xi$ for an isothermal third sound wave. From (41-10,19) the relationship between p', v_s', ξ' is

$$v_s' = \frac{u_3}{\bar{\rho}_s/\rho}\frac{\xi'}{d}, \tag{48-18}$$

$$p' = \rho u_3 v_s', \tag{48-19}$$

The term $(\partial u_3/\partial p)p'$ is of order u_3^2/u_1^2 when compared with the other terms and will be neglected. From (41-28) we have

$$\frac{\partial u_3}{\partial d} = \frac{(\rho_s/\rho)u_3}{2(\bar{\rho}_s/\rho)d}\left(\frac{4D}{d} - 3\right). \tag{48-20}$$

The Doppler shift of third sound determines $\partial u_3/\partial v_s$ or

$$\frac{\partial u_3}{\partial v_s} = \frac{1}{2}\left(\frac{\bar{\rho}_s}{\rho} + \frac{\rho_s}{\rho}\right), \tag{48-21}$$

where we have used (42-14) but have dropped the terms multiplied by $(\partial\Omega_v/\partial d)d$ since they lead to a correction of a maximum of 10% (decrease).

Substituting (48-21,20) into (48-10) yields

$$\frac{\mathrm{d}u_3}{\mathrm{d}\xi} = \frac{(\rho_s/\rho)u_3}{2(\bar{\rho}_s/\rho)d}\left(\frac{3D}{d} - 1\right), \tag{48-22}$$

so that the absorption of third sound is finally

$$\alpha_3 = \frac{3\omega}{\pi u_3}\left(\frac{\rho_s}{\rho}\right)^2 \frac{\hbar^2}{m^2 u_3^2 d(d-D)}\left|\frac{3D}{d} - 1\right|. \tag{48-23}$$

This calculated absorption of third sound is given by the dashed line in Fig. 52. The agreement is good at all thicknesses, in particular there is

Notes p. 285

a thickness $d = 3D$ at which the quantum corrections to third sound absorption vanish. At this thickness the non-linear corrections to third sound velocity $du_3/d\xi$ is zero.

If the absorption of a wave is so large that it decays to 1/e of its amplitude in travelling a wavelength then it has become diffusive rather than propagating. The thickness for which this happens can be used to determine a frequency independent onset condition by

$$\alpha_3 = \omega/u_3,$$

or:

$$u_3^2 = \frac{3}{\pi}\left(\frac{\rho_s}{\rho}\right)^2 \frac{\hbar^2}{m^2 d(d-D)}\left|\frac{3D}{d} - 1\right|, \tag{48-24}$$

which is a generalization of (48-8).

A striking result is that the fluid uncertainty principle leads to a large attenuation in the thick as well as the thin films. This happens because the Van der Waals force decreases more rapidly with d than does the zero point motion.

Since third sound is analogous to long gravity waves we now investigate the effects of the uncertainty principle on the propagation of such waves. First dimensionally we find the critical thickness below which the uncertainty in v_s becomes greater than the speed of a long gravity wave:

$$\Delta v_{s,y} \geqslant u_{g'}. \tag{48-25}$$

This thickness is

$$d < \left[\frac{3\hbar^2}{m^2 g(\rho_s/\rho)}\right]^{1/3} \tag{48-26}$$

where as with third sound we consider gravity waves where $v_n = 0$ or the frequency must be such that

$$d < \sqrt{2\eta/\omega\rho_n}, \tag{48-27}$$

so that

$$u_{g'} = \sqrt{(\rho_s/\rho)gd}. \tag{48-28}$$

At low temperatures (48-26) implies that the uncertainty motion will wash out these long gravity waves when

$$d < 4 \times 10^{-4}\ \text{cm}, \tag{48-29}$$

which is certainly a macroscopic geometry.

Notes p. 285

An application of a condition similar to (48-25) to classical fluids would yield a thickness below which the zero point motion of the individual degrees of freedom would contain greater energy than the driving potential of the long gravity wave. However, for the classical fluid this would be of no consequence to the propagation of the gravity waves as the uncertainty motion of the individual degrees of freedom would be incoherent. The uncertainty in the degrees of freedom would not reflect themselves in the macroscopic fluid velocity. This is in contrast to He II where the coherent uncertainty reflects itself in v_s.

By the same procedure whereby we calculated the absorption of third sound we find for the gravity waves

$$\alpha_{g'} = \frac{2\omega d'}{\pi (u_{g'})^2} \left| \frac{du_{g'}}{d\xi} \right|, \tag{48-30}$$

where now

$$gd' \approx \frac{\rho_s}{\rho} \frac{(\Delta v_s)^2}{2} \approx \frac{\rho_s}{\rho} \frac{3\hbar^2}{m^2 d^2}, \tag{48-31}$$

$$\frac{du_{g'}}{d\xi} = \frac{3u_{g'}}{2d}, \tag{48-32}$$

so that the contribution of zero point motion to the absorption is

$$\alpha_{g'} = \frac{9\omega}{\pi} \left(\frac{\rho_s}{\rho} \right)^2 \frac{\hbar^2}{m^2 (u_{g'})^3 d^2}, \tag{48-33}$$

and the thickness at which the wave becomes diffusive is determined by

$$(u_{g'})^2 = \frac{9}{\pi} \left(\frac{\rho_s}{\rho} \right)^2 \frac{\hbar^2}{m^2 d^2}. \tag{48-34}$$

The absorption increases dramatically as d diminishes. Experiments on this macroscopic quantum effect remain to be performed.

It may turn out that the uncertainty relation (48-4) or zero point motion is related to the need for a boundary condition on the wave function. To see how this may come about, consider the Madelung transformation (46-4) of the momentum conservation law implied by the Schrödinger equation:

Notes p. 285

$$\frac{\partial \rho_s v_{s,i}}{\partial t} + \frac{\partial}{\partial r_j}\left[\rho_s v_{s,i} v_{s,j} + \frac{\hbar^2}{2m^2}\left(\frac{\partial\sqrt{\rho_s}}{\partial r_i}\frac{\partial\sqrt{\rho_s}}{\partial r_j} - \sqrt{\rho_s}\frac{\partial^2\sqrt{\rho_s}}{\partial r_i\, \partial r_j}\right)\right] = 0. \tag{48-35}$$

If one imposes a boundary condition on Ψ (i.e., ρ_s) then even at zero degrees the stress tensor is not zero. But in the limit of zero degrees the vapor pressure becomes arbitrarily small. Hence there might be an unbalanced force on the free surface. We conclude that a stationary free surface is perhaps inconsistent with a boundary condition on the macroscopic wave function [12]. An unbalanced force will cause the surface to wiggle, which fact we have motivated via the uncertainty relation for the fluid variables.

Notes

[1] L. Onsager, Nuovo Cimento Suppl. **6**(1949)249.
[2] O. Penrose, Phil. Mag. **42**(1951)1373.
[3] E. Madelung, Z. Phys. **40**(1927)322.
[4] V. M. Kantorovich, Zh. Eksp. Teor. Fiz. **30**(1956)805 [Sov. Phys. JETP **3**(1956)770].
[5] E. S. Sabisky and C. H. Anderson, Phys. Rev. **A7**(1973)790.
[6] W. E. Keller, Phys. Rev. Letters **24**(1970)569.
[7] S. J. Putterman and I. Rudnick, Physics Today (August 1971).
[8] J. D. Reppy and C. T. Lane, Phys. Rev. **140**(1965)A106.
[9] The experiment of R. Little and K. Atkins, Phys. Rev. Letters **19**(1967)1224, observed a shrunken meniscus in a rotating He II film which played centrifugal effects against Van der Waals forces. This experiment was performed in a turbulent, highly-non-equilibrium geometry and is difficult to interpret. Indeed, recently E. van Spronsen, H. J. Verbeek, R. de Bruyn Ouboter, K. Taconis and H. van Beelen, Physica **61**(1972) 129, have done the same experiment in a far cleaner geometry and always observed a classical meniscus.
[10] It should be clear that the inability of a moving film to become thinner must be blamed on some property of the film and not on the vapor, since the mean free path of the gas is over ten times larger than the change in thickness searched for. Furthermore Bernoulli's law implies that for a classical Euler fluid a moving film should become thinner [Eq. (47-9) with $\rho_s/\rho = 1$]. Any trouble appears to be with the Bernoulli law for He II and not with the vapor.
[11] S. J. Putterman, R. Finkelstein and I. Rudnick, Phys. Rev. Letters **27**(1971)1697. S. J. Putterman, Paper presented at Thirteenth International Conference on Low Temperature Physics, Boulder, Colorado (1972).
[12] Thus the stationary solution for the order parameter in a film, provided by V. Ginzburg and L. Pitaevskii, Zh. Eksp. Teor. Fiz. **34**(1958)1240 [Sov. Phys. JETP **7**(1958) 858], is perhaps not applicable to the He II film.
[13] D. V. Osborne, Proc. Phys. Soc. (London) **63**(1950)909.

[14] H. Verbeek, H. Mars, H. van Beelen, R. de Bruyn Ouboter and K. W. Taconis, see Chapter VI reference [25].
[15] K. Telschow, Ph. D. Thesis, UCLA (1973).
[16] E. van Spronsen, H. Verbeek, R. de Bruyn Ouboter, K. W. Taconis and H. van Beelen, Phys. Letters **45A**(1973)49; see also Addendum, J. Low Temp. Phys. (in press). G. A. Williams and R. E. Packard, Phys. Rev. Letters **32**(1974)587.
[17] D. L. Goodstein and P. G. Saffman, Proc. Roy. Soc. **A325**(1971)447. This approach has been criticized on grounds of Galilean non-covariance by D. Bergmann, Proc. Roy. Soc. **A333**(1973)261.

CHAPTER VIII

Properties of the Condensed Ideal Bose Gas

49 *The Condensation of the Ideal Bose Gas and Some Analogies with Superfluid Helium*

By this point one sees that the thermo-hydrodynamics of superfluid helium is strikingly different and more complex than that of classical fluids. Even the most steadfast hydrodynamicist cannot help but wonder how this fluid with the simplest interatomic forces has such a complex macroscopic description.

One is led to ask if there is some means by which these different macroscopic properties can be understood from the microscopic or first principles approach. For instance, how come two velocity fields are required to describe the state of this single component fluid; why is one field's circulation quantized?

The simplest model which answers these questions is that of the condensation of the non-interacting quantum gas obeying Bose statistics. We pursue this model in this chapter since it provides a very elegant explanation of the two fluid approach. As interactions are ignored this model in general provides a very poor description of the equations of state of helium, and is at best a paradigm of superfluidity.

As the temperature of a non-interacting or ideal quantum gas obeying Bose statistics is lowered past a critical temperature,

$$T_c = \frac{h^2}{2\pi m k_B}\left(\frac{N}{2.61\,V}\right)^{2/3}, \tag{49-1}$$

where N is the given number of particles in the container of volume V, a macroscopic fraction N_0/N 'condenses' into the ground state with

$$\frac{N_0}{N} = 1 - \left(\frac{T}{T_c}\right)^{3/2}, \quad \text{for } T < T_c. \tag{49-2}$$

Notes p. 348

This phase transition known as the Bose condensation was first remarked by Einstein [1] in 1924. In 1938, F. London [2] proposed that the mechanism responsible for the Bose condensation would also account for the lambda transition in liquid helium and furthermore that the unusual dynamic properties of He II (which had only just become known) could at least be qualitatively understood in terms of the condensed Bose gas.

London was motivated by his knowledge of superconductivity and his suspicion that superfluids and superconductors must be understood in terms of similar microscopic mechanisms. In many metals it is found that as the temperature is lowered past a critical temperature all resistance to the flow of a steady electric current vanishes. As London remarked, this superconductivity (to be discussed further in Chapter IX) is strikingly similar to superflow in He II. Directly related to the zero resistance of a superconductor is its diamagnetism on a macroscopic level. Namely, a (small enough) magnetic field cannot penetrate the superconductor. Diamagnetism must be rooted in quantum mechanics thus London reasoned that the transition to the superconducting state and by analogy the transition to the superfluid state must be essentially quantum phase transitions. Especially they should reflect quantum theory on a macroscopic level. The Bose condensation fulfills these requirements particularly when we note that the macroscopic fraction of particles in the ground state (49-2) all have de Broglie wavelengths on the order of the size of the container. Finally, the value of T_c (49-1) for helium parameters is 3.13 °K which is remarkably close to T_λ. London realized the immediate difficulty of understanding superconductivity and superfluidity from the same point of view, since the Bose statistics play such a crucial role and the electrons in a metal obey Fermi statistics. He hoped that this problem could be worked out in the future. As we will mention in Chapter IX, the transition to superconductivity consists of the formation or condensation of correlated *pairs* of electrons.

Motivation aside, the ideal Bose gas must then be investigated on its own to see what properties of He II it describes. In this chapter we will see that based on the condensed ideal Bose gas, one can simply understand the two fluid model, the fountain effect, $\nabla \times \boldsymbol{v}_s = 0$, the quantization of circulation, the existence of a thermal sound mode, the macroscopic quantum jumps in angular momentum that result when a bucket of superfluid is rotated, and the equilibrium relations (6-12,13,14,15) and (16-8,9,10).

Notes p. 348

Even though the ideal Bose gas provides a means of understanding many of the most interesting and unique properties of He II from the microscopic point of view, it has, except for the work of London, and Blatt and Butler [3], received little attention. This is particularly surprising since for an ideal Bose gas all calculations, starting from first principles, can be made. Also any work on interacting systems must reduce to the ideal Bose gas when the interaction is switched off.

Criticisms of the ideal Bose gas as a model for He II were first strenuously proposed by Landau [4] in 1941 and are based on the opinion that a fluid is more like a solid than a gas. For instance at the lowest temperatures, the specific heat should be characteristic of a system whose elementary excitations are phonons. These points were in fact first raised by London in 1938. One naturally expects that the values of the compressibility and other equations of state for a gas will be quite different from the strongly interacting fluid. But the new and interesting properties of He II lie mostly in its unusual dynamical properties which express relationships between space and time variations of the variables. It is with respect to these relationships that the ideal Bose gas bears a striking resemblance to He II.

An analogy with classical physics lies in attempts to understand classical hydrodynamics based on Newtonian point mechanics. No one can begin to describe the Newtonian mechanics of a classical fluid, so at best one works with the Boltzmann equation of a *dilute* gas. Here again a gas is not a fluid, the ideal gas equation of state being different from that of a fluid. But the relationships between changes in variables of the gas, or its thermo-hydrodynamics is just the Navier–Stokes hydrodynamics.

It is with this situation in mind that we in this chapter discuss the properties of the ideal Bose gas. The complete thermo-hydrodynamics are derived in § 53. We will see that the *macroscopic* theory of the ideal Bose gas is *more* complicated than the Landau two fluid theory, but it still contains many of the new properties of the He II hydrodynamics. This might turn out to be an advantage of the ideal Bose gas since as we remarked in Chapter VII, various experiments have suggested the need to more fully incorporate quantum effects in the macroscopic theory of He II.

In this section we present the mathematical derivations of (49-1,2) and other properties of an ideal Bose gas in a container at rest [5]. In the next section the basic question of how one goes from the micro-

Notes p. 348

scopic first principles to the macroscopic dynamics is introduced and discussed in terms of reduced density matrices. The behavior of a condensed ideal Bose gas in a rotating container is discussed in § 51. The hydrodynamics of a semi-classical ($T > T_c$) and condensed ($T < T_c$) ideal Bose gas is derived in §§ 52,53. Finally, some solutions to these equations are presented in § 54.

The starting point is the quantum canonical ensemble wherein the quantum-statistical expectation of a quantity q is

$$\langle q \rangle = \frac{\sum' q_m \, \mathrm{e}^{-\beta E_m}}{\sum' \mathrm{e}^{-\beta E_m}}, \tag{49-3}$$

where $\beta = 1/k_B T$, E_m is the total energy of the mth, N particle energy eigenstate and the prime on the sum indicates that the sum runs over all states with total number of particles restricted to N; q_m is the quantum expectation of q in the state m:

$$q_m = \langle m | \hat{q} | m \rangle, \tag{49-4}$$

where $\hat{q}$ is the operator corresponding to the observable q. So far we have made no use of the Bose statistics, or lack of interactions.

Probability enters quantum statistical mechanics in two ways. One is the 'classical' uncertainty as to which state the system is in. This results from incomplete knowledge of the degrees of freedom which describe the system. The other way in which probability enters is through the basic quantum uncertainty which results even when the degrees of freedom are exactly specified. The canonical ensemble (49-3) is a special case of equilibrium quantum statistical mechanics which is assumed to apply when T, N are known. In general, quantum statistics is described by the density matrix

$$\hat{w} = \sum_m |m\rangle \, w(m) \, \langle m|, \tag{49-5}$$

where $|m\rangle$ is one of the complete set of states consistent with our knowledge of the system and $w(m)$ is the quantum statistical probability that the system is characterized by state vector $|m\rangle$. The basic assumption of quantum statistical mechanics is that the density matrix provides a complete description of the system. The combined quantum and statistical expectation of an observable q is

$$\langle q \rangle = \sum_k \langle k | \hat{q} \, \hat{w} | k \rangle, \tag{49-6}$$

Notes p. 348

where $|k\rangle$ is *any* complete set of states. When the $|k\rangle$ are chosen equal to $|m\rangle$

$$\langle q\rangle = \sum_m w(m)\, q_m, \tag{49-7}$$

of which (49-3) is a special case.

When the chemical potential, $\mu = (\log Z)/\beta m$ or equivalently the *average* number of particles is known instead of the exact total number, the system is described by the grand-canonical ensemble which follows from (49-3) and where now

$$w(m) = \frac{Z^N\, \mathrm{e}^{-\beta E_m}}{\sum_j Z^N\, \mathrm{e}^{-\beta E_j}}. \tag{49-8}$$

For the grand canonical ensemble there is a probability of observing various numbers N of particles in the system. The sum now goes over a set of states $|m\rangle$ complete for all possible numbers of particles [note: $N = N(m)$]. The chemical potential is determined by the expected number of particles

$$\langle N\rangle = \frac{\sum_m Z^N N\, \mathrm{e}^{-\beta E_m}}{\sum_m Z^N\, \mathrm{e}^{-\beta E_m}} = Z\left(\frac{\partial \log G}{\partial Z}\right)_{\beta,V}, \tag{49-9}$$

where $G(Z, V)$ is the grand canonical partition function:

$$G(Z, V) = \sum_m Z^N\, \mathrm{e}^{-\beta E_m}. \tag{49-10}$$

The expected energy is similarly

$$\langle E\rangle = -\left(\frac{\partial \log G}{\partial \beta}\right)_{Z,V}. \tag{49-11}$$

If one introduces the expressions for the expected values of entropy and pressure:

$$\frac{\langle S\rangle}{k_{\mathrm{B}}} = \log G - \beta\left(\frac{\partial \log G}{\partial \beta}\right)_{Z,V} - Z \log Z\left(\frac{\partial \log G}{\partial Z}\right)_{\beta,V}, \tag{49-12}$$

$$\langle p\rangle = k_{\mathrm{B}} T\left(\frac{\partial \log G}{\partial V}\right)_{Z,\beta}, \tag{49-13}$$

Notes p. 348

then it can be shown from (49-9,11,12,13) that

$$\mathrm{d}\langle E\rangle = T\mathrm{d}\langle S\rangle + m\mu\,\mathrm{d}\langle N\rangle - \langle p\rangle\,\mathrm{d}V, \tag{49-14}$$

which is the first and second laws of thermodynamics for reversible processes. Having been led to (49-14) demonstrates that (49-9,11,12,13) are the desired relationships between the microscopic description (i.e., $|m\rangle$) and the phenomenological thermodynamics.

To derive the basic relation between pressure and chemical potential and temperature:

$$V\mathrm{d}\langle p\rangle = \langle N\rangle\,\mathrm{d}(m\mu) + \langle S\rangle\,\mathrm{d}T \tag{49-15}$$

one must *assume* that the system or in particular $k_{\mathrm{B}}T\log G$ can be made extensive by an appropriate convention. In this case (49-13) becomes

$$p = \frac{k_{\mathrm{B}}T}{V}\log G.$$

For a non-interacting gas obeying Bose symmetry the energy of a given N particle wave function is

$$\sum_k N_k\varepsilon_k, \tag{49-16}$$

where N_k is the number of particles in the kth single particle level with energy ε_k determined by the eigenstates of the Schrödinger equation:

$$-\frac{\hbar^2}{2m}\nabla^2\psi_k = \varepsilon_k\psi_k. \tag{49-17}$$

In this way (49-10) becomes

$$G(Z, V) = \sum_{N_0, N_1, \ldots} Z^N \exp\left(-\beta\sum_k N_k\varepsilon_k\right), \tag{49-18}$$

where

$$N = \sum_k N_k. \tag{49-19}$$

By straightforward transformations (49-18) leads to

$$G(Z, V) = \prod_k \frac{1}{1 - Z\,\mathrm{e}^{-\beta\varepsilon_k}} = \exp\left[-\sum_{k=0}^{\infty}\log\left(1 - Z\,\mathrm{e}^{-\beta\varepsilon_k}\right)\right], \tag{49-20}$$

where Π indicates a product. To go from (49-18) to (49-20) the Bose statistics has been explicitly used by letting N_k be unrestricted and by

Notes p. 348

assigning a weight of unity to each state. From (49-9), (49-20) the expected number is

$$\langle N \rangle = \sum_k \frac{Z}{e^{\beta\varepsilon_k} - Z}, \qquad (49\text{-}21)$$

and the expected density is

$$\rho = m\frac{\langle N \rangle}{V} = \frac{m}{V}\sum_k \frac{Z}{e^{\beta\varepsilon_k} - Z}, \qquad (49\text{-}22)$$

which shows that for the grand-canonical ensemble the expected number of particles in the kth single particle level is

$$\langle N_k \rangle = \frac{1}{e^{\beta\varepsilon_k}/Z - 1}, \qquad (49\text{-}23)$$

which is the well known Bose distribution function. This classic result (49-23) can only be justified in the grand-canonical ensemble. In the canonical ensemble (49-23) is *not* valid [6], especially as regards the Bose condensation.

Expanding (49-21) as a geometric series yields

$$\langle N \rangle = \sum_{k=0,\, n=1}^{\infty} Z^n \, e^{-n\beta\varepsilon_k}. \qquad (49\text{-}24)$$

To evaluate (49-24) we take the thermodynamic limit by expanding the volume to arbitrary size maintaining its shape. In this large volume limit Weyl's theorem [8] applies:

$$\frac{1}{V}\sum_k e^{-n\beta\varepsilon_k} = \frac{1}{\lambda^3 n^{3/2}}, \qquad (49\text{-}25)$$

where the thermal de Broglie wavelength is

$$\lambda = h/\sqrt{2\pi m k_B T}. \qquad (49\text{-}26)$$

Using this asymptotic expression in (49-24) yields

$$\frac{\langle N \rangle}{V} = \frac{1}{\lambda^3}\sum_{n=1}^{\infty}\frac{Z^n}{n^{3/2}}. \qquad (49\text{-}27)$$

Notes p. 348

Let us first consider the case of periodic boundary conditions, so that the energy of the ground state is zero. Then from (49-23) one must have

$$Z < 1, \tag{49-28}$$

otherwise the population of the ground state could be negative which is nonsense. Equation (49-27) is monotonic increasing in Z and hence (49-28) implies a maximum or critical density

$$\frac{\rho_c}{m} \equiv \frac{\langle N \rangle_c}{V} = \frac{1}{\lambda^3}\,\zeta(\tfrac{3}{2}), \tag{49-29}$$

where

$$\zeta(\tfrac{3}{2}) = 2.612... \tag{49-30}$$

is the Riemann Zeta function. Equation (49-29) says that the average density which can be considered as given in the grand-canonical ensemble cannot be larger than a critical amount. This is troublesome and of course incorrect since one can put as many particles into the box as desired.

Looking at (49-22) or (49-23) one sees that in fact for Z arbitrarily close to 1, the population of just the ground state can be made as large as desired in conflict with (49-29). Somewhere an error had to be made in deriving the critical density. This occurred when we switched the order of summation over k, n in going from (49-24) to (49-27) via Weyl's theorem. Such a switch can be justified only for a uniformly convergent series. However, $Z = 1$ is a singular point of the geometric expansion performed for the summand of (49-22), as regards the contribution only of the ground state. To overcome this difficulty the ground state must be treated separately. Thus we split it off and write

$$\langle N \rangle = \langle N_0 \rangle + \sum_{k=1}^{\infty} \langle N_k \rangle, \tag{49-31}$$

$$\langle N \rangle = \frac{Z}{e^{\beta\varepsilon_0} - Z} + \sum_{k=1,\,n=1}^{\infty} Z^n\, e^{-n\beta\varepsilon_k}. \tag{49-32}$$

One can switch the order of summations on the right hand side of (49-32) since for the excited states, the geometric series are uniformly convergent. Weyl's theorem can still be applied to the sum over k, the neglected ground state leading to a correction of order λ^3/V which

Notes p. 348

vanishes in the thermodynamic limit of arbitrarily large volume. Remembering the periodic boundary conditions ($\varepsilon_0 = 0$) (49-32) becomes

$$\langle N \rangle = \frac{Z}{1-Z} + \frac{V}{\lambda^3} \sum_{n=1}^{\infty} \frac{Z^n}{n^{3/2}}, \tag{49-33}$$

which is the basic result describing the Bose condensation. Now for any $\langle N \rangle$ there exists a value of Z so that (49-33) is satisfied.

For $\langle N \rangle > \langle N \rangle_c$ there exists a value of Z,

$$Z = 1 - \frac{1}{\langle N \rangle - \langle N \rangle_c}, \tag{49-34}$$

which is *very close* to unity and which satisfies (49-33) except for corrections of order $(1 - Z)$, which is small when $\langle N \rangle - \langle N \rangle_c$ is of order $\langle N \rangle_c$.

For an ideal Bose gas of density much less than the critical density the value of Z determined by (49-27) will be substantially less than unity thus justifying its derivation. For this case the population of the ground state will be of order $1/\langle N \rangle$ which is negligible. As the density approaches the critical density, Z increases to unity until a point is reached where the Z determined by (49-27) is unity indicating the breakdown of its derivation and the need to explicitly include the ground state population as in (49-33). For densities larger than the critical density, Z is given by (49-34) indicating that the additional particles all drop into the ground state. Now the occupation of the ground state is of the same order as the total number of particles. This transition or Bose condensation takes place over a width near $\langle N \rangle_c$ which vanishes in the limit of large volume. Instead of a critical number (49-29) can be solved for a critical temperature T_c below which the system for given average density displays the Bose condensation. This leads to (49-1). The expected occupation of the ground state follows from (49-23,33) and is given by (49-2). The expected occupation of the first excited state is down by a factor of $N^{1/3}$ from that of the ground state as is verified from (49-23) and the ideal gas spectrum (49-17). Only the ground state is macroscopically occupied.

The population of the ground state is just like the superfluid density in He II. At the critical temperature it vanishes and at 0 °K it becomes the entire density. As far as the ideal Bose gas is concerned we will

Notes p. 348

always have in mind the relations $\rho_s/\rho \leftrightarrow \langle N_0 \rangle / \langle N \rangle$ and $\rho_n/\rho \leftrightarrow \langle N \rangle_c / \langle N \rangle$.

It was based on the properties of the Bose condensation that Tisza [7] was first led in 1938 to the two fluid idea. He reasoned that since a single quantum state has become macroscopically occupied it has now become a fluid variable. Thus an additional variable would be needed in the hydrodynamics, in particular it would be important to know the drift velocity of the excitations relative to the ground state. Next Tisza reasoned that a transformation of a given microstate would be time reversible, as is Schrödinger's equation, and thus show no dissipation. Therefore a flow of the ground state relative to the excitations or boundary could take place with no friction and explain superflow. We can also note that in view of the Madelung transformation (§ 46) a macroscopically occupied quantum state immediately leads to an explanation of the quantization of circulation. As the condensate occupies a single quantum state it will not contribute to the entropy of the system, explaining the unusual thermal effects in He II. These qualitative statements will be made precise in the remainder of this chapter.

The remaining thermodynamic variables can be obtained from the Gibbs free energy

$$k_B T \log G = -k_B T \sum_{k=0}^{\infty} \log(1 - Z\,\mathrm{e}^{-\beta\varepsilon_k})$$

$$= k_B T \left[-\log(1-Z) + \frac{V}{\lambda^3} \sum_{n=1}^{\infty} \frac{Z^n}{n^{5/2}} \right], \quad (49\text{-}35)$$

where we have used (49-20,33). From (49-13) the pressure of an ideal Bose gas is then

$$\langle p \rangle = \frac{k_B T}{\lambda^3} \sum_{n=1}^{\infty} \frac{Z^n}{n^{5/2}}, \quad (49\text{-}36)$$

where the term involving $\log(1-Z)$ is at most of order $\log\langle N_0 \rangle$ (for $T < T_c$) and hence can be neglected compared with (49-36) in the limit of large volume. In the semi-classical region ($T > T_c$) one uses (49-27) to determine Z and then (49-36) determines $\langle p \rangle$. In the Bose condensed region Z is determined by (49-34) and then (49-36) becomes

$$\langle p \rangle = \frac{k_B T}{\lambda^3} \zeta(\tfrac{5}{2}), \quad (49\text{-}37)$$

Notes p. 348

where

$$\zeta(\tfrac{5}{2}) = 1.342... \tag{49-38}$$

and terms of order $1/\langle N \rangle$ compared with (49-36) have been neglected. Below T_c the pressure is a function of only the temperature. This is similar to the classical liquid–vapor phase transition where in the coexistence region the pressure is also a function only of the temperature. For the ideal Bose gas ($T < T_c$) the normal and superfluids (excitations and ground state) are the two coexistent phases, $\langle N_0 \rangle / \langle N \rangle$ represents the relative mole fractions present and the transition starts at T_c and is complete at 0 °K. The similarity stops here. For a condensed Bose gas there is no separation of phases. Even in an external field the phases cannot be geometrically separated. We will see this explicitly in § 54 for a gravitational field. For this reason the Bose condensation is referred to as condensation in momentum space. More exactly it should be referred to as condensation in energy space, since energy eigenstates become momentum eigenstates only for periodic boundary conditions.

Returning to (49-37) we see that if for given T and $\langle N \rangle$ the pressure is increased above the value (49-37) there is no solution for the volume or in fact the volume has shrunk to zero. Such a situation could not take place in a more physical interacting system.

The periodic boundary conditions which have been used lead to $\varepsilon_0 = 0$ and would thus violate the uncertainty principle for the ground state in a container of finite volume. Since the ground state is macroscopically occupied one would like to show that the boundary condition that the wave function vanish, so that $\varepsilon_0 \neq 0$, leaves the discussion of the Bose condensation unaffected. In fact if $\varepsilon_0 \neq 0$ then it is straightforward to show that

$$Z = e^{\beta\varepsilon_0}\left(1 - \frac{1}{\langle N_0 \rangle}\right) \tag{49-39}$$

is the desired generalization of (49-34).

The entropy follows from (49-12,35) and is

$$\langle S \rangle = \frac{5}{2}\frac{k_B V}{\lambda^3}\sum_{n=1}^{\infty}\frac{Z^n}{n^{5/2}}. \tag{49-40}$$

Notes p. 348

Below the transition temperature

$$\langle S\rangle = \frac{5}{2}\frac{k_{\mathrm{B}}V}{\lambda^3}\zeta(\tfrac{5}{2}) = \frac{5}{2}\frac{\zeta(\frac{5}{2})}{\zeta(\frac{3}{2})}k_{\mathrm{B}}\langle N\rangle_{\mathrm{c}}, \tag{49-41}$$

so that for the condensed ideal Bose gas the entropy density is proportional to the normal fluid density or

$$\rho s/\rho_{\mathrm{n}} = \text{constant}. \tag{49-42}$$

We remark that in deriving (49-40) only the contributions to G from the excitations entered. The entropy vanishes at 0 °K and furthermore from (49-41,37) one sees that ($T < T_{\mathrm{c}}$)

$$\frac{\mathrm{d}\langle p\rangle}{\mathrm{d}T} = \frac{\langle S\rangle}{V}, \tag{49-43}$$

which is related to the fact that a condensed ideal Bose gas exhibits the fountain effect. Equation (49-43) is also Clapeyron's equation for the flat isotherms (pressure is a function only of T independent of V) of this *first* order phase transition. For given T the two coexistent phases are the $V = V_{\mathrm{c}}$ and $V = 0$ phases. As with such a transition the specific heat at constant pressure is infinite. The specific heat at constant volume follows from (49-41) and is per gram ($T < T_{\mathrm{c}}$)

$$C_V = \frac{15k_{\mathrm{B}}\zeta(\frac{5}{2})}{4m\zeta(\frac{3}{2})}\langle N\rangle_{\mathrm{c}}. \tag{49-44}$$

For the grand-canonical ensemble there are large fluctuations of the density about its average value in the condensed region. These are best calculated through the expectation value of the characteristic function [5]

$$\langle \mathrm{e}^{i\xi N/V}\rangle = \sum_{N_0, N_1,\dots} Z^N \mathrm{e}^{i\xi N/V} \exp\left(-\beta \sum_k N_k \varepsilon_k\right)/G(Z, V). \tag{49-45}$$

From (49-10) this becomes

$$\begin{aligned}\langle \mathrm{e}^{i\xi N/V}\rangle &= G(Z\mathrm{e}^{i\xi/V}, V)/G(Z, V)\\ &= \exp\left[\sum_k \log(1 - Z\mathrm{e}^{-\beta\varepsilon_k}) - \sum_k \log(1 - Z\mathrm{e}^{i\xi/V}\,\mathrm{e}^{-\beta\varepsilon_k})\right]. \end{aligned}\tag{49-46}$$

For $\langle N\rangle < \langle N\rangle_{\mathrm{c}}$ so that $T > T_{\mathrm{c}}$ one can expand the logarithms in a

Notes p. 348

Taylor series and use Weyl's theorem (49-25) to obtain to lowest order in $1/N$:

$$\langle e^{i\xi N/V} \rangle = e^{i\xi \langle N \rangle / V}. \tag{49-47}$$

If we introduce the probability distribution function $w(X, \rho/m)\,dX$ which gives the probability that the number density N/V is between X and $X + dX$, when the average is given as $\rho/m = \langle N \rangle / V$ then for $T > T_c$ (49-47) implies

$$w(X, \rho/m) = \delta(X - \rho/m), \tag{49-48}$$

or that for large volume the fluctuations around the average value are zero.

For the Bose condensed state $T < T_c$ one must again be careful to treat the ground state separately. So we split off the $k = 0$ state from (49-46), but treat the other states as above with a Taylor expansion and Weyl's theorem. Then to lowest order in $1/N$ we obtain

$$\langle e^{i\xi N/V} \rangle = \exp\left[\log(1 - Z) - \log(1 - Ze^{i\xi/V}) + i\xi\rho_c/m\right], \tag{49-49}$$

where Z is given by (49-34). Putting

$$e^{i\xi/V} \approx 1 + i\xi/V$$

yields

$$\langle e^{i\xi N/V} \rangle = \frac{e^{i\xi\rho_c/m}}{1 - i\xi(\rho - \rho_c)/m}. \tag{49-50}$$

Equating powers of ξ yields all the desired moments, in fact (49-50) implies that the distribution for $T < T_c$ is

$$\begin{aligned} w(X, \rho/m) &= \frac{m}{\rho - \rho_c} \exp\left(-\frac{mX - \rho_c}{\rho - \rho_c}\right), \quad \text{for } X > \rho_c/m, \\ &= 0, \quad \text{for } X < \rho_c/m. \end{aligned} \tag{49-51}$$

For the condensed ideal Bose gas there are huge fluctuations of the density around its average value. These fluctuations are on the order of the ground state fluctuations. From (49-51) one finds for the standard deviation

$$\langle (X - \langle X \rangle)^2 \rangle^{1/2} = (\rho - \rho_c)/m. \tag{49-52}$$

Notes p. 348

This behavior is quite different from what would be expected from a classical liquid–vapor phase transition. In that case $w(X, \rho/m)$ would exhibit two δ functions, one at the density of the saturated vapor and one at the liquid density indicative of the existence of a phase separation.

50 *The Quantum Hierarchy, Reduced Density Matrices and Off Diagonal Long Range Order*

A general question in physics is that of deriving the macroscopic or collective properties from the first principles microscopic theory. This question especially applies to He II where there is no derivation of the two fluid *hydrodynamics* from first principles for *any* microscopic model.

Classically the corresponding problem consists of deriving the Euler or Navier–Stokes hydrodynamics from Newton's laws of motion applied to the microscopic degrees of freedom. This classical problem has not been solved in a self-consistent or systematic fashion when interactions must be considered [9]. From this point of view, one cannot even justify the Boltzmann equation which does yield an excellent description of a *dilute* gas for it is well known that an extension to denser systems leads to difficulties which at present have not been satisfactorily answered. These difficulties naturally limit the possible success of any microscopic theory of superfluidity.

Nevertheless, we will here derive the quantum parallel of the classical procedure [10]. Although at a certain point we will not be able to proceed further (as is the case classically) the results will indicate the essential difference between the microscopic properties of classical and superfluids. Furthermore, a derivation of the Euler equations can be obtained for a *non-interacting* system. Similarly we will in this chapter obtain a derivation of the non-interacting Bose gas hydrodynamics. While this is perhaps a partial success, it leaves the very deep problem of the approach to equilibrium unresolved. We elaborate on this problem in Chapter X.

As mentioned in § 49, the complete description of the quantum system is assumed to be contained in the density matrix (49-5)

$$\hat{w}_N = \sum_m |m\rangle \, w(m) \, \langle m|, \tag{50-1}$$

where we are now dealing with an N particle system. The combined

Notes p. 348

quantum and statistical expectation of an observable q corresponding to the operator $\hat{q}$ is

$$\langle q \rangle = \sum_k \langle k | \hat{q} \hat{w}_N | k \rangle, \tag{50-2}$$

where the statistical probability $w(m)$ that the system is in state $|m\rangle$ is assumed normalized to unity.

The development in time of the density matrix is contained in the Schrödinger equation and is the quantum Liouville equation or

$$i\hbar \frac{\partial \hat{w}_N}{\partial t} = \left\{ \sum_{i=1}^{N} - \frac{\hbar^2}{2m} (\nabla_i'^2 - \nabla_i''^2) + \sum_{i<j=2}^{N} [V(r_{ij}') - V(r_{ij}'')] \right\} \hat{w}_N, \tag{50-3}$$

where for use in hydrodynamics we have written the density matrix in coordinate representation so that

$$\hat{w}_N = \hat{w}_N(\boldsymbol{r}_1' \ldots \boldsymbol{r}_N'; \boldsymbol{r}_1'' \ldots \boldsymbol{r}_N''), \tag{50-4}$$

central force interactions have been assumed and

$$r_{ij}' = |\boldsymbol{r}_i' - \boldsymbol{r}_j'|$$

and $\nabla_i'^2$ is the Laplacian with respect to the coordinates of r_i'.

The reduced density matrix is defined by

$$w_n(\boldsymbol{r}_1' \ldots \boldsymbol{r}_n'; \boldsymbol{r}_1'' \ldots \boldsymbol{r}_n'')$$
$$= m \frac{N!}{(N-n)!} \int \hat{w}_N(\boldsymbol{r}_1' \ldots \boldsymbol{r}_n' \boldsymbol{r}_{n+1}' \ldots \boldsymbol{r}_N'; \boldsymbol{r}_1'' \ldots \boldsymbol{r}_n'' \boldsymbol{r}_{n+1}' \ldots \boldsymbol{r}_N') \, \mathrm{d}^3 r_{n+1}' \ldots \mathrm{d}^3 r_N'. \tag{50-5}$$

Its equation of motion follows from (50-3) by mathematic induction [11]:

$$i\hbar \frac{\partial w_n}{\partial t} = - \frac{\hbar^2}{2m} \sum_{i=1}^{n} (\nabla_i'^2 - \nabla_i''^2) w_n + \sum_{i<j=2}^{n} [V(r_{ij}') - V(r_{ij}'')] w_n$$
$$+ \sum_{i=1}^{n} \int [V(\boldsymbol{r}_i' - \boldsymbol{Y}) - V(\boldsymbol{r}_i'' - \boldsymbol{Y})] w_{n+1}(\boldsymbol{r}_1' \ldots \boldsymbol{r}_n' \boldsymbol{Y}; \boldsymbol{r}_1'' \ldots \boldsymbol{r}_n'' \boldsymbol{Y}) \, \mathrm{d}^3 Y. \tag{50-6}$$

The following special cases of (50-6) are important:

$$i\hbar \frac{\partial w_1}{\partial t} = - \frac{\hbar^2}{2m} (\nabla_1'^2 - \nabla_1''^2) w_1$$
$$+ \int [V(\boldsymbol{r}_1' - \boldsymbol{Y}) - V(\boldsymbol{r}_1'' - \boldsymbol{Y})] w_2(\boldsymbol{r}_1' \boldsymbol{Y}; \boldsymbol{r}_1'' \boldsymbol{Y}) \, \mathrm{d}^3 Y, \tag{50-7}$$

Notes p. 348

$$i\hbar \frac{\partial w_2}{\partial t} = -\frac{\hbar^2}{2m}(\nabla_1'^2 + \nabla_2'^2 - \nabla_1''^2 - \nabla_2''^2)w_2 + [V(r_{12}') - V(r_{12}'')]w_2$$

$$+ \int [V(\boldsymbol{r}_1' - \boldsymbol{Y}) + V(\boldsymbol{r}_2' - \boldsymbol{Y}) - V(\boldsymbol{r}_1'' - \boldsymbol{Y}) - V(\boldsymbol{r}_2'' - \boldsymbol{Y})]$$

$$\times\, w_3(\boldsymbol{r}_1'\boldsymbol{r}_2'\boldsymbol{Y}\,;\boldsymbol{r}_1''\boldsymbol{r}_2''\boldsymbol{Y})\,\mathrm{d}^3 Y. \quad (50\text{-}8)$$

From the equations of motion of w_1, w_2 one can derive the macroscopic laws of mass, momentum and energy conservation. The definition of the density matrix and normalization of the reduced density matrices shows that the mass density of fluid at point $\boldsymbol{r}_1$ is

$$\rho(\boldsymbol{r}_1) = w_1(\boldsymbol{r}_1, \boldsymbol{r}_1). \quad (50\text{-}9)$$

This relation between a fluid variable and microscopic description also follows from (50-2) and the mass density operator

$$\hat{\rho}(\boldsymbol{r}) = m \sum_{i=1}^{N} \delta(\boldsymbol{r} - \boldsymbol{r}_i). \quad (50\text{-}10)$$

Use of (50-7,9) leads to the mass conservation law

$$\frac{\partial \rho}{\partial t} + \nabla \cdot \boldsymbol{J} = 0, \quad (50\text{-}11)$$

where

$$\boldsymbol{J}(\boldsymbol{r}_1) = \frac{\hbar}{mi} \lim_{\xi_1 \to 0} \nabla_{\xi_1} w_1(\boldsymbol{r}_1, \xi_1), \quad (50\text{-}12)$$

and is equivalent to the expectation value of the operator,

$$\hat{\boldsymbol{J}}(\boldsymbol{r}) = \frac{1}{2} \sum_{j=1}^{N} [\hat{\boldsymbol{p}}_j\, \delta(\boldsymbol{r} - \boldsymbol{r}_j) + \delta(\boldsymbol{r} - \boldsymbol{r}_j)\, \hat{\boldsymbol{p}}_j],$$

where $\hat{\boldsymbol{p}}_j \equiv -i\hbar\nabla_j$. In (50-12) the more convenient variables $\boldsymbol{r}_i, \boldsymbol{\xi}_i$ have been introduced:

$$\boldsymbol{r}_i \equiv \tfrac{1}{2}(\boldsymbol{r}_i' + \boldsymbol{r}_i''), \qquad \boldsymbol{\xi}_i \equiv \boldsymbol{r}_i' - \boldsymbol{r}_i'', \quad (50\text{-}13)$$

so that

$$\boldsymbol{r}_i = \tfrac{1}{2}(2\boldsymbol{r}_i + \boldsymbol{\xi}_i), \qquad \boldsymbol{r}_i'' = \tfrac{1}{2}(2\boldsymbol{r}_i - \boldsymbol{\xi}_i), \quad (50\text{-}14)$$

and

$$\nabla = \nabla' + \nabla'', \qquad \nabla_\xi = \tfrac{1}{2}(\nabla' - \nabla''), \qquad \nabla \cdot \nabla_\xi = \tfrac{1}{2}(\nabla'^2 - \nabla''^2). \quad (50\text{-}15)$$

Notes p. 348

By the function $w_n(\boldsymbol{r}_i, \xi_i)$ we mean the function obtained by transforming the variables of $w_n(\boldsymbol{r}'_i, \boldsymbol{r}''_i)$ according to (50-13). The process of taking $\boldsymbol{r}''_1$ equal to $\boldsymbol{r}'_1$ (or letting $\xi_1 \to 0$) does not commute with differentiation with respect to ξ_1 and this accounts for the form of (50-12).

The mass current density $\boldsymbol{J}$ is also the momentum density. From the equation of motion for w_1 (50-7) one obtains the momentum conservation law

$$\frac{\partial J_\alpha}{\partial t} + \frac{\partial}{\partial r_{1\alpha}} P_{\alpha\beta} = 0, \tag{50-16}$$

where

$$P_{\alpha\beta}(\boldsymbol{r}_1) = -\frac{\hbar^2}{m^2}\lim_{\xi_1\to 0} \nabla_{\xi_{1\alpha}}\nabla_{\xi_{1\beta}} w_1(\boldsymbol{r}_1, \xi_1)$$

$$-\frac{1}{2m}\int \mathrm{d}^3 Y \frac{\mathrm{d}V(\boldsymbol{Y})}{\mathrm{d}|\boldsymbol{Y}|}\frac{Y_\alpha Y_\beta}{|\boldsymbol{Y}|^2}\int_0^{|\boldsymbol{Y}|} \mathrm{d}v\, \rho_2\left[\boldsymbol{r}_1 + (v - |\boldsymbol{Y}|)\frac{\boldsymbol{Y}}{|\boldsymbol{Y}|}, \boldsymbol{r}_1 + v\frac{\boldsymbol{Y}}{|\boldsymbol{Y}|}\right], \tag{50-17}$$

and

$$\rho_2(\boldsymbol{r}_1, \boldsymbol{r}_2) \equiv w_2(\boldsymbol{r}_1\boldsymbol{r}_2, \boldsymbol{r}_1\boldsymbol{r}_2). \tag{50-18}$$

By $\rho_2(\boldsymbol{r}_1 + \boldsymbol{a}, \boldsymbol{r}_1 + \boldsymbol{b})$ is meant $\rho_2(\boldsymbol{r}_1, \boldsymbol{r}_2)$ with $\boldsymbol{r}_1 + \boldsymbol{a}$ substituted for $\boldsymbol{r}_1$ and $\boldsymbol{r}_1 + \boldsymbol{b}$ substituted for $\boldsymbol{r}_2$. The following relations assist the straightforward but involved derivation of (50-16,17)

$$\frac{\partial \rho_2}{\partial v} = \frac{\partial \rho_2}{\partial r_{1\beta}}\frac{Y_\beta}{|\boldsymbol{Y}|}, \quad \text{(sum over } \beta\text{)}, \tag{50-19}$$

$$\rho_2(\boldsymbol{r}_1, \boldsymbol{r}_1 + \boldsymbol{Y}) - \rho_2(\boldsymbol{r}_1 - \boldsymbol{Y}, \boldsymbol{r}_1)$$

$$= \int_0^{|\boldsymbol{Y}|} dv \frac{\partial}{\partial v}\rho_2\left[\boldsymbol{r}_1 + (v - |\boldsymbol{Y}|)\frac{\boldsymbol{Y}}{|\boldsymbol{Y}|}, \boldsymbol{r}_1 + v\frac{\boldsymbol{Y}}{|\boldsymbol{Y}|}\right], \tag{50-20}$$

$$\rho_2(\boldsymbol{r}_1, \boldsymbol{r}_2) = \rho_2(\boldsymbol{r}_2, \boldsymbol{r}_1),$$

$$\lim_{\xi_1\to 0} \nabla_{\xi_{1\alpha}} V(\boldsymbol{r}'_1 - \boldsymbol{r}_1 - \boldsymbol{Y}) = \frac{\mathrm{d}V(\boldsymbol{Y})}{\mathrm{d}|\boldsymbol{Y}|}\frac{Y_\alpha}{2|\boldsymbol{Y}|}. \tag{50-21}$$

Notes p. 348

From the quantum-mechanical Hamiltonian of the N particle system

$$-\frac{\hbar^2}{2m}\sum_{i=1}^{N}\nabla_i'^2+\sum_{i<j=2}^{N}V(r'_{ij}), \tag{50-22}$$

one is led to the quantum-mechanical energy density:

$$U_Q(\boldsymbol{r}_1)=-\frac{\hbar^2}{4m^2}\lim_{\xi_1\to 0}(\nabla_1'^2+\nabla_1''^2)w_1(\boldsymbol{r}'_1,\boldsymbol{r}''_1)+\frac{1}{2m}\int V(\boldsymbol{r}_1-\boldsymbol{r}_2)\,\rho_2(\boldsymbol{r}_1,\boldsymbol{r}_2)\mathrm{d}^3r_2, \tag{50-23}$$

which corresponds to the operator

$$\hat{U}_Q(\boldsymbol{r})=\frac{1}{4m}\sum_{j=1}^{N}[\hat{\boldsymbol{p}}_j^2\,\delta(\boldsymbol{r}-\boldsymbol{r}_j)+\delta(\boldsymbol{r}-\boldsymbol{r}_j)\,\hat{\boldsymbol{p}}_j^2]+\sum_{i<j=2}^{N}\delta(\boldsymbol{r}-\boldsymbol{r}_j)\,V(r_{ij}).$$

The term involving the Laplacian represents the quantum kinetic energy and the other term includes the effects of interactions. The quantum mechanical energy density is not uniquely determined from the requirements that it be real, have the proper classical limit, and lead to the same total energy as the Hamiltonian. For instance it can be modified by the divergence of a vector quantity which vanishes at infinity. In this way one can also consider the energy density:

$$U(\boldsymbol{r}_1)=-\frac{\hbar^2}{2m^2}\lim_{\xi_1\to 0}\nabla_{\xi_1}^2 w_1(\boldsymbol{r}_1,\xi_1)+\frac{1}{2m}\int V(\boldsymbol{r}_1-\boldsymbol{r}_2)\,\rho_2(\boldsymbol{r}_1,\boldsymbol{r}_2)\,\mathrm{d}^3r_2, \tag{50-24}$$

which corresponds to the operator

$$\hat{U}(\boldsymbol{r})=\frac{1}{8m}\sum_{j=1}^{N}[\hat{\boldsymbol{p}}_j^2\,\delta(\boldsymbol{r}-\boldsymbol{r}_j)+2\hat{\boldsymbol{p}}_j\,\delta(\boldsymbol{r}-\boldsymbol{r}_j)\,\hat{\boldsymbol{p}}_j+\delta(\boldsymbol{r}-\boldsymbol{r}_j)\,\hat{\boldsymbol{p}}_j^2]$$
$$+\sum_{i<j=2}^{N}\delta(\boldsymbol{r}-\boldsymbol{r}_j)\,V(r_{ij}).$$

We then have

$$U_Q(\boldsymbol{r}_1)=U(\boldsymbol{r}_1)-\frac{\hbar^2}{8m^2}\nabla_1^2\rho(\boldsymbol{r}_1). \tag{50-25}$$

There is no basis for selecting between (50-23,24). This problem will be commented upon briefly in § 52. Substitution of the time derivative of (50-24) into (50-7,8) yields the energy conservation law

Notes p. 348

$$\frac{\partial U}{\partial t} + \nabla \cdot \boldsymbol{Q} = 0, \tag{50-26}$$

where

$$\begin{aligned}
Q(\boldsymbol{r}_1)_\alpha = & -\frac{\hbar^3}{2m^3 i} \lim_{\xi_1 \to 0} \nabla^2_{\xi_1} \nabla_{\xi_{1\alpha}} w_1(\boldsymbol{r}_1, \xi_1) \\
& + \frac{\hbar}{2m^2 i} \int \mathrm{d}^3 Y \{ V(\boldsymbol{r}_1 - \boldsymbol{Y}) \lim_{\xi_1 \to 0} \nabla_{\xi_{1\alpha}} w_2(\boldsymbol{r}'_1 \boldsymbol{Y}, \boldsymbol{r}''_1 \boldsymbol{Y}) \} \\
& - \frac{\hbar}{2m^2 i} \int \mathrm{d}^3 Y \frac{\mathrm{d}V(\boldsymbol{Y})}{\mathrm{d}|\boldsymbol{Y}|} \frac{Y_\alpha Y_\beta}{|\boldsymbol{Y}|^2} \\
& \times \int_0^{|\boldsymbol{Y}|} \mathrm{d}\upsilon \lim_{\xi_2 \to 0} \nabla_{\xi_{2\beta}} w_2 \left[\boldsymbol{r}_1 + (\upsilon - |\boldsymbol{Y}|) \frac{\boldsymbol{Y}}{|\boldsymbol{Y}|}, \boldsymbol{r}_1 + \frac{\boldsymbol{Y}}{|\boldsymbol{Y}|} \upsilon; 0, \xi_2 \right].
\end{aligned} \tag{50-27}$$

By

$$w_2 \left[\boldsymbol{r}_1 + (\upsilon - |\boldsymbol{Y}|) \frac{\boldsymbol{Y}}{|\boldsymbol{Y}|}, \boldsymbol{r}_1 + \frac{\boldsymbol{Y}}{|\boldsymbol{Y}|} \upsilon; 0, \xi_2 \right]$$

we mean first form $w_2(\boldsymbol{r}_1, \boldsymbol{r}_2; \xi_1, \xi_2)$ from $w_2(\boldsymbol{r}'_1, \boldsymbol{r}'_2; \boldsymbol{r}''_1, \boldsymbol{r}''_2)$ by the variable transformation (50-13) then substitute $\boldsymbol{r}_1 + (\upsilon - |\boldsymbol{Y}|)\boldsymbol{Y}/|\boldsymbol{Y}|$ for $\boldsymbol{r}_1$, etc... When the expression (50-23) for the energy density is used, one finds that the energy flux density is

$$\boldsymbol{Q}_{\mathrm{Q}}(\boldsymbol{r}_1) = \boldsymbol{Q}(\boldsymbol{r}_1) - \frac{\hbar^2}{8m^2} \nabla_1 [\nabla_1 \cdot \boldsymbol{J}(\boldsymbol{r}_1)]. \tag{50-28}$$

The equations of motion for the reduced density matrices (50-6) along with the conservation laws form the quantum generalization of the classical hierarchy [10] of equations for the reduced distribution functions. These equations in principle provide a direct path, from the microscopic properties of the system as embodied in the density matrix, to the macroscopic dynamics as contained in (50-11,16,26). The problem (which is unsolved) is to somehow close the description.

For a classical fluid the five conservation laws are a complete set of equations, since five variables are empirically found to constitute a complete set (§ 1). The five conservation laws (50-11,16,26) derived above are not a complete set because there are no relations giving P_{ij}, $\boldsymbol{Q}$ as functions of ρ, $\boldsymbol{J}$, U. So to speak, the general conservation laws

Notes p. 348

are not yet closed. To close them, two steps are necessary; first, an ansatz about the off-equilibrium behavior of w_1 must be made so that it is characterized completely by five independent moments; second, one must provide an expression giving w_2 as a function of w_1. We note that for a non-interacting system, this second step is not necessary since the dependence on w_2 identically vanishes. In this case, one can, working from (50-11,16,26), justify the Euler (but obviously not the Navier–Stokes) equations. This we do in § 52 for an ideal Bose gas with $T > T_c$.

The above *five* conservation laws cannot possibly give a *complete* description of the hydrodynamics of a superfluid. From the phenomenological point of view, we have seen that additional variables and equations are required. From the Bose condensation we have seen that the wave function of the ground state becomes an additional macroscopic variable due to the macroscopic occupation of that quantum state. Thus the ansatz as to the off-equilibrium properties of w_1 must be quite different for a condensed ideal Bose gas; one had better *not* choose a form where it is completely characterized by five moments. Below we will calculate the equilibrium expressions for the reduced density matrix $w_1(\boldsymbol{r}_1', \boldsymbol{r}_1'')$ for an ideal Bose gas. It will be seen that as T is lowered below T_c its form changes drastically in that it acquires off diagonal long range order (ODLRO) which by definition means

$$\lim_{\xi_1 \to \infty} w_1(\boldsymbol{r}_1, \boldsymbol{\xi}_1) \neq 0. \tag{50-29}$$

The fundamentally different form of w_1 below T_c naturally lends itself to a different off-equilibrium generalization where an additional independent variable, the ODLRO, enters. The additional equations of a superfluid describe the time development of the ODLRO.

In the remainder of this section, we derive the equilibrium density matrix of the stationary ideal Bose gas [5]. In the next section we do the same for the rotating Bose gas. The 'off-equilibrium' dynamics is discussed in § 53.

The quantum hierarchy applies, as derived here, to a system with a given total number of particles. Thus the density matrix must be calculated for the canonical ensemble. From (50-1) and (49-3) we find that

$$w_N(\boldsymbol{r}_1' \ldots \boldsymbol{r}_N'; \boldsymbol{r}_1'' \ldots \boldsymbol{r}_N'') = \sum_{N_0, N_1 \ldots}' \exp\left(-\beta \sum_k N_k \varepsilon_k\right) \times \Psi_{\text{sym}}^{(N_i)}(\boldsymbol{r}_1' \ldots \boldsymbol{r}_N') \Psi_{\text{sym}}^{*(N_i)}(\boldsymbol{r}_1'' \ldots \boldsymbol{r}_N'')/Q_N(V), \tag{50-30}$$

Notes p. 348

where the canonical partition function is

$$Q_N(V) = \sum_{N_0, N_1 \dots}' \exp\left(-\beta \sum_k N_k \varepsilon_k\right), \tag{50-31}$$

the prime on the sum indicates that the total number of particles is restricted to N and by $\Psi^{(N_i)}_{\text{sym}}$ is meant the N particle Bose symmetric wave function corresponding to N_1 particles in the 1st energy level, N_2 in the second, etc. These wave functions are normalized to unity.

The reduced density matrices are defined by (50-5); forming in this way w_1 yields directly

$$\sum_{N=0}^{\infty} Z^N w_1(\boldsymbol{r}_1', \boldsymbol{r}_1'', N/V)\, Q_N(V) = m\, G(Z, V)\, A(\boldsymbol{r}_1', \boldsymbol{r}_1'', Z, V), \tag{50-32}$$

where

$$A(\boldsymbol{r}_1', \boldsymbol{r}_1'', Z, V) = \sum_k \frac{Z\psi_k(\boldsymbol{r}_1')\, \psi_k^*(\boldsymbol{r}_1'')}{e^{\beta\varepsilon_k} - Z} = \sum_k \langle N_k \rangle \psi_k(\boldsymbol{r}_1')\, \psi_k^*(\boldsymbol{r}_1''). \tag{50-33}$$

Our object, of course, is to ascertain $w_1(\boldsymbol{r}_1', \boldsymbol{r}_1'', N/V)$ where its explicit dependence on the given total number of particles is now demonstrated. Dividing (50-32) by $G(Z, V)$ we see that $mA(\boldsymbol{r}_1', \boldsymbol{r}_1'', Z, V)$ is just the average of $w_1(\boldsymbol{r}_1', \boldsymbol{r}_1'', X)$ in the grand-canonical ensemble ($X = N/V$). Thus

$$\int w(X, Z)\, w_1(\boldsymbol{r}_1', \boldsymbol{r}_1'', X)\, \mathrm{d}X = mA(\boldsymbol{r}_1', \boldsymbol{r}_1'', Z, V), \tag{50-34}$$

where $w(X, Z)$ is the probability distribution in the grand-canonical ensemble previously introduced in § 49. An inversion of (50-34) yields the desired expression for the reduced density matrix.

In the limit of large volume, the expression for $w(X, Z)$ is given by (49-48) for $T > T_c$ and in this case

$$w_1(\boldsymbol{r}_1', \boldsymbol{r}_1'') = m \lim_{V \to \infty} A(\boldsymbol{r}_1', \boldsymbol{r}_1'', Z, V). \tag{50-35}$$

For $T < T_c$, $w(X, Z)$ is given by (49-51) and to obtain w_1 one must invert the Laplace transform. The evaluation of A is based on the observation that

$$\sum_k \exp(-it\varepsilon_k/\hbar)\, \psi_k(\boldsymbol{r}_1')\, \psi_k^*(\boldsymbol{r}_1'') \tag{50-36}$$

is the Green's function of the diffusion equation (i.e., Schrödingers equation). For small t or equivalently large volume, it can be replaced by the Green's function of the infinite domain or

$$\sum_k \exp(-it\varepsilon_k/\hbar)\psi_k(\boldsymbol{r}_1')\, \psi_k^*(\boldsymbol{r}_1'') \approx (m/ith)^{3/2} \exp(im\xi_1^2/2\hbar t). \tag{50-37}$$

Notes p. 348

Now for $T > T_c$ one can evaluate A by expanding in a Taylor series and using (50-37) for the sum over states to obtain

$$w_1(\boldsymbol{r}'_1, \boldsymbol{r}''_1) = \frac{m}{\lambda^3} \sum_n \frac{Z^n}{n^{3/2}} \exp\left(- \frac{\pi \xi_1^2}{n\lambda^2} \right). \tag{50-38}$$

For $T < T_c$ one must be careful to split off the lowest state and apply (50-37) only to the excited states with now Z determined by (49-34); then

$$A(\boldsymbol{r}'_1, \boldsymbol{r}''_1) = \langle N_0 \rangle \psi_0(\boldsymbol{r}'_1)\, \psi_0^*(\boldsymbol{r}''_1) + \frac{1}{\lambda^3} \sum_n \frac{1}{n^{3/2}} \exp\left(- \frac{\pi \xi_1^2}{n\lambda^2} \right). \tag{50-39}$$

Noting that

$$\langle N_0 \rangle = (\rho - \rho_c) V/m, \tag{50-40}$$

one can invert the Laplace transform in (50-34) to obtain the first reduced density matrix ($T < T_c$):

$$w_1(\boldsymbol{r}'_1, \boldsymbol{r}''_1) = m \langle N_0 \rangle \psi_0(\boldsymbol{r}'_1)\, \psi_0^*(\boldsymbol{r}''_1) + \frac{m}{\lambda^3} \sum_{n=1}^{\infty} \frac{1}{n^{3/2}} \exp\left(- \frac{\pi \xi_1^2}{n\lambda^2} \right). \tag{50-41}$$

By the same procedure, one can also evaluate the second reduced density matrix. Instead of (50-32) one obtains

$$\sum_{N=0}^{\infty} Z^N w_2(\boldsymbol{r}'_1\boldsymbol{r}'_2, \boldsymbol{r}''_1\boldsymbol{r}''_2, N/V)\, Q_N(V)$$

$$= mG(Z, V) \left[A(\boldsymbol{r}'_1, \boldsymbol{r}''_1)\, A(\boldsymbol{r}'_2, \boldsymbol{r}''_2) + A(\boldsymbol{r}'_1, \boldsymbol{r}''_2)\, A(\boldsymbol{r}'_2, \boldsymbol{r}''_1) \right]. \tag{50-42}$$

Above T_c one then finds

$$w_2(\boldsymbol{r}'_1\boldsymbol{r}'_2, \boldsymbol{r}''_1\boldsymbol{r}''_2) = \frac{1}{m} \left[w_1(\boldsymbol{r}'_1, \boldsymbol{r}''_1)\, w_1(\boldsymbol{r}'_2, \boldsymbol{r}''_2) + w_1(\boldsymbol{r}'_1, \boldsymbol{r}''_2)\, w_1(\boldsymbol{r}'_2, \boldsymbol{r}''_1) \right], \tag{50-43}$$

whereas below T_c:

$$w_2 = \frac{1}{m} \left[w_1(\boldsymbol{r}'_1, \boldsymbol{r}''_1)\, w_1(\boldsymbol{r}'_2, \boldsymbol{r}''_2) + w_1(\boldsymbol{r}'_1, \boldsymbol{r}''_2)\, w_1(\boldsymbol{r}'_2, \boldsymbol{r}''_1) \right]$$

$$- m \langle N_0 \rangle^2 \psi_0(\boldsymbol{r}'_1)\, \psi_0^*(\boldsymbol{r}''_1)\, \psi_0(\boldsymbol{r}'_2)\, \psi_0^*(\boldsymbol{r}''_2). \tag{50-44}$$

To arrive at this result one uses the fact that the Laplace transformation of X^2 is $2/s^3$ where s is the Laplace transform variable.

Notes p. 348

The expressions (50-38,41) indicate that a fundamental change in the properties of the system takes place as the temperature is lowered past T_c. Above T_c, w_1 goes to zero as r_1' goes away from r_1''; below T_c, due to the macroscopic occupation of a single quantum state ψ_0, the system exhibits off diagonal long range order, so that the limit of w_1 for large ξ_1 is on the order of the fluid density. The higher order density matrices have the same properties as w_1.

Long range order is always characteristic of phase transitions and London [12] was the first to propose that this type of order was particularly characteristic of the quantum phase transition. This was expressed in density matrix language by Penrose [11] and Yang [13]. A classical (e.g., liquid–vapor) phase transition is characterized by long range order in the two point distribution function. This can be referred to as diagonal long range order. From (50-44,43) one can evaluate the two point distribution (50-18) for an ideal Bose gas above and below T_c: in each case

$$\lim_{|r_1 - r_2| \to \infty} \rho_2(\boldsymbol{r}_1, \boldsymbol{r}_2) = \rho^2/m. \tag{50-45}$$

There is *no* change in the diagonal long range limit as T is lowered below T_c, so that there is *no* diagonal long range order due to the transition

51 *The Rotating Condensed Ideal Bose Gas*

In Chapter II we saw that many of the most interesting and unique properties of superfluid helium manifest themselves when it is contained in a rotating bucket. For instance, at low enough velocities, the superfluid component remains at rest ignoring the walls, while the normal fluid rotates as a solid body. Under rotation, the behavior of $\boldsymbol{v}_n$ and $\boldsymbol{v}_s$ is split because of the restriction $\nabla \times \boldsymbol{v}_s = 0$. In view of these facts, and because the condensed ideal Bose gas is such a suggestive model of He II, and because rotation can be treated unambiguously as an equilibrium situation according to statistical mechanics, Blatt and Butler [3] were led to consider the behavior of a rotating condensed ideal Bose gas. We will see in this section that not only does the Bose condensation display the above properties, but it also has transitions due to the entrance of quantized vortices as the angular velocity increases.

Notes p. 348

For the observer in the inertial reference frame, Schrödingers equation will be

$$\hat{\mathscr{H}}_0 \Psi = i\hbar \partial\Psi/\partial t. \tag{51-1}$$

The wave equation which describes the development in time of the same wave function but as measured by an observer rotating at angular velocity ω is

$$(\hat{\mathscr{H}}_0 - \boldsymbol{\omega} \cdot \hat{\boldsymbol{L}})\Psi = i\hbar \partial\Psi/\partial t', \tag{51-2}$$

as follows from a coordinate transformation; $\hat{L}$ is the operator for angular momentum (relative to the inertial system), and t' is time as measured by the rotating observer ($t' = t$ *but* $\partial/\partial t \neq \partial/\partial t'$). Eigenstates of the inertial Hamiltonian have physical observables which are stationary or time independent in the inertial system. Eigenstates of the transformed Hamiltonian

$$\hat{\mathscr{H}} = \hat{\mathscr{H}}_0 - \boldsymbol{\omega} \cdot \hat{\boldsymbol{L}}, \tag{51-3}$$

will have properties stationary in the rotating system. With ω given we assume that the rotational equilibrium is described by the ensemble determined by the effective Hamiltonian (51-3). In this way, the generalized canonical ensemble (N also given) is

$$w(m) = \frac{\exp[-\beta(E - \omega L)_m]}{\sum_j{}' \exp[-\beta(E - \omega L)_j]}, \tag{51-4}$$

or the generalized grand-canonical ensemble ($\langle N \rangle$ or Z given)

$$w(m) = \frac{Z^N \exp[-\beta(E - \omega L)_m]}{\sum_j Z^N \exp[-\beta(E - \omega L)_j]}, \tag{51-5}$$

where we note again that $N = N(m)$.

In the grand-canonical ensemble the total expected angular momentum is

$$\langle L \rangle = \frac{\sum_m L_m Z^N \exp[-\beta(E - \omega L)_m]}{G(Z, V, \omega)}, \tag{51-6}$$

and points along the axis of the cylindrical rotating vessel,

$$G(Z, V, \omega) = \sum_j Z^N \exp[-\beta(E - \omega L)_j]. \tag{51-7}$$

Notes p. 348

In terms of $G(Z, V, \omega)$

$$\langle L \rangle = \frac{1}{\beta}\left(\frac{\partial \log G}{\partial \omega}\right)_{Z,V,\beta}, \tag{51-8}$$

and as before:

$$\langle N \rangle = Z\left(\frac{\partial \log G}{\partial Z}\right)_{\beta,V,\omega}. \tag{51-9}$$

For a gas of non-interacting particles the effective energy of a state with N_k particles in the single particle state k is

$$E - \omega L = \sum_k N_k(\varepsilon - \omega\hbar\ell)_k, \tag{51-10}$$

where single particle angular momentum states have eigenvalues $\ell\hbar$ (ℓ an integer). The grand-canonical partition is then

$$G(Z, V, \omega) = \exp\left[-\sum_{k=0}^{\infty} \log\{1 - Z\exp[-\beta(\varepsilon - \omega\hbar\ell)_k]\}\right] \tag{51-11}$$

which is a generalization of (49-20) to rotation. Use of (51-11) yields

$$\langle N \rangle = \sum_k \frac{Z}{\exp\beta(\varepsilon - \hbar\omega\ell)_k - Z}, \tag{51-12}$$

$$\langle L \rangle = \sum_k \frac{Z\hbar\ell_k}{\exp\beta(\varepsilon - \hbar\omega\ell)_k - Z}. \tag{51-13}$$

Evaluation of (51-13) will lead to the *total* angular momentum of the rotating Bose gas. Rather than evaluate it directly we will calculate the first reduced density matrix which contains *all* the information about this situation. The reason for this procedure is that in rotational equilibrium the thermodynamic quantities, such as the velocities, are not uniform. To describe their variations in space, one must work with the density matrix as opposed to say (51-12,13).

The N particle density matrix for rotation is

$$w_N(\mathbf{r}'_1\ldots\mathbf{r}'_N;\mathbf{r}''_1\ldots\mathbf{r}''_N) = \sum_{N_0,N_1\ldots}{}' \exp[-\beta\sum_k N_k(\varepsilon - \hbar\omega\ell)_k]$$
$$\times\, \Psi^{(N_i)}_{\text{sym}}(\mathbf{r}'_1\ldots\mathbf{r}'_N)\, \Psi^{*(N_i)}_{\text{sym}}(\mathbf{r}''_1\ldots\mathbf{r}''_N)/Q_N(V,\omega), \tag{51-14}$$

Notes p. 348

where the canonical partition function is

$$Q_N(V,\omega) = \sum_{N_0,N_1\ldots}{}' \exp\left[-\beta \sum_k N_k(\varepsilon - \hbar\omega\ell)_k\right]. \tag{51-15}$$

These relations are generalizations of (50-30,31) to rotation. Forming the first reduced density matrix, w_1, from (51-14) leads to

$$\sum_{N=0}^{\infty} Z^N w_1(\boldsymbol{r}_1', \boldsymbol{r}_1'', N/V, \omega)\, Q_N(V,\omega) = m\, G(Z, V, \omega)\, A(\boldsymbol{r}_1', \boldsymbol{r}_1'', Z, V, \omega), \tag{51-16}$$

where

$$A(\boldsymbol{r}_1', \boldsymbol{r}_1'', Z, V, \omega) = \sum_k \frac{Z\psi_k(\boldsymbol{r}_1')\,\psi_k^*(\boldsymbol{r}_1'')}{\exp\beta(\varepsilon - \hbar\omega\ell)_k - Z} = \sum_k \langle N_k\rangle \psi_k(\boldsymbol{r}_1')\,\psi_k^*(\boldsymbol{r}_1''). \tag{51-17}$$

With $A(\boldsymbol{r}_1', \boldsymbol{r}_1'')$ calculated one must invert (50-16) as in § 50 to obtain w_1. In terms of the probability distribution $w(X, N/V, \omega)$ for the density, Eq. (51-16) becomes

$$\int w(X, Z, \omega)\, w_1(\boldsymbol{r}_1', \boldsymbol{r}_1'', X, \omega)\, \mathrm{d}X = mA(\boldsymbol{r}_1', \boldsymbol{r}_1'', Z, V, \omega). \tag{51-18}$$

As in the case of the stationary Bose gas, $w(X, Z, \omega)$ describes the fluctuations in the *total* (as opposed to local) number of particles in the system. As before it is given by

$$w(X, Z, \omega) = \delta(X - \langle N\rangle/V), \tag{51-19}$$

when the system is not Bose condensed, and

$$\begin{aligned} w(X, Z, \omega) &= \frac{V}{\langle N_0\rangle} \exp\left(-\frac{XV - \langle N\rangle_c}{\langle N_0\rangle}\right), \quad \text{for } X > \langle N\rangle_c/V, \\ &= 0, \quad \text{for } X < \langle N\rangle_c/V, \end{aligned} \tag{51-20}$$

when the system is Bose condensed. The dependence of $\langle N_0\rangle$, $\langle N\rangle_c$ on β, ω, V, Z for rotation will be determined below.

To evaluate A for the semi-classical region expand in a geometric series to obtain

$$A(\boldsymbol{r}_1', \boldsymbol{r}_1'', Z, V, \omega) = \sum_{k,n} Z^n \exp\left[-n\beta(\varepsilon - \hbar\omega\ell)_k\right]\psi_k(\boldsymbol{r}_1')\,\psi_k^*(\boldsymbol{r}_1''). \tag{51-21}$$

We have in mind that the ψ_k are the Bessel function solutions to (51-3) appropriate to the cylindrical symmetry. Hence

$$\psi_k = C_k\, J_\ell(k_{n\ell} r/R)\, \mathrm{e}^{i\ell\theta} \cos(\pi p z/H), \tag{51-22}$$

Notes p. 348

where C_k is a normalization constant chosen so that

$$\int \psi_k \psi_k^* \, \mathrm{d}V = 1 \tag{51-23}$$

and R is the radius of the bucket of height H. If one works with the boundary condition that $\nabla_\perp \psi = 0$ at the boundaries then the $k_{n\ell}$ are roots of

$$J'_\ell(x) = 0, \tag{51-24}$$

if $\psi = 0$ at the boundaries the $k_{n\ell}$ are roots of

$$J_\ell(x) = 0. \tag{51-25}$$

In view of (51-22), (51-21) can be written:

$$A(\boldsymbol{r}'_1, \boldsymbol{r}''_1, Z, V, \omega) = \sum_n Z^n \exp\left(- in\beta\hbar\omega \frac{\mathrm{d}}{\mathrm{d}\theta'_1} \right) \sum_k \mathrm{e}^{-n\beta\varepsilon_k} \psi_k(\boldsymbol{r}'_1)\, \psi_k^*(\boldsymbol{r}''_1). \tag{51-26}$$

In § 50 we mentioned that from the Green's function (50-37) one obtains in the thermodynamic limit

$$\sum_k \mathrm{e}^{-n\beta\varepsilon_k} \psi_k(\boldsymbol{r}'_1) \psi_k^*(\boldsymbol{r}''_1) = \frac{1}{\lambda^3 n^{3/2}} \exp\left(- \frac{\pi \xi_1^2}{n\lambda^2} \right). \tag{51-27}$$

Using

$$\left[\exp\left(\alpha \frac{\mathrm{d}}{\mathrm{d}x} \right) \right] f(x) = f(x + \alpha), \tag{51-28}$$

we find

$$\exp\left(- in\beta\hbar\omega \frac{\mathrm{d}}{\mathrm{d}\theta'_1} \right) \sum_k \mathrm{e}^{-n\beta\varepsilon_k} \psi_k(\boldsymbol{r}'_1) \psi_k^*(\boldsymbol{r}''_1)$$
$$= \frac{1}{\lambda^3 n^{3/2}} \exp\{ -(\pi/n\lambda^2)[r_1'^2 + r_1''^2 - 2r'_1 r''_1 \cos(\theta'_1 - \theta''_1 - in\beta\hbar\omega)] \}. \tag{51-29}$$

Substitution of (51-29) into (51-26) yields A and thus the first reduced density matrix $w_1 = mA$, for all ω. Our immediate goal is to discuss the effect of ω on the Bose condensation. As a result of the Bose statistics a single quantum state will again, for given ω, become macroscopically occupied. The values of ω at which the various states become macroscopically occupied will depend on the properties of the discrete quantum levels and thus also upon R. In this way we see that the thermodynamic limit must also be taken on ω.

Notes p. 348

There are two characteristic limiting examples which we will discuss

$$\omega \text{ of order } \hbar/mR^2, \tag{51-30}$$

$$\omega \text{ of order } \sqrt{k_B T/mR^2}, \tag{51-31}$$

which can be referred to as slow (or quantum) and fast (or classical) rotation respectively. In each case the thermodynamic limit is realized by keeping the terms of lowest order in λ/R.

For the case (51-30) we obtain

$$\begin{aligned} w_1(\boldsymbol{r}_1', \boldsymbol{r}_1'') &= mA(\boldsymbol{r}_1', \boldsymbol{r}_1'', Z, V, \omega) \\ &= \frac{m}{\lambda^3} \sum_n \frac{Z^n}{n^{3/2}} \exp\left(-\frac{\pi\xi_1^2}{n\lambda^2}\right) \exp\left[i\frac{2\beta\hbar}{\lambda^2}\boldsymbol{\omega}\cdot(\boldsymbol{r}_1' \times \boldsymbol{r}_1'')\right]. \end{aligned} \tag{51-32}$$

In the second case (51-31) we find

$$\begin{aligned} w_1(\boldsymbol{r}_1', \boldsymbol{r}_1'') = \frac{m}{\lambda^3} \sum_n \frac{Z^n}{n^{3/2}} \exp\left(-\frac{\pi\xi_1^2}{n\lambda^2}\right) \\ \times \exp\left(\frac{n\pi\beta^2\hbar^2\omega^2\boldsymbol{r}_1' \cdot \boldsymbol{r}_1''}{\lambda^2}\right) \exp\left[i\frac{2\beta\hbar}{\lambda^2}\boldsymbol{\omega}\cdot(\boldsymbol{r}_1' \times \boldsymbol{r}_1'')\right]. \end{aligned} \tag{51-33}$$

The critical number of particles will be determined by the condition

$$\langle N \rangle_c = \max_Z \int \frac{1}{m} w_1(\boldsymbol{r}, \boldsymbol{r})\, d^3 r. \tag{51-34}$$

In the case of slow rotation (51-30) the critical density is unchanged. One can say that the centrifugal corrections to the density are vanishingly small in the thermodynamic limit. For fast rotation the critical density is determined by

$$\langle N \rangle_c = \max_Z \frac{2H\pi}{\lambda^3 m\omega^2 \beta} \sum_n \frac{Z^n}{n^{5/2}} \left[\exp\left(\tfrac{1}{2}m\omega^2 R^2 \beta n\right) - 1\right]. \tag{51-35}$$

This relation is monotonic increasing in Z and hence the maximum allowed value of Z determines $\langle N \rangle_c$. Since none of the occupation numbers are permitted to be negative (51-12) implies

$$\max Z = \min_k \exp\left[\beta(\varepsilon - \hbar\omega\ell)_k\right]. \tag{51-36}$$

Notes p. 348

The energy eigenvalues corresponding to (51-22) are

$$\beta\varepsilon_{n,\ell,p} = \frac{\lambda^2}{R^2}\frac{(k_{n,\ell})^2}{4\pi} + \frac{\lambda^2}{H^2}\frac{\pi^2 p^2}{4\pi}. \tag{51-37}$$

The minimum of the right hand side of (51-36) clearly occurs for $p = 0$ and the first root $n = 1$ of the Bessel function; thus

$$\max Z = \exp\left\{\min_{\ell}\left[\frac{\lambda^2}{R^2}\frac{(k_{1,\ell})^2}{4\pi} - \beta\hbar\omega\ell\right]\right\}. \tag{51-38}$$

Now for large ℓ

$$k_{1,\ell} \to \ell, \tag{51-39}$$

and the minimum is achieved for

$$\ell = \frac{R^2}{\lambda^2}\beta\omega h, \tag{51-40}$$

corresponding to

$$\max Z = \exp\left(-\tfrac{1}{2}\beta m\omega^2 R^2\right). \tag{51-41}$$

So for rotation the critical number is modified to:

$$\langle N\rangle_c = \frac{2H\pi}{\lambda^3 m\omega^2\beta}\sum_n \frac{1}{n^{5/2}}\left[1 - \exp\left(-\tfrac{1}{2}n\beta m\omega^2 R^2\right)\right]. \tag{51-42}$$

For $\omega \to 0$ one recovers the previous expression (49-29) for $\langle N\rangle_c$ and for $\omega \to \infty$ one obtains that the critical number per unit length along the axis of rotation is

$$\langle N\rangle_c/H = 2\pi\zeta(\tfrac{5}{2})/\lambda^3 m\omega^2\beta. \tag{51-43}$$

As ω is given by (51-31) it is best to write

$$\omega = \bar{\omega}\sqrt{\frac{k_B T}{mR^2}}, \tag{51-44}$$

where $\bar{\omega}$ is a dimensionless angular velocity. Then for large $\bar{\omega}$ the critical total density is

$$\frac{\langle N\rangle_c}{V} = \frac{2\zeta(\frac{5}{2})}{\lambda^3\bar{\omega}^2}, \tag{51-45}$$

which goes to zero for large $\bar{\omega}$.

Notes p. 348

If the average density is greater than the critical density for the respective domains, the extra particles will all drop into the ground state of the effective Hamiltonian (51-3). Thus the macroscopically occupied quantum state depends on the angular velocity of rotation. From (51-12) one sees that the state of maximum occupation is the one for which

$$\varepsilon - \hbar\omega\ell = \text{minimum.} \tag{51-46}$$

If we set

$$k \equiv (n, \ell, p), \tag{51-47}$$

then the minimum always occurs for

$$k_0 = (1, \ell_0, 0), \tag{51-48}$$

where ℓ_0 follows from (51-46,37) for the given ω. The occupation of this state is as before

$$\langle N_0 \rangle = \langle N \rangle - \langle N \rangle_c. \tag{51-49}$$

In calculating the reduced density matrices for the condensed phase these states must be split off as before. It is straightforward to show that the reduced density matrices are

$$w_1(\boldsymbol{r}_1', \boldsymbol{r}_1'') = m\langle N_0 \rangle \psi_{k_0}(\boldsymbol{r}_1')\, \psi_{k_0}^*(\boldsymbol{r}_1'') + \frac{m}{\lambda^3} \sum_n \frac{\exp(-\pi\xi_1^2/n\lambda^2)}{n^{3/2}} \exp\left[i\frac{2\beta\hbar}{\lambda^2}\boldsymbol{\omega}\cdot(\boldsymbol{r}_1' \times \boldsymbol{r}_1'')\right], \tag{51-50}$$

for (51-30) and in the case of 'fast' rotation (51-31) we find

$$w_1(\boldsymbol{r}_1', \boldsymbol{r}_1'') = m\langle N_0 \rangle \psi_{k_0}(\boldsymbol{r}_1')\, \psi_{k_0}^*(\boldsymbol{r}_1'') + \frac{m}{\lambda^3} \sum_n \frac{Z'^n}{n^{3/2}} \exp\left(-\frac{\pi\xi_1^2}{n\lambda^2}\right) \exp\left[i\frac{2\beta\hbar}{\lambda^2}\boldsymbol{\omega}\cdot(\boldsymbol{r}_1' \times \boldsymbol{r}_1'')\right], \tag{51-51}$$

where we have set

$$Z' \equiv Z \exp\left[\frac{\pi\beta^2\hbar^2}{\lambda^2} v_n^2(r_1)\right] = \exp\left[\frac{\pi\beta^2\hbar^2\omega^2}{\lambda^2}(r_1^2 - R^2)\right],$$

and have used $\omega^2 \boldsymbol{r}_1' \cdot \boldsymbol{r}_1'' = v_n^2(r_1) - \frac{1}{4}\omega^2\xi_1^2$ and the fact that the term in $\frac{1}{4}\omega^2\xi_1^2$ is negligible in the thermodynamic limit.

Notes p. 348

In each of these cases the density matrix is in the form of a local order plus an off diagonal long range order or

$$w_1(\boldsymbol{r}', \boldsymbol{r}'') = m\langle N_0\rangle\, \psi_{k_0}(\boldsymbol{r}')\, \psi^*_{k_0}(\boldsymbol{r}'') + \Lambda(\boldsymbol{r}', \boldsymbol{r}''), \tag{51-52}$$

where

$$\lim_{\xi\to\infty} \Lambda(\xi, \boldsymbol{r}) = 0. \tag{51-53}$$

We will always have in mind that the local order describes the normal fluid and the ODLRO describes the superfluid. In fact the fluid density is

$$\rho(\boldsymbol{r}) = m\langle N_0\rangle\, \psi_{k_0}(\boldsymbol{r})\, \psi^*_{k_0}(\boldsymbol{r}) + \Lambda(\boldsymbol{r}, \boldsymbol{r}), \tag{51-54}$$

and with an eye to He II we make the associations

$$\rho_s = m\langle N_0\rangle\, \psi_{k_0}(\boldsymbol{r})\, \psi^*_{k_0}(\boldsymbol{r}), \qquad \rho_n = \Lambda(\boldsymbol{r}, \boldsymbol{r}). \tag{51-55}$$

For the case of slow rotation the normal fluid density is as before:

$$\rho_n = \frac{m}{\lambda^3} \sum_n \frac{1}{n^{3/2}} = \frac{m}{\lambda^3}\, \zeta(\tfrac{3}{2}), \tag{51-56}$$

but for fast rotation it is from (51-51)

$$\rho_n(\boldsymbol{r}) = \frac{m}{\lambda^3} \sum_n \frac{\exp\left[(n\pi\beta^2\hbar^2\omega^2/\lambda^2)(r^2 - R^2)\right]}{n^{3/2}} \tag{51-57}$$

in the Bose condensed region. At the wall where $r = R$, $\rho_n(\boldsymbol{r})$ is a maximum and equal to ρ_n as given by (51-56).

The local momentum density of the system follows from (50-12):

$$\boldsymbol{J}(\boldsymbol{r}) = \rho_n(\boldsymbol{r})\, \boldsymbol{\omega} \times \boldsymbol{r} + \rho_s(\boldsymbol{r})\, \ell_0 \frac{\hbar}{mr}\, \hat{\boldsymbol{e}}_\theta. \tag{51-58}$$

Since $\boldsymbol{J} = \rho_n \boldsymbol{v}_n + \rho_s \boldsymbol{v}_s$, we see that

$$\boldsymbol{v}_n = \boldsymbol{\omega} \times \boldsymbol{r}, \tag{51-59}$$

$$\boldsymbol{v}_s = \ell_0 \frac{\hbar}{mr}\, \hat{\boldsymbol{e}}_\theta, \tag{51-60}$$

or in rotational equilibrium the normal fluid is in solid body rotation whereas the superfluid executes irrotational flow corresponding to motion about a quantized vortex of strength $\ell_0\hbar/m$, situated on the axis of rotation.

Notes p. 348

The total angular momentum can be found by integrating $\boldsymbol{r} \times \boldsymbol{J}$ over the volume and is

$$L = \langle N_0 \rangle \ell_0 \hbar + \tfrac{1}{2} \langle N \rangle_c m R^2 \omega, \tag{51-61}$$

where we now specialize to the case (51-30) so that ρ_n is independent of r. This result would also have followed from a direct evaluation of (51-13). It was first presented by Blatt and Butler [3].

Equation (51-46) which determines the angular momentum of the superfluid is quite similar to the free energy which was minimized in § 18. Here too, one finds that up to a critical angular velocity the superfluid is in a state $\ell = 0$ but as ω increases the free energy (51-46) becomes degenerate for the states (1,1,0) and (1,0,0) at

$$\omega = \omega_{cr} = \frac{\varepsilon_{11}}{\hbar} = \frac{\hbar k_{11}^2}{2mR^2} \approx 1.7 \frac{\hbar}{mR^2}, \tag{51-62}$$

for higher ω the state of minimum free energy is (1,1,0). Thus as an ideal Bose gas is brought into rotation the superfluid stays at rest ignoring the walls until the angular velocity of the container reaches (51-62); at this point a quantized vortex line forms on the axis of rotation. As ω increases further, higher critical angular velocities are reached, at which the quantum of circulation of the superfluid increases by h/m. Denoting the angular velocity at which the circulation changes to $\ell h/m$ by ω_ℓ one finds

$$\omega_\ell = \frac{\varepsilon_{1,\ell} - \varepsilon_{1,\ell-1}}{\hbar} = \frac{\hbar}{2mR^2} (k_{1,\ell}^2 - k_{1,\ell-1}^2). \tag{51-63}$$

The angular momentum versus ω is shown in Fig. 54.

This behavior bears strong qualitative similarities to the unusual properties of rotating He II and of course there are some differences, which can all be attributed to the difference in compressibility of the superfluids. In He II the successive vortices repel each other because of the incompressibility of the superfluid. A vortex of double strength is then energetically less favorable than two single strength vortices off center. For the Bose gas, the enormous compressibility acts to coalesce the vortices. The compressibility also accounts for the different numeric multiplying $\hbar/mR^2$ in the formula for ω_{cr} [compare (51-62) and (18-24)].

Since the condensed ideal Bose gas is a system that can be handled from first principles and since it bears such a strong resemblance to He II, one is motivated to ask how the vortices enter the Bose gas.

Notes p. 348

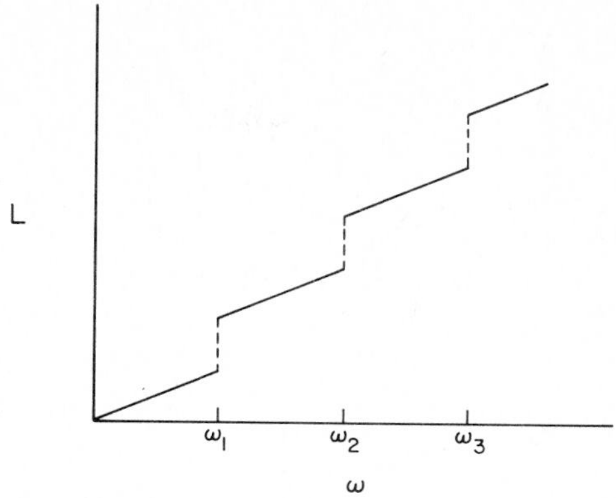

Fig. 54. The angular momentum versus angular velocity ω of an ideal condensed Bose gas in a rotating cylindrical vessel.

At the critical angular velocity ω_ℓ at which the quantum phase transitions occur, there is a degeneracy between the two states of lowest free energy. As the lowest state is macroscopically occupied, the effect of a small perturbation which will break the degeneracy may be crucial. The degeneracy is a consequence of the cylindrical symmetry hence we will investigate the effects of a small 'bump' on the wall of the rotating bucket. Such a bump can, for instance, be represented by a potential $m\Omega(r, \theta)$ which has a small constant value δ in a cylindrical strip along the wall of the bucket (with cross-sectional area $\mathscr{S}$) and is zero otherwise.

We are interested in the effects of this perturbation on the two lowest states. To describe this, one must solve the eigenvalue equation

$$(\hat{\mathscr{H}}_0 - \boldsymbol{\omega} \cdot \hat{\boldsymbol{L}} + m\Omega)\psi = \mathscr{F}\psi \tag{51-64}$$

for the two lowest single particle states. Let us focus on the first critical angular velocity and the boundary condition $\nabla_\perp \psi = 0$. With no perturbation, the free energies $\mathscr{F}_0, \mathscr{F}_1$ of the two lowest states cross (are degenerate at ω_1, but with the bump they become the solid lines in Fig. 55. The ground state is therefore no longer degenerate. Near ω_1 the splitting between the two lowest levels is of order

$$\mathscr{S}\delta/R^2, \tag{51-65}$$

which is to be compared with the characteristic spacing between unperturbed energy levels which is of order

$$h^2/mR^2. \tag{51-66}$$

Notes p. 348

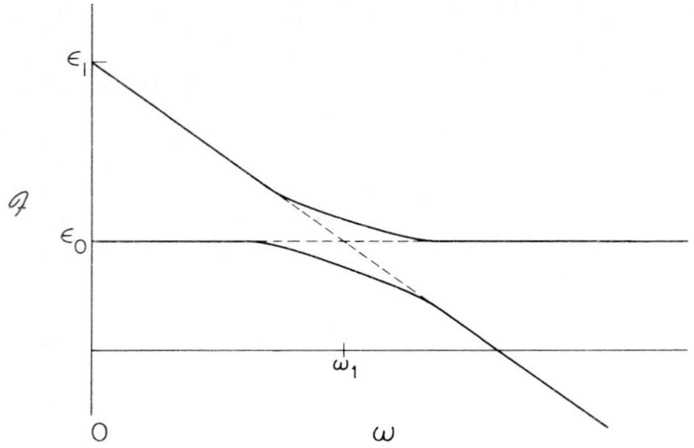

Fig. 55. The free energies $\mathscr{F}_0$, $\mathscr{F}_1$ for the two lowest single-particle states without (dashed line) and with (solid line) a 'bump' on the wall of the rotating bucket.

The perturbation theory applies when

$$\mathscr{S}\delta \ll \hbar^2/m, \tag{51-67}$$

which we assume. Although the splitting is small it is not thermodynamically small, which means that the ratio of (51-65) to (51-66) does not go to zero in the thermodynamic limit ($R \to \infty$).

With the perturbation the occupation numbers (51-12) are modified to

$$\langle N_k \rangle = \frac{Z}{e^{\beta \mathscr{F}_k} - Z}. \tag{51-68}$$

The ratio of occupation of the first to lowest level is then

$$\frac{e^{\beta \mathscr{F}_0} - Z}{e^{\beta \mathscr{F}_1} - Z} \tag{51-69}$$

so that the occupation of the first level is down by a factor of

$$R^2/\langle N_0 \rangle \mathscr{S}\delta, \tag{51-70}$$

which still goes to zero as $V^{-1/3}$ in the limit of large volume. Hence the perturbation leads to a sufficient splitting between the two lowest levels so that in the thermodynamic limit, only *one* of the levels can be macroscopically occupied.

Notes p. 348

Next, let us consider what happens when the bucket is brought from rest *slowly* into rotation. From the adiabatic theorem one can conclude that if ω, and hence the effective Hamiltonian, varies slowly, the occupation of the energy levels will not change (no quantum jumping) and the wave function will change continuously. In particular, the wave function for the condensate at rest will smoothly transform as ω_1 is passed into the wave function of a quantized vortex on the axis of rotation. One can say that in this case the vortex enters the fluid by an *adiabatic transformation* of the ground state.

These remarks about the perturbation theory can be made clear in the approximation where one includes only the two lowest states in the perturbation expansion. Our object is to find the eigenstates ψ_+, ψ_-, and eigenvalues $\mathscr{F}_+, \mathscr{F}_-$ of the transformed wave equations (51-64):

$$(\hat{\mathscr{H}}_0 - \boldsymbol{\omega}\cdot\hat{\boldsymbol{L}} + m\Omega)\psi_+ = \mathscr{F}_+\psi_+, \tag{51-71}$$

$$(\hat{\mathscr{H}}_0 - \boldsymbol{\omega}\cdot\hat{\boldsymbol{L}} + m\Omega)\psi_- = \mathscr{F}_-\psi_-, \tag{51-72}$$

in terms of the eigenvalues and eigenstates of the unperturbed, transformed wave equations:

$$(\hat{\mathscr{H}}_0 - \boldsymbol{\omega}\cdot\hat{\boldsymbol{L}})\psi_0 = \varepsilon_0\psi_0, \tag{51-73}$$

$$(\hat{\mathscr{H}}_0 - \boldsymbol{\omega}\cdot\hat{\boldsymbol{L}})\psi_1 = \varepsilon_1\psi_1, \tag{51-74}$$

where ψ_0, ψ_1, are the lowest energy wave functions (51-22) corresponding to $\ell = 0, 1$. We look for solution to (51-71,72) of the form

$$\psi = a\psi_0 + b\psi_1. \tag{51-75}$$

Substituting in (51-64) and taking the inner product with ψ_0^* and ψ_1^* yields two equations

$$a\varepsilon_0 + a\Omega_{00} + b\Omega_{01} = a\mathscr{F}, \tag{51-76}$$

$$a\Omega_{10} + b[\varepsilon_0 + \hbar(\omega_1 - \omega) + \Omega_{11}] = b\mathscr{F}, \tag{51-77}$$

where we have set

$$\Omega_{ij} \equiv \int \psi_i^*(\boldsymbol{r})\, m\Omega(\boldsymbol{r})\, \psi_j(\boldsymbol{r})\, \mathrm{d}^3 r \tag{51-78}$$

and recall that $\varepsilon_1 - \hbar\omega_1 = \varepsilon_0$. Equations (51-76,77) are two homogeneous equations in two unknowns. To have a non-trivial solution the determinant must vanish and this yelds the energy eigenvalues $\mathscr{F}_\pm$:

Notes p. 348

$$2(\mathscr{F}_{\pm} - \varepsilon_0) = [\Omega_{00} + \Omega_{11} + \hbar(\omega_1 - \omega)] \\ \pm[(\Omega_{00}-\Omega_{11})^2+\hbar^2(\omega_1-\omega)^2+2\hbar(\omega_1-\omega)(\Omega_{11}-\Omega_{00})+4\Omega_{01}\Omega_{10}]^{1/2}, \tag{51-79}$$

where the subscript minus denotes the lower eigenvalue. For *any* ω the splitting between the levels is on the order of the square root which is in turn on the order of Ω_{ij}. For the perturbation under consideration these integrals (51-78) are on the order (51-65) as previously asserted. Now consider the lowest level $\mathscr{F}_-$. For small ω such that $\omega_1 - \omega \approx \omega_1 = (\varepsilon_1 - \varepsilon_0)/\hbar$ we find from (51-79) that $\mathscr{F}_- \approx \varepsilon_0$. As ω increases past ω_1, $\mathscr{F}_-$ varies continuously and approaches $\varepsilon_1 - \hbar\omega$ for $\omega - \omega_1 \gg |\Omega_{ij}|$. Thus the perturbation which removes the degeneracy leads to a lowest level with properties indicated by the lower solid line in Fig. 55. Similarly, the level $\mathscr{F}_+$ behaves like the higher state.

The wave function corresponding to $\mathscr{F}_-$ can be found by substituting (51-79) into (51-76) and is

$$\psi_- = \sqrt{1-f}\,\psi_0 + \sqrt{f}\,\psi_1, \tag{51-80}$$

where f depends on ω and the perturbation such that for $\omega \to 0, f \to 0$ and for $\omega - \omega_1 \gg |\Omega_{ij}|$ f goes continuously to unity.

Due to the perturbation the wave function of the ground state is seriously affected for ω near ω_1, and the off diagonal long range order becomes

$$m\langle N_0\rangle\, \psi_-(\boldsymbol{r}_1')\, \psi_-^*(\boldsymbol{r}_1''), \tag{51-81}$$

where one must simply replace ψ_{k_0} in (51-50) with ψ_-. Using (50-12) for the mass flux density we find

$$\boldsymbol{J}(\boldsymbol{r}) = \rho_n \boldsymbol{\omega} \times \boldsymbol{r} + \rho_s(\boldsymbol{r})\frac{\hbar}{m}\nabla\varphi \tag{51-82}$$

where ρ_s is given by (51-55) and φ is defined by

$$\psi = \sqrt{\psi^*\psi}\, e^{i\varphi}. \tag{51-83}$$

Therefore the superfluid velocity for this case is $\boldsymbol{v}_s = \hbar\nabla\varphi/m$ where φ is the phase of (51-80). The velocity field found in this way from (51-80) corresponds to a quantized vortex line located *off-center* at the node of ψ_- and rotating with the normal fluid. Thus as the bucket is brought slowly into rotation, the continuous change of f from 0 to 1 corresponds

Notes p. 348

to the development of a node (vortex) of the ground state at the wall which then moves continuously to the center of the bucket. The origin of the vortex results from an *interference* of the two lowest unperturbed levels.

If we had worked with the boundary condition $\psi \to 0$ at the boundary, this procedure would have to be modified somewhat. In order to split the degeneracy, the perturbation would have to be appreciable in a region of cross-sectional area $\mathscr{S}$ which is at least proportional to R times a constant length. In this way, $\mathscr{S}$ increases with R. Now the interference (51-81) which results, corresponds to the formation of two parallel vortex lines of opposite polarization off-center. As ω increases, this adiabatically formed state develops into a single vortex at the axis with the vortex of polarization opposite to rotation disappearing at the wall.

From time-dependent perturbation theory, it follows that for a sudden change of ω the eigenfunctions will not change. Hence, if for $\omega > \omega_1$ one suddenly *stops* the rotation, the first state with $\ell = 1$ will remain macroscopically occupied corresponding to a 'metastable' vortex at the center. From this picture, metastable states will occur. Coupling to a bump on the wall will *not* lead to a decay of this state unless the perturbation is time dependent. The only way in which a metastable vortex in an ideal Bose gas can decay is through interactions with *vibrations* of the *boundary*. In this way one is led to the approach discussed in § 45. If C_0, C_1 are the amplitudes of occupation of the two lowest states, then

$$i\hbar \frac{\partial C_0}{\partial t} = \mathscr{F}_0 C_0 + K(t)\, C_1, \tag{51-84}$$

$$i\hbar \frac{\partial C_1}{\partial t} = \mathscr{F}_1 C_1 + K(t)\, C_0, \tag{51-85}$$

where $K(t)$ is the time dependent perturbation that couples the two lowest states. There will be an appreciable transition amplitude only for components of K close to $(\mathscr{F}_1 - \mathscr{F}_0)/\hbar$ in frequency. So we set

$$K(t) = K' \exp\left(i \frac{\mathscr{F}_1 - \mathscr{F}_0}{\hbar} t\right). \tag{51-86}$$

If at $t = 0$: $C_1 = 1$, $C_0 = 0$, then at a small time later

Notes p. 348

$$|C_0^2| = (K't/\hbar)^2, \tag{51-87}$$

which describes a stimulated transition which takes place during a characteristic time

$$\hbar/|K'|. \tag{51-88}$$

Since the off diagonal long range order ψ obeys the Schrödinger equation (51-1) and since $\boldsymbol{v}_s = \hbar\nabla\varphi/m$ as suggested by (51-82) one has in equilibrium:

$$\frac{D_s\boldsymbol{v}_s}{Dt} = \frac{\partial\boldsymbol{v}_s}{\partial t} + \nabla\tfrac{1}{2}v_s^2 = -\nabla\left(-\frac{\hbar^2}{2m^2}\frac{\nabla^2\sqrt{\rho_s}}{\sqrt{\rho_s}}\right), \tag{51-89}$$

which is just the Madelung transformation discussed in Chapter VII. Comparison with the superfluid He II equations suggests the relation for the ideal Bose gas:

$$\mu \leftrightarrow -\frac{\hbar^2}{2m^2}\frac{\nabla^2\sqrt{\rho_s}}{\sqrt{\rho_s}}. \tag{51-90}$$

We will see below that with this association the ideal Bose gas explains additional properties of He II. One is, of course, free to call any quantity the chemical potential, what must be done to justify this choice is to show that it *also* obeys a *thermodynamic* relation which is a generalization of (49-15) to the superfluid state, and that it determines the change in energy due to a change in mass.

First, let us note that since the equilibrium state is stationary in the rotating system

$$\frac{D_n\varphi}{Dt} = \frac{\partial\varphi}{\partial t} + \boldsymbol{v}_n\cdot\nabla\varphi = 0,$$

and hence (51-89) becomes

$$\mu + \tfrac{1}{2}v_s^2 - \boldsymbol{v}_n\cdot\boldsymbol{v}_s = \text{constant}, \tag{51-91}$$

which is the equilibrium condition (16-10) for He II. The quantity Z which determines the particle distribution (51-68) is related to the chemical potential of the system as defined thermodynamically (see § 49) and is clearly to be treated as a constant. Thus, if our relation (51-90) has any validity, Z must be a function of μ in the form (51-91) which we

Notes p. 348

now demonstrate. In order to have a Bose condensation, Z must equal the exponential of the Boltzmann factor times the effective energy $\mathscr{F}_-$ of the lowest state, or generalizing (49-39)

$$Z = e^{\beta \mathscr{F}_-}, \tag{51-92}$$

where the term involving V^{-1} is negligible for present considerations. From the eigenvalue equation for $\mathscr{F}_-$ (51-72) one finds

$$\mathscr{F}_- = m(\mu + \tfrac{1}{2}v_s^2 - \boldsymbol{v}_n \cdot \boldsymbol{v}_s), \tag{51-93}$$

where we are temporarily neglecting Ω. We conclude

$$\begin{aligned} \log Z &= \beta m(\mu + \tfrac{1}{2}v_s^2 - \boldsymbol{v}_n \cdot \boldsymbol{v}_s), \\ \log Z' &= \beta m[\mu + \tfrac{1}{2}(\boldsymbol{v}_n - \boldsymbol{v}_s)^2]. \end{aligned} \tag{51-94}$$

One might argue that without the bump on the wall $\boldsymbol{v}_n \cdot \boldsymbol{v}_s$ is also constant and hence one cannot distinguish between (51-91) and $\mu + \frac{1}{2}v_s^2$ constant. Including Ω, (51-89) becomes

$$\frac{D_s \boldsymbol{v}_s}{Dt} = -\nabla(\mu + \Omega), \tag{51-95}$$

and (51-91) is modified to

$$\mu + \tfrac{1}{2}v_s^2 - \boldsymbol{v}_n \cdot \boldsymbol{v}_s + \Omega = \text{constant}, \tag{51-96}$$

which is identical with the behavior of rotating He II in an external field and wherein $\boldsymbol{v}_n \cdot \boldsymbol{v}_s$ is not now constant. In this case:

$$\log Z = \beta m(\mu + \tfrac{1}{2}v_s^2 - \boldsymbol{v}_n \cdot \boldsymbol{v}_s + \Omega). \tag{51-97}$$

One can take Ω arbitrarily small and still resolve the degeneracy leading to states which are not stationary in the inertial system. Thus, one concludes that (51-91) is proven.

The rotating condensed ideal Bose gas has many properties in common with superfluid helium. In particular, a macroscopic fraction of the fluid moves without friction, ignoring the walls and with circulation quantized. Nevertheless a number of authors [4,14] assert that an ideal Bose gas is *not* a superfluid. These arguments are invariably based upon some arbitrary definition of what constitutes superfluidity, and always involve some property of the critical velocity. Landau said that a superfluid must have a non-zero critical velocity at zero temperature in an *infinite* geometry. That is: an object should be able to move without

Notes p. 348

friction up to this critical velocity at 0 °K. In He II all experiments on steady flow indicate that as the geometry goes to infinity, the critical velocity drops to zero. Furthermore, the hydrodynamic drag on a sphere moving through He II increases exponentially as the temperature is lowered towards 0 °K. Thus, the question of how the limit of 0 °K is taken becomes important and this point of view loses any *operational* meaning. Bloch defines a superfluid as a system which can exhibit a persistent current in an annular geometry where the width of the annular region is much less than the radius. The magnitude of this current must remain finite in the limit of large radius for the system to be defined as superfluid. This geometry is realized when a He II film coats the outside of a cylinder, and as mentioned in Chapter VI, the experimental factors controlling such film flows are not understood.

It may be misleading to base definitions of superfluidity on the least understood aspect of He II: the critical velocity. Such definitions might show that He II is not a superfluid. We would rather define superfluidity in terms of the macroscopic occupation of a single microscopic quantum state. Operationally, this point of view has two consequences. First, extra variables, which are required to describe this quantum degree of freedom, will enter the *macroscopic* description. Secondly, this new degree of freedom will possess no entropy. Therefore, as some critical temperature is passed, it will be possible to observe transformations of some new degree of freedom which correspond to no transfer of entropy. It is important to realize that these properties must be retained by the system in the thermodynamic limit as is implied by the word macroscopic. For instance, the ideal Bose gas for $T > T_c$ has a ground state with no entropy and a quantized circulation. However, the fraction of the system in this state goes to zero for large volumes.

By the above definition of superfluidity, He II, superconductors, the condensed ideal Bose gas, are all superfluids [15].

For the case of slow rotation (51-30) which we have emphasized so far, there is no centrifugal density distortion or pressure gradient in the thermodynamic limit. This is because

$$\beta m\omega^2 R^2 \approx \lambda^2/R^2.$$

To investigate centrifugal effects, one must consider the 'fast' rotation (51-31) for which

$$\beta m\omega^2 R^2 \approx 1.$$

Notes p. 348

Then the normal fluid density is given by (51-57). The stress tensor follows from (50-16) and is in equilibrium

$$P_{ij} = p_n \delta_{ij} - \frac{\hbar^2}{2m^2}\left(\sqrt{\rho_s}\frac{\partial^2 \sqrt{\rho_s}}{\partial r_i\, \partial r_j} - \frac{\partial \sqrt{\rho_s}}{\partial r_i}\frac{\partial \sqrt{\rho_s}}{\partial r_j}\right) + \rho_s v_{s,i} v_{s,j} + \rho_n v_{n,i} v_{n,j}, \tag{51-98}$$

where

$$p_n = \frac{k_B T}{\lambda^3} \sum_n \frac{\exp\left[n\pi\beta^2\hbar^2\omega^2(r^2 - R^2)/\lambda^2\right]}{n^{5/2}} \tag{51-99}$$

and (51-51) has been used and a term which vanishes in the thermodynamic limit has been dropped from p_n. The stresses within the ideal Bose gas are not isotropic even when the momentum fluxes are ignored. From (51-99) and (51-57) one finds that the normal fluid contribution to the pressure satisfies:

$$\nabla p_n = \rho_n \nabla \tfrac{1}{2} v_n^2. \tag{51-100}$$

There are two contributions to the stresses within the ideal Bose gas. One is the isotropic contribution p_n of the normal fluid, and the other is the superfluid contribution which depends on the curvature of the wave function. This contribution is not isotropic *but*, it is always strictly normal to any boundary of the system, because of the boundary condition that either $\rho_s \to 0$ or $\nabla_\perp \rho_s \to 0$. Thus, any attempt to measure this stress by introducing a surface will affect it seriously.

Using the expression (50-24) leads to (neglecting a surface term)

$$U = \tfrac{3}{2} p_n - \frac{\hbar^2}{2m^2}\sqrt{\rho_s}\nabla^2\sqrt{\rho_s} + \tfrac{1}{2}\rho_n v_n^2 + \tfrac{1}{2}\rho_s v_s^2 \tag{51-101}$$

for the energy density of the rotating Bose gas in equilibrium. Next let us consider the relation obtained for the variation of the energy density when $T, Z, v_n, \psi\ (=\rho_s, v_s)$ are changed slightly in each volume element, as can happen say when the bucket velocity ω is changed while heat is supplied, etc.. As opposed to the stationary Bose gas rotation makes $\boldsymbol{v}_n$ indepent of $\boldsymbol{v}_s$ and also makes Z independent of $T, \boldsymbol{v}_n$. One obtains at a given r

$$\mathrm{d}U = \frac{\log Z}{\beta m}\mathrm{d}\rho_n + \mathrm{T}\,\mathrm{d}\rho s + \boldsymbol{v}_n \cdot \mathrm{d}\rho_n \boldsymbol{v}_n + \mathrm{d}(\tfrac{1}{2}\rho_s v_s^2 + \rho_s \mu), \tag{51-102}$$

Notes p. 348

where p_n has been written as a function of Z, T, v_n by use of (51-41) and we have introduced for the entropy density

$$\rho s = \frac{5}{2}\frac{p_n}{T} - \frac{\rho_n}{T}\left(\frac{\log Z}{\beta m} + \frac{v_n^2}{2}\right). \tag{51-103}$$

In terms of ρs as given by (51-103) we have

$$\mathrm{d}p_n = \rho_n \,\mathrm{d}\left(\frac{\log Z}{\beta m} + \frac{v_n^2}{2}\right) + \rho s \,\mathrm{d}T. \tag{51-104}$$

In the first and second law of thermodynamics (51-102), μ is the *dynamically* defined driving force of the single macroscopically occupied quantum state (51-90) and Z is the *thermodynamic* chemical potential of the excited particles. *The condition that there be a Bose condensation relates these two quantities.* This condition (51-94) must be used to supplement the thermo-hydrodynamics.

Then one obtains for the first and second laws of thermodynamics:

$$\mathrm{d}U = (\mu + \tfrac{1}{2}v_s^2 - \boldsymbol{v}_n \cdot \boldsymbol{v}_s)\,\mathrm{d}\rho + T\,\mathrm{d}\rho s + \boldsymbol{v}_n \cdot \mathrm{d}\boldsymbol{J} + \rho_s(\boldsymbol{v}_s - \boldsymbol{v}_n)\cdot \mathrm{d}\boldsymbol{v}_s + \rho_s\,\mathrm{d}\mu, \tag{51-105}$$

which except for the term $\rho_s\,\mathrm{d}\mu$ is the first and second law for He II (4-5,6). We remark that the relation for p_n becomes

$$\mathrm{d}p_n = \rho_n\,\mathrm{d}\mu + \rho s\,\mathrm{d}T + \rho_n\,\mathrm{d}\tfrac{1}{2}(\boldsymbol{v}_n - \boldsymbol{v}_s)^2. \tag{51-106}$$

The term $\rho_s\,\mathrm{d}\mu$ is in fact a surface contribution to any variational process which results in an energy change. To see this, one must use the identity

$$\rho_s\,\mathrm{d}\mu \equiv -\frac{\hbar^2}{2m^2}\frac{\partial}{\partial r_j}\left[\sqrt{\rho_s}\frac{\partial}{\partial r_j}(\mathrm{d}\sqrt{\rho_s}) - \mathrm{d}\sqrt{\rho_s}\frac{\partial\sqrt{\rho_s}}{\partial r_j}\right], \tag{51-107}$$

which follows only when μ is given by (51-90). In any variation of ρ_s, the term $\rho_s\,\mathrm{d}\mu$ can be removed to a surface bounding the system where it vanishes. This remark applies only to *variations*, one cannot ignore $\rho_s\nabla\mu$ since then the expression inside the divergence of (51-107) does *not* vanish at a boundary. We will discuss this again in § 53 where the general thermo-hydrodynamics of the condensed ideal Bose gas is presented. For the time being, it is very interesting to note that by use of (51-106) and the identity (51-107) the divergence of the Bose stress tensor (51-98) becomes

Notes p. 348

$$\frac{\partial P_{i\alpha}}{\partial r_\alpha} = \frac{\partial}{\partial r_\alpha}(\rho_s v_{s,i} v_{s,\alpha} + \rho_n v_{n,i} v_{n,\alpha}) + \rho \frac{\partial \mu}{\partial r_i} + \rho s \frac{\partial T}{\partial r_i} + \rho_n \frac{\partial \frac{1}{2}(\boldsymbol{v}_n - \boldsymbol{v}_s)^2}{\partial r_i},$$

which is precisely the expression obeyed by He II (4-4,8).

From the expression for the entropy (51-103) we find that in rotation

$$\frac{\rho s}{\rho_n} \neq \text{constant}.$$

Also from the behavior of ρ_n (51-57) we see that it is a function only of $T, \mu + \frac{1}{2}(\boldsymbol{v}_n - \boldsymbol{v}_s)^2$ and not of three independent variables as would be the case in He II.

We conclude this section with the following qualm. One might think that instead of (51-15) one could equally well describe the equilibrium state of a rotating Bose gas by the canonical distribution

$$Q_N(V, L) = \sum_{N_0, N_1 \ldots}'' \exp\left(-\beta \sum_k N_k \varepsilon_k\right), \tag{51-108}$$

where now the total angular momentum, as opposed to the angular velocity, is given. The double prime on the summation indicates this extra restriction. In fact, in the classical domain $T > T_c$, or for strict cylindrical symmetry when $T < T_c$, one finds no difference between the two approaches. However, if there is a bump (51-108) no longer has any meaning since with a time dependent potential there is no meaning to energy in the inertial system. The ensemble (51-108) leads only to states which are stationary in the inertial system, which clearly rules out the off-center vortex states. The reason for this dilemma is that the equilibrium state without a bump is stationary in both the inertial and rotating systems. However, this equivalence is in general not necessarily true as the experience with rotating He II has taught us.

One can argue that quantum-mechanically measurements of ω and L do not commute. In fact these variables form a canonical pair. Knowledge that there is a bump on the wall and hence that the system is rotating, rules out precise knowledge of L. Thus, the action of measurement seriously affects the equilibrium state of the system. One might say that the process of measurement affects the approach to equilibrium in the condensed region. These quantum contributions to irreversibility are not accounted for in the He II hydrodynamics or the ideal Bose gas hydrodynamics, since the hydrodynamic laws describe the time development of the system regardless of how the measurement is made. Like the Schrödinger equations, the hydrodynamics are causal, and say nothing

Notes p. 348

about the effects of measurement. As previously expressed (Chapter VII), including such effects is one of the major outstanding problems. Further insight would also require a solution of the problem of the approach to equilibrium in a macroscopic quantum system.

52 *Hydrodynamics of the Semi-Classical Ideal Bose Gas*

In this section we will see that the equations of motion of the ideal Bose gas in the semi-classical region ($T > T_c$) are just the Euler equations (§ 1). However, the equations of state which are needed to complete the hydrodynamics [e.g., $p = p(\rho, s)$] will be that of the ideal quantum gas obeying Bose statistics.

To discuss hydrodynamics the fluid velocity $\boldsymbol{v}$ must somehow be brought into the problem in addition to the thermodynamic variables ρ, T. Thus we first derive the generalization of the reduced density matrix to the case of uniform flow. This amounts to a Galilean transformation of (50-38).

We consider a system moving at velocity $\boldsymbol{v}$ with respect to the laboratory observer. In the rest frame of the moving system denote the energy eigenvalues by ε_k as before. The density matrix for the laboratory observer is then still given by (50-30) but now the wave functions are those which describe the eigenstate k as seen by the laboratory observer. Equations (50-32,33) then follow but wherein ψ_k should be replaced by $\psi_{k,0}$ which is the wave function ascribed by the laboratory to the state of eigenvalue ε_k in the moving reference frame. From the Galilean covariance of the Schrödinger equation (51-1) one obtains

$$\psi_{k,0}(\boldsymbol{r}_1')\,\psi_{k,0}^*(\boldsymbol{r}_1'') = \psi_k(\boldsymbol{r}_1')\psi_k^*(\boldsymbol{r}_1'')\exp\left(i\frac{m}{\hbar}\boldsymbol{v}\cdot\boldsymbol{\xi}_1\right). \tag{52-1}$$

Substituting (52-1) into (50-33) and using (50-37) now leads to the reduced density matrix as seen by the laboratory:

$$w_1(\boldsymbol{r}_1', \boldsymbol{r}_1'') = \frac{m}{\lambda^3}\sum_{n=1}^{\infty}\frac{Z^n}{n^{3/2}}\exp\left(-\frac{\pi\xi_1^2}{n\lambda^2}\right)\exp\left(i\frac{m}{\hbar}\boldsymbol{v}\cdot\boldsymbol{\xi}_1\right). \tag{52-2}$$

To go from the equilibrium density matrix (52-2) to the off-equilibrium state we make an assumption of local equilibrium. Namely, the fluid will be close to equilibrium in that it can be divided into small volume

Notes p. 348

elements where (52-2) provides the local description, but different volume elements may have different Z, T, $\boldsymbol{v}$. We thus assume that the off-equilibrium density matrix is obtained from (52-2) by letting

$$T = T(\boldsymbol{r}_1, t), \quad \boldsymbol{v} = \boldsymbol{v}(\boldsymbol{r}_1, t), \quad Z = Z(\boldsymbol{r}_1, t), \tag{52-3}$$

where we recall that $\boldsymbol{r}_1 = \frac{1}{2}(\boldsymbol{r}_1' + \boldsymbol{r}_1'')$. By making this ansatz we are implicitly assuming that there are enough interactions in the system to bring about local equilibrium but that these interactions can be neglected so far as their contributions to the fluid properties are concerned.

This off-equilibrium ansatz (52-2,3) now makes $w_1(\boldsymbol{r}_1, \xi_1)$ completely determined by five quantities. Since the potential is zero, the five conservation laws (50-11,16,26) will provide a closed description of the motion on the Euler level. From (50-9) we see that the mass density is

$$\rho = \frac{m}{\lambda^3} \sum_{n=1}^{\infty} \frac{Z^n}{n^{3/2}}, \tag{52-4}$$

in agreement with (49-27). The mass flow or momentum density in terms of the density matrix follows from (50-12) and (52-2) and is

$$\boldsymbol{J} = \rho \boldsymbol{v}, \tag{52-5}$$

where $\boldsymbol{J}$ can vary from point to point since λ, Z, $\boldsymbol{v}$ can vary. The stress tensor follows from (50-17) and (52-2) and is

$$P_{\alpha\beta} = \rho v_\alpha v_\beta + p \delta_{\alpha\beta}, \tag{52-6}$$

where we have set

$$p = \frac{2\pi\hbar^2}{m\lambda^5} \sum_{n=1}^{\infty} \frac{Z^n}{n^{5/2}}, \tag{52-7}$$

which agrees with (49-36). The energy density and energy flux density follow from (50-24,27) and are

$$U = U_0 + \tfrac{1}{2}\rho v^2, \tag{52-8}$$

$$\boldsymbol{Q} = (U + p)\boldsymbol{v}, \tag{52-9}$$

where

$$U_0 = \tfrac{3}{2}p, \tag{52-10}$$

Notes p. 348

which also agrees with (49-11,20,25). The relations (52-5,6,8,9) are exactly those which describe the motion of an Euler fluid. Use of the (ideal gas) equation of state (52-10) leads to a closed description, in terms of the five independent variables ρ, U_0, $\boldsymbol{v}$.

Taking the differential of U_0 leads to

$$\mathrm{d}U_0 = \mu\,\mathrm{d}\rho + T\,\mathrm{d}\rho s, \tag{52-11}$$

where we have set

$$\mu = \frac{\log Z}{\beta m}, \tag{52-12}$$

and

$$\rho s = \frac{5}{2}\frac{p}{T} - \frac{\mu}{T}\rho, \tag{52-13}$$

so that (52-13) is the expression for the entropy density of the ideal Bose gas. From these relations we also verify:

$$\mathrm{d}\mu = -s\,\mathrm{d}T + \frac{1}{\rho}\mathrm{d}p. \tag{52-14}$$

From (52-11) and the hydrodynamics, one verifies that the ideal Bose gas obeys a law of entropy conservation:

$$\frac{\partial \rho s}{\partial t} + \nabla \cdot \rho s \boldsymbol{v} = 0. \tag{52-15}$$

The ideal Bose gas for $T > T_c$ can be referred to as semi-classical, since, although Planck's constant appears in the equations of state (see 52-7), the macroscopic dynamics are the Euler equations which do not have Planck's constant and which would have also been arrived at, had we discussed a Maxwell–Boltzmann gas obeying Newton's laws.

Starting from Schrödinger's equation plus the assumption of local equilibrium we have been able to show that an ideal Bose gas obeys the Euler hydrodynamics. Since we deal with a non-interacting system we can say nothing about the approach to equilibrium, and thus nothing about the Navier–Stokes hydrodynamics.

As commented in § 50 the expression for the energy density has an uncertainty as far as surface corrections (terms in the form of a divergence) are concerned. We know of no way to determine which if any of

Notes p. 348

the expressions (50-23,24) or linear combination thereof is preferable. Each leads to the same total energy, has the same classical limit and is real. Perhaps this lack of uniqueness in the hydrodynamics can even be extended to quantities other than the energy density.

Since the differences are always surface terms it appears that as far as phenomena inside the fluid are concerned the consequences of the hydrodynamics will be independent of these ambiguities. For instance the speed of sound will be the same for the different approaches.

However, as far as hydrodynamic boundary conditions are concerned, these surface ambiguities might lead to different consequences which are in principle observable. We do not delve further into this unresolved question here since it is aside the point of understanding the difference between the hydrodynamics of the semi-classical and condensed Bose gases.

53 *Thermo-Hydrodynamics of the Condensed Ideal Bose Gas*

In this section we generalize the procedure of the previous section to derive the hydrodynamics and thermodynamics of the condensed ideal Bose gas. It will be seen that the macroscopic description of the ideal Bose gas is in some sense a slight generalization of the Landau two fluid equations of He II.

The starting point for the procedure must be a generalization of the off-equilibrium density matrix (52-2,3) to the case of Bose condensation. Once we have the density matrix the equation of motion (50-7) determines it uniquely at later times and hence also determines the hydrodynamics. For rotational equilibrium we have derived from first principles the density matrix. In this situation $\boldsymbol{v}_n \neq \boldsymbol{v}_s$ are both varying in space and so are μ, ρ_s. We thus assume, in complete parallel with the derivation of classical hydrodynamics (§ 52), that when the condensed ideal Bose gas is near to equilibrium, the density matrix has the same form except that the variables which determine the distribution might vary from point to point. Thus, off-equilibrium (51-51) implies

$$w_1(\boldsymbol{r}_1', \boldsymbol{r}_1'') = \Psi(\boldsymbol{r}_1')\Psi^*(\boldsymbol{r}_1'') + \frac{m}{\lambda^3}\sum_n \frac{Z'^n \exp(-\pi\xi_1/n\lambda^2)}{n^{3/2}} \exp\left(i\frac{m}{\hbar}\xi_1 \cdot \boldsymbol{v}_n\right), \tag{53-1}$$

Notes p. 348

where now

$$Z = Z(\boldsymbol{r}_1, t), \quad T = T(\boldsymbol{r}_1, t), \quad \boldsymbol{v}_{\mathrm{n}} = \boldsymbol{v}_{\mathrm{n}}(\boldsymbol{r}_1, t). \tag{53-2}$$

The constant multiplicative factor of the off diagonal long range order has been absorbed into it so that now

$$\Psi^* \Psi = m \langle N_0 \rangle \psi^*_{k_0} \psi_{k_0}. \tag{53-3}$$

The distribution (53-1) is characterized by the independent variables Z, T, $\boldsymbol{v}_{\mathrm{n}}$, Ψ and hence we need equations for the time development of these quantities. When we have as many independent equations as variables, they will constitute the macroscopic description. Such a theory is macroscopic since the number of degrees of freedom is much less than the number needed for a first principles approach.

In order to derive the hydrodynamic equations the velocity must be introduced into the description. For the semi-classical Bose gas (§ 52), it was brought in through the Galilean transformation of the stationary equilibrium state. It could also have been brought in via the rotational equilibrium state. The generalization of each of these possibilities to off-equilibrium through the local equilibrium assumption would lead to identical results (hydrodynamics). For the condensed Bose gas this is not the case since it is only under rotation that $\boldsymbol{v}_{\mathrm{n}}$ is split from $\boldsymbol{v}_{\mathrm{s}}$. The rotational equilibrium state brings out additional degrees of freedom and is thus more general for the condensed Bose gas. For this reason we applied the postulate of local equilibrium to the rotational density matrix in order to arrive at (53-1,2).

The reduced density matrix (53-1) has the form of (52-2) plus ODLRO, but where the properties of the local order depend on the normal fluid. The justification for replacing $\boldsymbol{v}$ in (52-2) with $\boldsymbol{v}_{\mathrm{n}}$ in (53-1) came from the rotational behavior. In order to show that Z' can vary and need not be identical to unity [as is the case for slow rotation (51-30)] the fast rotation was provided as an example.

The total density is

$$\rho(\boldsymbol{r}) = w_1(\boldsymbol{r}, \boldsymbol{r}) = \rho_{\mathrm{n}} + \rho_{\mathrm{s}}, \tag{53-4}$$

where we have introduced (as before) the normal and superfluid densities

$$\rho_{\mathrm{s}}(\boldsymbol{r}) = \Psi^*(\boldsymbol{r})\, \Psi(\boldsymbol{r}), \tag{53-5}$$

$$\rho_{\mathrm{n}}(\boldsymbol{r}) = \frac{m}{\lambda^3} \sum_n \frac{Z'^n}{n^{3/2}}, \tag{53-6}$$

Notes p. 348

From (50-11,12) we see that mass is conserved and in fact

$$\frac{\partial \rho}{\partial t} + \nabla \cdot (\rho_n \boldsymbol{v}_n + \rho_s \boldsymbol{v}_s) = 0, \tag{53-7}$$

if one introduces

$$\boldsymbol{v}_s = \frac{\hbar}{m} \nabla \varphi, \tag{53-8}$$

where

$$\Psi = \sqrt{\rho_s}\, e^{i\varphi}. \tag{53-9}$$

From (50-16,17) one finds that (53-1) leads to the momentum conservation law:

$$\frac{\partial}{\partial t}(\rho_n v_n + \rho_s v_s)_i + \frac{\partial}{\partial r_\alpha}\Bigg[p_n \delta_{i\alpha} + \rho_s v_{s,i} v_{s,\alpha} + \rho_n v_{n,i} v_{n,\alpha} - \frac{\hbar^2}{2m^2}\left(\sqrt{\rho_s}\frac{\partial^2 \sqrt{\rho_s}}{\partial r_i\, \partial r_\alpha} - \frac{\partial \sqrt{\rho_s}}{\partial r_i}\frac{\partial \sqrt{\rho_s}}{\partial r_\alpha}\right)\Bigg] = 0, \tag{53-10}$$

where we have set

$$p_n = \frac{k_B T}{\lambda^3} \sum_n \frac{Z'^n}{n^{5/2}}. \tag{53-11}$$

The energy density can be taken to be given by (50-24) which then leads to

$$U = \tfrac{3}{2} p_n + \tfrac{1}{2}\rho_n v_n^2 + \tfrac{1}{2}\rho_s v_s^2 - \frac{\hbar^2}{4m^2}(\sqrt{\rho_s}\nabla^2\sqrt{\rho_s} - \nabla\sqrt{\rho_s}\cdot\nabla\sqrt{\rho_s}). \tag{53-12}$$

This can also be written

$$U = \tfrac{3}{2} p_n + \tfrac{1}{2}\rho_n v_n^2 + \tfrac{1}{2}\rho_s v_s^2 - \frac{\hbar^2}{2m^2}(\sqrt{\rho_s}\nabla^2\sqrt{\rho_s} - \tfrac{1}{4}\nabla\cdot\nabla\rho_s). \tag{53-13}$$

The energy conservation law follows from (50-26,27):

$$\frac{\partial U}{\partial t} + \nabla \cdot \boldsymbol{Q} = 0, \tag{53-14}$$

where

$$Q_i = \tfrac{1}{2}\rho_n v_n^2 v_{n,i} + (U_n + p_n) v_{n,i} + \rho_s v_{s,i}\left[\frac{v_s^2}{2} - \frac{\hbar^2}{2m^2}\frac{\nabla^2\sqrt{\rho_s}}{\sqrt{\rho_s}}\right] -$$

Notes p. 348

$$-\frac{\hbar^2}{2m^2}v_{s,j}\left\{\sqrt{\rho_s}\frac{\partial^2\sqrt{\rho_s}}{\partial r_i\,\partial r_j}-\frac{\partial\sqrt{\rho_s}}{\partial r_i}\frac{\partial\sqrt{\rho_s}}{\partial r_j}\right\}-\frac{\hbar^2}{4m^2}\frac{\partial}{\partial r_j}\left\{\rho_s\frac{\partial v_{s,i}}{\partial r_j}\right\} \tag{53-15}$$

where $U_n \equiv \frac{3}{2}p_n$, and from now on the term in the form of a perfect divergence $\nabla \cdot \nabla\rho_s$ in U has been dropped and thus its contribution to $\boldsymbol{Q}$ has been ignored in (53-15).

For a superfluid the five basic conservation laws are *not* a complete set. Additional equations are required to describe the ODLRO or macroscopically occupied quantum state. For the ideal Bose gas, the equation of motion for Ψ is just the Schrödinger equation. To see this, one need only apply (50-7) to (53-1) when ξ_1 is large so that the normal contribution vanishes. Thus

$$-\frac{\hbar^2}{2m}\nabla^2\Psi = i\hbar\frac{\partial\Psi}{\partial t}, \tag{53-16}$$

or

$$\frac{\mathrm{D_s}\boldsymbol{v}_s}{\mathrm{D}t} = -\nabla\mu, \tag{53-17}$$

$$\frac{\partial\rho_s}{\partial t} + \nabla\cdot\rho_s\boldsymbol{v}_s = 0, \tag{53-18}$$

where we have set

$$\mu = -\frac{\hbar^2}{2m^2}\frac{\nabla^2\sqrt{\rho_s}}{\sqrt{\rho_s}}. \tag{53-19}$$

Equations (53-7,10,14,16) constitute a complete description for the time development of the system as described by (53-1). In these equations appear two quantities μ, Z' which enter on the footing of a chemical potential; μ is the driving force of the superfluid or dynamic chemical potential and Z' is the thermodynamic chemical potential determining the properties of the normal fluid. As discussed previously in § 51, in the case of rotation *Z' and μ must be related in order for there to exist a Bose condensation.* We carry over that restriction (51-94) to the general off-equilibrium behavior. Thus (53-1) is to be supplemented with

$$\log Z' = \beta m[\mu + \tfrac{1}{2}(\boldsymbol{v}_s - \boldsymbol{v}_n)^2]. \tag{53-20}$$

This relation is an extension of the local equilibrium postulate. It says that the normal and superfluid phases are locally in equilibrium with

Notes p. 348

each other (i.e., the chemical potentials are equal). This condition couples the behavior of the macroscopic wave function (ODLRO) to that of the normal fluid or excited states. To see this, consider the thermodynamic relation for p_n:

$$\mathrm{d}p_n = \rho_n \,\mathrm{d}\mu + \rho s \,\mathrm{d}T + \rho_n \,\mathrm{d}\tfrac{1}{2}(\boldsymbol{v}_n - \boldsymbol{v}_s)^2, \tag{53-21}$$

where as with rotation we have introduced

$$\rho s = \frac{5}{2}\frac{p_n}{T} - \frac{\rho_n}{T}\frac{\log Z'}{\beta m} = \frac{5}{2}\frac{p_n}{T} - \frac{\rho_n}{T}[\mu + \tfrac{1}{2}(\boldsymbol{v}_n - \boldsymbol{v}_s)^2]. \tag{53-22}$$

Relation (53-21) shows that changes in μ are coupled by the Bose condensation condition to changes in the thermodynamic quantities $p_n, T, \frac{1}{2}(\boldsymbol{v}_n - \boldsymbol{v}_s)^2$.

Use of (53-21) and the identity (51-107) allows the equation for the time development of momentum (53-10) to be written

$$\frac{\partial}{\partial t}(\rho_s v_s + \rho_n v_n)_i + \frac{\partial}{\partial r_\alpha}(\rho_s v_{s,i} v_{s,\alpha} + \rho_n v_{n,i} v_{n,\alpha})$$
$$= -\rho \frac{\partial \mu}{\partial r_i} - \rho s \frac{\partial T}{\partial r_i} - \rho_n \frac{\partial \frac{1}{2}(\boldsymbol{v}_n - \boldsymbol{v}_s)^2}{\partial r_i}, \tag{53-23}$$

which is identical with the momentum law for He II. Although the equation for the time development is identical, the stresses exerted on a given plane are of quite a different form, being anisotropic even when $\boldsymbol{v}_n = \boldsymbol{v}_s = 0$.

The first and second law of thermodynamics follows from (53-13) and is

$$\mathrm{d}U = (\mu + \tfrac{1}{2}v_s^2 - \boldsymbol{v}_n \cdot \boldsymbol{v}_s)\,\mathrm{d}\rho + T\,\mathrm{d}\rho s + \boldsymbol{v}_n \cdot \mathrm{d}\boldsymbol{J}$$
$$+ \rho_s(\boldsymbol{v}_s - \boldsymbol{v}_n)\cdot \mathrm{d}\boldsymbol{v}_s + \rho_s\,\mathrm{d}\mu, \tag{53-24}$$

which except for the term $\rho_s\,\mathrm{d}\mu$ is the same as the expression for He II. From (53-24) one can then derive an expression for the time change of the entropy density by using the other equations to eliminate the time derivatives. One finds

$$\frac{\partial \rho s}{\partial t} + \nabla \cdot \rho s \boldsymbol{v}_n = 0, \tag{53-25}$$

which states that only the excitations transport the entropy as in He II.

Notes p. 348

As mentioned in the last section one can regard $\rho_s \, d\mu$ as a surface term with respect to variations in the parameters that describe the system. Identity (51-107) shows that when ρ_s is changed at *each* point by an amount $\delta\rho_s$ then the contribution to the local energy is in the form of a divergence which if removed to the boundary, vanishes. Thus, for situations where one is concerned with *changes* at a point it appears to be justified to drop $\rho_s \, d\mu$. Thus, in calculating $\partial U/\partial t$ we now ignore $\rho_s \, \partial\mu/\partial t$ and obtain instead of (53-15)

$$Q_i = (\mu + \tfrac{1}{2}v_s^2)J_i + \rho s T v_{n,i} + \rho_n \boldsymbol{v}_n \cdot (\boldsymbol{v}_n - \boldsymbol{v}_s) v_{n,i}, \qquad (53\text{-}26)$$

where use has been made of (53-22) and which is identical with the Landau energy conservation law (4-7).

Equations (53-7,17,23) and either (53-25) or (53-14) now form eight independent equations (provided that we count $\boldsymbol{v}_s$ as three variables) for the time development of the condensed ideal Bose gas which are identical with the eight Landau two fluid equations. One also has from the single valuedness of Ψ the quantization of circulation.

However, there are differences with the Landau two fluid hydrodynamics. First, there does *not* here exist a scalar p so that

$$\nabla p = \rho \nabla \mu + \rho s \nabla T + \rho_n \nabla \tfrac{1}{2}(\boldsymbol{v}_n - \boldsymbol{v}_s)^2. \qquad (53\text{-}27)$$

For the Landau theory (53-27) holds and the stresses are isotropic. For the Bose gas, the fact that in calculating ∇U one cannot ignore $\rho_s \nabla \mu$ prevents one from obtaining such a relation. As we remarked, $\rho_s \, \delta\mu$ can be removed to a surface where it will vanish when δ is a variation of ρ_s in each volume element, but $\rho_s \nabla \mu$ is a little too much non-local and although it can be removed to a surface, it will *not* vanish there. Thus, from the Landau theory expression for the pressure

$$p = -U + \rho(\mu + \tfrac{1}{2}v_s^2 - \boldsymbol{v}_n \cdot \boldsymbol{v}_s) + \rho s T + \boldsymbol{J} \cdot \boldsymbol{v}_n, \qquad (53\text{-}28)$$

one will not get from (53-24) the expression (53-27) since $\rho_s \nabla \mu$ cannot be ignored. In fact, the left hand side of (53-28) for an ideal Bose gas is p_n.

The appearance of this extra term is probably related to the fact that for an ideal Bose gas, knowledge of the *thermodynamic* variables, μ, $\boldsymbol{v}_s$, $\boldsymbol{v}_n$, T does *not* imply knowledge of ρ_s. For the condensed ideal Bose gas ρ_s is a *ninth* independent variable and it obeys a *conservation* law (53-18). The relation (53-20) determines some properties of ρ_s in terms of the thermodynamic variables, but (53-20) by no means yields

Notes p. 348

an equation of state $\rho_s = \rho_s(\mu, T, \mathbf{v}_n, \mathbf{v}_s)$. Conservation of ρ_s and thus ρ_n is contrary to the behavior of He II.

In summary, the equations for the *time development* of the condensed ideal Bose gas are the same as the Landau two fluid theory except that ρ_s is conserved. Quantization of circulation is built in automatically. The thermodynamics are somewhat more complicated. If one is interested in the first and second laws of thermodynamics for a volume of fluid, then the term $\rho_s \, d\mu$ is a surface term for any variation and one is led to the basic relation obeyed by He II. We will use this explicitly in an example in § 54. On the other hand, there is no justification for dropping $\rho_s \, d\mu$ from gradients of the energy and thus pressure. In this way, the stresses have a peculiar quantum anisotropic character, depending on the deformation so that in contrast with the Landau two fluid theory, Pascal's law does *not* hold for the condensed Bose gas!

While the non-interacting Bose gas is certainly not He II, it bears a strong resemblance and has the advantage of being a quantum fluid for which everything can be calculated from first principles. Perhaps the ideal Bose gas hydrodynamics has in it the form of the modifications which must be made in the two fluid hydrodynamics to include wave function curvature.

We close this section with some speculations on modifications in the approach which will have to be made in order to include interactions. Although we expect a thermodynamic relation like (52-21) to still hold for μ, there undoubtedly will be a change in the dynamic relation (53-19). For instance, we expect that instead of (53-19) interactions might lead to

$$\mu = -\frac{\hbar^2}{2m^2} \frac{\nabla^2 \sqrt{\rho_s}}{\sqrt{\rho_s}} + \alpha F(\rho_s), \tag{53-29}$$

where F is some function. If $F(\rho_s) = \rho_s$ then condition (53-29) and (51-91) lead to the Ginsburg–Pitaevskii equation [16]. In particular, a characteristic length is introduced over which the wave function drops to zero at a boundary or vortex core. This healing length is in general much less than the radius of the container in strong contrast to the ideal Bose gas. As a result of this term the ground state will be far more incompressible.

The other major modification to expect as a result of introducing interactions is in the relationship between ρ_s and the microscopic properties as contained in the reduced density matrix. Onsager and

Notes p. 348

Penrose [17] have shown that for an *interacting* system similar to He^4 the off-diagonal long range order comprises only about 8% of the system at 0 °K. The ODLRO is a measure of the single particle condensate, but in an interacting system one might expect also to have correlated pairs of particles. For the particles condensed in this pair state, the center of mass velocity is the same as the velocity of the single particle condensate, but the individual mates of the pair move with different velocities. The condensed pairs will show up as an ODLRO contribution to the second reduced density matrix w_2 [13]. It is suggestive to speculate [18] that if one *adds* together the single particle condensate, to the pair condensate, to the three particle condensate, etc., that one will arrive at the superfluid density ρ_s.

54 Some Solutions to the Condensed Bose Gas Hydrodynamics

In the previous section we saw that although the equations of *state* of the condensed Bose gas are quite different from He II, the equations of *motion* bear a striking similarity to the Landau two fluid theory. In this section we will work on the assumption that one has a *fluid* which obeys the condensed Bose hydrodynamics and solve some special cases thereof.

Many of the interesting properties of the condensed Bose gas were made apparent from an investigation of the statistical mechanics in a rotating vessel. Now let us *start from the hydrodynamics* and follow the procedure of § 18 by maximizing the entropy to obtain the equilibrium properties. We will arrive at the same conclusions as in § 51 which fact will demonstrate the consistency of our procedure.

An ideal Bose gas in a rotating container will be in thermodynamic equilibrium if the entropy is a maximum:

$$\int \rho s \, \mathrm{d}V = \text{maximum}, \tag{54-1}$$

subject to the constraints

$$\int \rho \, \mathrm{d}V = \text{constant}, \tag{54-2}$$

$$\int U \, \mathrm{d}V = \text{constant}, \tag{54-3}$$

Notes p. 348

$$\int \boldsymbol{r} \times \boldsymbol{J} \, \mathrm{d}V = \text{constant}. \tag{54-4}$$

Multiplying (54-2,3,4) by Lagrange multipliers $C_a, C_b, \boldsymbol{C}_c$ and incorporating in (54-1) yields

$$\int [\rho s + C_a \rho + C_b U + \boldsymbol{C}_c \cdot (\boldsymbol{r} \times \boldsymbol{J})] \, \mathrm{d}V = \text{maximum}. \tag{54-5}$$

We regard all quantities as functions of the independent variables $\rho, \rho s, \boldsymbol{J}, \boldsymbol{v}_s, \rho_s$. From the vanishing of the variations of $\rho, \rho s, \boldsymbol{J}$ we find

$$\mu + \tfrac{1}{2}v_s^2 - \boldsymbol{v}_n \cdot \boldsymbol{v}_s = -C_a/C_b, \tag{54-6}$$

$$T = -\frac{1}{C_b}, \tag{54-7}$$

$$v_n = -\frac{\boldsymbol{C}_c \times \boldsymbol{r}}{C_b}, \tag{54-8}$$

which express the fact that in equilibrium, the entropy is an extremum. As before, we don't perform the variation of $\boldsymbol{v}_s$ since it will be restricted by $\nabla \times \boldsymbol{v}_s = 0$. For the condensed Bose gas, there is a ninth independent variable ρ_s. However, its variation identically vanishes since it appears only through the term $\rho_s \, \delta\mu$ which by use of identity (51-107) becomes a surface term that vanishes at the boundary.

Equations (54-6,7,8) are consistent with the Bose condensed hydrodynamics provided that the equilibrium is stationary in the rotating system, $\nabla \times \boldsymbol{v}_s = 0$, and $\nabla \cdot \rho_s(\boldsymbol{v}_n - \boldsymbol{v}_s) = 0$.

There are still many solutions consistent with these restrictions. To obtain further information, the stability criteria must be investigated. Substituting (54-6,7,8) into (54-5) yields that in equilibrium

$$\int p_n \, \mathrm{d}V = \text{minimum}. \tag{54-9}$$

For given temperature changes in p_n are determined by

$$\delta p_n = \rho_n \, \delta[\mu + \tfrac{1}{2}(\boldsymbol{v}_n - \boldsymbol{v}_s)^2]. \tag{54-10}$$

If we use the fact that ρ_n increases as $\mu + \frac{1}{2}(\boldsymbol{v}_n - \boldsymbol{v}_s)^2$ increases, then the condition (54-9) becomes that in *stable* equilibrium

$$\mu + \tfrac{1}{2}(\boldsymbol{v}_n - \boldsymbol{v}_s)^2 = \text{minimum}, \tag{54-11}$$

Notes p. 348

or if now we compare equilibrium states with the same $\boldsymbol{v}_n$, the one which will be stable satisfies

$$\mu + \tfrac{1}{2}v_s^2 - \boldsymbol{v}_n \cdot \boldsymbol{v}_s = \text{minimum}. \tag{54-12}$$

That ρ_n is an increasing function of $\mu + \frac{1}{2}(\boldsymbol{v}_n - \boldsymbol{v}_s)^2$ follows directly from taking the second variation of (54-5); it also can be seen from the calculated result in § 51.

There are still many solutions to (54-12). However, if we now introduce the quantization of circulation, there is a unique solution which is identical with that obtained from the statistical mechanics of § 51. In order to modify this procedure to include a bump on the wall, the condition (54-4) must be replaced by the statement that the total angular momentum of fluid plus massive bucket is known. This in turn is equivalent to giving $\boldsymbol{v}_n$ and we don't go further into the details, since all results are identical with § 51.

When an external field, say gravity acts on the fluid, Eqs. (53-17,23) become modified to

$$\frac{D_s \boldsymbol{v}_s}{Dt} = -\nabla\mu + \boldsymbol{g}, \tag{54-13}$$

$$\frac{\partial J_i}{\partial t} + \frac{\partial}{\partial r_\alpha}(\rho_s v_{s,i} v_{s,\alpha} + \rho_n v_{n,i} v_{n,\alpha}) = -\rho\frac{\partial \mu}{\partial r_i} - \rho s\frac{\partial T}{\partial r_i} - \rho_n \frac{\partial \frac{1}{2}(\boldsymbol{v}_n - \boldsymbol{v}_s)^2}{\partial r_i} + \rho g_i. \tag{54-14}$$

We look for a solution with the fluid at rest ($v_n = v_s = 0$): these equations yield

$$\nabla\mu = \boldsymbol{g}, \tag{54-15}$$

and

$$\nabla T = 0, \tag{54-16}$$

which implies that the normal contribution to the pressure is

$$\nabla p_n = \rho_n \boldsymbol{g}. \tag{54-17}$$

The dynamic equation for the chemical potential (53-19) yields an equation for the superfluid distribution in the gravitational field

$$-\frac{\hbar^2}{2m^2}\nabla^2\sqrt{\rho_s} + gz\sqrt{\rho_s} = \frac{\varepsilon_0}{m}\sqrt{\rho_s}, \tag{54-18}$$

where ε_0 is an integration constant and gravity is in the z direction.

Notes p. 348

The solution to this equation takes the form of Bessel functions of order 1/3 multiplied by exponentials in the x and y direction:

$$\sqrt{\rho_s} = [C_1 \zeta^{1/2} J_{1/3}(\tfrac{2}{3} i \zeta^{3/2}) + C_2 \zeta^{1/2} J_{-1/3}(\tfrac{2}{3} i \zeta^{3/2})]\, e^{ik_1 x}\, e^{ik_2 y}, \tag{54-19}$$

where

$$\zeta = \frac{z}{\ell} - \frac{\varepsilon_0}{mg\ell}, \qquad \ell \equiv \left(\frac{\hbar^2}{2m^2 g}\right)^{1/3}. \tag{54-20}$$

Imposing boundary conditions in general leads to a restriction on the allowed values of ε_0. However, as with rotation, there is only one value which is most stable. The stability condition follows as before and is, in this case:

$$\mu + gz = \varepsilon_0/m = \text{minimum}. \tag{54-21}$$

This solution will be achieved for $k_1 = k_2 = 0$.

The dependence of the normal fluid density on height z can be obtained from (54-21) and (53-20) which imply

$$Z = \exp \beta(\varepsilon_0 - mgz),$$

so one finds from (53-1) that

$$\rho_n = \frac{m}{\lambda^3} \sum_n \frac{\exp n\beta(\varepsilon_0 - mgz)}{n^{3/2}}.$$

Note that in contrast with (51-97) we do not now include the external field in the definition of Z. The characteristic length over which the normal fluid density varies is

$$\ell_n = k_B T/mg.$$

In order that one be justified in describing the system hydrodynamically it had better be true that the length over which the macroscopic variable ρ_n changes be much greater than the interatomic spacing:

$$(\rho/m)^{-1/3} \ll \ell_n,$$

which implies a restriction on the strength of the external field. This also implies that ℓ is much larger than the interatomic spacing as can be shown by noting that $(\rho/m)^{-1/3} = \alpha\lambda$ where $\alpha \approx 1$ at the critical temperature and decreases for decreasing T (with volume fixed). It is possible

Notes p. 348

in principle to satisfy $(\rho/m)^{-1/3} \ll \ell_{\mathrm{n}}$ and still have (for $T \approx 0.01\ T_{\mathrm{c}}$): $\ell \approx \ell_{\mathrm{n}}$ so that even in an external field there is no separation of phases.

In a stationary arrangement, two connected containers of a Bose fluid will have the same chemical potential as implied by (53-17). The thermodynamic relation for μ, (53-21), then yields

$$\Delta p_{\mathrm{n}} = \rho s \Delta T, \tag{54-22}$$

which describes the fountain effect. To see that this relation has the same consequences as the He II fountain effect, consider a condensed Bose fluid in a gravitational field; then

$$\nabla p_{\mathrm{n}} = \rho_{\mathrm{n}} \boldsymbol{g}, \qquad \rho_{\mathrm{s}} \nabla \mu = \rho_{\mathrm{s}} \boldsymbol{g}. \tag{54-23}$$

If there are two containers of Bose fluid each in equilibrium with a Maxwell–Boltzmann vapor as in Fig. 56, the condition that the stresses on the free surface be equal becomes

$$(p_{\mathrm{n}} + p_{zz})_{\mathrm{A}} = (p_{\mathrm{n}} + p_{zz})_{\mathrm{B}}, \tag{54-24}$$

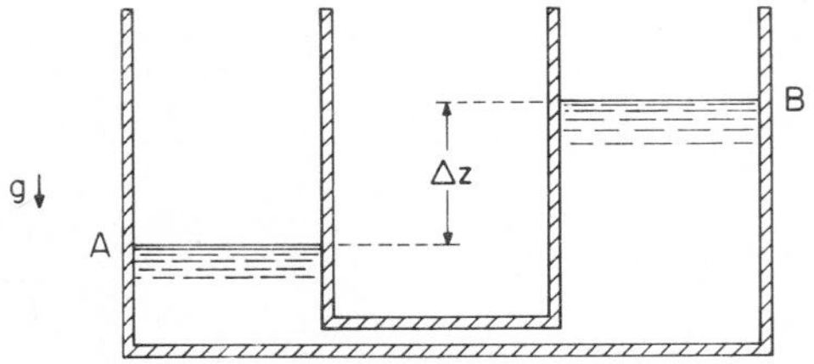

Fig. 56. The level difference Δz developed between two vessels of superfluid connected by a narrow constriction.

where the subscripts A, B denote the respective surfaces which are perpendicular to the z direction and we have introduced the superfluid stress tensor

$$p_{ij} = -\frac{\hbar^2}{2m^2}\left(\sqrt{\rho_{\mathrm{s}}}\,\frac{\partial^2 \sqrt{\rho_{\mathrm{s}}}}{\partial r_i\, \partial r_j} - \frac{\partial \sqrt{\rho_{\mathrm{s}}}}{\partial r_i}\frac{\partial \sqrt{\rho_{\mathrm{s}}}}{\partial r_j}\right). \tag{54-25}$$

For simplicity we work with the boundary condition that the perpendicular derivative of the $\sqrt{\rho_{\mathrm{s}}}$ vanish at a boundary. In this case $\sqrt{\rho_{\mathrm{s}}}$ is a function of z alone. Then (54-23) yields

$$\frac{\partial p_{zz}}{\partial z} = -\rho_{\mathrm{s}}\, g, \tag{54-26}$$

Notes p. 348

since the only non-zero component of p_{ij} is p_{zz}. Now if we set $p = p_n + p_{zz}$ we have proven

$$p_A = p_B$$

at the surface;

$$\nabla p = \rho \boldsymbol{g}$$

within the bulk liquid, and

$$\Delta p = \rho s \Delta T$$

across the superleak. These three relations are identical with those that describe the fountain effect in He II. In particular, one finds that the level difference is

$$g\Delta z = s\Delta T.$$

The anisotropy of the stresses in a condensed Bose fluid is most clearly brought out by considering a situation in which a single quantized vortex line is on the axis of a cylindrical bucket at 0 °K. Then

$$\sqrt{\rho_s} = CJ_1(k_{11}r/R), \qquad \boldsymbol{v}_s = \frac{\hbar}{mr}\hat{\boldsymbol{e}}_\theta,$$

for the boundary condition that the perpendicular derivative of the wave function vanish. The force per unit area exerted radially outward by the fluid on the wall $r = R$, z arbitrary, is from (54-25)

$$\rho_s(R)\left(\frac{\varepsilon_{1,1,0}}{m} - \frac{\hbar^2}{2m^2R^2}\right), \tag{54-27}$$

where $\varepsilon_{1,1,0}$ is given by (51-37). The force on the top and bottom walls, $z = 0$, H and r arbitrary is similarly zero. Thus at the location $r = R$, $z = H$, the forces on two arbitrarily close but perpendicular walls is different or the stresses are anisotropic.

This anisotropy has striking consequences. Since any plane, $z =$ constant, is a plane of constant (perpendicular) stress a vortex in a condensed Bose fluid should *not* show a dimple at the free surface at the location of the core. In a classical fluid a radial stress gradient is necessary to maintain the centripetal acceleration of fluid around a vortex line. As the stresses are isotropic this reflects itself in a varying force on a plane perpendicular to the vortex axis and thus leads to a dimple. For the

Notes p. 348

Bose condensed fluid a radial stress gradient is also necessary for maintaining the centripetal acceleration, however, it is uncoupled from the z behavior by the anisotropy.

Another situation where anisotropy may play a crucial role is in the flow of a Bose condensed fluid in a converging pipe as in Fig. 57. For

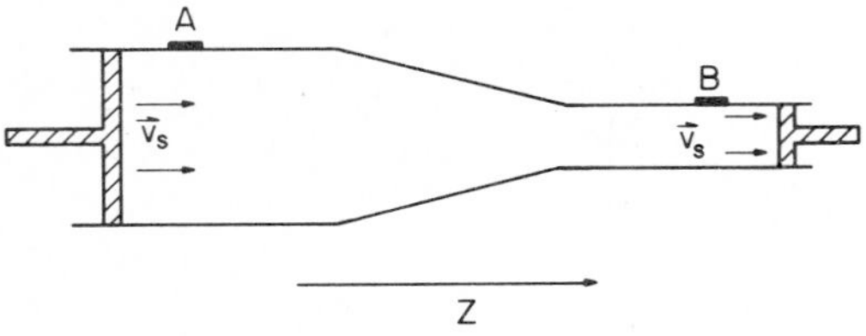

Fig. 57. Apparatus used to discuss the forces exerted on pressure sensitive diaphragms located parallel to a converging flow.

simplicity we will take $T = 0\,°\mathrm{K}$. Then from the Landau two fluid theory there exists a pressure gradient in the tube which is necessary to accelerate the fluid through the constriction:

$$p_{\mathrm{B}} - p_{\mathrm{A}} = -\tfrac{1}{2}\rho[v_{\mathrm{s}}(\mathrm{B})^2 - v_{\mathrm{s}}(\mathrm{A})^2], \tag{54-28}$$

where we ignore pressure induced changes in ρ. According to the two fluid theory this pressure difference should be observable by placing pressure sensitive diaphragms at A and B. We mentioned in § 30 that if, however, one tried to observe this pressure change through the level difference developed in standpipes connected to points A and B, no effect would be observed, because the restriction $\nabla \times \boldsymbol{v}_{\mathrm{s}} = 0$ forces the superfluid streamlines to enter the standpipes.

For a Bose condensed fluid, the standpipes will similarly show no effect, but in contrast to the Landau two fluid theory the anisotropy of the stresses may also imply, as with the vortex flow, that no force difference can be recorded on the pressure sensitive diaphragms which are located *parallel* to the streamlines. Of course there would have to be a stress difference on the pistons which force the accelerated flow and are located *perpendicular* to the streamlines.

An essential difference between the ideal Bose gas and the Landau two fluid theory are the anisotropic stresses. This difference can only be observed through the different boundary conditions implied, since the divergence of the stress tensor is the same for the two theories. In a real

Notes p. 348

system there will exist in addition to the wave function curvature an isotropic contribution to the superfluid stress tensor which is due to the mutual interaction between the superfluid component atoms. Although these isotropic stresses will dominate within the fluid one might wonder if at the surface (where the curvature is localized) there will remain some quantum anisotropy in the He II stresses. This is best investigated by careful measurements on the meniscus of He II, and in § 47 we saw that the related experimental situation is controversial. Perhaps arrangements as in Fig. 57 should also be accurately investigated [19]. Finally it should be noted that the anisotropic stresses result directly from the need to impose a boundary condition on $\sqrt{\rho_s}$ and are in conflict with Pascal's law which was a basic assumption involved in deriving the Landau two fluid equations in § 3.

To discuss the propagation of sound in a condensed Bose fluid, we take as independent variables, μ, T, v_n, v_s, ρ_s. Then the linearized hydrodynamics yield

$$-\omega\frac{\partial\rho}{\partial\mu}\mu' - \omega\frac{\partial\rho}{\partial T}T' - \omega\frac{\partial\rho}{\partial\rho_s}\rho_s' + \rho_s k v_s' + \rho_n k v_n' = 0, \quad (54\text{-}29)$$

$$-\omega\frac{\partial\rho s}{\partial\mu}\mu' - \omega\frac{\partial\rho s}{\partial T}T' - \omega\frac{\partial\rho s}{\partial\rho_s}\rho_s' + \rho s k v_n' = 0, \quad (54\text{-}30)$$

$$-\omega v_s' + k\mu' = 0, \quad (54\text{-}31)$$

$$-\omega\rho_s v_s' - \omega\rho_n v_n' + k\rho\mu' + \rho s k T' = 0, \quad (54\text{-}32)$$

$$-\omega\rho_s' + \rho_s k v_s' = 0, \quad (54\text{-}33)$$

where we look for a traveling wave solution of amplitude denoted by a prime. If the dependence on the ninth internal variable ρ_s is ignored [i.e., ignoring $(\partial\rho/\partial\rho_s)_{\mu,T}$ and $(\partial\rho s/\partial\rho_s)_{\mu,T}$] then (54-29,30,31,32) lead to the same dispersion law as obeyed by He II (7-14). For the Bose fluid, one must not only include the ninth variable, but also the dual nature of μ which leads to the additional restriction

$$\mu' = \frac{\hbar^2 k^2}{4m^2\rho_s}\rho_s', \quad (54\text{-}34)$$

where quantities without primes are to be evaluated in the unperturbed state.

Notes p. 348

From (54-34) the equations (54-31,33) lead to the dispersion law:

$$\left(\frac{\omega}{k}\right)^2 = \frac{\hbar^2 k^2}{4m^2}, \tag{54-35}$$

which is just the single particle mode of a non-interacting system. For the ideal Bose gas (53-6) and (53-22) imply

$$\left(\frac{\partial \rho}{\partial \rho_s}\right)_{\mu,T} = 1, \qquad \left(\frac{\partial \rho s}{\partial \rho_s}\right)_{\mu,T} = 0. \tag{54-36}$$

Hence (54-29,30,32) become

$$-\frac{\omega^2}{k}\frac{\partial \rho}{\partial \mu} v_s' - \omega \frac{\partial \rho}{\partial T} T' + \rho_n k v_n' = 0, \tag{54-37}$$

$$-\frac{\omega^2}{k}\frac{\partial \rho s}{\partial \mu} v_s' - \omega \frac{\partial \rho s}{\partial T} T' + \rho s k v_n' = 0, \tag{54-38}$$

$$\omega \rho_n v_s' - \omega \rho_n v_n' + \rho s k T' = 0. \tag{54-39}$$

The only solution to these equations which satisfies (54-34) and (54-31,33) is

$$v_s' = \rho_s' = \mu' = 0,$$

and

$$\frac{\omega^2}{k^2} = \frac{(\rho s)^2}{\rho_n}\left(\frac{\partial \rho s}{\partial T}\right)_\mu^{-1}, \tag{54-40}$$

which is the speed of propagation of a thermal sound wave in an ideal Bose gas.

Finally, it should be mentioned that if the joint distribution of a mixture of a rotating condensed Bose gas and a Maxwell–Boltzmann gas is investigated, one arrives directly at the equilibrium conditions (6-12,13,14) which are analogous to the conditions obeyed by a He^3–He^4 mixture or He^4 in equilibrium with its vapor.

Notes

[1] A. Einstein, Sitzber. Preuss. Akad. Wiss. (1924) p. 261; (1925) p. 3.

[2] F. London, Nature **141**(1938)643; Phys. Rev. **54**(1938)947; J. Phys. Chem. **43**(1939) 49; *Superfluids* (Wiley, New York, 1954) Vol. 2, p. 40.

[3] J. M. Blatt and S. T. Butler, Phys. Rev. **100**(1955)476.

[4] L. D. Landau, J. Phys. USSR **5**(1941)71; Phys. Rev. **75**(1949)884.

[5] We follow closely the mathematical procedure developed by M. Kac, unpublished.

[6] I. Fujiwara, D. ter Haar and H. Wergeland, J. Statistical Phys. **2**(1970)329.

[7] L. Tisza, Nature **141**(1938)913; Compt. Rend. **207**(1938)1035,1186; J. Phys. Radium **1**(1940)164,350.

[8] See M. Kac, Amer. Math. Monthly, **73 II**(1966)No. 4, for a discussion of Weyl's theorem.

[9] E. G. D. Cohen, in: *The Boltzmann Equation Theory and Applications*, eds. E. G. D. Cohen and W. Thirring (Springer-Verlag, Wien, 1973) p. 157.

[10] G. E. Uhlenbeck and G. W. Ford, *Lectures in Statistical Mechanics* (American Mathematical Society, Providence, 1963) Chap. 7.

[11] O. Penrose, Phil. Mag. **42**(1951)1373; H. Frohlich, Physica **37**(1967)215; J. Phys. Soc. Japan **26** Suppl. (1969)189; Phys. Kondens. Materie **9**(1969)350; Proc. Phys. Soc. (London) **87**(1966)330.

[12] F. London, J. Chem. Phys. **11**(1943)203.

[13] C. N. Yang, Rev. Mod. Phys. **34**(1962)694.

[14] F. Bloch, Phys. Rev. **7A**(1973)2187.

[15] By this definition the observation of fourth sound in He^3 at milli-Kelvin temperatures suggests that it undergoes a superfluid transition [viz. Eq. (39-10)]. See H. Kojima, D. Paulson and J. Wheatley, Phys. Rev. Letters **32**(1974)141.

[16] V. L. Ginsburg and L. P. Pitaevskii, Zh. Eksp. Teor. Fiz. **34**(1958)1240 [Sov. Phys. JETP **7**(1958)858]. See also E. Gross, J. Math. Phys. **4**(1963)195.

[17] O. Penrose and L. Onsager, Phys. Rev. **104**(1956)576.

[18] This idea was proposed and developed by C. Cambero and M. Zaidi (unpublished).

[19] H. E. Corke and A. F. Hildebrandt, Phys. Fluids **11**(1968)465, have measured the Bernoulli pressure drop in He II but on surfaces which deflect the flow.

CHAPTER IX

Superconducting Magneto-Hydrodynamics

55 *Introduction: The Similarities of Superfluids and Superconductors*

In many metals it is found that as the temperature is lowered past a critical temperature (e.g., 4 °K for Sn) the electrical resistance vanishes abruptly. An electric current then can flow with no potential difference. This phenomenon of superconductivity was discovered in 1911 by Kamerlingh Onnes [1] who was also the first to liquefy helium. It is obviously comparable with the frictionless flow of liquid helium below T_λ. In fact as soon as superfluidity in He II was observed in 1938, London [2] proposed that superfluidity and superconductivity should be understood from the same point of view. This has turned out to be an extremely successful hypothesis. For instance, in superconductors there exist macroscopic quanta of magnetic flux which are analogous to the quanta of circulation in He II.

Besides these similarities there are also differences of which the most obvious are consequences of the fact that the electron fluid is a *charged superfluid*, so that interaction with the electromagnetic field must be taken into account. There are, however, also differences which cannot be simply attributed to the charge as for instance the fact that the ability of a superconductor to transport heat does not in passing through the critical temperature show the remarkable increase observed in He II (§ 29).

On the theoretical side, the macroscopic theory of superconductivity proposed by London [3] in 1935, and which was so successful in describing the electrical and magnetic properties of superconductors, had similarities with the Landau two fluid theory of He II. London envisaged the electron fluid as being composed of normal and super electrons. The super electrons could flow without friction through the lattice

Notes p. 385

(i.e., the background of positive ions), but the normal electrons would flow according to Ohm's law just as in a normal metal. It is this assumption which is the real difference between the two fluid theories of He II and superconductivity. According to London the normal current in a superconductor always involves dissipation (the Joule heat). In fact in the approximation where one neglects dissipation one must say that there is no normal current, or that the normal electrons are clamped by the lattice [4]. This is in contrast with the flow of He II where in the approximation that dissipation is neglected, the normal component is able to flow.

Clearly the similarities between superconductors and superfluids will be much closer if one compares the behavior of a superconductor with the flow of He II *when the normal fluid is clamped* ($v_n = 0$) as can be realized when the He II is contained in a superleak which then plays the role of the lattice for the superconductor. One may then expect that the *only* difference which remains from the macroscopic point of view, is the charge of the electron fluid [5].

It is this point of view which will be developed in this chapter. It leads to a slight generalization of the London equations.

56 *Two Fluid Hydrodynamics of Superconductivity*

Our basic postulate (see § 55) is that the equations of superconductivity on the hydrodynamic level follow from the equations of *clamped* He II (Chapter V) *by including the charge.* In this way we obtain from (40-1,6) the law of conservation of electrons (i.e., charge):

$$\frac{\partial \rho}{\partial t} + \nabla \cdot (\rho_s \boldsymbol{v}_s + \boldsymbol{J}_n) = 0, \qquad (56\text{-}1)$$

where to first order in the deviation from equilibrium the normal fluid electric current density is

$$\frac{q}{m} \boldsymbol{J}_n = \sigma \left[\boldsymbol{E} - \frac{m}{q} \nabla(\mu + \tfrac{1}{2} v_s^2) \right] + \sigma \alpha \nabla T, \qquad (56\text{-}2)$$

where ρ, ρ_s are the mass densities of all, super, electrons; $\boldsymbol{E}$ is the electric field, q/m is the charge to mass ratio of a superconducting particle, σ is the electrical conductivity, α the normal fluid thermal-power, and

Notes p. 385

μ the electron chemical potential. From (40-3,8) we obtain the equation of motion of the superelectron fluid:

$$\frac{\mathrm{D_s}\boldsymbol{v}_\mathrm{s}}{\mathrm{D}t} = -\nabla\mu + \frac{q}{m}\left(\boldsymbol{E} + \frac{1}{c}\boldsymbol{v}_\mathrm{s} \times \boldsymbol{B}\right) - \nabla H, \tag{56-3}$$

where

$$H = -\zeta\nabla \cdot \rho_\mathrm{s}\boldsymbol{v}_\mathrm{s}. \tag{56-4}$$

$\boldsymbol{B}$ is the magnetic field, c the speed of light. The electron entropy law follows from (40-2,4) by including the charge:

$$\frac{\partial\rho s}{\partial t} + \nabla \cdot \frac{\boldsymbol{q}}{T} = \frac{\Sigma}{T} \tag{56-5}$$

where

$$\boldsymbol{q} = -\kappa\nabla T - \sigma\beta T\left[\boldsymbol{E} - \frac{m}{q}\nabla(\mu + \tfrac{1}{2}v_\mathrm{s}^2)\right] \tag{56-6}$$

and

$$\Sigma = \boldsymbol{J}_\mathrm{n} \cdot \left[\boldsymbol{E} - \frac{m}{q}\nabla(\mu + \tfrac{1}{2}v_\mathrm{s}^2)\right] - \frac{\boldsymbol{q} \cdot \nabla T}{T} - H\nabla \cdot \rho_\mathrm{s}\boldsymbol{v}_\mathrm{s}. \tag{56-7}$$

By the Onsager relations:

$$\alpha = \beta, \tag{56-8}$$

and in order for the entropy production to be positive definite, κ, σ, ζ are positive and

$$(\alpha + \beta)^2 < \frac{4\kappa}{\sigma T}. \tag{56-9}$$

The first and second law of thermodynamics follows from (39-4) by including the charge and is

$$\mathrm{d}U = (\mu + \tfrac{1}{2}v_\mathrm{s}^2)\,\mathrm{d}\rho + T\,\mathrm{d}\rho s + \rho_\mathrm{s}\boldsymbol{v}_\mathrm{s} \cdot \mathrm{d}\boldsymbol{v}_\mathrm{s} + \mathrm{d}U_{\mathrm{e.m.}}, \tag{56-10}$$

where the electromagnetic energy density is

$$U_{\mathrm{e.m.}} = \frac{1}{8\pi}(E^2 + B^2). \tag{56-11}$$

To complete these equations they must be supplemented with equations of state for μ, T, ρ_s, and Maxwell's equations which are in Gaussian units:

Notes p. 385

$$\nabla \times \boldsymbol{B} = \frac{4\pi}{c}\boldsymbol{j} + \frac{1}{c}\frac{\partial \boldsymbol{E}}{\partial t}, \tag{56-12}$$

$$\nabla \times \boldsymbol{E} = -\frac{1}{c}\frac{\partial \boldsymbol{B}}{\partial t}, \tag{56-13}$$

$$\nabla \cdot \boldsymbol{B} = 0, \qquad \nabla \cdot \boldsymbol{E} = 4\pi\rho_{\text{net}}, \tag{56-14}$$

where ρ_{net} is the net charge density and the total electric current density is

$$\boldsymbol{j} = \frac{q}{m}(\rho_s \boldsymbol{v}_s + \boldsymbol{J}_n). \tag{56-15}$$

Equations (56-1,3,5,12,13) form eleven equations for the eleven basic variables ρ, ρs, $\boldsymbol{v}_s$, $\boldsymbol{E}$, $\boldsymbol{B}$ which describe the state of a superconductor [5]. It is straightforward to show that (56-10) implies the energy conservation law

$$\frac{\partial U}{\partial t} + \nabla \cdot \left[(\mu + \tfrac{1}{2}v_s^2)(\rho_s \boldsymbol{v}_s + \boldsymbol{J}_n) + \boldsymbol{q} + \rho_s \boldsymbol{v}_s H + \frac{c}{4\pi}(\boldsymbol{E} \times \boldsymbol{B})\right] = 0. \tag{56-16}$$

In the limit that the charge q goes to zero these equations reduce to the equations of clamped He II. The easiest way to see that these are a *unique* generalization of the He II equations to include charge is to first write down (56-10) and (56-3). These two generalizations are obvious since they amount to adding in the energy of the electromagnetic field, and including the Lorentz force in the acceleration equation. Then using methods discussed in § 21 one shows that the most general equations consistent with the entropy law and mass (charge), energy, conservation are (56-1,5) supplemented by (56-2,6).

As in He II the super (electron) fluid accelerates as though it were able to flow without friction. From (56-3) we immediately see that in the steady state with v_s = constant $\neq 0$,

$$\boldsymbol{E} - \frac{m}{q}\nabla(\mu + \tfrac{1}{2}v_s^2) = 0$$

in the direction of the current. Thus there is no electro-chemical potential difference, or the flow of current is taking place at zero voltage drop, in much the same way as He II can flow at zero chemical potential drop.

Except for the $\frac{1}{2}v_s^2$ modification of the chemical potential (56-2) is identical with the Ohm law in a classical metal. In the limit where there

Notes p. 385

is no dissipation (56-7) shows us that $\boldsymbol{J}_n = 0$ or there is no normal current. Equation (56-2) for the normal current was first proposed by Ginsburg [6].

Except for the term in ∇H the fundamental superfluid equation (56-3) was first proposed by London [3]. He also usually ignored the $\nabla\mu$ term since its effects were expected to be small.

If one introduces the scalar and vector potentials so that

$$\boldsymbol{E} = -\nabla\Phi - \frac{1}{c}\frac{\partial \boldsymbol{A}}{\partial t}, \tag{56-17}$$

$$\boldsymbol{B} = \nabla \times \boldsymbol{A}, \tag{56-18}$$

then from (56-3) follows the superconducting analogue of the Kelvin circulation theorem or

$$\frac{\mathrm{D_s}\Gamma_\mathrm{s}}{\mathrm{D}t} = 0, \tag{56-19}$$

where

$$\Gamma_\mathrm{s} \equiv \oint\left(\boldsymbol{v}_\mathrm{s} + \frac{q}{mc}\boldsymbol{A}\right)\cdot \mathrm{d}\boldsymbol{\ell}. \tag{56-20}$$

Thus the circulation of $\boldsymbol{v}_\mathrm{s}$ plus q/mc multiplied by the magnetic flux through a given contour is a constant of the motion. This is another way of understanding the existence of persistent electric currents in superconductors. From (56-19) follows the analogue of the Lagrange theorem which says that if

$$\nabla \times \left(\boldsymbol{v}_\mathrm{s} + \frac{q}{mc}\boldsymbol{A}\right) = 0, \qquad \text{or: } \boldsymbol{v}_\mathrm{s} + \frac{q}{mc}\boldsymbol{A} = \nabla\chi \tag{56-21}$$

everywhere, it stays zero (χ is the canonical velocity potential). This last result also follows directly from (56-3) which by use of (56-17,18) becomes

$$\frac{\partial}{\partial t}\left(\boldsymbol{v}_\mathrm{s} + \frac{q}{mc}\boldsymbol{A}\right) = -\nabla\left(\mu + \tfrac{1}{2}v_\mathrm{s}^2 + \frac{q}{m}\Phi + H\right) + \boldsymbol{v}_\mathrm{s} \times \left[\nabla \times \left(\boldsymbol{v}_\mathrm{s} + \frac{q}{mc}\boldsymbol{A}\right)\right]. \tag{56-22}$$

Now taking the curl of (56-22) leads to

$$\frac{\partial}{\partial t}\left[\nabla \times \left(\boldsymbol{v}_\mathrm{s} + \frac{q}{mc}\boldsymbol{A}\right)\right] = \nabla \times \left\{\boldsymbol{v}_\mathrm{s} \times \left[\nabla \times \left(\boldsymbol{v}_\mathrm{s} + \frac{q}{mc}\boldsymbol{A}\right)\right]\right\}, \tag{56-23}$$

Notes p. 385

so that if (56-21) holds everywhere at an initial time, (56-23) shows that its time derivative is zero so that it will stay zero.

London proposed that not only would (56-21) be consistent with superconductivity, but that it would characterize it. Thus he always supplemented the equations for the time development of the system with this restriction, which is clearly the parallel of the Landau condition, $\nabla \times \boldsymbol{v}_s = 0$, for He II. Historically the London condition (56-21) came first.

Using (56-21) Eq. (56-22) becomes

$$\frac{\partial \boldsymbol{v}_s}{\partial t} = \frac{q}{m}\boldsymbol{E} - \nabla(\mu + \tfrac{1}{2}v_s^2 + H). \qquad (56\text{-}24)$$

In the remaining sections of this chapter we discuss various applications of the macroscopic theory of superconductivity.

57 *The Meissner Effect*

After the observation of a flow of electricity with no resistance, it was natural to attempt to interpret the transition to superconductivity as one in which the classical electrodynamics were valid but with $\sigma = \infty$. If this was the case then the state of a superconductor would not be thermodynamically determined by temperature and the external field but would depend on how the state was produced. To see this consider two ways in which a superconductor at temperature $T < T_c$ (where T_c is the critical temperature) in an external magnetic field can be reached. On the one hand it can be cooled through T_c while always maintaining a magnetic field on it. On the other hand the field can be turned on after it has been cooled through T_c with no external field. An infinite conductivity implies that the magnetic field inside the substance cannot change, otherwise its time derivative would create an electric field and an infinite current. Thus in the first situation the material would have a magnetic field penetrating it throughout for $T < T_c$ and in the other case the field would be kept out. This dichotomy is comparable to the one that would arise in rotating He II as a consequence of interpreting the lambda transition as one in which viscosity went to zero (§ 19).

Meissner and Ochsenfeld [7] came to grips with this superconductivity problem in 1933 long before the comparable problem arose with He II.

Notes p. 385

They found that (for small enough magnetic fields) the final state always consisted of no magnetic field in the superconductor, provided that the sample was pure.

In terms of the London equation (56-21) one can see that this Meissner state must always be reached. First take the curl of (56-21) to obtain

$$\nabla \times \nabla \times \boldsymbol{v}_{\mathrm{s}} = -\frac{q}{mc}\nabla \times \boldsymbol{B}. \tag{57-1}$$

By use of (56-12,15) we obtain

$$\nabla \times \nabla \times \boldsymbol{v}_{\mathrm{s}} = -\frac{4\pi q^2}{m^2c^2}\rho_{\mathrm{s}}\boldsymbol{v}_{\mathrm{s}} - \frac{4\pi q^2}{m^2c^2}\boldsymbol{J}_{\mathrm{n}} - \frac{q}{mc^2}\frac{\partial \boldsymbol{E}}{\partial t}. \tag{57-2}$$

In the steady state, $\partial v_{\mathrm{s}}/\partial t = 0$, $\partial \rho/\partial t = 0$ and with no temperature gradient (57-2) becomes

$$\nabla \times \nabla \times \boldsymbol{v}_{\mathrm{s}} = -\frac{4\pi q^2}{m^2c^2}\rho_{\mathrm{s}}\boldsymbol{v}_{\mathrm{s}}. \tag{57-3}$$

Taking the curl again and using (56-21,14) yields

$$\nabla^2 \boldsymbol{B} = \frac{4\pi q^2}{m^2c^2}\rho_{\mathrm{s}}\boldsymbol{B}, \tag{57-4}$$

where the spatial variations in ρ_{s} have been ignored.

Equation (57-4) is the basic equation of the Meissner effect. According to it a magnetic field imposed on a superconductor decays from its value at the boundary to zero over a characteristic distance

$$\lambda_{\mathrm{L}} = \sqrt{\frac{m^2c^2}{4\pi q^2\rho_{\mathrm{s}}}} \tag{57-5}$$

referred to as the London penetration depth. A typical value for this distance is 10^{-5} cm. Near the critical temperature $\lambda_{\mathrm{L}} \to \infty$ and the external field penetrates deeper and deeper into the superconductor.

Since there is no second sound in superconductors one principally uses measurements of λ_{L} to determine ρ_{s}. Experimentally λ_{L} is determined through the magnetization of the superconducting specimen. For instance, consider a coil located inside a large solenoid. If a superconducting material initially within the inner coil is separated from it, an induced E.M.F. will result since the region initially occupied by the superconductor will now have a magnetic field (due to the outer sole-

Notes p. 385

noid). The amount of flux displaced by the superconductor when located within the inner coil depends on its geometry and λ_L. Thus measurements of the E.M.F. yield λ_L. The results [8] indicate that near the critical temperature $\lambda_L \to \infty$ ($\rho_s \to 0$) and that for most substances $\lambda_L \approx 10^{-5}$ cm at 0 °K.

These experiments face the difficulty that in order to see appreciable effects in the magnetization due to the finite penetration depth λ_L, the sample must be on the order of λ_L in width. Another experimental technique has been able to determine the temperature dependence of λ_L in bodies large compared with it. Casimir [9] suggested that if two coils are wound around the same superconducting cylinder then their mutual trapped flux or inductance will depend upon the degree, λ_L to which the magnetic field penetrates the superconductor. In fact since one expects ρ_s to increase as T decreases, the mutual inductance should diminish with temperature. Observation of this small change then yields the temperature variation of λ_L. These experiments [10] are consistent with the magnetization measurements.

Once (57-4) has been used to solve for $\boldsymbol{B}$ the superfluid velocity $\boldsymbol{v}_s$ follows from (56-21). It is found that in order for the material to keep out the external magnetic field, currents are generated over a region of depth λ_L from the surface. We see that if one characterizes superconductivity as a state in which the canonical momentum is irrotational then regardless of how the superconducting state was reached the material will act so as to expel the magnetic field.

In a neutral superfluid such as He II the characteristic distance over which the superfluid velocity varies in equilibrium is infinite or at least the size of the container restraining it. One need only remember the velocity of a vortex line (10-2) to realize its long range effects. For a superconductor we have just seen that due to the coupling with the electromagnetic phenomena the characteristic distance over which v_s varies in equilibrium is λ_L as given by (57-5). (Note that $\lambda_L \to \infty$ as $q \to 0$) The appearance of a finite characteristic length λ_L raises the following important difficulty. The Landau two fluid hydrodynamics have been observed to break down when the distance over which v_s varies is on the order of the coherence length a of the fluid. This situation for instance arises in the thin films. In general the Landau two fluid theory does not account for phenomena where the coherence length plays a role. For bulk samples of He II, however, the healing length can be made unimportant since the characteristic length over which v_s

Notes p. 385

changes is at least the size of the sample. Even for large superconducting specimens it is possible for the coherence length to be on the order of λ_L since λ_L is a material constant independent of the size of the sample. As the London equations (§ 56) are a transformation of the Landau two fluid theory we naturally expect that it will be applicable to superconductors where the coherence length is significantly smaller than λ_L. These are referred to as type II superconductors. For the other case where the coherence length is on the order of, or longer than λ_L (type I superconductors) the London equations cannot be expected to yield more than a qualitative picture. It is interesting to note that the early experiments on which London based his phenomenological theory were performed on type I superconductors. We will here limit our discussion to type II superconductors though many of these results do in fact also apply to type I systems. This is analogous with the situation in thin He II films where some of the Landau two fluid ideas (e.g., $\nabla \times \boldsymbol{v}_s = 0$) still appear to be valid.

As with rotation in He II one observes a Meissner effect ($v_s = 0$ in He II) only when the external field is small enough. When it increases past a critical field quantized flux lines analogous to quantized vortices enter the material. This mixed state will be discussed in § 59.

58 *Quantization of the Fluxoid*

As the 'fluxoid' or canonical circulation

$$\Gamma_s = \oint \left(\boldsymbol{v}_s + \frac{q}{mc} \boldsymbol{A} \right) \cdot d\boldsymbol{\ell} \tag{58-1}$$

is a constant of the motion for the electron fluid in a superconductor one is led by analogy with the Onsager [11] quantization in He II (§ 10) to impose a similar restriction here, or

$$\oint \left(\boldsymbol{v}_s + \frac{q}{mc} \boldsymbol{A} \right) \cdot d\boldsymbol{\ell} = \frac{nh}{m}, \tag{58-2}$$

where n is an integer. It was precisely from this point of view that London [12] was first to propose (58-2).

Consider the superconducting ring in Fig. 58. If the width of the ring is large compared with the London penetration depth then a contour

Notes p. 385

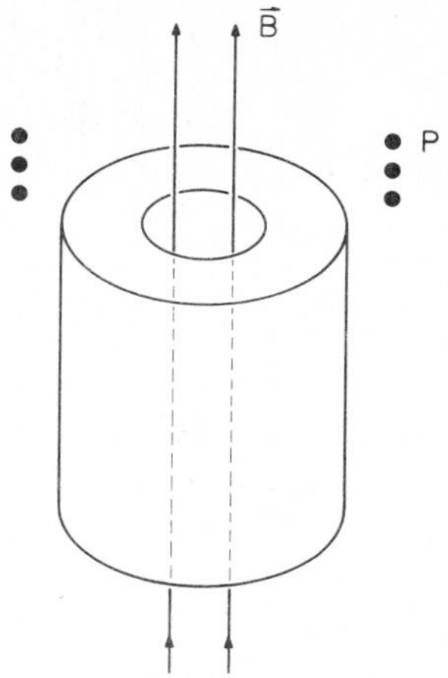

Fig. 58. Apparatus used to measure the flux trapped by a superconducting ring. The pick-up coils P receive an induced E.M.F. when the flux linkage changes as a result of oscillating the superconductor.

can be chosen for which $\boldsymbol{v}_s = 0$. Integrating once around the hole then yields

$$\frac{q}{c}\oint \boldsymbol{A} \cdot \mathrm{d}\ell = nh, \tag{58-3}$$

or the magnetic flux bounded by this contour is quantized:

$$\phi = \int \boldsymbol{B} \cdot \mathrm{d}\boldsymbol{S} = n\frac{hc}{q}. \tag{58-4}$$

The magnetic flux which is quantized includes that which is in the vacuum space plus that which penetrates a distance λ_L into the superconductor.

One might wonder, if by placing a solenoid in the hole of the ring, an arbitrary magnetic flux could be forced through the superconductor by varying the solenoid's current. In this circumstance (58-3) will still always be obeyed since surface currents will flow on the superconductor so that the *total* flux is quantized.

This macroscopic quantization was first observed by Deaver and Fairbank [13] and by Doll and Näbauer [14]. The method consisted of measuring the E.M.F. generated in a pick-up coil P when the flux

Notes p. 385

linkage between coil and superconductor was varied by oscillating the superconductor (Fig. 58).

A striking and fundamental result was that the lowest quantum of flux which could be observed corresponded to

$$q = 2e, \tag{58-5}$$

where e is the charge of an electron. That this should be the case was first suggested by Onsager [15] in 1959 based on considerations of the superfluid nature of the Bose condensate. He reasoned that in order to have a macroscopic quantum coherence the electrons would have to form bound pairs. These are referred to a Cooper pairs since he was first to present the mechanism under which they bind [16]. Although the electrons must form correlated pairs in order to display superconductivity the fact that each mate of the pair obeys Fermi statistics is crucial for the microscopic understanding [17] of superconductivity.

The basic unit of flux is

$$\phi_0 = \frac{hc}{2e} = 2 \times 10^{-7} \text{ gauss cm}^2. \tag{58-6}$$

The magnetic field of the Earth is 0.3 gauss. For these experiments the typical cylindrical radius is about 10^{-3} cm so that the Earth's magnetic flux is comparable to the flux quantum. Hence it is obvious that care must be used to perform these experiments in field free regions.

In terms of the canonical velocity potential χ introduced in (56-21) the quantization condition (58-2) becomes

$$\oint \nabla\chi \cdot d\ell = \frac{nh}{m}, \tag{58-7}$$

so that the states with $n = 0$ correspond to multiple valued potentials as is the case also with He II.

59 *The Mixed State of Type II Superconductivity*

When an external magnetic field is imposed on a superconductor 'surface' currents are generated so as to keep the field from entering the bulk of the material. For a type II superconductor this fact remains true only up to a critical external field H_{c1} above which the external field begins to penetrate the sample in the form of quantized flux lines. This

Notes p. 385

property is entirely comparable to the acquiring of rotation by the superfluid component of He II above a critical angular velocity. In that case we have already seen that the rotation is due to the formation of quantized vortex lines.

The existence of type II superconductivity was first predicted by Abrikosov [18]. Although his work was published in 1957, it was completed in the early 1950's. Landau, who believed the irrotationality conditions (e.g., $\nabla \times \boldsymbol{v}_s = 0$) and their relationship to macroscopic quantum states, nevertheless thought that the quantization of flux was a ridiculous idea [19], and held up publication. His objections vanished after Feynman's article in 1955 proposing quantization of vorticity in He II.

In this section we present a discussion of the thermodynamics of this mixed state of superconductivity, in parallel with our treatment of rotating He II.

The fundamental thermodynamic condition, from which all others must follow, is that the entropy of a *closed* system is a maximum in the equilibrium state. As we wish to consider a superconductor in an external or applied field, $\boldsymbol{H}$, the only way in which we can talk about a closed system is to include the currents which generate $\boldsymbol{H}$ in our thermodynamic system. To be explicit, we will let the superconductor sit inside a large solenoid whose current generates the applied field. It should be emphasized that $\boldsymbol{H}$ is the field in the absence of the superconductor or equivalently the field far from the superconductor. Resistance of the solenoid coil is neglected or in fact let it be a superconductor.

The state of thermodynamic equilibrium is now characterized by the condition

$$\int \rho s \, \mathrm{d}V = \text{maximum}, \tag{59-1}$$

where ρs is the entropy density of the superconductor. There are, however, subsidiary restrictions which express the fact that the system is closed. These are:

Conservation of charge:

$$\int \rho \, \mathrm{d}V = \text{constant}, \tag{59-2}$$

Conservation of energy:

$$\text{energy of superconductor} + \text{energy of solenoid} = \text{constant}. \tag{59-3}$$

Notes p. 385

In addition to the thermal energy of the superconductor, the energy of the system will be due to the currents in the superconductor and the current in the solenoid. When the currents in the superconductor, and hence the magnetic field $\boldsymbol{B}_s$ which they generate, vary there will be a contribution to the change in energy which follows from (56-10,11) with $\boldsymbol{B}$ replaced by $\boldsymbol{B}_s$. In general a change in currents within the superconductor will also involve a change in the total magnetic moment, $\mathcal{M}$ generated by the superconductor. In turn this implies a change in magnetic flux in the superconductor and thus also in the solenoid. This causes a back E.M.F. in the solenoid which means that its energy will change at a rate equal to the back E.M.F. multiplied by the current in the solenoid.

Since the current in the solenoid is related to $\boldsymbol{H}$ one is led to the expression

$$-\boldsymbol{H}\cdot \mathrm{d}\mathcal{M} \tag{59-4}$$

for this additional contribution to the change in energy of the system caused by the change in $\boldsymbol{B}_s$ [20]. We assume that the solenoid has an arbitrarily large self-inductance, so that its change in energy (59-4) reflects an infinitesimal change in current or $\boldsymbol{H}$.

In general the magnetic moment is given by

$$\mathcal{M} = \frac{1}{c}\sum_n \boldsymbol{A}_n i_n, \tag{59-5}$$

where A_n is the area of the nth circuit with current i_n and is assigned a direction by the right hand rule. For our considerations the currents in (59-5) are to be those within the superconductor. The expressions (59-4,5) are equivalent to a change in energy of

$$-\frac{1}{4\pi}\boldsymbol{H}\cdot \mathrm{d}\int \boldsymbol{B}_s\,\mathrm{d}V = -\mathrm{d}\left(\frac{1}{4\pi}\boldsymbol{H}\cdot\int \boldsymbol{B}_s\,\mathrm{d}V\right), \tag{59-6}$$

where we recall that the changes in $\boldsymbol{H}$ are negligible. When the boundary conditions at the surface of the superconductor are homogeneous the total magnetic field is

$$\boldsymbol{B} = \boldsymbol{H} + \boldsymbol{B}_s. \tag{59-7}$$

We shall always have in mind a cylindrical solenoid inside of which is a cylindrical superconductor with axis parallel so that (59-7) is valid.

Notes p. 385

In view of (59-4) the energy condition (59-3) becomes

$$\int U\,\mathrm{d}V - \frac{1}{4\pi}\int \boldsymbol{H}\cdot\boldsymbol{B}_{\mathrm{s}}\,\mathrm{d}V = \text{constant}, \tag{59-8}$$

where for the energy density of the superconductor one can use

$$\mathrm{d}U = \left(\mu + \tfrac{1}{2}v_{\mathrm{s}}^2 + \frac{q}{m}\Phi\right)\mathrm{d}\rho + T\,\mathrm{d}\rho s + \rho_{\mathrm{s}}\boldsymbol{v}_{\mathrm{s}}\cdot\mathrm{d}\boldsymbol{v}_{\mathrm{s}} + \frac{1}{8\pi}\mathrm{d}B_{\mathrm{s}}^2, \tag{59-9}$$

where the electrostatic energy has been written in terms of the electrostatic potential instead of the field $\boldsymbol{E}$. This is valid in stationary situations, $\partial\boldsymbol{B}/\partial t = 0$, which we assume obtains in equilibrium.

Multiplying (59-2,8) with Lagrange multipliers C_{a}, C_{b} and incorporating in (59-1) leads to the basic result describing the equilibrium state:

$$\int [\rho s + C_{\mathrm{a}}\rho + C_{\mathrm{b}}U - C_{\mathrm{b}}(1/4\pi)\boldsymbol{H}\cdot\boldsymbol{B}_{\mathrm{s}}]\,\mathrm{d}V = \text{maximum}. \tag{59-10}$$

From the vanishing of the first variations of $\delta\rho$, $\delta\rho s$ one finds the extremum conditions

$$\mu + \tfrac{1}{2}v_{\mathrm{s}}^2 + \frac{q}{m}\Phi = -\frac{C_{\mathrm{a}}}{C_{\mathrm{b}}} \tag{59-11}$$

$$T = -\frac{1}{C_{\mathrm{b}}}, \tag{59-12}$$

so that in equilibrium the electrochemical potential, and temperature are constant. As in the case of He II we did not perform the variation of $\boldsymbol{v}_{\mathrm{s}}$ from point to point in anticipation of a restriction which it must obey. Similarly for $\boldsymbol{B}_{\mathrm{s}}$ which is related to $\boldsymbol{v}_{\mathrm{s}}$ by the Maxwell equations.

Now in equilibrium (59-11,12) must be exactly consistent with (56-1,3,5) neglecting $\boldsymbol{J}_{\mathrm{n}}$, $\boldsymbol{q}$, H. The result is that in equilibrium

$$\nabla\cdot\rho_{\mathrm{s}}\boldsymbol{v}_{\mathrm{s}} = 0, \qquad \nabla\times\left(\boldsymbol{v}_{\mathrm{s}} + \frac{q}{mc}\boldsymbol{A}\right) = 0, \tag{59-13}$$

which could naturally be anticipated by the transformation which took us from He II to superconductivity.

There are many ways in which (59-13) can be satisfied. It can hold *everywhere* as in the Meissner state, or it might hold everywhere except in small non-superconducting one dimensional regions around which

Notes p. 385

the circulation will be quantized. These are called quantized flux lines. The equilibrium state is not further specified until we determine the number and locations of the flux lines. As with He II this is a *stability* property of the system and is best discussed directly from (59-10) which becomes from (59-11,12)

$$\iint \left[\int \rho_s \, d\tfrac{1}{2} v_s^2 + \frac{1}{8\pi} B_s^2 - \frac{1}{4\pi} \boldsymbol{H} \cdot \boldsymbol{B}_s \right] dV = \text{minimum}. \tag{59-14}$$

We now show that this relation leads to a critical field H_{c1} above which the entrance of quantized flux lines is favored. To discuss H_{c1} we must evaluate the energy and magnetic field of a flux line.

In cylindrical coordinates (58-2) implies

$$\boldsymbol{v}_s + \frac{q}{mc} \boldsymbol{A} = \frac{\hbar}{mr} \hat{\boldsymbol{e}}_\theta, \tag{59-15}$$

which is the generalization of (10-2). The differential equation obeyed by $\boldsymbol{v}_s$ follows from (59-13) and (56-12) and is in equilibrium

$$\nabla^2 \boldsymbol{v}_s = (1/\lambda_L^2) \boldsymbol{v}_s, \tag{59-16}$$

where for the cylindrical symmetry we take $\boldsymbol{v}_s = v_s(r)\, \hat{\boldsymbol{e}}_\theta$. Combining this equation with (59-15) yields the differential equation for $\boldsymbol{A}$:

$$\nabla^2 \boldsymbol{A} = \frac{1}{\lambda_L^2} \boldsymbol{A} - \frac{\hbar c}{q \lambda_L^2} \frac{\hat{\boldsymbol{e}}_\theta}{r}. \tag{59-17}$$

The solution to (59-17) which obeys cylindrical symmetry:

$$\boldsymbol{A} = A(r)\, \hat{\boldsymbol{e}}_\theta,$$

is the sum of a particular solution and the Bessel function solution to the homogeneous equation

$$A(r) = C_1 J_1(ir/\lambda_L) + C_2 Y_1(ir/\lambda_L) + \hbar c/qr. \tag{59-18}$$

The restriction that the magnetic field of the vortex goes to zero for $r \to \infty$ leads to

$$A = C H_1^+(ir/\lambda_L) + \hbar c/qr, \tag{59-19}$$

where the Henkel functions are defined by

$$H_n^{\pm}(x) \equiv J_n(x) \pm i Y_n(x) \underset{x \to \infty}{\simeq} \sqrt{2/\pi x} \exp\{\pm i[x - \tfrac{1}{4}(2n+1)\pi]\}, \tag{59-20}$$

Notes p. 385

and so far C is an undetermined integration constant. The magnetic field follows from

$$\boldsymbol{B} = \nabla \times \boldsymbol{A}, \tag{59-21}$$

and is

$$\boldsymbol{B} = (iC/\lambda_L)\, H_0^+(ir/\lambda_L)\, \hat{\boldsymbol{e}}_z, \tag{59-22}$$

where we have used

$$H_{n-1}(x) = (n/x)H_n(x) + H_n'(x). \tag{59-23}$$

The coefficient C can be determined from the integral form of (59-21):

$$\int \boldsymbol{B} \cdot \mathrm{d}\boldsymbol{S} = \oint \boldsymbol{A} \cdot \mathrm{d}\boldsymbol{\ell} \tag{59-24}$$

as the singular behavior of $\boldsymbol{A}$ near $r = 0$ has been lost by use of the differential relations. Evaluating (59-24) for large r yields

$$\frac{iC}{\lambda_L} \int_0^\infty H_0^+(ir/\lambda_L)\, 2\pi r\, \mathrm{d}r = \frac{hc}{q}, \tag{59-25}$$

or

$$C = -\frac{hc}{4q\lambda_L}, \tag{59-26}$$

where we have used the behavior near $x = 0$:

$$Y_1(x) \approx \frac{2}{\pi} J_1(x)(\log \tfrac{1}{2}x + \gamma_e) - \frac{2}{\pi x} - \frac{x}{2\pi}, \tag{59-27}$$

where $\gamma_e = 0.577...$ is Euler's constant.

The velocity field of the singly quantized flux line is now given by (59-15):

$$\boldsymbol{v}_s = -C \frac{q}{mc} H_1^+(ir/\lambda_L)\, \hat{\boldsymbol{e}}_\theta. \tag{59-28}$$

We can now evaluate the contribution to the free energy (59-14) which is of the form

$$-\frac{1}{4\pi} \boldsymbol{H} \cdot \int \boldsymbol{B}_s\, \mathrm{d}V, \tag{59-29}$$

Notes p. 385

where $\boldsymbol{B}_s$ is the magnetic field generated by currents in the superconductor: These are of two kinds: first there are the Meissner currents on the surface which screen out $\boldsymbol{H}$ from the bulk of the medium and then there are the quantized flux lines which allow penetration in a cylindrical region of radius λ_L. The Meissner currents are independent of the number of vortices present and since we are really interested in free energy differences between various states we ignore their contribution to (59-29). We then find that due to a flux line:

$$-\frac{1}{4\pi}\boldsymbol{H}\cdot\int \boldsymbol{B}_s\,\mathrm{d}V = -\frac{hc}{4\pi q}LH, \tag{59-30}$$

where L is the length of the superconductor.

To calculate the contribution of the energy to the free energy we first write

$$\rho_s\,\mathrm{d}\tfrac{1}{2}v_s^2 = \mathrm{d}\tfrac{1}{2}\rho_s v_s^2 - \tfrac{1}{2}v_s^2\,\mathrm{d}\rho_s \tag{59-31}$$

and ignore the term in $\mathrm{d}\rho_s$. Then the term of interest is

$$\int\left(\rho_s\frac{v_s^2}{2} + \frac{1}{8\pi}B_s^2\right)\mathrm{d}V = \frac{1}{8\pi}\int[B_s^2 + \lambda_L^2(\nabla\times\boldsymbol{B}_s)^2]\,\mathrm{d}V, \tag{59-32}$$

where we have used (57-3), (59-13) and are specializing to the energy of the quantized flux line. Since

$$\boldsymbol{B}_s = \lambda_L^2\nabla^2\boldsymbol{B}_s$$

(59-32) becomes

$$\int\left(\rho_s\frac{v_s^2}{2} + \frac{1}{8\pi}B_s^2\right)\mathrm{d}V = \frac{\lambda_L^2}{8\pi}\int\nabla\cdot[\boldsymbol{B}_s\times(\nabla\times\boldsymbol{B}_s)]\,\mathrm{d}V, \tag{59-33}$$

where we have used

$$\nabla\cdot\boldsymbol{B} = 0, \qquad \nabla\cdot(\boldsymbol{a}\times\boldsymbol{b}) \equiv \boldsymbol{b}\cdot\nabla\times\boldsymbol{a} - \boldsymbol{a}\cdot\nabla\times\boldsymbol{b}. \tag{59-34}$$

As with the vortex lines in He II there must be a region near the quantized flux line in which ρ_s is depleted. We approximate this behavior by saying that ρ_s drops to zero abruptly at a distance a from the flux line. The total energy of the flux line will then equal the integral (59-33) taken over the superconducting volume with core excluded, plus the integral of $B_s^2/8\pi$ over the core region. The integral (59-33) can be converted to a surface integral over the boundary of superconductor

Notes p. 385

and the surface of the core. If the sample is large compared with λ_L the boundary integral vanishes. The surface integral over the core yields

$$-i\frac{C^2La}{4\lambda_L}H_0^+(ia/\lambda_L)\,H_1^+(ia/\lambda_L), \tag{59-35}$$

and the *total* energy of the flux line is

$$\int\left(\rho_s\frac{v_s^2}{2}+\frac{1}{8\pi}B_s^2\right)\mathrm{d}V = -i\frac{C^2La}{4\lambda_L}H_0^+(ia/\lambda_L)\,H_1^+(ia/\lambda_L) - \frac{C^2La^2}{8\lambda_L^2}[H_0^+(ia/\lambda_L)]^2, \tag{59-36}$$

where the last term in (59-36) is the energy of the magnetic field inside the core region ($r < a$). The critical field $H = H_{c1}$ at which it will be favorable for a flux line to enter will be that for which (59-30) cancels (59-36). This expression assumes a much more transparent form when

$$a \ll \lambda_L. \tag{59-37}$$

Then using the expansions for small x

$$H_0^+(x) \approx 1 + \frac{2i}{\pi}(\log\tfrac{1}{2}x + \gamma_e), \qquad H_1^+(x) \approx -\frac{2i}{\pi x}, \tag{59-38}$$

leads to the energy

$$\int\left(\rho_s\frac{v_s^2}{2}+\frac{1}{8\pi}B_s^2\right)\mathrm{d}V = \frac{LC^2}{\pi^2}\left(\log\frac{\lambda_L}{a}+\log 2-\gamma_e\right). \tag{59-39}$$

The free energy (59-14) will now decrease by the entrance of a flux line if the external field is larger than the critical field:

$$H_{c1} = \frac{\phi_0}{4\pi\lambda_L^2}\log\frac{\lambda_L}{a}, \tag{59-40}$$

where in view of (59-37) the term $(\log 2 - \gamma_e)$ has been dropped and ϕ_0 is the basic quantum of flux (58-6). As H passes H_{c1} many flux lines will all of the sudden enter, because if they are a distance λ_L separated there will be no interaction between them. Thus at H_{c1} there is a sharp increase in the magnetic field in the superconductor, or a sharp drop in its *total* magnetization [21]. This is indicated schematically by the magnetization curve in Fig. 59. When the external field gets so large that the flux cores

Notes p. 385

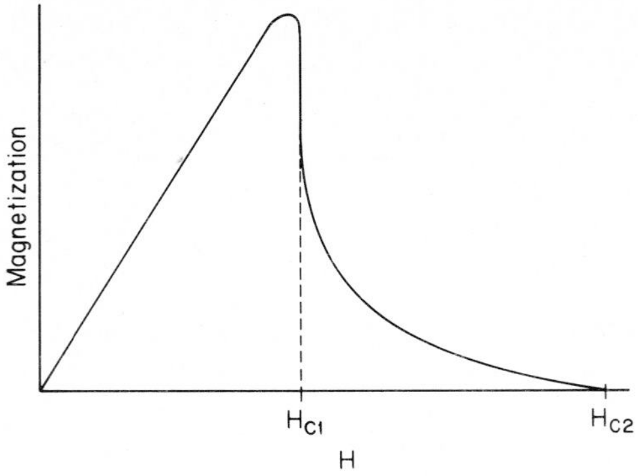

Fig. 59. The magnetization curve of a typical type II superconductor.

start to overlap, then superfluidity has been destroyed. This field is indicated by H_{c2}. It is important to realize that the total magnetization is due to the surface Meissner currents plus the flux lines and that these in general have opposite sense.

The lattice which the flux lines form can be observed directly by evaporating small metal particles over the superconductor which are then attracted to the locations where flux lines enter the superconductor [22].

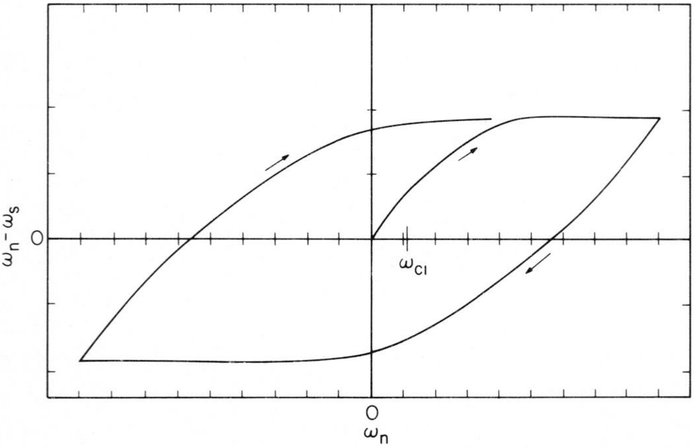

Fig. 60. The relative angular velocity $(\omega_n - \omega_s)$ versus the speed of rotation ω_n for He II in a superleak. If the y axis is relabeled magnetization and the x axis relabeled external field this graph becomes the behavior of a type II irreversible superconductor.

Notes p. 385

For a superconductor the imposition of an external field is analogous to rotation in He II. If the type II superconductor is a little bit dirty or irreversible so that the flux lines can be pinned then the hysteresis effects are also extremely similar to those observed in He II contained in a rotating superleak. In Fig. 60 the behavior of rotating He II as discussed in § 39 is plotted for relative rotation (instead of ω_s) versus the angular velocity of the container for an initial state of rest. This is just the behavior that is exhibited in a type II irreversible superconductor when the relative rotation is reinterpreted as magnetization and ω_n is reinterpreted as the external magnetic field [23].

60 *Superconducting Bernoulli and Chemical Potential Effects*

The magneto-hydrodynamics of the superconducting electron fluid have been developed by analogy with clamped superfluid helium. When He II is clamped in a superleak (§ 39) the characteristic wave made is fourth sound which propagates with a velocity u_4:

$$u_4^2 = \rho_s \left(\frac{\partial \mu}{\partial \rho}\right)_{\rho s} . \tag{60-1}$$

Now we will see that in a superconductor there should exist a propagating mode which is the analogue of fourth sound.

If one linearizes the *non-dissipative* equations of superconductivity, i.e., (56-1,3,5,12,13) neglecting $\boldsymbol{J}_n$, $\boldsymbol{q}$, H one obtains

$$-i\omega\rho' + ik\rho_s v_s' = 0, \tag{60-2}$$

$$-i\omega v_s' + ik\mu' = \frac{q}{m} E', \tag{60-3}$$

$$-i\omega(\rho s)' = 0, \tag{60-4}$$

$$\frac{4\pi q}{m} \rho_s v_s' - i\omega E' = 0, \tag{60-5}$$

where we look for a travelling *longitudinal* wave with frequency ω and wave vector k; the primed quantities denote deviations from equilibrium and the unprimed quantities are to be evaluated in the equilibrium state; (60-2,3,4,5) are four homogeneous equations in four unknowns, the consistency condition (§ 1) for a non-trivial solution yields the dispersion law for the speed ω/k of superconducting fourth sound:

$$\frac{\omega^2}{k^2} - \frac{c^2}{k^2\lambda_L^2} = u_4^2, \tag{60-6}$$

where $\mu = \mu(\rho, \rho s)$ and μ_4 is given by (60-1). In the zero charge limit (60-6) becomes (60-1). As λ_L is on the order of 10^{-5} cm one finds that a superconducting fourth sound wave will decay over a distance $u_4\lambda_L/c$ unless ω is on the order of 10^{15} sec^{-1}. Such longitudinal fields may be very difficult to create and so this mode is perhaps only of academic interest. Also at these frequencies $h\omega \gg k_B T$ so that the validity of a hydrodynamic approach is doubtful.

Following London and the analogy with He II the canonical superfluid momentum is irrotational:

$$\boldsymbol{v}_s + \frac{q}{mc}\boldsymbol{A} = \nabla\chi, \tag{60-7}$$

where χ is some scalar. In this way (56-3) becomes

$$\frac{\partial\chi}{\partial t} + \mu + \tfrac{1}{2}v_s^2 + \frac{q}{m}\Phi - \zeta\nabla\cdot\rho_s\boldsymbol{v}_s = \text{constant}, \tag{60-8}$$

which is the Bernoulli law for the electron fluid.

First consider a stationary situation so that $\partial\rho/\partial t = \partial\chi/\partial t = 0$. Then neglecting terms quadratic in the dissipative coefficients,

$$\mu + \tfrac{1}{2}v_s^2 + \frac{q}{m}\Phi = \text{constant}, \tag{60-9}$$

or the electrochemical potential $\equiv (\partial U/\partial\rho)m/q$ is constant throughout the superconductor. As an electromotive force, E.M.F., or reading on a voltmeter represents an electrochemical potential difference we see that in the stationary state the superconductor cannot develop an E.M.F. However, there *can* be an electric field.

A situation in which this happens has been investigated by Bok and Klein, and Morris and Brown [24] and is shown in Fig. 61. Consider a cylindrical superconductor with axis perpendicular to an externally imposed magnetic field $\boldsymbol{H}$ which is uniform at infinity. Inside the bulk of the superconductor the magnetic field must vanish. As the normal component of magnetic field is continuous at a surface (it is unaffected

Notes p. 385

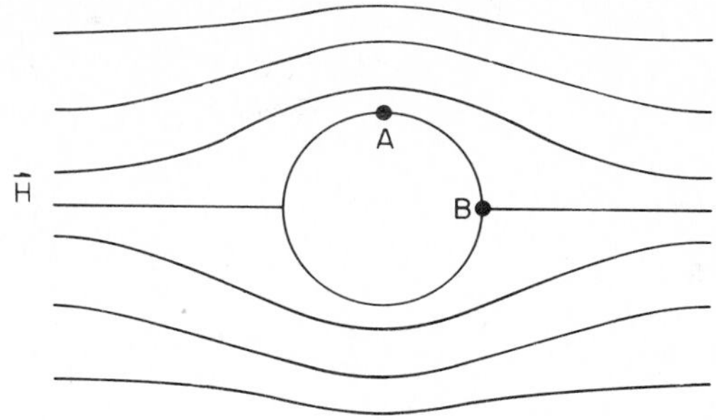

Fig. 61. A magnetic field imposed perpendicular to the axis of a superconducting cylinder will have flux lines bunched up at A so that the tangential field there is grèater than at B. This results in an electric field, somewhat analogous to a contact potential between these points.

by surface currents) it must vanish at the surface of the superconductor (in the steady state). Thus the magnetic field around the cylindrical superconductor will be distorted similar to the flow of an Euler fluid around a cylinder. In this way the magnetic field at point A will be greater than at point B. According to the London equations super-surface currents must exist so as to prevent the magnetic field from penetrating the bulk of the sample. These currents must be stronger at A than at B. Hence v_s^2 will be greater at A than at B and there will be an electric field between these points, (60-9).

This electric field must be measured by the Kelvin capacitance technique [25]. As mentioned, experiments [26] which connect a voltmeter between A and B are doomed to observing a null effect. Using the capacitance technique Bok and Klein found an electric field in qualitative agreement with (60-9). That is the best which can be hoped for since their experiment was performed on a type I superconductor where one expects the local hydrodynamics to be insufficient. No experiments on this effect have been performed on type II superconductors.

In the same way that a variation in the electron convective velocity can lead to an electric field so can a temperature gradient. With the same conditions that led to (60-9) one finds that a temperature difference leads to an electric potential difference:

$$\left(\frac{\partial \mu}{\partial T}\right)_{\rho} \delta T = \frac{q}{m} \delta \Phi, \qquad (60\text{-}10)$$

Notes p. 385

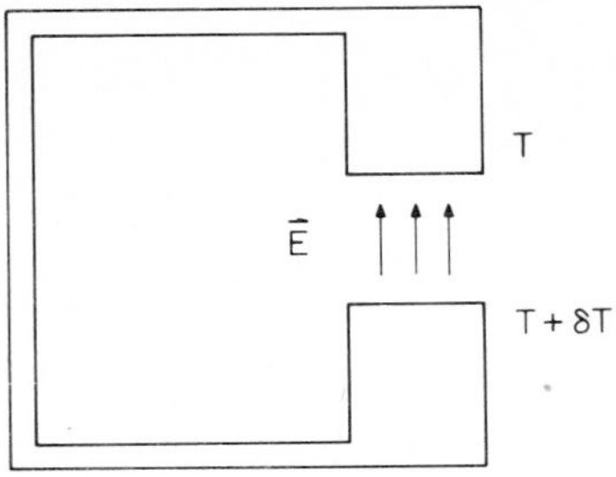

Fig. 62. A temperature difference across a superconductor leads to an electric field as shown.

as shown in Fig. 62. This is clearly analogous to the fountain effect in He II (§ 2) wherein a temperature difference leads reversibly to a pressure difference.

Attempts [27] to observe this superconducting fountain effect have run into difficulty, either because of irreproducible results or large surface dipole layers which also result from the temperature variation. As before, this is again an electric field with no E.M.F.

61 *The Josephson Effect*

Some of the most striking and useful effects in low temperature physics occur when two superconductors are separated by a weak, non-superconducting link, in such a way that the superfluid on the two sides remains coherent. These effects, first predicted by Josephson [28] are derived in this section from the London two fluid equations plus quantization of circulation.

Let us assume as in Fig. 63a that a weak link L interrupts a superconductor. Application of the superconducting Bernoulli law (60-8) to points 1 and 2 implies

$$\frac{\partial\,\delta\chi}{\partial t} + \delta\left(\mu + \tfrac{1}{2}v_s^2 + \frac{q}{m}\Phi\right) = 0, \qquad (61\text{-}1)$$

where δ indicates the difference between the value of a quantity at points 1 and 2:

$$\delta\chi = \chi_1 - \chi_2 . \qquad (61\text{-}2)$$

Notes p. 385

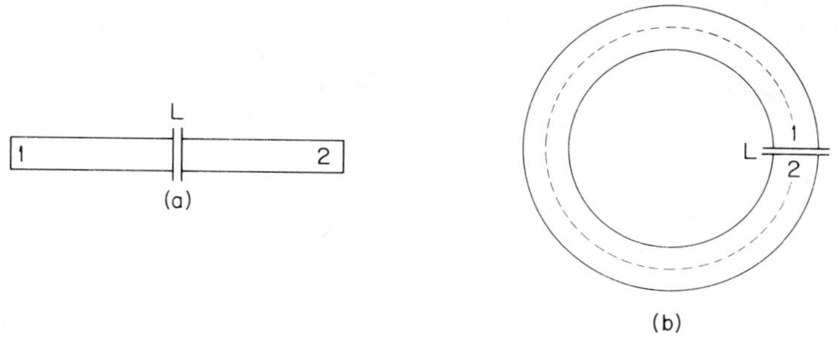

Fig. 63. Two superconductors separated by a weak link L (a). In (b) is shown a superconducting ring interrupted by a weak link.

We have assumed that point 1 is far enough from point 2 so that the term involving the superconducting bulk viscosity ζ can be neglected. From the first and second laws of thermodynamics (59-9) we see that

$$\frac{\partial U}{\partial \rho} = \mu + \tfrac{1}{2}v_s^2 + \frac{q}{m}\Phi. \tag{61-3}$$

As the energy required to add an electron is the electrochemical potential, and a voltage difference is an electrochemical potential difference (61-1) becomes

$$\frac{m}{\hbar}\frac{\partial\, \delta\chi}{\partial t} = \frac{q}{\hbar}V, \tag{61-4}$$

where V is the voltage across the superconductor.

If the link L is very weak, as, for instance, when it is a centimeter of normal metal, then there will be no supercurrent across it; or at each side of the link one has (neglecting dissipation):

$$v_{s\perp} = 0. \tag{61-5}$$

As the link is made thinner and thinner a point will eventually be reached at which the superelectrons can leak through. This will be determined by the material properties of the link, but phenomenologically one can argue that the most general boundary condition on the supercurrent at the link is that it be proportional to a function of the phase difference:

$$v_{s\perp} = \alpha f(\delta\chi). \tag{61-6}$$

Notes p. 385

From (60-7) we see that a supercurrent requires a phase difference especially when we note that at any point the vector potential can be made to vanish by an appropriate choice of gauge. In fact the most general expression for the supercurrent at the junction must depend on the quantities which might change across it; these are the phase, voltage and temperature or to lowest order:

$$v_{s\perp} = \alpha f(\delta\chi) + \alpha_1\, \delta T + \alpha_2 V. \tag{61-7}$$

The dependence on temperature and voltage must be dissipative corrections since they have different time reversal character from v_s, thus to lowest order we ignore them, arriving at (61-6).

Now it can be argued that [29]:

$$f(m\,\delta\chi/\hbar + 2n\pi) = f(m\,\delta\chi/\hbar), \tag{61-8}$$

which follows from the quantization principle (58-7) which states that $m\,\delta\chi/\hbar$ is determined at best to modulo 2π. To see this consider Fig. 63b where we imagine that there is a superfluid circulation in the ring corresponding to a fluxoid quantum number n. Integrating from point 1 to point 2 across the junction leads to a phase difference of $m\,\delta\chi/\hbar$, continuing around again over the dashed line implies that the phase difference between these points is $m\,\delta\chi/\hbar + 2n\pi$. As v_s is well defined, the physics for these two phase differences must be the same, hence (61-8).

Any function satisfying (61-8) can be expanded as a series of harmonics:

$$\sin(nm\delta\chi/\hbar), \qquad \cos(nm\delta\chi/\hbar); \tag{61-9}$$

for simplicity we take $n = 1$ and are led to the Josephson relation for the superelectron current through the junction [38]:

$$I_s = j_0 \sin(m\,\delta\chi/\hbar), \tag{61-10}$$

where j_0 is a material constant characteristic of superconductor and junction. Equations (61-4,10) describe the Josephson effects. Combining them we obtain

$$I_s(t) = j_0 \sin\left[\delta_0 + \int_0^t \frac{q}{\hbar} V(t')\,dt'\right], \tag{61-11}$$

where δ_0 is an integration constant.

When a D.C. voltage is applied across the junction, the supercurrent oscillates very rapidly with frequency $qV/\hbar$ and there is no net flow,

Notes p. 385

but when the voltage is zero there can be a flow determined by δ_0. This is the D.C. Josephson effect. If in addition to the D.C. voltage one imposes an A.C. modulation so that

$$V = V_0 + V' \cos \omega t, \tag{61-12}$$

$$V'/V_0 \ll 1, \tag{61-13}$$

then there can be a supercurrent even when the total voltage is non-vanishing provided that the frequency is at resonance, e.g.:

$$\omega = qV_0/\hbar. \tag{61-14}$$

To arrive at this result expand (61-11) to lowest order in V' to obtain,

$$I_s = j_0 \sin [\delta_0 + (q/\hbar)V_0 t] + j_0(qV'/\hbar\omega) \sin \omega t \cos [\delta_0 + (q/\hbar)V_0 t]. \tag{61-15}$$

The first term corresponds to no net flow but the second term on the right hand side of (61-15) will have a non-zero time average at resonance (61-14).

Experimentally [30] these effects can be shown by the arrangement in Fig. 64. By varying the resistance various currents can be sent through

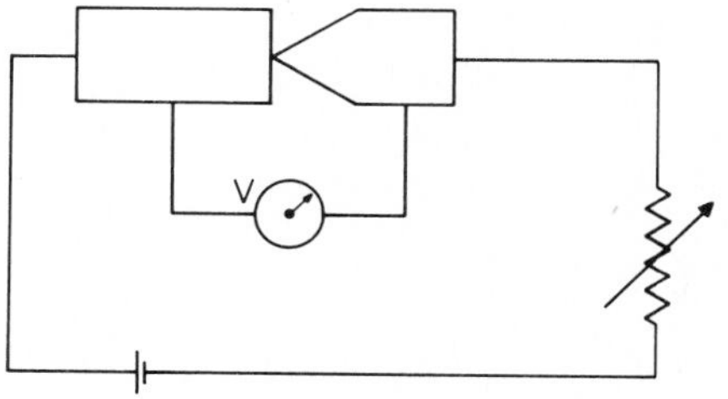

Fig. 64. Two superconductors separated by a weak link point contact. A voltmeter reads the voltage drop across the junction.

the Josephson junction which in this case is pictured as a point contact. If the sharpness of the point is on the order of a coherence length then the point behaves like a normal metal. As the current is increased no voltage drop V is observed across the superconductor until the maximum current j_0 is reached. Then for still larger currents the voltage approaches the value appropriate to a normal (or Ohmic) electron flow through the

Notes p. 385

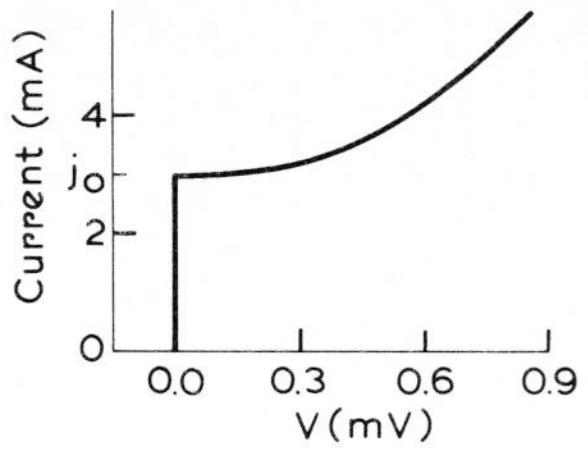

Fig. 65. Voltage drop versus given current in the D.C. Josephson effect. The total current is the sum of super and normal currents. For currents less than j_0 there is no voltage drop and hence no normal current. For currents greater than j_0 the supercurrent oscillates quickly with small net flow while the normal current is Ohmic (note that current is proportional to V for large V) for a point contact junction.

link as displayed in Fig. 65 where some typical numbers have been indicated. When the current is chosen so that the voltage drop is non-zero there still is a supercurrent contribution to the total current. This happens because for a given *current* the voltage oscillates rapidly around its mean value. The components of oscillation at resonance lead to the supercurrent. These effects can be calculated as follows. First the total current through the junction, I, equals the sum of super and normal currents:

$$I = I_s + I_n.$$

The supercurrent is given by (61-10) and the normal current is given by Ohm's law (taking T constant):

$$I_n = V/R_n,$$

where R_n is the resistance of the junction to normal flow as can be obtained from the behavior of the junction at large V. Thus the total current is

$$I = j_0 \sin\left(\frac{m}{\hbar}\,\delta\chi\right) + \frac{m}{qR_n}\frac{\partial\,\delta\chi}{\partial t},$$

where we have used (61-4). The total current, I, is given and independent of time for the specific arrangement under consideration. Thus this equation yields a solution for $\delta\chi$, and also therefore V [note (61-4)].

Notes p. 385

The time averaged value of the voltage so obtained is, for times much longer than a period:

$$\frac{2\pi R_n}{\int_0^{2\pi} [I - j_0 \sin(m\,\delta\chi/\hbar)]^{-1}\, \mathrm{d}(m\,\delta\chi/\hbar)},$$

which has the behavior qualitatively indicated in Fig. 65. Junctions can also be constructed where the electrons must tunnel through instead of overcoming Ohmic resistance. In these cases the behavior above j_0 is different since the 'normal' flow within the junction is more complicated.

A still more striking Josephson effect occurs when a supercurrent is diffracted through two junctions as in Fig. 66. The total current through the superconductor is

$$I_s = I_a + I_b = j_0 \sin \delta_a + j_0 \sin \delta_b, \qquad (61\text{-}16)$$

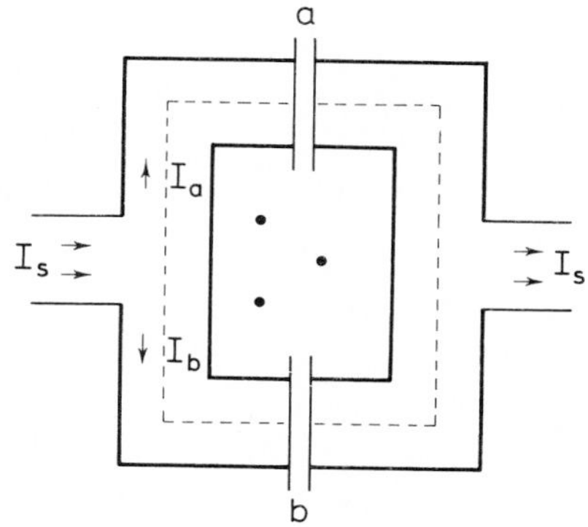

Fig. 66. The two slit Josephson effect. By varying the magnetic flux through the circuit the relative phases of the junctions can be varied so as to cause the currents to interfere or reinforce.

where δ_a, δ_b are the phase jumps across junctions 'a' and 'b' and we assume the junctions have same j_0. Now we consider a situation with no voltage across the double junction but with magnetic flux trapped by the junction as indicated by the dots. Integrating once around the circuit as indicated by the dashed lines leads to a relation for $\delta_b - \delta_a$:

$$\delta_b - \delta_a = \frac{q}{\hbar c} \oint \left(\boldsymbol{A} + \frac{mc}{q} \boldsymbol{v}_s \right) \cdot \mathrm{d}\ell - 2n\pi, \qquad (61\text{-}17)$$

Notes p. 385

where there are n quanta trapped by the circuit. A phase difference of $2n\pi$ can be neglected since the currents are determined only modulo 2π. If the superconductors are thick enough then the path of integration can be removed to the interior where $v_s \to 0$ (Meissner effect).

Then we have

$$\delta_b - \delta_a = \frac{q}{\hbar c}\phi, \tag{61-18}$$

where ϕ is the trapped magnetic flux. The magnetic flux through the circuit determines the relative phases of the two weak links. From (61-18) we can set

$$\delta_a = \delta_0 + \frac{q}{2\hbar c}\phi, \tag{61-19}$$

$$\delta_b = \delta_0 - \frac{q}{2\hbar c}\phi, \tag{61-20}$$

so that the total current through the junctions is, (61-16):

$$I_s = 2j_0 \sin\delta_0 \cos\left[(q/2\hbar c)\phi\right]. \tag{61-21}$$

By varying the magnetic flux through the circuit the currents can be caused to interfere! When

$$\phi = \frac{2\hbar c}{q} n\pi, \tag{61-22}$$

the currents reinforce; but when

$$\phi = \frac{2\hbar c}{q}(n + \tfrac{1}{2})\pi, \tag{61-23}$$

the currents cancel. The current described by (61-21) is analogous to the diffraction pattern observed when electrons are sent through the two slit arrangement. These effects were first observed by Mercereau et al. [31]. Since the changes in total current are very large when the total flux change is less than a flux quantum, which is very small, these macroscopic quantum interference devices are used for extremely sensitive measurements of the magnetic field.

As discussed by De Bruyn Ouboter and De Waele [30] the total flux ϕ is due to the externally imposed flux plus the self-induced flux which is given by the product of the self-inductance of the circuit and circulating

Notes p. 385

current ($j_0 \sin \delta_a - j_0 \sin \delta_b$). In geometries where the self induced flux is non-negligible it turns out to be impossible to choose a value of externally controlled flux so that the total flux is given by (61-23) when the maximum (or critical) current for the given external flux flows through the junction. The observed behavior does, however, have the same periodicity as when ϕ is the externally imposed flux.

Our success in deriving the Josephson effects from the London two fluid equations plus quantization of fluxoid raises the question as to in what sense these effects are interference effects. Are they comparable with the classical diffraction of sound waves or with the fundamental quantum principle of superposition of the probability amplitude as is invoked to understand the diffraction of single particles [32]? The fact that the London equations are *deterministic* suggests that the London theory plus quantization is on the level of the *old quantum theory* where the quantization of adiabatic invariants was employed to select out a discrete set of allowed states. From this point of view the Josephson effect is semi-classical in that the full glory of quantum theory need *not* be invoked on the macroscopic level in order to understand it. In particular, no use need be made of an uncertainty relation or the principle of the reduction of the wave packet as a result of interaction between observer and system. It remains to be seen whether in superfluid systems there will be macroscopic analogues to these fundamental quantum effects.

62 *Are There Thermoelectric Effects in Superconductors?*

It is commonly accepted that there can be no thermoelectric effects in superconductors. This view is based on the early experiments of Casimir and Rademakers on the Seebeck effect and of Daunt and Mendelssohn on the Thompson heat which show that in the usual stationary state arrangement these effects vanish in the superconducting state [33]. At first sight these observations would appear to be in conflict with the expression (56-2) for the normal current density which shows that there are thermoelectric contributions to $\boldsymbol{J}_n$. We will see in this section that the superconducting hydrodynamics do imply the vanishing of these effects in the *stationary* state: $\partial T/\partial t = 0$, but for non-stationary configurations there can be a thermal power.

Consider the arrangement in Fig. 67 in which metal 2 is sandwiched between two samples of metal 1, and the temperature variation is as

Notes p. 385

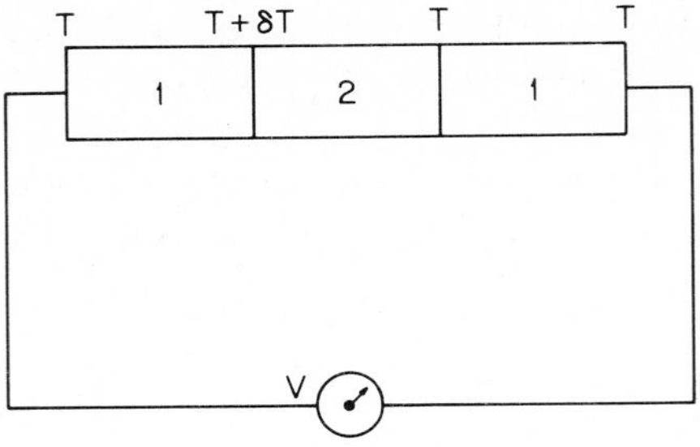

Fig. 67. The arrangement used to measure the Seebeck thermoelectric E.M.F.

indicated. If these are normal metals then there will exist a Seebeck E.M.F.

$$V = (\alpha_2 - \alpha_1)\,\delta T. \tag{62-1}$$

To arrive at this result, we note that the normal current equals the total current and under the condition where the voltage is determined the resistance is infinite so that no current flows, then from (56-2)

$$\boldsymbol{E} - \frac{m}{q}\nabla\mu = \alpha\nabla T, \tag{62-2}$$

so that a temperature gradient leads to an electrochemical potential gradient or voltage. Integrating (62-2) across the sample leads to (62-1).

If these metals are superconductors then it follows from the London equation (56-24) that regardless of the temperature variation the electrochemical potential is constant and there can be no Seebeck voltage. But from (56-2) there must be a normal current. One can say following Ginsburg that although a normal current flows:

$$\frac{q}{m}\boldsymbol{J}_{\rm n} = \sigma\alpha\nabla T, \tag{62-3}$$

a supercurrent also flows so that

$$\rho_{\rm s}\boldsymbol{v}_{\rm s} + \boldsymbol{J}_{\rm n} = 0. \tag{62-4}$$

In the stationary state the energy conservation law (56-16) becomes

$$\frac{\partial U}{\partial t} = \nabla\cdot(\kappa\nabla T), \tag{62-5}$$

Notes p. 385

so that unlike a normal metal there is no contribution to the energy developed which changes sign upon reversal of the current (i.e., no Thompson heat).

There can be voltages in a superconductor only when the superfluid is accelerating, $\partial v_s/\partial t \neq 0$. This suggests that one look for thermoelectric effects in *non*-stationary arrangements such as when

$$\delta T = T' \, e^{i\omega t}. \tag{62-6}$$

Solve (56-24) for the electrochemical potential and substitute into (56-2) for $\boldsymbol{J}_n$ to obtain the total current density:

$$\boldsymbol{j} = \frac{q}{m} \rho_s \boldsymbol{v}_s + \sigma \frac{m}{q} \frac{\partial \boldsymbol{v}_s}{\partial t} + \sigma \alpha \nabla T = 0. \tag{62-7}$$

This equation determines $\boldsymbol{v}_s$ for a given driving temperature gradient; one obtains

$$\frac{m}{q} \frac{\partial \boldsymbol{v}_s}{\partial t} = \frac{-\omega^2 \tau^2 \alpha - i\omega\tau\alpha}{1 + \omega^2 \tau^2} \nabla T, \tag{62-8}$$

where $\tau = m^2\sigma/q^2\rho_s$ is the normal electron collision time. Since $\tau < 10^{-10}$ sec except near T_c we keep lowest order in $\omega\tau$, so

$$V = \int \frac{m}{q} \frac{\partial \boldsymbol{v}_s}{\partial t} \cdot \mathrm{d}\ell = i\omega(\tau_2 \alpha_2 - \tau_1 \alpha_1) T' \, e^{i\omega t}, \tag{62-9}$$

or the magnitude of the oscillating Seebeck E.M.F. is $\omega\tau\alpha\,\delta T$. For $\delta T \approx 10^{-3}$ °K, $\omega = 10^4$ sec^{-1} this thermoelectric voltage is of order 10^{-16} volt if we use the value of $\alpha = 10^{-7}$ volt/°K observed above the critical temperature [34]. It lags the temperature by a phase $\omega\tau$. Although one can perhaps do better close to the transition temperature, the non-stationary thermoelectric effects will clearly be very difficult to observe.

63 The Superconducting Bulk Viscosity

As with the super component of He II the motion of the super electron fluid is *not* strictly reversible. This is reflected by the appearance of a bulk viscosity [5] in the acceleration equation (56-3). In He II the bulk viscosity plays a role in the absorption of the sound modes. It will be hard to generate the comparable modes in a superconductor (§ 60), but

Notes p. 385

it has been pointed out [35] that this term can play a role at a superconducting normal metal junction when an electric current is flowing.

Let us consider the stationary state with constant temperature, then (56-1,2) and (56-3) become

$$\nabla \cdot \rho_s \boldsymbol{v}_s = -\nabla \cdot \boldsymbol{J}_n, \tag{63-1}$$

$$\frac{q}{m} \boldsymbol{J}_n = -\sigma \frac{m}{q} \nabla \mu^*, \tag{63-2}$$

$$\nabla \mu^* = \zeta \nabla (\nabla \cdot \rho_s \boldsymbol{v}_s), \tag{63-3}$$

where we have set

$$\mu^* \equiv \mu + \tfrac{1}{2} v_s^2 + \frac{q}{m} \Phi. \tag{63-4}$$

Combining the above yields

$$\nabla \mu^* = \sigma \zeta \frac{m^2}{q^2} \nabla^2 \nabla \mu^*, \tag{63-5}$$

or equivalently:

$$\boldsymbol{J}_n = \sigma \zeta \frac{m^2}{q^2} \nabla^2 \boldsymbol{J}_n. \tag{63-6}$$

These relations show that when *dissipative* effects are included there can exist voltages and normal currents within the superconductor even when the temperature is constant (no thermoelectric effects). This effect penetrates over a characteristic distance [36]

$$\delta = [\sigma \zeta (m^2/q^2)]^{1/2}. \tag{63-7}$$

In order for a current to flow in the normal metal there must be an electric field. In the *bulk* of the superconductor there can be no electric field in the steady state since with temperature constant:

$$\boldsymbol{E} = -\frac{m}{q} \nabla \mu^*, \tag{63-8}$$

when small quadratic terms are neglected. Thus there must be at the surface of the superconductor which borders the metal a net charge. It will be distributed over the distance δ given by (63-7).

Notes p. 385

Due to this effect there exists a voltage drop *in the superconductor* of order

$$E\delta, \tag{63-9}$$

where E is the electric field driving the current in the normal metal. The total voltage drop across a super–normal–super sandwich will for a given current be greater by an amount $2E\delta$ than would take place across the normal metal alone. The superconductor will contribute to the total resistance!

Experimental [37] investigations of this off-equilibrium effect reveal that $\delta \approx 10^{-4}$ cm.

64 *Fluctuating Corrections to the Equations of Superconductivity*

Any theory which is closed but describes a number of degrees of freedom which is less than the complete set must have shortcomings. This will be reflected for instance in the existence of thermal fluctuations which are not described by the deterministic equations. This trouble which occurs also in classical hydrodynamics was discussed in Chapter IV. Here we present the fluctuating corrections to the superconducting equations.

In the presence of fluctuations there will be a fluctuating normal fluid current $\check{\boldsymbol{J}}_{\mathrm{n}}$ so that (56-1) becomes

$$\frac{\partial \rho}{\partial t} + \nabla \cdot (\rho_{\mathrm{s}} \boldsymbol{v}_{\mathrm{s}} + \boldsymbol{J}_{\mathrm{n}} + \check{\boldsymbol{J}}_{\mathrm{n}}) = 0. \tag{64-1}$$

The fluctuating contribution to the irreversible chemical potential is $\check{H}$ so that (56-3) becomes

$$\frac{\mathrm{D_s}\boldsymbol{v}_{\mathrm{s}}}{\mathrm{D}t} = -\nabla\mu + \frac{q}{m}\left[\boldsymbol{E} + \frac{1}{c}(\boldsymbol{v}_{\mathrm{s}} \times \boldsymbol{B})\right] - \nabla(H + \check{H}). \tag{64-2}$$

The entropy law becomes

$$T\left[\frac{\partial\, \rho s}{\partial t} + \nabla \cdot \left(\frac{\boldsymbol{q} + \check{\boldsymbol{q}}}{T}\right)\right] = -\frac{\boldsymbol{q} + \check{\boldsymbol{q}}}{T} \cdot \nabla T - (H + \check{H})\nabla \cdot \rho_{\mathrm{s}}\boldsymbol{v}_{\mathrm{s}}$$
$$+ (\boldsymbol{J}_{\mathrm{n}} + \check{\boldsymbol{J}}_{\mathrm{n}}) \cdot \left[\boldsymbol{E} - \frac{m}{q}\nabla(\mu + \tfrac{1}{2}v_{\mathrm{s}}^2)\right]. \tag{64-3}$$

Notes p. 385

The fluctuation dissipation relations follow as before and are

$$\langle \check{H}(\boldsymbol{r}, t)\, \check{H}(\boldsymbol{r}', t')\rangle = 2k_{\mathrm{B}}T\zeta\, \delta(\boldsymbol{r} - \boldsymbol{r}')\, \delta(t - t'), \tag{64-4}$$

$$\langle \check{q}_i(\boldsymbol{r}, t)\, \check{q}_j(\boldsymbol{r}', t')\rangle = 2k_{\mathrm{B}}T^2\kappa\delta_{ij}\, \delta(\boldsymbol{r} - \boldsymbol{r}')\, \delta(t - t'), \tag{64-5}$$

$$\langle \check{J}_{\mathrm{n},i}(\boldsymbol{r}, t)\, \check{J}_{\mathrm{n},j}(\boldsymbol{r}', t')\rangle = 2k_{\mathrm{B}}T\sigma \frac{m^2}{q^2} \delta_{ij}\, \delta(\boldsymbol{r} - \boldsymbol{r}')\, \delta(t - t'), \tag{64-6}$$

$$\langle \check{J}_{\mathrm{n},i}(\boldsymbol{r}, t)\, \check{q}_j(\boldsymbol{r}', t')\rangle = 2k_{\mathrm{B}}T^2\sigma\alpha \frac{m}{q} \delta_{ij}\, \delta(\boldsymbol{r} - \boldsymbol{r}')\, \delta(t - t'), \tag{64-7}$$

all other correlations vanish.

As a simple application of these equations we will show that there is no noise or thermally induced fluctuating E.M.F. in a superconductor. First let us calculate the noise in a normal metal. Taking $\rho_{\mathrm{s}} = 0$ we have

$$\frac{\partial \rho}{\partial t} + \nabla \cdot (\boldsymbol{J}_{\mathrm{n}} + \check{\boldsymbol{J}}_{\mathrm{n}}) = 0, \tag{64-8}$$

$$\nabla \cdot \boldsymbol{E} = 4\pi\rho_{\mathrm{net}}, \tag{64-9}$$

$$\frac{q}{m} \boldsymbol{J}_{\mathrm{n}} = \sigma\left(\boldsymbol{E} - \frac{m}{q} \nabla\mu\right), \tag{64-10}$$

and the correlation for $\check{\boldsymbol{J}}_{\mathrm{n}}$ is given by (64-6). For simplicity we take $\alpha = 0$ so that any possible thermoelectric E.M.F.'s are ignored. Combining the time derivative of (64-9) with (64-8) yields

$$\nabla \cdot \left[\frac{1}{4\pi} \frac{\partial \boldsymbol{E}}{\partial t} + \sigma\left(\boldsymbol{E} - \frac{m}{q} \nabla\mu\right) + \frac{q}{m} \check{\boldsymbol{J}}_{\mathrm{n}}\right] = 0. \tag{64-11}$$

Since $4\pi\sigma \approx 10^{19}\ \mathrm{sec}^{-1}$ we can ignore the term in $\partial E/\partial t$ as far as hydrodynamic frequencies are concerned.

For the one dimensional problem of the fluctuating voltage in a wire (64-11) becomes

$$E_x - \frac{m}{q} \frac{\partial \mu}{\partial x} = -\frac{q}{m\sigma} \check{J}_{\mathrm{n},x}, \tag{64-12}$$

where the wire lies on the x axis.

The E.M.F., V, is the line integral of the electric field minus chemical potential gradient or

$$V(t) = -\frac{q}{m\sigma A} \int \check{J}_{\mathrm{n},x}(\boldsymbol{r}, t)\, \mathrm{d}^3 r, \tag{64-13}$$

Notes p. 385

where A is the cross-sectional area of the wire. The correlation function for the voltage:

$$\langle V(t)\, V(t+\tau)\rangle = \left(\frac{q}{m\sigma A}\right)^2 \iint \langle \check{J}_{\mathrm{n},x}(\boldsymbol{r}, t)\, \check{J}_{\mathrm{n},x}(\boldsymbol{r}', t+\tau)\rangle\, \mathrm{d}^3 r\, \mathrm{d}^3 r', \quad (64\text{-}14)$$

can be evaluated by use of (64-6) and is

$$\langle V(t)\, V(t+\tau)\rangle = \frac{2k_{\mathrm{B}} T \ell}{\sigma A}\, \delta(\tau), \quad (64\text{-}15)$$

where ℓ is the length of the wire. Noting that the resistance is $\ell/\sigma A$ enables one to put Eq. (64-15) into the well known form for the noise in a resistor.

In the superconducting state the fluctuating London equation is

$$\frac{\partial \boldsymbol{v}_{\mathrm{s}}}{\partial t} = \frac{q}{m} \boldsymbol{E} - \nabla(\mu + \tfrac{1}{2} v_{\mathrm{s}}^2) + \nabla(\zeta \nabla \cdot \rho_{\mathrm{s}} \boldsymbol{v}_{\mathrm{s}}) - \nabla \check{H}. \quad (64\text{-}16)$$

Again the E.M.F. is the line integral of

$$\boldsymbol{E}^* \equiv \boldsymbol{E} - \frac{m}{q} \nabla(\mu + \tfrac{1}{2} v_{\mathrm{s}}^2).$$

Also time derivatives are neglected for the same reason as in the normal metals. As $\boldsymbol{E}^*$ is the gradient of a single valued function its line integral around a closed path will vanish regardless of the fluctuations, i.e., $\check{H}$. Thus for instance a superconducting galvanometer will show no thermally fluctuating E.M.F.. The absence of noise in a superconductor is not surprising since as we noted a current can flow without resistance in a closed superconducting path.

Notes

[1] H. Kamerlingh Onnes, Proc. Roy. Acad. Amsterdam **13**(1911)1903.
[2] F. London, Phys. Rev. **54**(1938)947.
[3] F. London and H. London, Physica **2**(1935)341. F. London, *Une Conception Nouvelle de la Supraconductibilité*, Act. Sci. Ind. (Paris) No. 458 (1937); *Superfluids* (Wiley, New York, 1950) Vol. 1; Proc. Roy. Soc. **A149**(1935)71.
[4] Compare with remarks by D. Pines, in: *Quantum Fluids*, ed. D. F. Brewer (North-Holland, Amsterdam, 1966) p. 34.
[5] S. J. Putterman and R. de Bruyn Ouboter, Phys. Rev. Letters **24**(1970)50.

[6] V. Ginsburg, Zh. Eksp. Teor. Fiz. **14**(1944)177.
[7] W. Meissner and R. Ochsenfeld, Naturwissenschaften **21**(1933)787.
[8] D. Shoenberg, Proc. Roy. Soc. **A175**(1940)49; M. Desirant and D. Shoenberg, Proc. Phys. Soc. (London) **60**(1948)413; J. M. Lock, Proc. Roy. Soc. **A208**(1951)391.
[9] H. B. G. Casimir, Physica **7**(1940)887.
[10] E. Laurmann and D. Shoenberg, Proc. Roy. Soc. **A198**(1949)560. A. I. Shalnikov and Y. V. Sharvin, Zh. Eksp. Teor. Fiz. **18**(1948)102.
[11] L. Onsager, Nuovo Cimento, Suppl. No. 2 to Vol. **6**(1949)249.
[12] F. London, *Superfluids* (Wiley, New York, 1950) Vol. 1, p. 152.
[13] B. S. Deaver and W. M. Fairbank, Phys. Rev. Letters **7**(1961)43.
[14] R. Doll and M. Näbauer, Phys. Rev. Letters **7**(1961)51.
[15] See footnote 3 of Ref. [13]. L. Onsager, Phys. Rev. Letters **7**(1961)50.
[16] L. Cooper, Phys. Rev. **104**(1956)1189.
[17] J. Bardeen, L. Cooper and J. Schrieffer, Phys. Rev. **108**(1957)1175.
[18] A. A. Abrikosov, Zh. Eksp. Teor. Fiz. **32**(1957)1442.
[19] A. A. Abrikosov, Speech accepting the London Award, Thirteenth International Conference on Low Temperature Physics, Boulder, Colorado (1972).
[20] A. B. Pippard, *Classical Thermodynamics* (Cambridge Univ. Press, Cambridge, 1960) p. 25.
[21] Experimental observations of this behavior have been made by D. Finnemore, T. F. Stromberg and C. A. Swenson, Phys. Rev. **149**(1966)231; A. Calverley and A. C. Rose-Innes, Proc. Roy. Soc. **A255**(1960)267; B. B. Goodman, J. Hillairet, J. Veyssie and L. Weil, in: *Proceedings of the VIIth International Conference on Low Temperature Physics*, eds. G. M. Graham and A. C. Hollis-Hallet (Univ. Press, Toronto, 1960) p. 350.
[22] U. Essman and H. Träuble, Scientific American (March 1971) p. 75. H. Träuble and U. Essman, J. Appl. Phys. **39**(1968)4052.
[23] Experiments on irreversible type II superconductors are: W. A. Fietz, M. R. Beasley, J. Silcox and W. W. Webb, Phys. Rev. **136**(1964)A335; C. P. Bean, Phys. Rev. Letters **8**(1962)250; F. J. Mortin, J. P. Maita, H. J. Williams, R. C. Sherwood, J. H. Wernick and J. E. Kunzler, Phys. Rev. Letters **8**(1962)275. The comparison with He II in a superleak is discussed by H. Kojima, W. Veith, S. J. Putterman, E. Guyon and I. Rudnick, Phys. Rev. Letters **27**(1971)714.
[24] J. Bok and J. Klein, Phys. Rev. Letters **20**(1968)660. J. B. Brown and T. D. Morris, in: *Proceedings Eleventh International Conference on Low Temperature Physics*, ed. J. F. Allen (St. Andrews, 1968) p. 768; Physica **55**(1971)760.
[25] For a discussion of the Kelvin technique see W. Zisman, Rev. Sci. Instr. **3**(1932)367; R. E. Simon, Phys. Rev. **116**(1959)613.
[26] H. Lewis, Phys. Rev. **92**(1953)1149; **100**(1955)641. R. Jaggi and R. Sommerhalder, Helv. Phys. Acta **32**(1959)167.
[27] J. Clarke and S. M. Freake, Phys. Rev. Letters **29**(1972)588; A. Th. A. M. de Waele, Thesis, Leiden (1972); and Paper presented at the Thirteenth International Conference on Low Temperature Physics, Boulder, Colorado (1972).
[28] B. D. Josephson, Phys. Letters **1**(1962)251.
[29] We follow the reasoning of B. D. Josephson, Advan. Phys. **14**(1965)419; see also F. Bloch, Phys. Rev. Letters **21**(1968)1241; Phys. Rev. **B2**(1970)109.
[30] The first observation of the D.C. Josephson effect was by P. W. Anderson and

J. Rowell, Phys. Rev. Letters **10**(1963)230. A review of experiments is given by J. E. Mercereau in: *Tunneling Phenomena in Solids*, eds. E. Burstein and S. Lundquist (Plenum Press, New York, 1969) p. 461; and D. N. Langenberg, Loc. cit., p. 519. See also R. de Bruyn Ouboter and A. Th. A. M. de Waele, in: *Progress in Low Temperature Physics*, ed. C. J. Gorter (North-Holland, Amsterdam, 1970) Vol. VI.

[31] R. Jaklevic, J. Lambe, A. Silver and J. Mercereau, Phys. Rev. Letters **12**(1964)159,274.

[32] This last point of view is taken by R. P. Feynman, *Lectures on Physics* (Addison Wesley, Reading, Mass., 1965) Vol. III, p. 21-1.

[33] H. B. G. Casimir and A. Rademakers, Physica **13**(1947)33; J. G. Daunt and K. Mendelssohn, Proc. Roy. Soc. **A185**(1946)225. Compare with the discussion in: D. Shoenburg, *Superconductivity* (Cambridge Univ. Press, New York, 1962) p. 87.

[34] G. Borelius and W. H. Keesom, Proc. Acad. Sci. Amsterdam **35**(1932)10.

[35] T. J. Rieger, D. J. Scalapino and J. E. Mercereau, Phys. Rev. Letters **27**(1971)1787; M. Tinkham and J. Clarke, Phys. Rev. Letters **28**(1972)1366.

[36] This derivation is due to R. de Bruyn Ouboter (private communication).

[37] M. L. Yu and J. E. Mercereau, Phys. Rev. Letters **28**(1972)1117; J. Clarke, Phys. Rev. Letters **28**(1972)1363.

[38] The term involving the cosine of the phase difference is of a different time reversal character and therefore dissipative. Thus in the approximation considered here we neglect it.

CHAPTER X

Open Problems for Future Research

65 The Macroscopic Problem

In this chapter I shall attempt to outline the unsolved problems which from the point of view emphasized in this book constitute the most important open questions. Naturally such an exposition is tentative and at best suggestive.

The problems which arise when one thinks of superfluidity from the hydrodynamic or macroscopic point of view (§ 65) have been separated from those which arise as a result of microscopic considerations (§ 66). Such a separation is somewhat artificial since as we have emphasized the hydrodynamics provides a good description of phenomena in microscopic configurations.

The central macroscopic problem is that of finding the modifications of the two fluid thermo-hydrodynamics to more fully include the macroscopic quantum effects. As described in Chapter VII one would like a macroscopic description which unifies the Landau two fluid theory with properties that follow from the curvature of the macroscopic wave function, as expressed in the boundary conditions on ρ_s. The hydrodynamics of the condensed Bose gas naturally allow (even require) a boundary condition on ρ_s, but in this case the stresses are not isotropic, depending on the deformation, so that Pascal's law is not obtained. The more complete quantum hydrodynamics of He II may have to incorporate these facts.

Another major problem will be related to understanding how the interaction between observer and quantum system is to be reflected in the macroscopic theory. Will a macroscopic quantum uncertainty principle be justified or will the superfluid hydrodynamics always be at the level of the old quantum theory? As the interaction between observer and quantum system is in principle an irreversible process will the act of observation affect the approach to equilibrium and provide *quantum* contributions to the entropy production? When the rotating condensed ideal Bose gas was discussed (§ 51) we saw that knowing the angular velocity and knowing the angular momentum led to two completely different macroscopic quantum equilibrium states. This suggests (at least for the ideal Bose gas) that measurements affect the thermodynamic equilibrium, and the approach to it. Such unique possibilities have yet to be investigated. In fact the general point of view has been that the basic quantum effect of interaction of system with observer is unimportant for thermodynamic considerations, as perhaps expressed by the following quote from Pauli (1948) to be found in Ref. [1]:

> 'In quantum mechanics the observation is a process irreversible in principle accompanied by an incontrollable amount of interaction between the observed system and the measuring instruments. It was often argued that for this reason a consideration of closed systems in statistical thermodynamics would be senseless and the entropy increase is caused by the external influences accompanying the observations. I do not believe however, that such an argument can be maintained, on the contrary I defend the standpoint that the otherwise so important difference between classical and quantum mechanics is not relevant in principle for thermodynamic questions. Indeed, the disturbance by observations defined as macroscopic can be made small and a single macroscopic observation is sufficient in principle for controlling whether or not the system has reached its thermal equilibrium. Moreover thermodynamics admits that after every "irreversible" change of a system its initial state can be re-established, if only as a compensation an external reservoir is supplied with heat at the expense of a sinking weight. On the other hand in quantum mechanics the observation is a process outside the description by physical laws, after which the initial state cannot be re-established by any means.'

66 *The Microscopic Problem*

From the density matrix approach we saw in Chapter VIII that the equations of motion of the condensed ideal Bose gas were quite similar to those of superfluid helium on the reversible level. However, the equations of state and thus the excitation spectrum of this non-inter-

Notes p. 397

acting system are qualitatively different from those of the real fluid, He II. So a natural problem arises in trying to incorporate interactions (especially repulsion) into the quantum hierarchy. There has been enormous work [2] on understanding the excitation spectrum of He II and a problem is to unify these results with the quantum hierarchy approach, which has here been carried out for the non-interacting case. Many difficulties will be encountered, for instance as soon as interactions are introduced one no longer knows the relationship between the superfluid density and the reduced density matrices or the off diagonal long range order.

From the microscopic approach the major problem will arise in attempts to understand the approach to equilibrium when a single quantum state is macroscopically occupied. We follow the discussion of Uhlenbeck [3] who was first to emphasize this problem.

Our discussion of the Bose condensation started with the density matrix description (see § 49)

$$\hat{w} = \sum_m |m\rangle w(m) \langle m|, \tag{66-1}$$

where it was assumed that in *equilibrium* the (classical) probability $w(m)$ that the quantum system is characterized by state $|m\rangle$ is

$$w(m) = \frac{e^{-\beta E_m}}{\sum' e^{-\beta E_m}}, \tag{66-2}$$

where E_m is the energy of the state $|m\rangle$ and the total number of particles is restricted to N as denoted by the prime on the sum. We call (66-2) the fine grained canonical ensemble since in it the energies are the exact eigenvalues of the N particle Hamiltonian.

A major problem in statistical mechanics both classically and quantum mechanically is that of justifying the equilibrium description and understanding the approach to it. While it is not completely solved the picture is as follows. First if one introduces the fine grained H function

$$H \equiv \sum_k \langle k|\hat{w} \log \hat{w}|k\rangle, \tag{66-3}$$

where $\hat{w}$ is now an arbitrary off-equilibrium density matrix and $|k\rangle$ is any complete set of states. Then from the quantum Liouville equation one finds

$$H(t) = H(0), \tag{66-4}$$

Notes p. 397

which emphasizes the fact that the microscopic behavior is time reversible and on this level there is no trace of the approach to equilibrium. Next one introduces the coarse grained probabilities

$$P_i = \frac{1}{g_i} \sum_{m=g_{i-1}}^{g_{i-1}+g_i} w(m), \tag{66-5}$$

which is the average probability that the system is in some 'region' including g_i neighboring states. In terms of the P_i one can now show that the coarse grained H function

$$\bar{\bar{H}} = \sum_i P_i \log P_i \tag{66-6}$$

has an irreversible time behavior:

$$\bar{\bar{H}}(t) \leqslant \bar{\bar{H}}(0) < H, \tag{66-7}$$

and for a closed system the minimum is achieved for a completely uniform distribution of P_i, or the so-called micro-canonical ensemble.

Thus one understands the approach to equilibrium as being due to the coarse graining. The *exact* description is time reversible, but the description of the *macroscopic* or coarse grained quantities P_i is time irreversible.

In order to justify the approach to the micro-canonical, or canonical ensemble the coarse graining is essential. But in a coarse grained description a single quantum state can have no meaning and there can be no Bose condensation. To discuss the Bose condensation we are forced to work with the fine grained distribution (66-2) but in doing this one loses the generally accepted view of the approach to equilibrium. That is the paradox. What new ideas must be incorporated in order to explain the approach to equilibrium when a single quantum state is macroscopically occupied? These questions might tie in with those raised in § 65.

67 *Might Relativistic Effects Be Observable in Superfluid Systems*

As superfluids are systems where the third law of thermodynamics is dominant and the energy is thus very low one might think that the observation of relativistic effects is out of the question, to say the least. However, since superconductors have such a low impedance they can

Notes p. 397

and have been used for measurements of great accuracy. In fact they are now used as the standard for the volt, and with them the ratio of Planck's constant to the electron charge has been already measured to over 6 places [4], by use of the Josephson effect.

Relativistic effects enter hydrodynamic theory in two ways. First there are effects which arise if the center of mass velocity gets to be on the order of the speed of light. Second, there can be relativistic effects due to large internal stresses. These two effects will play a role depending on the magnitude of the dimensionless quantities

$$\frac{v_s^2}{c^2}, \tag{67-1}$$

$$\frac{\mu}{c^2}, \tag{67-2}$$

where v_s is the fluid velocity, c the speed of light and μ the chemical potential. While $v_s^2/c^2 \approx 10^{-17}$ one can have superconductors where $\mu/c^2 \approx 10^{-5}$ so that five place accuracy might in principle see relativistic hydrodynamic effects wherein the internal stresses affect the inertia. The large μ in superconductors is due to the Pauli exclusion principle which assures a large Fermi velocity even at zero temperature. In this section we develop these ideas in more detail. It should be noted that relativistic hydrodynamics (no less quantum relativistic hydrodynamics) has not yet been amenable to laboratory tests. Naturally we discuss only those relativistic effects which are not directly attributable to the electromagnetic field. For instance the He II Van der Waals potential of attraction of film to substrate (§ 41) and the transition from the d^{-3} to d^{-4} dependence is a relativistic effect derived from electromagnetic considerations. Of course one could not have observed these effects had it not been for the superfluidity that maintains a uniform film!

The London equations for the temporal and spatial behavior of the phase χ are from (60-7,8)

$$\mu + \tfrac{1}{2}v_s^2 + \frac{q}{m}\Phi = -\frac{\partial \chi}{\partial t}, \tag{67-3}$$

$$\boldsymbol{v}_s + \frac{q}{mc}\boldsymbol{A} = \nabla \chi, \tag{67-4}$$

where we recall that

Notes p. 397

$$\boldsymbol{B} = \nabla \times \boldsymbol{A}, \tag{67-5}$$

$$\boldsymbol{E} = -\nabla \Phi - \frac{1}{c}\frac{\partial \boldsymbol{A}}{\partial t}, \tag{67-6}$$

The two London equations are contained in the single relativistic equation:

$$\left(1 + \frac{\mu}{c^2}\right) v_{s,\mu} + \frac{q}{mc} A_\mu = \frac{\partial \chi}{\partial r_\mu}, \tag{67-7}$$

where the four-vectors are

$$A_\mu \equiv (\boldsymbol{A}, i\Phi), \tag{67-8}$$

$$\frac{\partial}{\partial r_\mu} \equiv \left(\nabla, -\frac{i}{c}\frac{\partial}{\partial t}\right), \tag{67-9}$$

$$v_{s,\mu} \equiv \left(\frac{\boldsymbol{v}_s}{\sqrt{1 - v_s^2/c^2}}, \frac{ic}{\sqrt{1 - v_s^2/c^2}}\right). \tag{67-10}$$

The space part of (67-7) yields (67-4) in the non-relativistic limit and the time part yields (67-3); we ignore dissipative effects. The Maxwell equations are

$$\frac{\partial F_{\mu\nu}}{\partial r_\alpha} + \frac{\partial F_{\nu\alpha}}{\partial r_\mu} + \frac{\partial F_{\alpha\mu}}{\partial r_\nu} = 0, \qquad \frac{\partial F_{\mu\nu}}{\partial r_\nu} = \frac{4\pi}{c} j_\mu, \tag{67-11}$$

where

$$F_{\mu\nu} = \frac{\partial A_\nu}{\partial r_\mu} - \frac{\partial A_\mu}{\partial r_\nu}, \tag{67-12}$$

$$j_\mu = (\boldsymbol{j}, ic\rho_{\text{net}}). \tag{67-13}$$

As a representative application we now ignore v_s^2/c^2 but not μ/c^2 and consider a rotating superconductor. The positive ions then move at velocity $\boldsymbol{\omega} \times \boldsymbol{r}$ and hence the total electric current will be

$$\boldsymbol{j} = \frac{q}{m} \rho_s(\boldsymbol{v}_s - \boldsymbol{\omega} \times \boldsymbol{r}), \tag{67-14}$$

so that Maxwell's equation (56-12) becomes

$$\nabla \times \boldsymbol{B} = \frac{4\pi q}{mc} \rho_s(\boldsymbol{v}_s - \boldsymbol{\omega} \times \boldsymbol{r}). \tag{67-15}$$

Notes p. 397

Use of (67-7) leads to

$$\nabla \times \nabla \times \boldsymbol{B} = -\lambda_{\mathrm{L}}^{2}\left[\boldsymbol{B} + \frac{2mc}{q}\left(1 + \frac{\mu}{c^{2}}\right)\boldsymbol{\omega}\right], \tag{67-16}$$

where

$$\lambda_{\mathrm{L}}^{2} = \frac{m^{2}c^{2}}{4\pi q^{2}\rho_{\mathrm{s}}}\left(1 + \frac{\mu}{c^{2}}\right) \tag{67-17}$$

is the relativistic generalization of the London penetration depth (57-5).

Equation (67-16) describes an exponential decay of

$$\boldsymbol{B} + \frac{2mc}{q}\boldsymbol{\omega}\left(1 + \frac{\mu}{c^{2}}\right),$$

so that far in the interior of a rotating superconductor the magnetic field is [10]:

$$\boldsymbol{B} = -\frac{2mc}{q}\boldsymbol{\omega}\left(1 + \frac{\mu}{c^{2}}\right). \tag{67-18}$$

This expression differs only by the relativistic correction to the inertia from that presented by London for a rotating superconductor [5]. This result has been tested to about 5% accuracy by Hildebrandt [6]. An observation of greater accuracy could in principle check the validity of relativistic hydrodynamics.

The equations of motion of superfluid helium:

$$\tfrac{1}{2}v_{\mathrm{s}}^{2} + \mu = -\frac{\partial\phi}{\partial t}, \tag{67-19}$$

$$\boldsymbol{v}_{\mathrm{s}} = \nabla\phi, \tag{67-20}$$

are similarly contained in

$$\left(1 + \frac{\mu}{c^{2}}\right)v_{\mathrm{s},\mu} = \frac{\partial\phi}{\partial r_{\mu}}. \tag{67-21}$$

In the Landau two fluid theory and in all microscopic theories one has $\nabla \times \boldsymbol{v}_{\mathrm{s}} = 0$ exactly at all points in the fluid at each instant of time. One might thus wonder if vorticity signals propagate according to these theories with infinite velocity in the same way that compressional waves travel with infinite velocity if $\nabla \cdot \boldsymbol{v} = 0$. Of course including sound in any description removes $\nabla \cdot \boldsymbol{v} = 0$, however, the Landau two fluid

Notes p. 397

theory includes sound and yet it still requires $\nabla \times \boldsymbol{v}_s = 0$. It is interesting to note from (67-21) that the exact relativistic generalization of $\nabla \times \boldsymbol{v}_s = 0$ is

$$\nabla \times \boldsymbol{v}_s + \frac{1}{c^2}\boldsymbol{v}_s \times \frac{\partial \boldsymbol{v}_s}{\partial t} = 0. \tag{67-22}$$

Does this imply that relativity will play a zeroth order role as regards deviations from $\nabla \times \boldsymbol{v}_s = 0$? Incidentally by performing a Madelung transformation (§ 46) on the Klein–Gordon equation Reyes [7] has derived these relativistic generalizations of the Landau equations.

For the relativistic theory the quantization condition becomes

$$\oint \left[\left(1 + \frac{\mu}{c^2}\right) v_{s,\mu} + \frac{q}{mc} A_\mu\right] \mathrm{d}r_\mu = \frac{nh}{m}, \tag{67-23}$$

or in the approximation considered here:

$$\oint \left[\left(1 + \frac{\mu}{c^2}\right) \boldsymbol{v}_s + \frac{q}{mc} \boldsymbol{A}\right] \cdot \mathrm{d}\boldsymbol{\ell} = \frac{nh}{m}, \tag{67-24}$$

so that in geometries where $\boldsymbol{v}_s \neq 0$ there is a relativistic correction to the trapped magnetic flux.

If any of these relativistic effects are observable one can wonder as to which relativistic quantum theory provides the first principles microscopic description.

68 *Some Very Speculative Final Remarks*

It should now be clear that with superfluid helium one has a system in which coherent quantum effects can be observed, in geometries varying continuously between Ångstroms and centimeters and also with masses varying over eight orders of magnitude. In this way He II provides perhaps the strongest check on the Schrödinger wave mechanics. The purpose of this section is to motivate the possibility of the presently formulated quantum mechanics *not* providing the first principles description of the system (relativity aside). We shall always have in mind the question of how a measurement gets made in the quantum theory.

In the quantum theory there are two different means whereby the wave function changes in time:

Notes p. 397

$$\mathscr{H}\Psi = i\hbar \frac{\partial \Psi}{\partial t}, \tag{68-1}$$

$$\Psi \rightarrow \Psi_i. \tag{68-2}$$

One is by unitary transformation as determined by the Hamiltonian and the other represents the reduction of the wave packet by a measurement, i.e., a measurement always finds the system in an eigenstate. If for simplicity we consider a two state system such as an electron which might have spin up or spin down then according to the orthodox quantum theory the wave function will develop according to (68-1) from any initial state until the measurement is performed. At that time the electron spin will in general be in a superposition of the two states but according to (68-2) it will be found to be either up or down (albeit with different probabilities) in any single measurement.

Von Neumann [8] investigated the mutual consistency of (68-1,2) and concluded that they were inconsistent. His argument was as follows. Instead of separating observer from the quantum system he considered a wave function that included the electron, the measuring apparatus and an alarm clock that determined when the measurement gets made. He could then show quite generally that for this *closed* system there can never be a reduction of the wave packet [i.e., (68-2)] since the closed system develops according to (68-1). If the electron is in a superposition at the time of measurement then the whole apparatus goes into the same superposition. This leads to the conclusion that 'in quantum mechanics the observation is a process outside the description by physical law' (see Pauli quote, § 65).

Bohr realized that if this is the case then the quantum theory becomes empty unless one knows how to separate the observer from the quantum system. He remarked that this is academic because the quantum system is always microscopic and the observer macroscopic, and in this way one knows when to apply (68-1) or (68-2). This resolution has led to general discussions as to whether quantum effects could be observed in macroscopic systems [9]. In view of the existence of superfluids where the mass and de Broglie wavelength can be on the order of the size of any measuring apparatus one must regard with skepticism this orthodox resolution of the measurement paradox.

Perhaps with superfluidity in mind one will be able to sharpen this old paradox. Possibly an investigation of the interaction between observer and macroscopic quantum system will lead to difficulties that

Notes p. 397

cannot be resolved by the Schrödinger wave mechanics with the Copenhagen interpretation [11].

Notes

[1] W. Pauli, discussion remarks on p. 166 of Supplement to Nuovo Cimento Vol. VI, Series IX (1949); they can also be found in: *Collected Papers* (Interscience, New York, 1964) Vol. II, p. 1112.

[2] See for instance, R. P. Feynman, *Progress in Low Temperature Physics*, Vol. 1, ed. C. J. Gorter (North-Holland, Amsterdam, 1955) p. 36.

[3] G. E. Uhlenbeck, in: *The Physicist's Conception of Nature*, ed. J. Mehra (Reidel, Den Haag, 1973).

[4] W. H. Parker, D. Langenberg and A. Denenstein, Phys. Rev. **177**(1969)639.

[5] F. London, *Superfluids* (Wiley, New York, 1950) Vol. 1, p. 78.

[6] A. F. Hildebrandt, Phys. Rev. Letters **12**(1964)190. See also N. Brickman, Phys. Rev. **184**(1969)460.

[7] J. Reyes, private communication.

[8] J. von Neumann, *Mathematical Foundations of Quantum Mechanics* (Princeton Univ. Press, Princeton, 1955); see also F. London and E. Bauer, *La Théorie de l'Observation en Mécanique Quantique* (Hemann et Cie, Paris, 1939); E. Wigner, Am. J. Phys. **31**(1963), and *Symmetries and Reflections* (Indiana Univ. Press, Bloomington, 1967) pp. 153, 171. These last references attribute the process of measurement to the consciousness of the observer which is beyond the description of physical law.

[9] A. Peres and N. Rosen, Phys. Rev. **135**(1964)B1486.

[10] This consequence of relativity for superconducting systems is discussed by P. W. Anderson, in: *Progress in Low Temperature Physics*, ed. C. J. Gorter (North-Holland, Amsterdam, 1967) Vol. V, p. 32.

[11] See also related comments by H. B. G. Casimir, in: *The Physicist's Conception of Nature*, ed. J. Mehra (Reidel, Den Haag, 1973).

APPENDIX I

Equality of the Momentum and Mass Current Densities in the Two Fluid Theory

Since there are so to speak two fluids present in the He II one might wonder if the fluids scatter off each other with the result that the momentum density will be different from the mass flux density. To investigate this possibility we assume $\mathscr{J} \neq \boldsymbol{J}$ and take as our eight independent variables $\rho, s, \mathscr{J}, \boldsymbol{v}_s$. In the transformation of energy it is the momentum $\mathscr{J}$ (instead of $\boldsymbol{J}$) which will enter on the right hand side of (3-6). Also in (3-11,12,13) $\mathscr{J}$ will now appear everywhere instead of $\boldsymbol{J}$. In going from (3-14) to (3-15), however, we must put

$$\frac{\partial \rho}{\partial t} = -\nabla \cdot (\mathscr{J} + \boldsymbol{D}),$$

where $\mathscr{J} + \boldsymbol{D} \equiv \boldsymbol{J}$ is the definition of $\boldsymbol{D}$. Then everything goes through as before and we obtain (3-23) with $\boldsymbol{J}$ replaced by $\mathscr{J}$ only on the right hand side and in addition the term

$$\boldsymbol{D} \cdot \nabla[\mu + \tfrac{1}{2}v_s^2 - (\boldsymbol{v}_s + \boldsymbol{w}) \cdot \boldsymbol{v}_s]$$

will appear on the right hand side. The only manner in which all the independent gradients on the right hand side of the thus modified Eq. (3-23) can vanish is if $\boldsymbol{D} = 0$, implying $\mathscr{J} = \boldsymbol{J}$. In arriving at this conclusion one must use the requirement that the Galilean transformation of the stress tensor is given by (AII-9).

APPENDIX II

The Galilean Transformation

For any system which obeys laws of mass, energy and momentum conservation the Galilean transformations of the fluxes $\boldsymbol{J}$, P_{ij}, Q_i follow from the transformation properties of ρ, U. Consider the law of mass conservation which in a given reference frame (subscript 1) takes the form

$$\frac{\partial \rho}{\partial t_1} + \nabla_1 \cdot \boldsymbol{J}_1 = 0, \qquad \text{(AII-1)}$$

where we attach no subscript to ρ since we assume that density is invariant just as for the classical fluid. Written in terms of the coordinates of a second Galilean reference frame (denoted by subscript 2) moving at relative velocity $\boldsymbol{v}_\mathrm{R}$ with respect to the first, (AII-1) becomes

$$\frac{\partial \rho}{\partial t_2} + \nabla_2 \cdot (\boldsymbol{J}_1 + \rho \boldsymbol{v}_\mathrm{R}) = 0, \qquad \text{(AII-2)}$$

where

$$\boldsymbol{r}_2 = \boldsymbol{r}_1 + \boldsymbol{v}_\mathrm{R} t, \qquad \text{(AII-3)}$$

$$t_2 = t_1, \qquad \text{(AII-4)}$$

so that

$$\nabla_1 = \nabla_2, \qquad \text{(AII-5)}$$

$$\frac{\partial}{\partial t_1} = \frac{\partial}{\partial t_2} + \boldsymbol{v}_\mathrm{R} \cdot \nabla_2. \qquad \text{(AII-6)}$$

Since conservation of mass is a law of physics, according to the Galilean principle it will also be conserved in system 2 according to the law

$$\frac{\partial \rho}{\partial t_2} + \nabla_2 \cdot \boldsymbol{J}_2 = 0. \qquad \text{(AII-7)}$$

Comparison of (AII-7) and (AII-2) yields the Galilean transformation of the mass current:

$$\boldsymbol{J}_2 = \boldsymbol{J}_1 + \rho \boldsymbol{v}_{\mathrm{R}}. \tag{AII-8}$$

Similarly from this transformation for $\boldsymbol{J}$ the momentum conservation law yields the transformation of P_{ij}:

$$P_{ij2} = P_{ij1} + v_{\mathrm{R}i} J_{j1} + v_{\mathrm{R}j} J_{i1}. \tag{AII-9}$$

If we assume that the transformation for the energy density is the same as for a classical fluid:

$$U_2 = U_1 + \boldsymbol{v}_{\mathrm{R}} \cdot \boldsymbol{J}_1 + \tfrac{1}{2}\rho v_{\mathrm{R}}^2, \tag{AII-10}$$

then the above method yields the transformation of $\boldsymbol{Q}$:

$$Q_{i2} = Q_{i1} + (\tfrac{1}{2}\rho v_{\mathrm{R}}^2 + \boldsymbol{v}_{\mathrm{R}} \cdot \boldsymbol{J}_1 + U_1) v_{\mathrm{R}i} + \tfrac{1}{2} v_{\mathrm{R}}^2 J_{i1} + P_{ij1} v_{\mathrm{R}j}. \tag{AII-11}$$

Similarly if entropy density is taken invariant as is the case for a classical fluid then the entropy flux density obeys the law

$$\boldsymbol{f}_2 = \boldsymbol{f}_1 + \rho s \boldsymbol{v}_{\mathrm{R}}. \tag{AII-12}$$

Finally since $\mathrm{D}_s \boldsymbol{v}_s/\mathrm{D}t$ is a Galilean invariant so must also be $\nabla\psi$ in (3-4). Hence ψ is an invariant.

In order to show that the mass density and energy density obey the same transformation as for a classical fluid it is best to consider a cyclic process in which the system in question can exchange energy, mass, and momentum with a classical fluid. The cycle consists of (1) exchanging some mass, energy and momentum, (2) accelerating the combined system to velocity $\boldsymbol{v}_{\mathrm{R}}$ without change of state, (3) exchanging mass, energy and momentum between the classical fluid and the system in question so that for the co-moving observer the classical fluid is brought back to its initial internal state, (4) decelerating the combined system to rest. From the fact that the combined system by this cycle must be returned to its initial state we conclude that the mass and the energy must obey the same transformation as for the classical fluid. For He II the classical fluid with which the exchange takes place can be taken to be its vapor. One must of course use the fact that the total energy, momentum, and mass of the combined system is conserved.

If we had taken the momentum density different from the mass flux density (see Appendix I) then the above cycle argument could be used to show that they obey the same Galilean transformation.

APPENDIX III

The Ideal Fluxes

The most general requirement to express the fact that (3-23) must be a conservation law is that the coefficients of the independent gradients ∇T, $\nabla\mu$, $\partial w_i/\partial r_j$, $\partial(v_s + w)_i/\partial r_j$, vanish.

We have shown in Appendix II that one can conclude from (3-4) that ψ is a scalar Galilean invariant. In He II the maximum number of independent scalar Galilean invariants is three as opposed to an Euler fluid where there are only two. Thus we can take ψ to be a function of μ, T, w^2, so that

$$\nabla\psi = \frac{\partial\psi}{\partial\mu}\nabla\mu + \frac{\partial\psi}{\partial T}\nabla T + \frac{\partial\psi}{\partial w^2}\nabla w^2. \tag{AIII-1}$$

Substituting this into (3-23) its right hand side becomes

$$\left\{\boldsymbol{f} - \rho s(\boldsymbol{v}_s + \boldsymbol{w}) + [\boldsymbol{J} - \rho(\boldsymbol{v}_s + \boldsymbol{w})]\frac{\partial\psi}{\partial T}\right\}\cdot\nabla T + [\boldsymbol{J} - \rho(\boldsymbol{v}_s + \boldsymbol{w})]$$
$$\times\left(\frac{\partial\psi}{\partial\mu} - 1\right)\nabla\mu + [\Pi_{ik} - v_{s,i}J_k - (v_s + w)_k(J - \rho v_s)_i]\frac{\partial(v_s + w)_i}{\partial r_k}$$
$$+ [J - \rho(v_s + w)]_k\frac{\partial\psi}{\partial w^2}2w_i\frac{\partial w_i}{\partial r_k}. \tag{AIII-2}$$

In order for this term to vanish the coefficient of each independent gradient must vanish. From the requirement that the coefficient of $\partial(v_s + w)_i/\partial r_k$ vanish we find the relation (3-26) for Π_{ik}. From the vanishing of the coefficient of $\partial w_i/\partial r_k$ we find $\partial\psi/\partial w^2 = 0$. Similarly from the coefficient of $\nabla\mu$ we find

$$\left(\frac{\partial\psi}{\partial\mu}\right)_{T,w^2} = 1. \tag{AIII-3}$$

Hence we conclude that

$$\psi = \mu + g(T), \tag{AIII-4}$$

where $g(T)$ is an arbitrary function of T. Finally from the coefficient of ∇T we find

$$\boldsymbol{f} = \rho s(\boldsymbol{v}_s + \boldsymbol{w}) + [\boldsymbol{J} - \rho(\boldsymbol{v}_s + \boldsymbol{w})]\frac{\mathrm{d}g}{\mathrm{d}T}, \tag{AIII-5}$$

where we used (AIII-4) for ψ. Except for the function $g(T)$ these results for the ideal fluxes are the same as (3-24,25,26).

Let us elucidate some properties of g. It must have the same units as μ (i.e., velocity squared) and thus must involve k_B/m where k_B is Boltzmann's constant and m the mass of a helium atom. One cannot however simply take $g = k_B T/m$ because then one would not have $\mathrm{d}g/\mathrm{d}T = 0$ at $T = 0$ which is a requirement of the third law (i.e., the entropy flux must vanish at $T = 0\,°\mathrm{K}$). Thus g must take the form

$$g = \frac{k_B T}{m} B\left(\frac{T}{T_0}\right), \tag{AIII-6}$$

where the function B cannot be a constant (except of course zero),

$$\lim_{T\to 0} [TB'(T) + B(T)] = 0,$$

and T_0 is a constant, characteristic temperature of the system.

The arbitrary function g can be excluded on the following grounds. We require that the quantities which appear in the continuum hydrodynamics be explicit functions of the basic variables and their conjugate variables in the expression for the energy, Eq. (3-13). This is a property of all continuum theories and implies that g must be an explicit function of only μ, ρ, T, ρs, w^2, $(J - \rho v_s)^2$, on the reversible level. In view of (AIII-6) this requirement means that some combination of the above variables *must* equal a constant which would therefore reduce the number of independent variables from eight to seven in contradiction with the basic assumption of the two fluid model.

It would be nicer to have a sharper argument for eliminating g. While we cannot provide it some properties of the equations including g are discussed below as they might be useful in developing such an argument.

When dissipative effects are incorporated it will be seen that the conjugate variable to $\boldsymbol{J}$ namely $\boldsymbol{v}_s + \boldsymbol{w}$ is restricted to shear flow. Thus in a superleak $\boldsymbol{v}_s + \boldsymbol{w} = 0$. From (AIII-5) we then see that a superflow through a superleak now involves an entropy flow $\boldsymbol{J}\,\mathrm{d}g/\mathrm{d}T$. Thus when $g \neq 0$ (clearly the case where g is constant is equivalent to taking g zero) it is impossible to reversibly transfer mass through a superleak if the reservoirs at the two ends are at different temperatures. The equilibrium fountain effect is in conflict with $g \neq 0$. We emphasize that this is not a theoretical basis for ruling out the terms in g.

By use of the continuity equation the entropy equation can be written

$$\frac{\partial}{\partial t}[\rho(s - g')] + \nabla \cdot [\rho(s - g')(\boldsymbol{v}_s + \boldsymbol{w})] + \rho\,\frac{\mathrm{D}_v g'}{\mathrm{D}t} = 0, \qquad \text{(AIII-7)}$$

where

$$g' \equiv \frac{\mathrm{d}g}{\mathrm{d}T}, \qquad \frac{\mathrm{D}_v}{\mathrm{D}t} \equiv \frac{\partial}{\partial t} + \boldsymbol{v}\cdot\nabla,$$

and where $\boldsymbol{J} \equiv \rho\boldsymbol{v}$. If one can take $\mathrm{D}_v g'/\mathrm{D}t$ zero or equivalently if

$$\frac{\mathrm{D}_v T}{\mathrm{D}t} = 0, \qquad \text{(AIII-8)}$$

then the entropy equation is the same as (3-5,24) with the entropy per gram rescaled. Similarly the superfluid acceleration equation can be viewed as a rescaling of μ. Also one can introduce the rescaled energy

$$U^* = U + \rho(g - Tg'), \qquad \text{(AIII-9)}$$

which will be conserved (and thus justified) only if (AIII-8) holds. The first and second laws for U^* is

$$\mathrm{d}U^* = [\mu + g + \tfrac{1}{2}v_s^2 - (\boldsymbol{v}_s + \boldsymbol{w})\cdot\boldsymbol{v}_s]\,\mathrm{d}\rho + T\,\mathrm{d}\rho(s - g')$$
$$+ (\boldsymbol{v}_s + \boldsymbol{w})\cdot\mathrm{d}\boldsymbol{J} + [\boldsymbol{J} - \rho(\boldsymbol{v}_s + \boldsymbol{w})]\cdot\mathrm{d}\boldsymbol{v}_s, \qquad \text{(AIII-10)}$$

which demonstrates that in this case the terms in g amount only to a rescaling of the basic variables. It is tempting to speculate that the only self-consistent solutions to the Landau two fluid equations including g are those for which (AIII-8) describes the flow. If this were the case the equations with $g = 0$ would be more general.

In view of the third law one can restrict g' so that $g' > 0$, otherwise the flow through a superleak would lead to a transfer of negative entropy.

APPENDIX IV

The Magnus Force

When the steady state flow velocities are much less than the speeds of first and second sound the variations of the quantities ρ, s, ρ_n can be neglected to accuracy of order the Mach number squared, where the Mach number is the ratio of the flow velocity to the appropriate sound velocity. We demonstrate this for steady state flow satisfying $\nabla \times \boldsymbol{v}_s = 0$, $\nabla \times \boldsymbol{A} = 0$. In this case a systematic iterative expansion for the flow can be obtained in terms of the Mach number.

In the steady state the entropy and continuity laws yield

$$\nabla \cdot (\rho s \boldsymbol{A} + \rho \boldsymbol{v}_s) = 0, \tag{AIV-1}$$

$$\nabla \cdot \left[\rho s \boldsymbol{v}_s + \frac{(\rho s)^2}{\rho_n} \boldsymbol{A} \right] = 0, \tag{AIV-2}$$

where we have used

$$\boldsymbol{v}_n = \boldsymbol{v}_s + \frac{\rho s}{\rho_n} \boldsymbol{A}. \tag{AIV-3}$$

Expanding (AIV-1,2) yields

$$s\nabla \cdot \boldsymbol{A} + \nabla \cdot \boldsymbol{v}_s = -\frac{1}{\rho}(\boldsymbol{A} \cdot \nabla \rho s + \boldsymbol{v}_s \cdot \nabla \rho), \tag{AIV-4}$$

$$\nabla \cdot \boldsymbol{v}_s + \frac{\rho s}{\rho_n} \nabla \cdot \boldsymbol{A} = -\frac{1}{\rho s}\left\{ \boldsymbol{v}_s \cdot \nabla \rho s + \boldsymbol{A} \cdot \nabla \left[\frac{(\rho s)^2}{\rho_n} \right] \right\}. \tag{AIV-5}$$

Now we expand the thermodynamic gradients on the right hand sides of (AIV-4,5) as

$$\nabla \rho = \left(\frac{\partial \rho}{\partial \mu} \right)_{T,w^2} \nabla \mu + \left(\frac{\partial \rho}{\partial T} \right)_{\mu,w^2} \nabla T + \left(\frac{\partial \rho}{\partial w^2} \right)_{\mu,T} \nabla w^2, \tag{AIV-6}$$

and similarly for $\nabla \rho s$ and $\nabla[(\rho s)^2/\rho_n]$. The superfluid and Bernoulli laws can be used to write the chemical potential and temperature gradients in terms of velocity gradients:

$$\nabla \mu = -\nabla \tfrac{1}{2} v_s^2, \tag{AIV-7}$$

$$\nabla T = -\nabla(\boldsymbol{v}_n \cdot \boldsymbol{A}), \tag{AIV-8}$$

so that we can write

$$\nabla \rho = -B_{\rho,\mu} \nabla \tfrac{1}{2} v_s^2 - B_{\rho,T} \nabla(\boldsymbol{v}_n \cdot \boldsymbol{A}) + B_{\rho,w^2} \nabla w^2, \tag{AIV-9}$$

where

$$B_{\rho,\mu} = \left(\frac{\partial \rho}{\partial \mu}\right)_{T,w^2},$$

and so on. In this way the equations (AIV-4,5) become

$$s\nabla \cdot \boldsymbol{A} + \nabla \cdot \boldsymbol{v}_s = \frac{1}{\rho}[(B_{\rho s,\mu}\boldsymbol{A} + B_{\rho,\mu}\boldsymbol{v}_s) \cdot \nabla \tfrac{1}{2} v_s^2$$

$$+ (B_{\rho s,T}\boldsymbol{A} + B_{\rho,T}\boldsymbol{v}_s) \cdot \nabla(\boldsymbol{v}_n \cdot \boldsymbol{A}) - (B_{\rho s,w^2}\boldsymbol{A} + B_{\rho,w^2}\boldsymbol{v}_s) \cdot \nabla w^2], \tag{AIV-10}$$

$$\nabla \cdot \boldsymbol{v}_s + \frac{\rho s}{\rho_n} \nabla \cdot \boldsymbol{A} = \frac{1}{\rho s}[(B_{\sigma,\mu}\boldsymbol{A} + B_{\rho s,\mu}\boldsymbol{v}_s) \cdot \nabla \tfrac{1}{2} v_s^2$$

$$+ (B_{\sigma,T}\boldsymbol{A} + B_{\rho s,T}\boldsymbol{v}_s) \cdot \nabla(\boldsymbol{v}_n \cdot \boldsymbol{A}) - (B_{\sigma,w^2}\boldsymbol{A} + B_{\rho s,w^2}\boldsymbol{v}_s) \cdot \nabla w^2], \tag{AIV-11}$$

where $\sigma \equiv (\rho s)^2/\rho_n$. The ratio of any term on the right hand side of (AIV-10,11) to a velocity gradient is of order the Mach number squared. This property suggests an expansion of $\boldsymbol{v}_s$, $\boldsymbol{A}$ in powers of the Mach number. Hence to second order we set

$$\boldsymbol{v}_s = \boldsymbol{v}_{s,0} + M^2 \boldsymbol{v}_{s,1}, \tag{AIV-12}$$

$$\boldsymbol{A} = \boldsymbol{A}_0 + M^2 \boldsymbol{A}_1. \tag{AIV-13}$$

To this order and for our purpose one need not distinguish between the first and second sound Mach numbers, so the Mach number M can be considered to be formed from the first or second sound velocity. Substituting (AIV-12,13) into (AIV-10,11) and equating terms of equal powers in M^2 yields

$$\nabla \cdot \boldsymbol{A}_0 = 0, \qquad \nabla \cdot \boldsymbol{v}_{s,0} = 0, \tag{AIV-14}$$

$$M^2(s_0\nabla\cdot \boldsymbol{A}_1 + \nabla\cdot \boldsymbol{v}_{s,1}) = \frac{1}{\rho_0}[(B_{\rho s,\mu}\boldsymbol{A} + B_{\rho,\mu}\boldsymbol{v}_s)_0\cdot\nabla\tfrac{1}{2}v_{s,0}^2 + (B_{\rho s,T}\boldsymbol{A} + B_{\rho,T}\boldsymbol{v}_s)_0\cdot\nabla(\boldsymbol{v}_n\cdot\boldsymbol{A})_0 - (B_{\rho s,w^2}\boldsymbol{A} + B_{\rho,w^2}\boldsymbol{v}_s)_0\cdot\nabla w_0^2], \tag{AIV-15}$$

$$M^2\left[\nabla\cdot \boldsymbol{v}_{s,1} + \left(\frac{\rho s}{\rho_n}\right)_0\nabla\cdot \boldsymbol{A}_1\right] = \frac{1}{\rho s_0}[(B_{\sigma,\mu}\boldsymbol{A} + B_{\rho s,\mu}\boldsymbol{v}_s)_0\cdot\nabla\tfrac{1}{2}v_{s,0}^2 + (B_{\sigma,T}\boldsymbol{A} + B_{\rho s,T}\boldsymbol{v}_s)_0\cdot\nabla(\boldsymbol{v}_n\cdot\boldsymbol{A})_0 - (B_{\sigma,w^2}\boldsymbol{A} + B_{\rho s,w^2}\boldsymbol{v}_s)_0\cdot\nabla w_0^2]. \tag{AIV-16}$$

When combined with the irrotationality conditions Eq. (AIV-14) yields the velocity fields to zeroth order (i.e., neglecting compressibility, and entropy or second sound, effects). Substituting the zeroth order behavior into (AIV-15,16) yields the lowest order correction to the velocity fields. From (AIV-15,16) we see that $\boldsymbol{A}_1$, $\boldsymbol{v}_{s,1}$ are on the order of $\boldsymbol{A}_0$, $\boldsymbol{v}_{s,0}$ so that the corrections to the velocity are indeed of order M^2.

We now focus attention on the lowest order flow properties $M \ll 1$ so that

$$\nabla\cdot \boldsymbol{v}_s = 0, \qquad \nabla\cdot \boldsymbol{A} = 0,$$

or equivalently to this order

$$\nabla\cdot \boldsymbol{v}_s = 0, \qquad \nabla\cdot \boldsymbol{v}_n = 0,$$
$$\nabla\times \boldsymbol{v}_s = 0, \qquad \nabla\times \boldsymbol{v}_n = 0, \tag{AIV-17}$$

where we now drop the subscript zero.

The normal fluid flow field, which is uniform at infinity with streaming velocity $\boldsymbol{U}_n$, has zero component perpendicular to a cylinder of radius $\frac{1}{2}d$ with axis at the origin and satisfies $\nabla\cdot \boldsymbol{v}_n = 0$, $\nabla\times \boldsymbol{v}_n = 0$ is

$$\boldsymbol{v}_n = U_n\left(1 - \frac{d^2}{4r^2}\right)\cos\theta\,\hat{\boldsymbol{e}}_r + \left[\frac{\Gamma_n}{2\pi r} - U_n\left(1 + \frac{d^2}{4r^2}\right)\sin\theta\right]\hat{\boldsymbol{e}}_\theta, \tag{AIV-18}$$

where the incident flow is along the x axis and there is a normal circulation Γ_n around the cylinder. Similarly the superfluid obeys

$$\boldsymbol{v}_s = U_s\left(1 - \frac{d^2}{4r^2}\right)\cos\theta\,\hat{\boldsymbol{e}}_r + \left[\frac{\Gamma_s}{2\pi r} - U_s\left(1 + \frac{d^2}{4r^2}\right)\sin\theta\right]\hat{\boldsymbol{e}}_\theta. \tag{AIV-19}$$

Our object is to calculate the resulting force on the cylinder due to this flow field. In terms of the stress tensor

$$P_{ij} = p\delta_{ij} + \rho_{\mathrm{n}} v_{\mathrm{n},i} v_{\mathrm{n},j} + \rho_{\mathrm{s}} v_{\mathrm{s},i} v_{\mathrm{s},j}, \qquad \text{(AIV-20)}$$

the force exerted by the fluid on the cylinder is

$$\int P_{ij}\, \mathrm{d}S_j, \qquad \text{(AIV-21)}$$

where the integral goes over the entire surface of the cylinder. Since

$$\nabla p = \rho\nabla\mu + \rho s \nabla T + \rho_{\mathrm{n}} \nabla \tfrac{1}{2} w^2, \qquad \text{(AIV-22)}$$

we find from (AIV-7,8)

$$\nabla p = -\rho\nabla\tfrac{1}{2}v_{\mathrm{s}}^2 - \rho s \nabla(\boldsymbol{v}_{\mathrm{n}} \cdot \boldsymbol{A}) + \rho_{\mathrm{n}} \nabla \tfrac{1}{2} w^2. \qquad \text{(AIV-23)}$$

To lowest (zeroth) order in M^2 we can neglect the variations in ρ_{n}, ρ, ρs so that (AIV-23) becomes

$$p + \tfrac{1}{2}\rho_{\mathrm{n}} v_{\mathrm{n}}^2 + \tfrac{1}{2}\rho_{\mathrm{s}} v_{\mathrm{s}}^2 = \text{constant}. \qquad \text{(AIV-24)}$$

Placing (AIV-24) in (AIV-20) and using (AIV-18,19) for $\boldsymbol{v}_{\mathrm{n}}$, $\boldsymbol{v}_{\mathrm{s}}$ enables one to evaluate the integral (AIV-21). The resulting force (Magnus force) is perpendicular to the plane determined by the axis of the cylinder and fluid flow at infinity. Per unit length of cylinder it is

$$\rho_{\mathrm{s}} \boldsymbol{U}_{\mathrm{s}} \times \boldsymbol{\Gamma}_{\mathrm{s}} + \rho_{\mathrm{n}} \boldsymbol{U}_{\mathrm{n}} \times \boldsymbol{\Gamma}_{\mathrm{n}}, \qquad \text{(AIV-25)}$$

which is just (10-6). We have assigned the circulation a direction by the right hand rule.

APPENDIX V

Energy, Velocity and Impulse of a Vortex Ring in a Classical Incompressible Fluid

The impulse required to change the size of a vortex ring is best evaluated by considering it to be situated in a *closed* container. Then the identity

$$\int \boldsymbol{v}\,\mathrm{d}V \equiv -\int \boldsymbol{r}(\nabla \cdot \boldsymbol{v})\,\mathrm{d}V + \int \boldsymbol{r}(\boldsymbol{v} \cdot \mathrm{d}\boldsymbol{S}) \qquad \text{(AV-1)}$$

implies that the fluid momentum vanishes in the approximation that it is incompressible. Therefore

$$\int \phi\,\mathrm{d}\boldsymbol{S} = 0, \qquad \text{(AV-2)}$$

because we naturally take

$$\nabla\phi = 0.$$

However, in applying (AV-2) one must be careful to use a surface for which ϕ is single valued. This can be accomplished by considering the fluid as bounded by the circular surface of the vortex ring in addition to the physical container boundary (B). The integral of ϕ over the circular surface bounded by the ring is $2\pi\gamma \boldsymbol{A}_{\mathrm{R}}$ where $2\pi\gamma$ is the circulation and $\boldsymbol{A}_{\mathrm{R}}$ is the area of the ring with direction equal to that in which the ring would move if located in an unbounded fluid.

Next imagine that as a result of some process the area of the ring changes at a rate $\mathrm{d}\boldsymbol{A}_{\mathrm{R}}/\mathrm{d}t$. Then (AV-2) yields:

$$\int_{\mathrm{B}} \frac{\partial\phi}{\partial t}\,\mathrm{d}\boldsymbol{S} + 2\pi\gamma\frac{\mathrm{d}\boldsymbol{A}_{\mathrm{R}}}{\mathrm{d}t} = 0. \qquad \text{(AV-3)}$$

The phase change can be related to the pressure by the Bernoulli law that follows from (1-16,17):

$$\frac{\partial\phi}{\partial t} + \tfrac{1}{2}v^2 + \frac{p}{\rho} = \text{constant}. \qquad \text{(AV-4)}$$

Substituting (AV-4) into (AV-3) we have that the force exerted by the boundary on the fluid during this process is

$$-\int_{\mathrm{B}} p\,\mathrm{d}\boldsymbol{S} = \int_{\mathrm{B}} \tfrac{1}{2}\rho v^2\,\mathrm{d}\boldsymbol{S} - 2\pi\rho\gamma\frac{\mathrm{d}\boldsymbol{A}_{\mathrm{R}}}{\mathrm{d}t}. \tag{AV-5}$$

The total momentum of the fluid stays zero as discussed above. Thus if we do nothing from outside to disturb it the surface integral of pressure vanishes and the ring's motion satisfies the relation

$$2\pi\gamma\frac{\mathrm{d}\boldsymbol{A}_{\mathrm{R}}}{\mathrm{d}t} = \int_{\mathrm{B}} \tfrac{1}{2}v^2\,\mathrm{d}\boldsymbol{S}, \tag{AV-6}$$

where we consider only the case where the ring does not deform out of the plane. Now through some process let the area of the ring increase by an amount $\delta\boldsymbol{A}_{\mathrm{R}}$ *more* than if it were free to move [i.e., move according to (AV-6)]. This can for instance be imagined as due to a thin expandable wire located inside the core which is magnetically controlled from outside. Then in this process the impulse exerted by the container walls is from (AV-5): $-2\pi\rho\gamma\,\delta\boldsymbol{A}_{\mathrm{R}}$. As the fluid momentum remains zero, an equal and opposite impulse

$$2\pi\rho\gamma\,\delta\boldsymbol{A}_{\mathrm{R}} \tag{AV-7}$$

had to be exerted from outside (e.g., by the wire) to enlarge the ring. Although the impulse required to change the radius of a vortex ring is unique the total momentum of a vortex ring is not unique [E. R. Huggins, Phys. Rev. Letters **17**(1966)1284]. For instance, if a ring of finite radius R is formed from a vanishingly small ring the net impulse supplied is

$$2\pi^2\gamma\rho R^2. \tag{AV-8}$$

If the ring is formed by squeezing in an initial ring of area A equal to the cross-sectional area of the container then the total impulse supplied is

$$-2\pi\gamma\rho(A - \pi R^2). \tag{AV-9}$$

We should note that to form a ring, of infinitesimal radius, or one of such a size that its core lies arbitrarily close to the boundary, requires an arbitrarily small perturbation of the initial flow. If in the limit of unbounded fluids one excludes infinite impulses then (AV-8) is the unique impulse of a vortex ring in such a geometry.

Turning to the velocity field of a vortex ring in an unbounded fluid we first note that by taking

$$\nabla \times \boldsymbol{v} = 0, \tag{AV-10}$$

$$\nabla \cdot \boldsymbol{v} = 0, \tag{AV-11}$$

the problem becomes completely analogous to the magnetic field generated by a current carrying loop especially when we use (AV-11) to introduce the vector velocity potential $\mathscr{A}$

$$\boldsymbol{v} = \nabla \times \mathscr{A}. \tag{AV-12}$$

We take the gauge $\nabla \cdot \mathscr{A} = 0$. Orient the ring so that it lies in the x,y plane and now introduce polar coordinates. By symmetry the velocity field has only r and z components and we can take

$$\mathscr{A} = \mathscr{A}(r,z)\,\hat{e}_\theta. \tag{AV-13}$$

Substituting into (AV-12), (AV-10) and using the gauge yields

$$\frac{\partial^2 \mathscr{A}}{\partial r^2} + \frac{1}{r}\frac{\partial \mathscr{A}}{\partial r} - \frac{\mathscr{A}}{r^2} + \frac{\partial^2 \mathscr{A}}{\partial z^2} = 0. \tag{AV-14}$$

We want a solution to (AV-14) which satisfies the requirement that every path which encircles the vortex ring core has a circulation $2\pi\gamma$. This restriction is best incorporated through a source term and is equivalent to solving

$$\frac{\partial^2 \mathscr{A}}{\partial r^2} + \frac{1}{r}\frac{\partial \mathscr{A}}{\partial r} - \frac{\mathscr{A}}{r^2} + \frac{\partial^2 \mathscr{A}}{\partial z^2} = -2\pi\gamma\,\delta(r - R)\,\delta(z), \tag{AV-15}$$

where R is the ring radius. Equation (AV-15) yields the vector potential and then Eq. (AV-12) yields the fluid velocity field:

$$v_r = -\frac{\partial \mathscr{A}}{\partial z}, \tag{AV-16}$$

$$v_z = \frac{1}{r}\frac{\partial (r\mathscr{A})}{\partial r}, \tag{AV-17}$$

We solve (AV-15) following the approach of A. G. van Vijfeijken, A. Walraven and F. Staas, Physica **44**(1969)415 [see also A. Walraven, Phys. Rev. **1A**(1970)145]. It is easiest to transform both the variables r, z which appear in $\mathscr{A}$. For r the Bessel transform is used:

$$\mathscr{A}(k,z) = \int_0^\infty \mathscr{A}(r,z)\, rJ_1(kr)\,\mathrm{d}r, \tag{AV-18}$$

where J_1 is the Bessel function of order one. The inverse transform is

$$\mathscr{A}(r,z) = \int_0^\infty \mathscr{A}(k,z)\, kJ_1(kr)\,\mathrm{d}k. \tag{AV-19}$$

On z a Fourier transform is used:

$$\mathscr{A}(k,p) = \int_{-\infty}^{\infty} \mathscr{A}(k,z)\,\mathrm{e}^{ipz}\,\mathrm{d}z, \tag{AV-20}$$

with inverse

$$\mathscr{A}(k,z) = \frac{1}{2\pi}\int_{-\infty}^{\infty} \mathscr{A}(k,p)\,\mathrm{e}^{-ipz}\,\mathrm{d}p. \tag{AV-21}$$

Transforming the basic equation (AV-15) yields

$$\mathscr{A}(k,p) = \frac{2\pi\gamma R}{k^2 + p^2} J_1(kR). \tag{AV-22}$$

In order to derive this result one must use the fact that $r\mathscr{A}(r,z)$ and $r\partial\mathscr{A}(r,z)/\partial r$ go to zero both as $r \to 0$ and $r \to \infty$. This follows from Eq. (AV-15) but can also be verified from the final results.

Now one must transform (AV-22) back to coordinate space. For the variable p one gets

$$\mathscr{A}(k,z) = 2\pi\gamma \frac{R}{2k} J_1(kR)\,\mathrm{e}^{-k|z|}. \tag{AV-23}$$

Transforming the variable k leads to

$$\mathscr{A}(r,z) = \pi\gamma R \int_0^\infty J_1(kR)\, J_1(kr)\,\mathrm{e}^{-k|z|}\,\mathrm{d}k, \tag{AV-24}$$

yielding

$$\mathscr{A}(r,z) = \frac{2\gamma}{q}\sqrt{\frac{R}{r}}\,[(1 - \tfrac{1}{2}q^2)\,K(q) - E(q)], \tag{AV-25}$$

where $K(q)$ and $E(q)$ are complete elliptic integrals of the first and second kind:

$$K(q) = \int_0^{\pi/2} \frac{d\theta}{\sqrt{1 - q^2 \sin^2\theta}}, \tag{AV-26}$$

$$E(q) = \int_0^{\pi/2} \sqrt{1 - q^2 \sin^2\theta}\, d\theta, \tag{AV-27}$$

and

$$q^2 = \frac{4rR}{(r + R)^2 + z^2}. \tag{AV-28}$$

Using (AV-16,17) we find for the velocity field of the vortex ring of circulation $2\pi\gamma$:

$$v_r(r,z) = \frac{\gamma z}{r\sqrt{(R + r)^2 + z^2}}\left[-K(q) + \frac{R^2 + r^2 + z^2}{(R - r)^2 + z^2} E(q)\right], \tag{AV-29}$$

$$v_z(r,z) = \frac{\gamma}{\sqrt{(R + r)^2 + z^2}}\left[K(q) + \frac{R^2 - r^2 - z^2}{(R - r)^2 + z^2} E(q)\right]. \tag{AV-30}$$

The kinetic energy of the ring is

$$\text{K.E.}_{\text{R}} = \tfrac{1}{2}\rho \int v^2\, dV = \tfrac{1}{2}\rho \int (\nabla \times \mathscr{A})^2\, dV. \tag{AV-31}$$

In order to get convergence for small $r - R$ and small z combined a model for the core must be supposed. We shall say that within a core radius a no fluid is present. Thus $\nabla \times \boldsymbol{v}$ is zero everywhere in the fluid region and (AV-31) can be transformed to a surface integral over the vortex core:

$$\text{K.E.}_{\text{R}} = \tfrac{1}{2}\rho \int (\mathscr{A} \times \nabla \times \mathscr{A}) \cdot d\boldsymbol{S}, \tag{AV-32}$$

the surface integral at infinity yielding zero. Substituting for $\mathscr{A}$ and ignoring correction terms of order a/R yields

$$\text{K.E.}_{\text{R}} = 2\pi^2\gamma^2\rho R\left(\log\frac{8R}{a} - 2\right),$$

which is just (10-8).

It follows from the Kelvin circulation theorem that each element of the vortex core moves with the local fluid velocity at the core. This motion can be decomposed into a rotation of the core into itself plus a translation of the core. The translation, which we are interested in calculating, is complicated by the fact that different elements of the core move at different velocities. This difficulty can be seen by expanding asymptotically the elliptic functions near the core. Thus taking

$$(r - R)^2 + z^2 \approx a^2,$$

we obtain from (AV-29,30):

$$v_r(r,z) = \frac{\gamma z}{(r - R)^2 + z^2} - \frac{\gamma}{2R} \frac{(r - R)z}{(r - R)^2 + z^2}, \tag{AV-33}$$

$$v_z(r,z) = -\frac{\gamma(r - R)}{(r - R)^2 + z^2} + \frac{\gamma}{2R}\left(\log \frac{8R}{\sqrt{(r - R)^2 + z^2}} - \frac{z^2}{(r - R)^2 + z^2}\right), \tag{AV-34}$$

where terms of order a/R smaller have been dropped.

The first term on the right hand side of these equations represents the rapid rotation of the core. The other terms lead to its translation. Consider first the ring's translational velocity $v_{z,\mathrm{T}}$ in the z direction; we find,

$$v_{z,\mathrm{T}}(R, \pm a) = (\gamma/2R)\,[\log (8R/a) - 1],$$
$$v_{z,\mathrm{T}}(R \pm a, 0) = (\gamma/2R) \log (8R/a);$$

so it is clear that the actual velocity v_{R} of the ring lies between these two values and that since these values are not equal the circular core will distort as it translates. By averaging the translational velocity $v_{z,\mathrm{T}}$ implied by (AV-34) over the perimeter of the core the desired result (10-9) is obtained. By averaging the small translational velocity in the r direction over the core perimeter one obtains zero as expected. The ring's radius does not change as it moves.

The analogy of these results with those of magnetostatics is best brought out by noting that the solution to (AV-10,12) corresponding to a vortex line located on a contour C is

$$\mathscr{A}(r) = \frac{\gamma}{2} \int_{\mathrm{C}} \frac{\mathrm{d}\boldsymbol{r}'}{|\boldsymbol{r} - \boldsymbol{r}'|},$$

where $\boldsymbol{r}'$ runs over the contour.

APPENDIX VI

The Dissipative Fluxes

In this appendix we derive the most general dissipative fluxes which make Σ positive definite and which are linear in the deviation from equilibrium or equivalently linear in the derivatives

$$\nabla T, \quad \nabla \cdot \rho_s(\boldsymbol{v}_s - \boldsymbol{v}_n), \quad \frac{\partial v_{n,i}}{\partial r_j}, \quad \nabla(\mu + \tfrac{1}{2}v_s^2 - \boldsymbol{v}_n \cdot \boldsymbol{v}_s). \qquad \text{(AVI-1)}$$

Choosing the fluxes linear in the derivatives will make Σ quadratic in them. Thus Σ is a positive definite quadratic form in the quantities (AVI-1). Inspection of (21-10) reveals that there is no way that a term quadratic in $\nabla(\mu + \frac{1}{2}v_s^2 - \boldsymbol{v}_n \cdot \boldsymbol{v}_s)$ can enter Σ, therefore none of the fluxes $\boldsymbol{q}$, τ_{ij}, H can depend on this quantity.

The dependence on the gradients of $\boldsymbol{v}_n$ must vanish in equilibrium when $\boldsymbol{v}_n = \boldsymbol{\omega} \times \boldsymbol{r}$, thus derivatives of $\boldsymbol{v}_n$ can enter the fluxes only through the combination

$$D_{ij} \equiv \frac{1}{2}\left(\frac{\partial v_{n,i}}{\partial r_j} + \frac{\partial v_{n,j}}{\partial r_i}\right). \qquad \text{(AVI-2)}$$

Now we argue that τ_{ij} must be symmetric in the indices. The only manner in which a quantity quadratic in D_{ij} could enter the entropy production is through the term $\tau_{\alpha\beta}\partial v_{n,\alpha}/\partial r_\beta$. Therefore if the deviation from equilibrium is to depend on the deformation D_{ij} it must be possible to write

$$\tau_{\alpha\beta}\frac{\partial v_{n,\alpha}}{\partial r_\beta} = \tau'_{\alpha\beta}D_{\alpha\beta},$$

where τ'_{ij} is an undetermined tensor. This relation immediately implies that τ_{ij} is symmetric.

Introduce the traceless tensors $\tilde{\tau}_{ij}$, $\tilde{D}_{ij}$ through the relations

$$\tau_{ij} = \tilde{\tau}_{ij} + \tfrac{1}{3}\delta_{ij}\tau_{\alpha\alpha}, \qquad \text{(AVI-3)}$$

$$D_{ij} = \tilde{D}_{ij} + \tfrac{1}{3}\delta_{ij}D_{\alpha\alpha}, \tag{AVI-4}$$

then from (21-10) we obtain

$$\Sigma = -\frac{\boldsymbol{q}\cdot\nabla T}{T} - \tilde{\tau}_{\alpha\beta}\tilde{D}_{\alpha\beta} - \tfrac{1}{3}\tau_{\alpha\alpha}D_{\beta\beta} + H\nabla\cdot\rho_s\boldsymbol{w}, \tag{AVI-5}$$

where $\boldsymbol{w} = \boldsymbol{v}_n - \boldsymbol{v}_s$.

We now show how to obtain the most general form for $\boldsymbol{q}$. The heat flux must depend only on ∇T, $\tilde{D}_{ij}$, $D_{\alpha\alpha}$ and $\nabla\cdot\rho_s\boldsymbol{w}$ and tensor coefficients. Dependence on other derivatives is impossible since there is no way that they can appear quadratically in (AVI-5). Thus

$$q_i = Q_{i\alpha}\frac{\partial T}{\partial r_\alpha} + R_i D_{\alpha\alpha} + S_i\nabla\cdot\rho_s\boldsymbol{w} + Y_{i\alpha\beta}\tilde{D}_{\alpha\beta}. \tag{AVI-6}$$

By the methods of Appendix II it follows from the equations (21-1,4,2,5) that τ_{ij}, H, $\boldsymbol{q}$ are Galilean invariants. Hence in (AVI-6), Q_{ij}, R_i, S_i, Y_{ijk} must all be Galilean invariants. Under rotation R_i must transform like a vector. So R_i must be proportional to a vector which is Galilean invariant: but furthermore this vector must not involve a gradient (otherwise $\boldsymbol{q}$ would not be linear in the gradients). The only possible choice left is $\boldsymbol{w}$. Hence

$$R_i = b_2 T w_i, \tag{AVI-7}$$

where $b_2 T$ is a new dissipative coefficient. Similarly Q_{ij} must be a tensor of rank two under rotation. The only Galilean invariant tensors at our disposal are $w_i w_j$ and δ_{ij}, hence

$$Q_{ij} = -\kappa\delta_{ij} - b_1 T w_i w_j, \tag{AVI-8}$$

where κ and $b_1 T$ are dissipative coefficients. Now Y_{ijk} must be a tensor of rank three under rotation and also Galilean invariant: but furthermore since we are only interested in its contraction with a symmetric, traceless tensor [see (AVI-6)] we can take Y_{ijk} symmetric and traceless in j and k:

$$Y_{ijk} = Y_{ikj}, \qquad Y_{ijj} = 0.$$

This leaves us with

$$Y_{ijk} = b_4 T[w_i w_j w_k - \tfrac{1}{2}w^2(w_j\delta_{ik} + w_k\delta_{ij})]. \tag{AVI-9}$$

Finally:

$$S_i = b_3 T w_i. \tag{AVI-10}$$

Substituting these expressions in (AVI-6) yields

$$q_i = -\kappa \frac{\partial T}{\partial r_i} - b_1 T w_i(\boldsymbol{w} \cdot \nabla T) + b_2 T w_i(\nabla \cdot \boldsymbol{v}_\mathrm{n}) + b_3 T w_i(\nabla \cdot \rho_\mathrm{s} \boldsymbol{w})$$
$$+ b_4 T[w_i w_j w_k - \tfrac{1}{2} w^2 (w_j \delta_{ik} + w_k \delta_{ij})]\tilde{D}_{jk}. \tag{AVI-11}$$

In exactly the same manner we find

$$H = -\zeta_4 \nabla \cdot \boldsymbol{v}_\mathrm{n} + \zeta_3 \nabla \cdot \rho_\mathrm{s} \boldsymbol{w} - c_1 \boldsymbol{w} \cdot \nabla T - b_5 w_i w_j \tilde{D}_{ij}, \tag{AVI-12}$$

$$\tfrac{1}{3}\tau_{\alpha\alpha} = -\zeta_2 \nabla \cdot \boldsymbol{v}_\mathrm{n} + \zeta_1 \nabla \cdot \rho_\mathrm{s} \boldsymbol{w} + c_2 \boldsymbol{w} \cdot \nabla T + b_6 w_i w_j \tilde{D}_{ij}, \tag{AVI-13}$$

$$\tilde{\tau}_{ij} = (w_i w_j - \tfrac{1}{3} w^2 \delta_{ij})(c_3 \nabla \cdot \boldsymbol{v}_\mathrm{n} + c_4 \nabla \cdot \rho_\mathrm{s} \boldsymbol{w} + c_5 \boldsymbol{w} \cdot \nabla T)$$
$$-\tfrac{1}{2} c_6 w^2 \left(w_i \frac{\partial T}{\partial r_j} + w_j \frac{\partial T}{\partial r_i} - \tfrac{2}{3} \delta_{ij} \boldsymbol{w} \cdot \nabla T \right)$$
$$+ (b_8 w^2 \delta_{ij} - b_7 w_i w_j) w_k w_\ell \tilde{D}_{k\ell} - 2\eta \tilde{D}_{ij}$$
$$+ \tfrac{1}{4}(b_7 w^2 - 3 b_8 w^2)(w_j w_k \delta_{\ell i} + w_i w_k \delta_{\ell j} + w_\ell w_i \delta_{jk} + w_\ell w_j \delta_{ik}) \tilde{D}_{k\ell}. \tag{AVI-14}$$

In order that the entropy production be positive definite it is necessary that $\kappa, b_1, \zeta_2, \zeta_3, b_7, \eta, 3b_8 - b_7$ are positive. The conditions which are sufficient for $\Sigma > 0$ are considerably more involved and will not be presented here. The Onsager principle furthermore requires that $c_1 = b_3$, $\zeta_1 = \zeta_4$, $c_2 = b_2$, $c_3 = b_6$, $c_4 = b_5$, $c_5 = c_6 = b_4$ so that in all there are thirteen independent transport coefficients.

Tables and Graph of the Equations of State of He^4

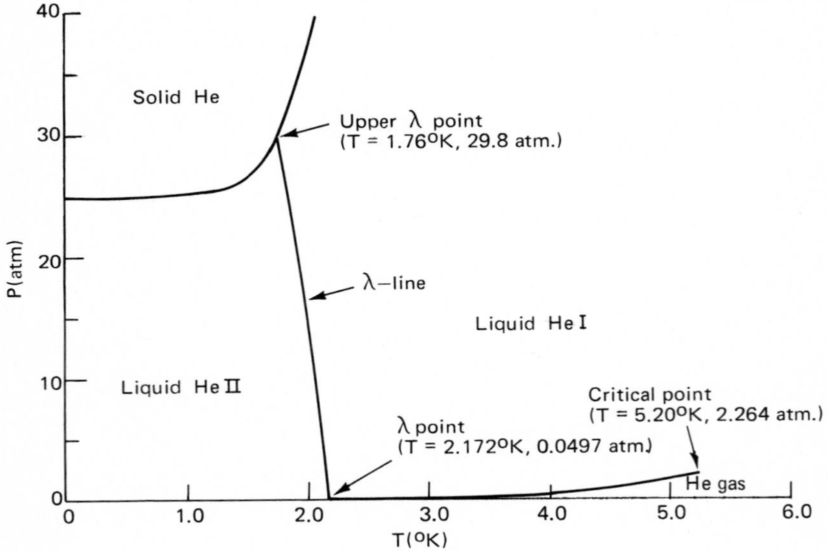

Fig. A. The phase diagram of He^4.

TABLE A

The density, expansion coefficient, saturated vapor pressure, specific heat, entropy and normal fluid viscosity as a function of temperature at the vapor pressure

T	ρ	$-\frac{1}{\rho}\left(\frac{\partial\rho}{\partial T}\right)_p$	p	$T\frac{\partial s}{\partial T}$	s	η
(°K)	(g/cm³)	(10^{-3} °K⁻¹)	(cm Hg)	(joule/g °K)	(joule/g °K)	(10^{-6} poise)
0.6	0.1452	0.227	2.812×10^{-5}	0.0044	0.0015	
0.7	0.1452	0.343	2.279×10^{-4}	0.0098	0.0025	
0.8	0.1452	0.464	1.144×10^{-3}	0.0222	0.0044	158
0.9	0.1452	0.522	4.158×10^{-3}	0.0510	0.0085	65
1.0	0.1452	0.484	1.200×10^{-2}	0.1042	0.0164	37
1.1	0.1452	0.301	2.922×10^{-2}	0.191	0.030	23
1.2	0.1452	−0.064	6.250×10^{-2}	0.322	0.051	17.7
1.3	0.1452	−0.633	1.208×10^{-1}	0.516	0.085	16
1.4	0.1452	−1.42	2.155×10^{-1}	0.780	0.132	15.1
1.5	0.1452	−2.44	3.599×10^{-1}	1.150	0.196	14.1
1.6	0.1452	−3.63	5.690×10^{-1}	1.619	0.284	13
1.7	0.1453	−5.14	8.590×10^{-1}	2.198	0.398	12.8
1.8	0.1454	−6.75	1.247	2.975	0.545	12.8
1.9	0.1455	−9.04	1.748	3.950	0.732	13.8
2.0	0.1457	−12.0	2.377	5.274	0.963	14.6
2.1	0.1459	−16.9	3.143	7.38	1.268	16.5
2.15	0.1460	−24.8	3.578	9.42	1.462	21.5

The vapor pressure is taken from F. G. Brickwedde, H. Van Dijk, M. Durieux, J. R. Clement and J. K. Logan, National Bureau of Standards Monograph 10 (1960).

The viscosity was measured by A. D. B. Woods and A. C. Hollis-Hallet, Can. J. Phys. **41**(1963)596; W. J. Heikkila and A. C. Hollis-Hallet, Can. J. Phys. **33**(1955)420.

The entropy and specific heat come from C. J. N. van den Meijdenberg, K. W. Taconis and R. de Bruyn Ouboter, Physica **27**(1961)197; H. C. Kramers, J. D. Wasscher and C. J. Gorter, Physica **18**(1952)329; O. V. Lounasmaa and E. Kojo, Ann. Acad. Sci. Fennicae, Ser. **A VI**(1959)36; G. J. C. Bots and C. J. Gorter, Physica **26**(1960)337; M. J. Buckingham and W. M. Fairbank, in: *Progress in Low Temperature Physics*, ed. C. J. Gorter (North-Holland, Amsterdam, 1961) Vol. III, Chap. 3. We have made use of the interpolated fit to the above works provided by R. G. Hussey, B. J. Good and J. M. Reynolds, Phys. Fluids **10**(1967)89.

The expansion coefficient and density are provided by E. C. Kerr and R. D. Taylor, Ann. Phys. **26**(1964)292. To obtain the expansion coefficient at constant pressure from that measured at the vapor pressure one must use the sound velocity: K. R. Atkins and R. A. Stasior, Can. J. Phys. **41**(1963)596. Note: 1 joule = 10^7 erg; 1 cm Hg = 1.333×10^4 dyne/cm^2.

TABLE B
The mass density ρ of He^4 in gram/cm^3

T (°K)	p (atm) 0.493	5.06	10.01	15.01	20.10	24.93	28.00
1.30	0.1460	0.1530	0.1592	0.1646	0.1692	0.1734	in solid
1.35	0.1460	0.1531	0.1593	0.1647	0.1693	0.1735	in solid
1.40	0.1460	0.1531	0.1593	0.1647	0.1694	0.1736	in solid
1.50	0.1461	0.1532	0.1594	0.1648	0.1696	0.1738	in solid
1.60	0.1461	0.1533	0.1596	0.1650	0.1699	0.1742	in solid
1.70	0.1462	0.1534	0.1598	0.1653	0.1702	0.1748	0.1777
1.80	0.1463	0.1536	0.1601	0.1657	0.1708	0.1758	0.1792
1.90	0.1464	0.1539	0.1605	0.1664	0.1719	0.1768	0.1793
2.00	0.1466	0.1542	0.1611	0.1674	0.1724	0.1767	0.1792
2.10	0.1468	0.1548	0.1618	0.1674	0.1723	0.1766	0.1791
2.20	0.1470	0.1550	0.1617	0.1673	0.1721	0.1764	0.1789
2.30	0.1467	0.1547	0.1615	0.1671	0.1719	0.1762	0.1787
2.40	0.1463	0.1544	0.1612	0.1669	0.1717	0.1760	0.1784
2.50	0.1458	0.1540	0.1609	0.1666	0.1714	0.1757	0.1782
2.70	0.1444	0.1531	0.1601	0.1659	0.1708	0.1752	0.1776
3.00	0.1420	0.1514	0.1588	0.1648	0.1698	0.1743	0.1767
3.20	0.1400	0.1501	0.1578	0.1639	0.1691	0.1736	0.1761
3.50	0.1363	0.1479	0.1561	0.1625	0.1678	0.1725	0.1750
3.80	in gas	0.1453	0.1542	0.1610	0.1665	0.1712	0.1739

From D. L. Elwell and H. Meyer, Phys. Rev. **164**(1967)245.

TABLE C

Thermal expansion coefficient $-\frac{1}{\rho}\left(\frac{\partial \rho}{\partial T}\right)_p$ for He^4 in units of $10^{-3}(°K)^{-1}$

T	p (atm)						
(°K)	0.493	5.06	10.01	15.01	20.10	24.93	28.00
1.30	− 0.88	− 2.69	− 3.79	− 5.09	− 6.40	− 8.70	in solid
1.35	− 1.39	− 3.26	− 4.68	− 6.07	− 7.94	− 9.83	in solid
1.40	− 1.89	− 4.06	− 5.94	− 7.29	− 9.48	−11.86	in solid
1.50	− 2.73	− 5.73	− 8.07	−11.10	−14.68	−19.0	in solid
1.60	− 3.79	− 7.79	−11.18	−15.27	−19.8	−28.3	in solid
1.70	− 5.22	−10.85	−15.5	−21.7	−29.6	−43.0	−65.5
1.80	− 7.16	−14.54	−21.7	−30.0	−45.1	−75.1	−34.8
1.90	− 9.38	−19.8	−29.8	−45.6	−77.5	− 1.5	+ 2.7
2.00	−12.9	−26.6	−46.3	−27.9	+ 1.6	+ 6.4	+ 8.5
2.10	−18.7	−48.0	0.0	+ 5.4	+ 8.7	+ 9.8	+10.6
2.20	+12.3	+ 9.7	+10.7	+11.0	+11.9	+11.9	+11.9
2.30	+27.0	+18.5	+15.3	+13.8	+12.6	+12.9	+12.9
2.40	+33.1	+23.2	+18.6	+16.2	+15.4	+13.7	+13.9
2.50	+38.9	+27.0	21.4	+18.4	+16.3	+14.6	+14.7
2.70	+50.8	+33.0	+25.1	+21.0	+19.0	+16.5	+16.0
3.00	+64.1	+40.3	+30.0	+24.4	+21.1	+19.1	+18.1
3.20	+78.7	+46.0	+33.6	+26.7	+23.5	+20.3	+18.9
3.50	+101.3	+54.1	+38.9	+31.0	+25.8	+22.4	+21.1
3.80	in gas	+64.5	+44.5	+34.5	+28.2	+25.0	+23.3

From D. L. Elwell and H. Meyer, Phys. Rev. **164**(1967)245.

TABLE D

The entropy of He^4 under pressure in joule/g °K

T (°K)	p (atm) 2.5	5.0	10	15	20	25
1.15	0.041	0.043	0.049	0.057	0.068	0.080
1.20	0.053	0.056	0.063	0.074	0.086	0.100
1.30	0.088	0.091	0.102	0.116	0.134	0.157
1.40	0.136	0.142	0.157	0.178	0.205	0.238
1.50	0.202	0.210	0.232	0.261	0.300	0.350
1.60	0.292	0.303	0.332	0.374	0.430	0.502
1.70	0.409	0.424	0.464	0.524	0.602	0.709
1.80	0.560	0.581	0.637	0.721	0.836	
1.90	0.752	0.782	0.863	0.982		
2.00	0.994	1.035	1.164			
2.05	1.149	1.209				

From C. J. N. van den Meijdenberg, K. W. Taconis and R. de Bruyn Ouboter, Physica **27**(1961)197.

TABLE E
The normal fluid fraction ρ_n/ρ as a function of temperature and pressure

T (°K)	p (atm)					
	saturated vapor pressure	5	10	15	20	25
1.10	0.015	(0.021)	(0.027)	(0.035)	(0.044)	(0.054)
1.20	0.029	(0.036)	(0.045)	(0.058)	(0.070)	(0.084)
1.30	0.048	(0.058)	(0.070)	(0.085)	(0.100)	(0.125)
1.40	0.074	(0.089)	(0.103)	(0.12)	(0.15)	(0.18)
1.50	0.110	(0.125)	(0.145)	(0.18)	(0.215)	0.30
1.55	0.134	(0.14)	(0.18)	(0.21)	(0.27)	0.35
1.60	0.162	(0.17)	(0.21)	(0.26)	0.33	0.41
1.65	0.191	(0.21)	(0.25)	0.33	0.39	0.47
1.70	0.229	(0.27)	0.315	0.39	0.46	0.55
1.75	0.265	0.31	0.36	0.45	0.52	0.65
1.80	0.313	0.355	0.42	0.52	0.61	0.78
1.85	0.376	0.42	0.49	0.60	0.72	1.00
1.90	0.424	0.48	0.57	0.70	0.87	
1.95	0.488	0.56	0.655	0.80		
2.00	0.566	0.645	0.78	1.00		
2.05	0.645	0.75	0.945			
2.10	0.756	0.90				
2.15	0.987					

The values of ρ_n/ρ at the saturated vapor pressure are from the experiments of V. P. Peshkov, Zh. Eksp. Teor. Fiz. **38**(1960)799 [Sov. Phys. JETP **11**(1960)580] as interpolated by R. G. Hussey, B. J. Good and J. M. Reynolds, Phys. Fluids **10**(1967)89. The values in parentheses are determined from second sound velocity under pressure ($u_2^2 = \rho_s s^2 T/\rho_n C_p$) as measured by R. D. Maurer and M. A. Herlin, Phys. Rev. **81**(1951)444. The other values were determined directly by R. H. Romer and R. J. Duffy, Phys. Rev. **186**(1969)255.

The Dependence of the Equations of State on $(\boldsymbol{v}_n - \boldsymbol{v}_s)^2$

When p, T, $w^2 \equiv (\boldsymbol{v}_n - \boldsymbol{v}_s)^2$ are chosen as the complete independent set of internal variables, equations of state for ρ, s, ρ_n/ρ are required in terms of these variables in order to complete the hydrodynamics. The dependence on p, T is discussed in the accompanying tables. The dependence of ρ,s on w^2 can be determined from the Maxwell relations:

$$2\left(\frac{\partial s}{\partial w^2}\right)_{p,T} = \left(\frac{\partial(\rho_n/\rho)}{\partial T}\right)_{p,w}, \qquad \frac{2}{\rho^2}\left(\frac{\partial \rho}{\partial w^2}\right)_{p,T} = \left(\frac{\partial(\rho_n/\rho)}{\partial p}\right)_{T,w},$$

which are implied by the basic identity

$$\mathrm{d}\mu = -s\,\mathrm{d}T + \frac{1}{\rho}\,\mathrm{d}p - \frac{\rho_n}{\rho}\,\mathrm{d}\tfrac{1}{2}w^2.$$

The dependence of ρ_n/ρ on w^2 has not been determined, but persistent current experiments by Kojima (Ph.D. Thesis) have set the upper bound

$$\left|\left(\frac{\partial(\rho_n/\rho)}{\partial w^2}\right)_{p,T}\right| < 6 \times 10^{-8}\ \mathrm{sec^2/cm^2}$$

for $T \leqslant 1.9$ °K.

Some Properties of the λ *Transition*

The observed behavior of the specific heat at constant pressure C_p is suggestive of a logarithmic singularity at T_λ which according to G. Ahlers [Phys. Rev. **A8**(1973)530] can be represented as

$$C_p = -A\log|\varepsilon| + B + D\varepsilon\log|\varepsilon| + E\varepsilon,$$

where

$$\varepsilon \equiv \frac{T - T_\lambda(p)}{T_\lambda(p)},$$

$$A' = 5.102 - 0.05652p + 9.643 \times 10^{-4}p^2$$
$$B' = 15.57 - 0.3601p + 4.505 \times 10^{-3}p^2$$

$$\begin{aligned}
D' &= -14.5 + 6.119p \\
E' &= 69.0 + 19.08p \\
A &= 5.357 - 0.03465p + 8.447 \times 10^{-4}p^2 \\
B &= -7.75 - 0.362p - 4.535 \times 10^{-4}p^2 \\
D &= 14.5 - 6.203p \\
E &= 103.0 - 16.55p.
\end{aligned}$$

The primed coefficients refer to the He II phase. When p is given in bars these relations yield C_p in joule/mole °K and are valid from $\varepsilon \approx 10^{-2}$ to at least a micro-degree from the transition.
The superfluid fraction can be represented as

$$\rho_s/\rho = k\,\varepsilon^{0.67}\,(1 + b\,\varepsilon^{0.5}),$$

where

$$\begin{aligned}
k &= 2.396 - 0.02883p \\
b &= 0.6514 - 0.04548p + 0.005265p^2,
\end{aligned}$$

as determined from second sound velocity by D. S. Greywall and G. Ahlers, Phys. Rev. **A7** (1973) 2145, and has been verified from $\varepsilon \approx 10^{-2}$ to about ten microdegrees from the λ transition. Again p must be given in bars.

As discussed in § 41 various experiments on the He II film suggest that for temperatures greater than 1 °K

$$a\rho_s/T \approx 0.243 \times 10^{-8}\ \text{g/cm}^2\ \text{°K}$$

is independent of temperature where a is the healing length or so-called coherence length. Measurements by R. Williams, S.E.A. Beaver, J.C. Fraser, R. S. Kagiwada and I. Rudnick, Phys. Letters **29A** (1969) 279, have shown that $a\rho_s/T$ is independent of T to at least a couple of microdegrees of the transition. These experiments generate second sound by vibrating a diaphragm with small holes. The normal fluid is clamped in the holes but the superfluid flows through creating a relative velocity as in second sound. When the temperature is so close to T_λ that the healing length is on the order of the hole size superflow and second sound disappear. By observing this effect one obtains information on how the healing length varies with temperature. An extension of this technique to pressures up to the melting pressure by G. Ihas, F. Pobell and R. Williams (private communication) has shown that furthermore $a\rho_s/T$ is independent of p.

Some Fundamental Constants

$\hbar$ = $1.0545919 \times 10^{-27}$ erg sec
k_B = 1.380623×10^{-16} erg/°K
$|e|$ = 4.803250×10^{-10} esu = $1.6021918 \times 10^{-19}$ coulomb
c = 2.9979250×10^{10} cm/sec
Avagadro's number = 6.022169×10^{23} mole^{-1}
m_e = 0.5110041 Mev = 9.109559×10^{-28} g
m_{He^4} = 6.648×10^{-24} g

Author Index

Page numbers in italics refer to the pages containing notes at the end of the introduction and the respective chapters.

Subject Index